DIGITAL COMPUTATION FOR CHEMICAL ENGINEERS

McGRAW-HILL SERIES IN CHEMICAL ENGINEERING

Max S. Peters, *Consulting Editor*

BUILDING THE LITERATURE OF A PROFESSION

Fifteen prominent chemical engineers first met in New York more than 30 years ago to plan a continuing literature for their rapidly growing profession. From industry came such pioneer practitioners as Leo H. Baekeland, Arthur D. Little, Charles L. Reese, John V. N. Dorr, M. C. Whitaker, and R. S. McBride. From the universities came such eminent educators as William H. Walker, Alfred H. White, D. D. Jackson, J. H. James, Warren K. Lewis, and Harry A. Curtis. H. C. Parmelee, then editor of *Chemical & Metallurgical Engineering,* served as chairman and was joined subsequently by S. D. Kirkpatrick as consulting editor.

After several meetings, this first Editorial Advisory Board submitted its report to the McGraw-Hill Book Company in September, 1925. In it were detailed specifications for a correlated series of more than a dozen texts and reference books which have since become the McGraw-Hill Series in Chemical Engineering.

Since its origin the Editorial Advisory Board has been benefited by the guidance and continuing interest of such other distinguished chemical engineers as Manson Benedict, John R. Callaham, Arthur W. Hixson, H. Fraser Johnstone, Webster N. Jones, Paul D. V. Manning, Albert E. Marshall, Charles M. A. Stine, Edward R. Weidein, and Walter G. Whitman. No small measure of credit is due not only to the pioneering members of the original board but also to those engineering educators and industrialists who have succeeded them in the task of building a permanent literature for the chemical engineering profession.

THE SERIES

ANDERSEN AND WENZEL—*Introduction to Chemical Engineering*
ARIES AND NEWTON—*Chemical Engineering Cost Estimation*
BADGER AND BANCHERO—*Introduction to Chemical Engineering*
BENNETT AND MYERS—*Momentum, Heat, and Mass Transfer*
COMINGS—*High Pressure Technology*
CORCORAN AND LACEY—*Introduction to Chemical Engineering Problems*
COUGHANOWR AND KOPPEL—*Process Systems Analysis and Control*
DODGE—*Chemical Engineering Thermodynamics*
GRISWOLD—*Fuels, Combustion, and Furnaces*
GROGGINS—*Unit Processes in Organic Synthesis*
HARIOTT—*Process Control*
HENLEY AND BIEBER—*Chemical Engineering Calculations*
HUNTINGTON—*Natural Gas and Natural Gasoline*
JOHNSTONE AND THRING—*Pilot Plants, Models, and Scale-up Methods in Chemical Engineering*
KATZ, CORNELL, KOBAYASHI, POETTMANN, VARY, ELENBAAS, AND WEINAUG—*Handbook of Natural Gas Engineering*
KIRKBRIDE—*Chemical Engineering Fundamentals*
KNUDSEN AND KATZ—*Fluid Dynamics and Heat Transfer*
KOHL AND RIESENFELD—*Gas Purification*
LAPIDUS—*Digital Computation for Chemical Engineers*
LEVA—*Fluidization*
LEWIS, RADASCH, AND LEWIS—*Industrial Stoichiometry*
MANTELL—*Adsorption*
MANTELL—*Electrochemical Engineering*
MCADAMS—*Heat Transmission*
MCCABE AND SMITH, J. C.—*Unit Operations of Chemical Engineering*
MICKLEY, SHERWOOD, AND REED—*Applied Mathematics in Chemical Engineering*
NELSON—*Petroleum Refinery Engineering*
PERRY (EDITOR)—*Chemical Business Handbook*
PERRY (EDITOR)—*Chemical Engineers' Handbook*
PETERS—*Elementary Chemical Engineering*
PETERS—*Plant Design and Economics for Chemical Engineers*
PIERCE—*Chemical Engineering for Production Supervision*
REID AND SHERWOOD—*The Properties of Gases and Liquids*
RHODES, T. J.—*Industrial Instruments for Measurement and Control*
ROBINSON AND GILLILAND—*Elements of Fractional Distillation*
SCHMIDT AND MARLIES—*Principles of High-polymer Theory and Practice*
SCHWEYER—*Process Engineering Economics*
SHERWOOD AND PIGFORD—*Absorption and Extraction*
SHREVE—*The Chemical Process Industries*
SMITH, B. D.—*Design of Equilibrium Stage Processes*
SMITH, J. M.—*Chemical Engineering Kinetics*
SMITH, J. M., AND VAN NESS—*Introduction to Chemical Engineering Thermodynamics*
TREYBAL—*Liquid Extraction*
TREYBAL—*Mass-transfer Operations*
TYLER AND WINTER—*Chemical Engineering Economics*
VILBRANDT AND DRYDEN—*Chemical Engineering Plant Design*
VOLK—*Applied Statistics for Engineers*
WALAS—*Reaction Kinetics for Chemical Engineers*
WALKER, LEWIS, MCADAMS, AND GILLILAND—*Principles of Chemical Engineering*
WILLIAMS AND JOHNSON—*Stoichiometry for Chemical Engineers*
WILSON AND RIES—*Principles of Chemical Engineering Thermodynamics*
WILSON AND WELLS—*Coal, Coke, and Coal Chemicals*

DIGITAL COMPUTATION FOR CHEMICAL ENGINEERS

LEON LAPIDUS

Professor of Chemical Engineering
Princeton University

New York San Francisco Toronto London 1962

McGRAW-HILL BOOK COMPANY, INC.

DIGITAL COMPUTATION FOR CHEMICAL ENGINEERS

 Library of Congress Catalog Card Number 61-14793

THE MAPLE PRESS COMPANY, YORK, PA.

36358

3 4 5 6 7 8 9 10 - MP - 1 0 9 8 7

To Elizabeth

PREFACE

It is apparent that the modern world is rapidly approaching an almost unmanageable degree of technical complexity. It is no longer possible, except in one's wildest dreams, to forecast the future level of the growth of complicated technological systems. An important factor in the rise of such systems has been the increased rate of communication between various combinations of man and machine. Whether the digital computer as the machine has contributed to increasing the complexity or has merely been a tool used in lifting the veil on our modern technology is not of real consequence. What is important is that digital computers are here to stay and will be used in the future to aid in attacking problems at the forefront of technology.

The optimum use of a digital computer for analyzing complex physical problems requires a level of mathematical sophistication which most chemical engineers do not possess at the present time. This follows, in part, because mathematics in engineering education has been considered as a junior partner whose presence was welcome but on whom no great and ultimate reliance was placed. In the same sense the mathematical tradition of pure abstraction coupled with an appreciation of clean, formal deductive logic has seemed far removed from engineering applications. The advent of the digital computer, however, has now made it more profitable to carry theoretical investigations through to their numerical conclusions before going to the hardware stage. In this way an extremely large number of possibilities can be examined at a minimum cost in time and labor.

The motivation for the present book lies in an attempt to point out in some detail the various areas of digital-computer mathematics which the chemical engineer will find of importance and at the same time to frame the material in a format which he can assimilate. To accomplish these points, only a minimum number of detailed proofs are included, and all examples, when possible, are directed toward problems of direct chemical-engineering interest. The material covered has been presented in various forms to a number of undergraduate and graduate classes taught by the author since about 1957 and in extended lectures to technical personnel in many chemical and petroleum companies.

Chapter 1 in the book is devoted to a concise introduction to some of the broad conceptual ideas inherent in the formation of digital computers and to the historical development of these machines. It is felt that this material will lend some perspective to the reader. Only the briefest mention of hardware and no mention of programming have been made, since these will probably be familiar to most students using the mathematical developments.

Following the technique which the author has found to be most useful, actual numerical examples are always given at the end of a specific chapter. In this way there is no break in the continuity of the mathematical presentation. While a large number of references are noted in the text material itself, each chapter also has a bibliography containing most of the pertinent available references dealing with the topics of that chapter. For the student who wishes to investigate a specific area in more detail these extra references should prove helpful.

Leon Lapidus

CONTENTS

CHAPTER 1

DIGITAL-COMPUTER SYSTEMS

1.1. The Basic Building Blocks and Concepts

The present-day digital computer may be thought of as an information-processing device or logic manipulator. Given a set of commands defining what it should do with a set of discrete data, the computer proceeds to process and manipulate these data. New information not inherent in the original data cannot be obtained. In carrying out these manipulations the computer adds, subtracts, multiplies, and divides just as a person would do, but at fantastically high speed and with extremely high reliability. Even a trivial and often used operation such as obtaining the square root of a real number must be carried out by this same series of four arithmetic operations, since special devices or circuits are not usually built into the computer for automatically calculating the square root. Thus the digital computer is restricted in its operation to those manipulations which man can tell it to do. Because of its speed, however, the computer can carry out calculations under suitable control or direction which man cannot, because of his limited time and energies. It seems fair to say that the number of arithmetic steps performed by existing digital computers to date exceeds all those performed by man throughout his history.

Since control of a digital computer is necessary, it is important to outline how this is accomplished. Another way of phrasing this is: How does man communicate with a computer? At the same time it seems advisable to indicate the macroscopic functioning areas within a digital computer.

Figure 1.1 illustrates the essential blocks of such functioning areas, with possible paths of data flow. The control unit is the over-all activator of the streams of data and information. It directs the arithmetic calculator and the memory and communicates with the external world of man through the input-output section. The arithmetic unit carries out the actual manipulation of the data, and the memory holds these data either before or after manipulation. The control unit may actually be an integral part of the memory in many present-day computers, but for discussion purposes the present division is made.

The primary function of the memory and/or storage unit in a digital computer is as a retainer of units of information such as data, numbers, and computer instructions. "Storage" and "memory" are used synonymously, as an outgrowth of early computer terminology. Any information handled as a unit in memory is referred to as a "word." Since there must be a means of distinguishing one word, or unit of information, from another, within the total word memory of the machine, each is identified uniquely by a number called the "address." When a word is taken from or entered into a specific portion of the memory, reference is made through electronic circuits to the necessary address. Thus the address is the means whereby a tag or label is put on a word locating its

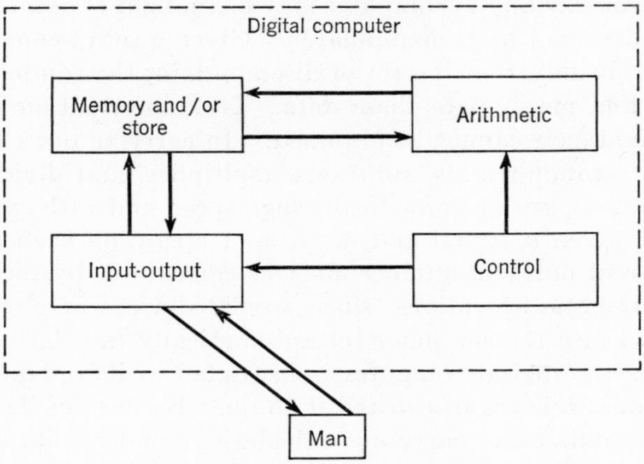

FIG. 1.1. Block areas of operation of a digital computer.

position in the memory, or storage unit. This corresponds to the normal addressing system for locating different houses within a city. Parenthetically, the address has no relation to the architecture of the house; this distinction, in the computer sense, is not always clear to beginners.

While memory units vary from machine to machine, there are a number of general characteristics which can be specified to achieve maximum storage efficiency:

1. The memory must have the ability to allow a word to be removed from any desired address for use in other areas of the machine. This corresponds to the ability of man to read out of a book a word to be used in his brain. In computer notation this process is referred to as reading out of memory.

2. In addition, the reverse of read-out, namely, read-in, in which a word is placed into a specific address, must be possible. This corresponds to man's writing a word on a piece of paper. In computer notation this process is often referred to as writing into memory.

3. The time required to remove a word from any address in memory and deliver it to the proper receiver should be as short as possible. In this way the over-all operating time of the computer can be kept to a minimum. This is called the access time of the memory. Two types of access time are frequently encountered, random access and minimum access. For certain types of memories the access time is a constant independent of the address chosen, or, stated in another way, the next position from which information is to be obtained is in no way dependent on the previous one—thus the notion of random access. In other cases the next position is dependent on the previous one. By suitable placement of words in storage this dependency can be minimized in a calculation—thus the notion of minimum access.

4. Once a word has been placed into a specific address in memory, it should be able to remain there for an indefinite length of time. If the memory is the type in which the words are not lost when the main electric power is turned off, then it is referred to as "permanent," or "nonvolatile"; if the words are lost after the power is cut off, the memory is referred to as "volatile." The former type of memory is, of course, preferable.

5. It should be possible to erase or cover up words in memory so that new information can be placed in the same address. An address may be used at the start of a calculation for storing a constant which is needed at the very beginning of a calculation. After this initial period the constant is no longer needed, and it should be possible to erase the number and replace it with an intermediate result or any other word.

6. The capacity of the memory unit should be as large as possible consistent with cost. The cost requirements frequently lead to a number of different types of memory, each with different access characteristics within the same machine.

7. The reliability of the memory unit should be as high as possible. Since thousands of read-out and read-in operations may be performed per second in a large-scale computer, it is essential that there be no question whether the memory is operating in a reliable manner or not. The speeds of these operations preclude human detection of any errors. Whenever possible, automatic checking features should be made an integral part of the machine operation to monitor the storage functions continuously.

8. The physical size of the memory unit should be kept as small as possible. Recent years have seen the advent of large-capacity memory of small physical size, and the trend seems to be progressing satisfactorily in this direction.

Input-output units form the important communication link between man and the computer. During the early years of computer operation there was an unbalance between the speed of the computer itself and the rate of data intake or output. It was not unusual for a short input or output operation to require a considerably longer time period than an entire machine calculation. The trend in recent years, however, has been to cut the communication time down by substantial amounts by the development of new devices. At the same time, of course, internal computer speeds have increased so that an unbalance still exists. The more important input or output devices include magnetic tape and punched cards for both input and output and printers and cathode-ray tubes as output units.

Figure 1.1 can be used to indicate a difference between what is termed a "scientific" digital computer and a "business" digital computer. In a scientific machine the contact links between man and the machine are kept at a minimum. The machine accepts a limited amount of original starting data and calculates at high speed and for a relatively long time period; it then communicates a limited number of results back to man. The amount of memory required is not large. In contrast the business machine communicates almost continuously with man by constantly receiving new input data, manipulating these data in some simple fashion, and sending back the required answers. The memory requirements in this case are usually quite large. This distinction between the two types of machines is, however, rapidly disappearing with newer and proposed machines which are multipurpose in operation.

A second difference between scientific and business machines is the word or number size to be used. For scientific calculations the number size is based upon the degree of accuracy required and may be fixed for all problems. On the other hand business calculations involve not only numbers but also alphabetic or other specially coded data. Because of this resulting lack of consistency in the size of the total words, the calculations are best performed with variable-sized words (or numbers).

While the present material is concerned solely with digital computers. a comparison between analog and digital computers would seem appropriate. It seems reasonably clear that the computation laboratory of the near future will require both digital and analog facilities. While there are distinct differences between the modes of operation and the problems applicable to each type of computer, there is still considerable compatible overlap between the two. As complementary tools in which a computing task is assigned to that computer for which it is best adapted, this arrangement will prove very efficient. In fact the combination of the two machines to form a hybrid type of computer is currently receiving much attention.

The basis of the analog machine is common to all our physical experiences. Continuous variables such as heat or fluid flow are represented within an analog by another continuous variable, namely, a voltage. Thus analog computers may be thought of as continuous system machines. In contrast, the digital computer is a discrete machine and cannot handle continuously varying parameters except in sampled or discrete number form. Counting instead of measuring is actually carried out with sequences of digits. In general the physical size and cost of digital machines are greater than with analogs, but no precise statement can be made on this point.

Digital computers are characterized as performing only the four simple arithmetic operations of addition, subtraction, multiplication, and division, plus certain logical operations. The analog can carry out the same arithmetic operations and, in addition, integration and differentiation.

All calculations in digital machines are carried out in a serial manner; i.e., one operation must be completed before a second can be started. In an analog all computations are carried out in a parallel manner. In this sense, then, an analog may be thought of as being faster than a digital machine. This difference, however, is being partly removed in the latest digital machines by providing for multiple operations. Two distinct advantages of analog machines result from their mode of parallel operation. First, they can be operated on a real-time basis and thus exactly correspond to the physical model being characterized. Second, all the dependent variables of the system being simulated are available at the same instant.

In terms of flexibility of operation, the digital machine is more powerful than the analog. The digital can handle a wider range of problems because of its memory and logical ability. An analog can basically handle only one independent variable in a specific problem, which implies applicability only to ordinary differential equations. While it can be adapted to handle partial differential equations (two or more independent variables), such operation is in a sense a simulation of a digital computer. As a result, problems which involve a time variable and one or more space variables are usually better suited for digital computation.

The output of analog computers is usually in the form of plotted curves of the dependent variables vs. the independent variables; the digital output, in contrast, is in the form of tables of numbers. In many chemical-engineering problems the plotted output is superior as an intermediate or final result. It must be realized, of course, that the tabulated data from a digital machine can be simply plotted up on auxiliary equipment, but usually not in real time.

It is in the area of precision of calculation results that digital computers exhibit complete superiority over analogs. In present-day analogs the maximum signal-to-noise ratio possible is about 10^{-4}, with little further improvement possible. Ratios of 10^{-15} to 10^{-30} can easily be achieved in digital machines. Since the signal-to-noise ratio is directly indicative of the precision of arithmetic numbers, the digital machine holds a clear edge of superiority. Perhaps another way of stating the same result is to point out that the analog computer involves a measurement problem. To insert values into the machine and to read values out, a voltage must be measured, and an accuracy of four figures is probably the maximum attainable in terms of measurement. In contrast the digital computer does not involve any measurement of this form, and any accuracy desired may be introduced or withdrawn. The reader may ask the logical question: Why the need for high precision in chemical-engineering calculations when the data in general may be good only to 10^{-2} or 10^{-3}? The answer is a simple one and is due to the present status of numerical computation. All calculations which are suitable for or require machine computation are long and complex. The errors involved as a result of such calculations may build up to intolerable levels if the precision of operation is low.

It is convenient at this point to emphasize the importance of the multiplication (or division) time for two numbers in a digital computer. Since this multiplication usually takes considerably longer than either addition or subtraction, the product of the number of multiplications, or the multiplication time, is usually a good criterion of the time spent in a calculation. In comparing different methods for evaluating a number or a function, this product may frequently determine the more efficient method. In actuality the real time spent by the computer on a problem is made up of a number of parts. Some of these are (1) the time required to place the problem into the machine and that required to get the answer out, (2) the time required to move intermediate numbers back and forth within the machine, and (3) the time required to carry out the arithmetic operations.

1.2. Tracing the Historical Development

The development of the digital computer from its conceptual beginning to its modern-day acceptance as a scientific and/or business tool is fascinating. Some of the high points of this development will be herein discussed. For an excellent discussion of this topic and also of the future of digital computers see the work of Bourne and Ford (44).

Stage I Development. The basic conceptual structure of the digital computer can be traced back to the work of Charles Babbage. In 1812 Babbage proposed the idea for a mechanical difference machine which could be used to tabulate mathematical functions such as logarithms by polynomial approximation. In 1822 he completed a small model of this machine which could calculate second differences with 6-digit accuracy. Once this working model was in operation, he proposed building a much larger version involving sixth-order differences and 20-digit accuracy and which could print out the answer to a set of calculations. In much the same manner as one might proceed today, he turned to the government for financial support of this second project. A portion of this machine was eventually finished, but Babbage himself lost interest in its development when he conceived his "analytic engine." Conceptually, this machine was far more advanced than the difference machine and bears a striking resemblance to the modern-day computer. It was to include a memory, or storage, for 1,000 words; a mill, or arithmetic unit to perform arithmetic calculations; input and output units; and logical control for the sequence of arithmetic steps. All these factors were completely detailed for operation and clearly prophesied the present-day computer. Unfortunately, Babbage's concepts were greeted with extreme skepticism, and in 1871 he died with only minor parts of the machine completed.

The development of the digital computer remained dormant after Babbage's death until 1937, when Howard Aiken of Harvard proposed the construction of the Automatic Sequence Controlled Calculator, or Mark I, as it was named. In conjunction with IBM this machine was completed in 1944 and was the first general-purpose automatic digital computer. It was electromechanical in nature, using standard IBM accounting relays and mechanical counters. Some of the features of this computer are listed in Table 1.1.

TABLE 1.1

Storage capacity	72 words of 24 digits (variables) 60 words of 24 digits (constants)
Addition time	3 sec
Multiplication time	7 sec
Division time	60 sec
Program sequence	Dictated by external sequenced punched tape
Special features	Included routines for calculating certain transcendental functions such as sin x

In 1947 the Electronic Numerical Integrator and Calculator, called ENIAC, was constructed at the University of Pennsylvania by Eckert and Mauchly. Eighteen hundred electronic tubes were used in this electronic version of the Mark I, with, of course, a major increase in the calculation speed. Some of the features are listed in Table 1.2.

Shortly after this development IBM made available its CPC calculator. This was the first commercial electronic computer and possessed a memory capacity of 36 words, each of six digits. The speed of calculation was much slower than that of the ENIAC, but still in the millisecond class. Punched-card program input and printer output were used. For a number of years this machine was the workhorse of the computer field, since one was available to almost any firm that could justify the small rental cost. Even as late as 1956, many large companies had the CPC as their sole computer.

TABLE 1.2

Storage capacity	20 words of 10 digits
Addition time	200 μsec
Multiplication time	2.3 msec
Divison time	2.8 msec
Program sequence	Dictated by external punched cards; this machine was comparatively sophisticated in its logical properties but its small memory capacity severely limited its utility for wide-range problems

Stage I development was featured by rapid increase in technological improvement but was characterized by external programming of the computer. Stored programs were not used, and in this sense the machines might be termed backward. No matter how fast the arithmetic unit operated, the over-all speed was dictated by the input speed.

Stage II Development. The stage II development was motivated by a report written in 1947 by Von Neumann, Goldstine, and Burks regarding the logical design of a large-scale digital computer. This report outlined the concepts of the stored program and the use of the binary number system and of cyclic memory. It was first used in the construction of the EDVAC, at the Aberdeen Proving Grounds, and the MANIAC, at the Advanced Institute in Princeton. The latter machine was completed in early 1952, with the features listed in Table 1.3.

TABLE 1.3

Storage capacity	1,024 words of 40 binary bits
Addition time	60 μsec
Multiplication time	700 μsec
Division time	1,100 μsec
Program sequence	Stored program
Special features	Punched-card input-output; electrostatic high-speed memory and magnetic-drum intermediate memory

Based on these concepts, a whole sequence of computers were built. These included the SEAC at the National Bureau of Standards, the ILLIAC at the University of Illinois, the ORACLE at Oak Ridge, the Whirlwind at MIT, and the Remington-Rand UNIVAC.

As each machine was completed, improvements in such items as memory units, input-output equipment, logical manipulation, and programming were further developed. Some of the more important contributions were the result of successive models of the Whirlwind at MIT. The development of the commercially available Remington-Rand Univac Scientific (or ERA 1103) and the IBM 701 was announced and then followed by the improved ERA 1103A and the IBM 704 and 709. These latter machines are characterized by magnetic-core memory, extensive magnetic-tape units, and floating-point arithmetic. Calculation speeds are in the microseconds range, and the logical commands possible and programming techniques available are outstanding. As this development of large-scale computers progressed, a number of medium-sized computers were made available. These included the popular IBM 650 and Burrough's Datatron.

The stage II development was one of rapidly expanding technology and techniques. The end result was the availability of a large number of extremely powerful commercial computers.

Stage III Development. The stage III development, sometimes referred to as the second generation, includes the present time period and has a number of definite offshoots in addition to a further refinement of the machines in stage II. A major development has been the filling of the gaps imposed by having available only certain restricted-sized machines. Now one may obtain almost any desired size of machine.

To illustrate the capabilities of some of these machines, a few of the features of the IBM 1620, with a rental figure of approximately $2,000 per month, include magnetic-core storage with 20,000 digits capacity, a variable word length, and an add time of about 560 μsec. In the same sense it is not unusual now to see a computer like the Control Data 1604, with a rental figure of approximately $36,000 per month and with 32,768 words storage, a 48-bit word, and 7.2 μsec, add time using a smaller IBM 1401 because of its versatile input-output. The latter machine rents for about $4,000 per month.

In addition, the stage III development has involved the construction of a limited number of very large machines by industry for the government. The three most important machines of this type are the NORC built by IBM for the Dahlgarn Proving Grounds of the Navy, the LARC built by Remington-Rand for the Livermore Atomic Energy Laboratory, and the STRETCH machine built by IBM for Los Alamos. In the order given, the machines become faster, bigger, and more costly. The STRETCH machine, for example, is about 100 times faster than the IBM 704, plus being much more versatile.

The STRETCH machine is speeded up first by the use of new transistor circuits and magnetic cores. In particular there is a main memory area with 2 μsec access time and a fast memory area with 0.5 μsec access. The fast memory is made up in units of 512 words and the main memory in units of 8,192 words. There also is a large magnetic-disk back-up memory. The arithmetic unit will operate with floating-point addition in 0.6 μsec and multiplication in 1.2 μsec. This latter operation is extremely fast as compared with the stage II machines. A single word in core storage consists of 64 binary bits plus 8 check bits, and the command structure of the machine is very versatile, with complete fixed and floating-point single and double precision operations. At least 16 index registers are provided and, of course, extensive input-output units with complete buffering.

Actually the STRETCH machine is a combination of a number of independent computers; the over-all sequencing of the individual components will be directed by a "scheduler." In this way many of the machine operations proceed concurrently or in parallel instead of serially as in the stage II machines.

The recent turn to solid-state circuitry has also been a significant feature of the stage III development. Thus machines such as the IBM 7090 and the Remington-Rand Univac 80 or 90 are all solid-state and comparable in capabilities with earlier vacuum-tube units, but at lower cost and with more capability at the same cost. The use of thin-film memories has also reached a commercial basis with the announcement of the Remington-Rand Univac 1107. Access times for such memories are not measured in microseconds (millionths) but rather in nanoseconds (billionths). It is to be expected that all competitive companies will shortly have memories of this type.

As a final point we should mention the advent of digital computers designed specifically for on-line process control (see Chap. 8). These are small to medium machines with completely revised input-output devices, i.e., analog-digital converters, so that they can connect directly to real systems. Typical examples are the Ramo-Wooldridge 300 and the RCA 110. This area is in such a state of flux at the present time that further discussion does not seem appropriate.

BIBLIOGRAPHY

Books

1. Alt, F. L.: "Electronic Digital Computers," Academic Press, Inc., New York, 1958.
2. Alt, F. L.: "Advances in Computers. I," Academic Press, Inc., New York, 1960.
3. Beckenbach, E. F.: "Modern Mathematics for the Engineer," McGraw-Hill Book Company, Inc., New York, 1957.
4. Bellman, R.: "Dynamic Programming," Princeton University Press, Princeton, N.J., 1957.
5. Bodewig, E.: "Matrix Calculus," Interscience Publishers, Inc., New York, 1959.
6. Buckingham, R. A.: "Numerical Methods," Pitman Publishing Corporation, New York, 1957.
7. Charnes, A., W. W. Cooper, and A. Henderson: "An Introduction to Linear Programming," John Wiley & Sons, Inc., New York, 1953.

8. Collatz, L.: "The Numerical Treatment of Differential Equations," 3d ed., Springer-Verlag OHG, Berlin, 1960.
9. Crandell, S. H.: "Engineering Analysis," McGraw-Hill Book Company, Inc., New York, 1956.
10. Eckert, W. J., and R. Jones: "Faster, Faster," McGraw-Hill Book Company, Inc., New York, 1956.
11. Ferguson, R. O., and L. F. Sargent: "Linear Programming," McGraw-Hill Book Company, Inc., New York, 1958.
12. Forsythe, G. E., and P. C. Rosenbloom: "Numerical Analysis and Partial Differential Equations," John Wiley & Sons, Inc., New York, 1958.
13. Fox, L.: "The Numerical Solution of Two-point Boundary Problems," Oxford University Press, New York, 1957.
14. Gass, S. I.: "Linear Programming," McGraw-Hill Book Company, Inc., New York, 1958.
15. Gotlieb, C. C., and J. N. P. Hume: "High-speed Data Processing," McGraw-Hill Book Company, Inc., New York, 1958.
16. Grabbe, E. M., S. Ramo, and D. E. Wooldridge: "Handbook of Automation, Computation and Control. I," John Wiley & Sons, Inc., New York, 1958.
17. Hartree, D. R.: "Numerical Analysis," Oxford University Press, New York, 1958.
18. Hastings, C.: "Approximations for Digital Computers," Princeton University Press, N.J., 1955.
19. Hildebrand, F. B.: "Introduction to Numerical Analysis," McGraw-Hill Book Company, Inc., New York, 1956.
20. Householder, A. S.: "Principles of Numerical Analysis," McGraw-Hill Book Company, Inc., New York, 1953.
21. Jeenel, J.: "Programming for Digital Computers," McGraw-Hill Book Company, Inc., New York, 1959.
22. Kantorovich, L. V., and V. I. Krylov: "Approximate Methods of Higher Analysis," P. Noordhoff, N. V., Groningen, Netherlands, 1958.
23. Kopal, Z.: "Numerical Analysis," John Wiley & Sons, Inc., New York, 1955.
24. Kunz, K. S.: "Numerical Analysis," McGraw-Hill Book Company, Inc., New York, 1957.
25. Lanczos, C.: "Applied Analysis," Prentice-Hall, Inc., Englewood Cliffs, N.J., 1956.
26. Langer, R. E.: "Boundary Value Problems in Differential Equations," University of Wisconsin Press, Madison, Wis., 1960.
27. Lowan, A. N.: "The Operator Approach to Problems of Stability and Convergence," *Scripta Mathematica Yeshiva University*, New York, 1957.
28. McCormick, E. M.: "Digital Computer Primer," McGraw-Hill Book Company, Inc., New York, 1959.
29. McCracken, D. D.: "Digital Computer Programming," John Wiley & Sons, Inc., New York, 1957.
30. Mickley, H. S., T. K. Sherwood, and C. E. Reed: "Applied Mathematics in Chemical Engineering," 2d ed., McGraw-Hill Book Company, Inc., New York, 1957.
31. Milne, W. E.: "Numerical Solution of Differential Equations," John Wiley & Sons, Inc., New York, 1953.
32. "Modern Computing Methods," National Physical Laboratory Notes on Applied Science, No. 16, H. M. Stationery Office, London, 1957.
33. Phister, M., Jr.: "Logical Design of Digital Computers," John Wiley & Sons, Inc., New York, 1958.
34. Richards, R. K.: "Arithmetic Operations in Digital Computers," D. Van Nostrand Company, Inc., Princeton, N.J., 1955.

35. Sasieni, M., A. Yaspan, and L. Friedman: "Operations Research," John Wiley & Sons, Inc., New York, 1958.
36. Scarborough, J. B.: "Numerical Mathematical Analysis," Johns Hopkins Press, Baltimore, 1958.
37. Smith, C. V. L.: "Electronic Digital Computers," McGraw-Hill Book Company, Inc., New York, 1959.
38. Stibitz, G. R., and J. A. Larrivee: "Mathematics and Computers," McGraw-Hill Book Company, Inc., New York, 1956.
39. Symonds, G. H.: "Linear Programming: The Solution of Refinery Problems," Esso Standard Oil Co., New York, 1955.
40. Vazsonyi, A.: "Scientific Programming in Business and Industry," John Wiley & Sons, Inc., New York, 1958.
41. Wilt, H. S., and A. Ralston: "Mathematical Methods for Digital Computations," John Wiley & Sons, Inc., New York, 1960.

Articles

42. Ashenhurst, R. L., and N. Metropolis: *J. Assoc. Comput. Mach.*, **6**: 415 (1959).
43. Booth, K. H. V.: *Research*, **10**: 437 (1957).
44. Bourne, C. P., and D. F. Ford: *Proc. Western Joint Computer Conf.*, May, 1960.
45. Bratman, H., et al.: *Communs. ACM*, **2**(10): 25 (1959).
46. Buchholz, W.: *Communs. ACM*, **2**(12): 3 (1959).
47. Clippinger, R. F., B. Dimsdale, and J. B. Levin: *J. SIAM*, **1**: 1, 91 (1953); **29**: 36, 113, 184 (1954).
48. *Control Engineering:* series of papers in digital-computer series and basic digital series, 1955–1959.
49. Cuthill, E., and J. W. Schot: A Class of Scientific Applications on LARC, *David Taylor Model Basin Rept.* 1248, 1958.
50. DeFrate, L. A., and A. E. Hoerl: *Chem. Eng. Progr. Symposium Ser.* 21, 1959.
51. Eckert, J. P., Jr.: *Proc. IRE*, **41**: 1393 (1953).
52. Elgot, C. C.: Single vs. Triple Address Computing Machines, *NAVORD Rept.* 2741, 1959.
53. Ferguson, D. E.: *J. Assoc. Comput. Mach.*, **7**: 1 (1960).
54. Green, J.: *Communs. ACM*, **2**(9): 25 (1959).
55. Hamming, R. W.: *Bell System Tech. J.*, **29**: 147 (1950).
56. Hamming, R. W.: *Sci. Monthly*, **85**: 169 (1957).
57. Hollander, F. H., and C. B. Tompkins: *Chem. Eng. Progr.*, **52**: 451 (1956).
58. Hubbard, L. C.: *Ind. Eng. Chem.*, **50**: 1662 (1958).
59. Humphrey, S. M.: *Communs. ACM*, **2**(12): 16 (1959).
60. Irons, E. T., and F. S. Acton: *Communs. ACM*, **2**(12): 14 (1959).
61. Perlis, A. J.: *Communs. ACM*, **2**(5): 1 (1959).
62. Rose, A., R. C. Johnson, and T. J. Williams: *Ind. Eng. Chem.*, **43**: 2459 (1951).
63. Rose, A., T. J. Williams, and N. A. Kahn: *Ind. Eng. Chem.*, **43**: 2502 (1951).
64. Samuel, A. L.: *Proc. IRE*, **41**: 1223 (1953).
65. Schmittroth, L. A.: *Communs. ACM*, **3**(3): 171 (1960).
66. Shell, D. L.: *J. Assoc. Comput. Mach.*, **6**: 123 (1959). (See other papers in same issue.)
67. Speckhard, A. E.: *Communs. ACM*, **3**(1): 2 (1960).
68. Suigals, J.: *Communs. ACM*, **3**(3): A11 (1960).
69. Thomas, W. H.: *Proc. IRE*, **41**: 1245 (1953).
70. Tocher, K. D.: *Quart. J. Mech. Appl. Math.*, **11**: 364 (1958).
71. Ulrich, W.: *Bell System Tech. J.*, **36**: 1341 (1957).
72. Williams, T. J., R. C. Johnson, and A. Rose: *J. Assoc. Comput. Mach.*, **4**: 393 (1957).

CHAPTER 2

POLYNOMIAL APPROXIMATION

A task which frequently confronts the chemical engineer is the necessity for a suitable fit or representation of a set of tabulated data. The data may derive from the discrete behavior of a known but extremely complicated analytical function or from experimental measurements. In the former case the numbers will usually contain errors only in the last figure retained, whereas the numbers derived from experimental measurements will include considerably more error (or less significant figures). Typical examples may involve the fit of output data from a chemical reactor in terms of an input variable or the calculation of the capacity of a packed tower.

The synthesis of a new analytical function to serve as a substitute for the original information is a necessary feature for many machine computations. If the data are given only in tabulated form, such a representation is mandatory for purposes of accurate interpolation, differentiation, or integration. In the same sense, if the data have evolved from an analytical form too complicated for integration (or too time-consuming to carry out), the new representation has the feature of computational simplicity.

In the present chapter polynomial functions are used for approximating the available data. Such functions are relatively easy to develop and are simple to manipulate, i.e., differentiate and integrate. In more concrete terms a polynomial of degree n, $\phi_n(x)$, is used to approximate the function $y = f(x)$ given either in analytical form or as $n + 1$ sets of tabulated data such as

$$\begin{array}{cc} x_0 & y_0 \\ x_1 & y_1 \\ x_2 & y_2 \\ \cdots & \cdots \\ x_{n-1} & y_{n-1} \\ x_n & y_n \end{array}$$

The values of $y_0, y_1, \ldots, y_n$ are assumed known at the discrete points of the independent variable x. $y_0 = f(x_0), y_1 = f(x_1), \ldots, y_n = f(x_n)$ is a convenient manner of representing this functional dependence.

$\phi_n(x)$ has the explicit form

$$\phi_n(x) = a_0 + a_1x + a_2x^2 + \cdots + a_nx^n$$

with the coefficients $a_0, a_1, a_2, \ldots, a_n$ to be determined by the data points.

A more general type of representation can also be formulated,

$$\phi_n(x) = b_0g_0(x) + b_1g_1(x) + \cdots + b_ng_n(x)$$

where the $g_0(x), g_1(x), \ldots, g_n(x)$ are trigonometric, exponential, or general orthogonal functions (see Sec. 2.11). The case of polynomial approximation, $g_i(x) = x^i$, is merely a special case of the more general formulation.

2.1. Linear Symbolic Operators

As a means of simplifying the operations which follow, some of the properties of certain linear symbolic operators will be developed. These operators apply only when the spacing between successive values of the independent variable is constant. If we call this constant spacing h, it follows that

$$x_{i+1} = x_i + h \qquad i = 0, 1, \ldots, n-1$$

or

$$x_i = x_0 + ih$$

The following linear operators are of importance,

E = shift operator
Δ = forward-difference operator
∇ = backward-difference operator
δ = central difference operator
μ = average operator
D = differential operator
I = integral operator

defined by the relationships

$$\begin{aligned}
Ef(x) &= f(x+h) \\
\Delta f(x) &= f(x+h) - f(x) \\
\nabla f(x) &= f(x) - f(x-h) \\
\delta f(x) &= f\left(x + \frac{h}{2}\right) - f\left(x - \frac{h}{2}\right) \\
\mu f(x) &= \frac{1}{2}\left[f\left(x + \frac{h}{2}\right) + f\left(x - \frac{h}{2}\right)\right] \\
Df(x) &= \frac{df(x)}{dx} = f'(x) \\
If(x) &= \int_x^{x+h} f(x)\,dx
\end{aligned} \tag{2.1.1}$$

The function of any operator is to transform $f(x)$ into another form; thus the shift operator E when applied to $f(x)$ yields $f(x + h)$, and the forward operator Δ yields $f(x + h) - f(x)$.

An operator or a group of different operators can be applied sequentially to $f(x)$. Under such conditions the accepted terminology is to write each new operator to the left of the function which is being transformed. As an example,

$$Df(x) = f'(x)$$

and

$$\Delta Df(x) = f'(x + h) - f'(x)$$

Positive integral powers of an operator are easily defined in this way, with E^n taken to mean

$$E^n f(x) = EE \cdots Ef(x) = f(x + nh) \tag{2.1.2}$$

When an operator is raised to the zero power, no change takes place in the function. Stated in another way, the zero power of any operator is identical to the identity operator 1. This definition can be extended to cover the application of any real positive power of an operator such that

$$E^\alpha f(x) = f(x + \alpha h)$$

where α = a real positive number.

It is easily shown that all the operators defined by (2.1.1) satisfy the distributive, commutative, and associative laws of algebra. If A_1 is one operator and $A_2, A_3, \ldots$ other operators, then

$$\begin{aligned} A_1 + A_2 &= A_2 + A_1 \\ A_1 + (A_2 + A_3) &= (A_1 + A_2) + A_3 \\ A_1A_2 &= A_2A_1 \\ A_1(A_2A_3) &= (A_1A_2)A_3 \\ A_1(A_2 + A_3) &= A_1A_2 + A_1A_3 \end{aligned}$$

As an illustration,

$$E^n Df(x) = E^n f'(x) = f'(x + nh) = Df(x + nh) = DE^n f(x)$$

or

$$E^n Df(x) = DE^n f(x)$$

which is written merely as

$$E^n D = DE^n$$

Real negative integer powers of the linear operators may also be defined. In particular, if A is any operator, then A^{-1} is defined by

$$AA^{-1} = 1 \tag{2.1.3}$$

with A^{-1} called the "inverse" of A. If

$$A^{-1}f(x) = h(x)$$

then

$$AA^{-1}f(x) = Ah(x)$$
$$f(x) = Ah(x)$$

Higher negative real powers may be defined in the same way as positive real powers.

Certain complications arise when the inverse of D and I is involved. To illustrate this point, note that

$$D^{-1}f(x) = \int f(x)\,dx + C$$

and thus

$$DD^{-1}f(x) = D\int f(x)\,dx + DC$$
$$f(x) = f(x) + 0$$

Any value of C will lead to the same value of $D^{-1}f(x)$, and D^{-1} is thus not uniquely defined. Care must thus be taken regarding the order of the application of the inverse operators.

Since the operators can be manipulated by the normal rules of algebra, it is a relatively simple matter to obtain a set of formal relations between any pair of (2.1.1). In particular, the following are useful:

$$\begin{aligned}
\Delta &= E - 1 = E\nabla \\
\nabla &= 1 - E^{-1} \\
\delta &= E^{\frac{1}{2}} - E^{-\frac{1}{2}} \\
\delta^2 &= \Delta - \nabla \\
\mu &= \tfrac{1}{2}(E^{\frac{1}{2}} + E^{-\frac{1}{2}}) \\
\mu^2 &= 1 + \tfrac{1}{4}\delta^2 \\
I &= \Delta D^{-1}
\end{aligned} \tag{2.1.4}$$

Expanding $f(x)$ in a Taylor series expansion about h leads to

$$f(x + h) = f(x) + \frac{h}{1!}f'(x) + \frac{h^2}{2!}f''(x) + \cdots$$

In operator notation

$$Ef(x) = \left(1 + \frac{hD}{1!} + \frac{h^2D^2}{2!} + \cdots\right)f(x)$$

and upon recognizing the infinite series in the parentheses as the exponential of hD there results

$$E = e^{hD} \tag{2.1.5}$$

From (2.1.5) the following relations are obtained:

$$\begin{aligned}
\Delta &= e^{hD} - 1 \\
\nabla &= 1 - e^{-hD} \\
\delta &= e^{\frac{1}{2}hD} - e^{-\frac{1}{2}hD} = 2\sinh \tfrac{1}{2}hD \\
\mu &= \cosh \tfrac{1}{2}hD
\end{aligned}$$

Since the linear operators serve as a convenient shorthand notation, it is also worth mentioning the binomial coefficients which serve the same purpose. The binomial expansion of the rth power of the sum of u and w is written as

$$(u + w)^r = \binom{r}{0} u^r + \binom{r}{1} u^{r-1}w + \binom{r}{2} u^{r-2}w^2 + \cdots + \binom{r}{r} w^r \qquad (2.1.6)$$

where

$$\binom{r}{k} = \frac{r!}{k!(r-k)!}$$

The coefficients given in (2.1.6) are called the binomial coefficients and are tabulated in the literature. For increasing values of k

$$\binom{r}{0} = 1$$
$$\binom{r}{1} = r$$
$$\binom{r}{2} = \frac{r(r-1)}{2!}$$
$$\binom{r}{3} = \frac{r(r-1)(r-2)}{3!}$$
$$\cdots\cdots\cdots\cdots$$
$$\binom{r}{r-1} = r$$
$$\binom{r}{r} = 1$$

An alternative way of writing these coefficients is

$$\binom{r}{k} = \frac{r(r-1)(r-2)\cdots(r-k+1)}{k!}$$

or symbolically $\binom{r}{k} = (r)_k$

2.2. Difference-table Notation

The higher-order linear operators bear a special relation to each other in a geometric sense. This feature will first be examined in terms of the forward-difference operator. Call

$$\begin{aligned} \Delta y_0 &= y_1 - y_0 \\ \Delta y_1 &= y_2 - y_1 \\ &\cdots\cdots \\ \Delta y_i &= y_{i+1} - y_i \end{aligned}$$

and successively

$$
\begin{aligned}
\Delta^2 y_0 &= \Delta y_1 - \Delta y_0 = y_2 - 2y_1 + y_0 \\
\Delta^2 y_1 &= \Delta y_2 - \Delta y_1 \\
&\cdots\cdots\cdots \\
\Delta^2 y_i &= \Delta y_{i+1} - \Delta y_i \\
\Delta^3 y_0 &= \Delta^2 y_1 - \Delta^2 y_0 = y_3 - 3y_2 + 3y_1 - y_0 \\
\Delta^3 y_1 &= \Delta^2 y_2 - \Delta^2 y_1 \\
&\cdots\cdots\cdots \\
\Delta^3 y_i &= \Delta^2 y_{i+1} - \Delta^2 y_i \\
&\cdots\cdots\cdots \\
\Delta^{r+1} y_0 &= \Delta^r y_1 - \Delta^r y_0 \\
\Delta^{r+1} y_1 &= \Delta^r y_2 - \Delta^r y_1 \\
&\cdots\cdots\cdots \\
\Delta^{r+1} y_i &= \Delta^r y_{i+1} - \Delta^r y_i
\end{aligned}
\tag{2.2.1}
$$

Δy_i is termed the first forward difference, $\Delta^2 y_i$ the second forward difference, . . . , and $\Delta^{r+1} y_i$ the $r + 1$ forward difference. $\Delta^{r+1} y_i$ can be calculated from the successive differences or directly from the original tabulated data by expanding the higher-order difference. All the differences of (2.2.1) can be arranged in the following manner:

x_0	y_0					
		Δy_0				
x_1	y_1		$\Delta^2 y_0$			
		Δy_1		$\Delta^3 y_0$		
					$\Delta^4 y_0$	
x_2	y_2		$\Delta^2 y_1$			
		Δy_2		$\Delta^3 y_1$		
				$\cdot$		$\Delta^n y_0$
x_3	y_3		$\Delta^2 y_2$			
$\cdot$	$\cdot$	Δy_3	$\cdot$	$\cdot$		
				$\cdot$	$\Delta^4 y_{n-4}$	
$\cdot$	$\cdot$	$\cdot$	$\cdot$			
$\cdot$	$\cdot$	Δy_{n-2}	$\cdot$	$\Delta^3 y_{n-3}$		
x_{n-1}	y_{n-1}		$\Delta^2 y_{n-2}$			
		Δy_{n-1}				
x_n	y_n					

In this arrangement each difference is placed between the two terms which form the basis of the particular difference and in the column to the right. This tabular form is termed a forward-difference table. The vertex of the table corresponds to $\Delta^n y_0$, and the subscripts remain constant along any diagonal line.

A difference table may also be constructed in terms of successive backward differences. It is observed that

$$\begin{aligned}
\nabla y_i &= y_i - y_{i-1} \\
\nabla^2 y_i &= \nabla y_i - \nabla y_{i-1} \\
\nabla^3 y_i &= \nabla^2 y_i - \nabla^2 y_{i-1} \\
&\cdots\cdots\cdots\cdots \\
\nabla^{r+1} y_i &= \nabla^r y_i - \nabla^r y_{i-1}
\end{aligned}$$

holds for the successive ith backward differences. These values may be arranged in a backward-difference table in which the vertex is $\nabla^n y_n$ and the subscript n remains constant along the lower rising values.

To construct a central-difference table, the subscript notation on the original tabulated data is first rearranged.

. . .	. . .
x_{-2}	y_{-2}
x_{-1}	y_{-1}
x_0	y_0
x_1	y_1
x_2	y_2
. . .	. . .

Upon using the central-difference operator applied to these data, there results

$$\begin{aligned}
\delta y_{\frac{1}{2}} &= y_1 - y_0 \\
\delta y_{-\frac{1}{2}} &= y_0 - y_{-1} \\
\delta y_{\frac{3}{2}} &= y_2 - y_1 \\
\delta y_{-\frac{3}{2}} &= y_{-1} - y_{-2} \\
&\cdots\cdots\cdots\cdots \\
\delta^2 y_0 &= \delta y_{\frac{1}{2}} - \delta y_{-\frac{1}{2}} = y_1 - 2y_0 + y_{-1} \\
\delta^2 y_1 &= \delta y_{\frac{3}{2}} - \delta y_{\frac{1}{2}} \\
\delta^2 y_{-1} &= \delta y_{-\frac{1}{2}} - \delta y_{-\frac{3}{2}} \\
&\cdots\cdots\cdots\cdots \\
\delta^2 y_{\frac{1}{2}} &= \delta^2 y_1 - \delta^2 y_0 = y_2 - 3y_1 + 3y_0 - y_{-1} \\
\delta^2 y_{-\frac{1}{2}} &= \delta^2 y_0 - \delta^2 y_{-1} \\
&\cdots\cdots\cdots\cdots
\end{aligned}$$

The general term in this representation is

$$\delta^r y_i = \sum_{k=0}^{r} (-1)^r \frac{r!}{k!(r-k)!} y_{i+r/2-k}$$

The coefficients are seen to be the binomial coefficients of (2.1.6). The central-difference table then has the form

$$
\begin{array}{cccccc}
\cdot & \cdot & & & & \\
\cdot & \cdot & & & & \\
\cdot & \cdot & & & & \\
x_{-2} & y_{-2} & & & & \\
 & & \delta y_{-\frac{3}{2}} & & & \\
x_{-1} & y_{-1} & & \delta^2 y_{-1} & & \\
 & & \delta y_{-\frac{1}{2}} & & \delta^3 y_{-\frac{1}{2}} & \\
x_0 & y_0 & & \delta^2 y_0 & & \delta^4 y_0 \\
 & & \delta y_{\frac{1}{2}} & & \delta^3 y_{+\frac{1}{2}} & \\
x_1 & y_1 & & \delta^2 y_1 & & \\
 & & \delta y_{\frac{3}{2}} & & & \\
x_2 & y_2 & & & & \\
\cdot & \cdot & & & & \\
\cdot & \cdot & & & & \\
\cdot & \cdot & & & &
\end{array}
$$

In this difference table the subscripts remain constant along horizontal rows, but only at every other column. Only in the case of even-order differences are the subscripts integral numbers.

The three difference tables are different only in the sense of nomenclature. By comparing the various terms it can be noted that

$$
\begin{aligned}
\Delta y_0 &= \nabla y_1 = \delta y_{\frac{1}{2}} \\
\Delta y_1 &= \nabla y_2 = \delta y_{\frac{3}{2}} \\
&\cdots\cdots\cdots \\
\Delta^2 y_0 &= \nabla^2 y_2 = \delta^2 y_1 \\
&\cdots\cdots\cdots \\
\Delta^r y_{i-r/2} &= \nabla^r y_{i+r/2} = \delta^r y_i
\end{aligned}
$$

As the next step in the present development consider the case of $f(x)$ a polynomial of degree n. For $n = 1$, $f(x)$ is merely a straight line written as

$$n = 1 \qquad y = a_0 x + b$$

The first forward difference is

$$
\begin{aligned}
\Delta y_0 &= (a_0 x_1 + b) - (a_0 x_0 + b) \\
&= a_0(x_1 - x_0) \\
&= a_0 h \\
&= \text{constant}
\end{aligned}
$$

The second difference is zero. For $n = 2$, $f(x)$ is a quadratic written as

$$n = 2 \qquad y = a_0 x^2 + a_1 x + b$$

The forward differences become

$$\begin{aligned}\Delta y_0 &= a_0(x_1^2 - x_0^2) + a_1(x_1 - x_0)\\ &= a_0(h^2 + 2hx_0) + a_1h\\ \Delta^2 y_0 &= 2a_0h^2 = \text{constant}\\ \Delta^3 y_0 &= 0\end{aligned}$$

From these two simple cases a number of important features of differencing a polynomial become apparent:

1. The nth difference of a polynomial of degree n is a constant,

$$\Delta^n y = a_0 h^n n!$$

2. The $(n + 1)$st difference of a polynomial of degree n is zero.
3. The first difference of a polynomial of degree n is a polynomial of degree $n - 1$.

These results correspond to the fact that the nth derivative of a polynomial of degree n is a constant, the $(n + 1)$st derivative zero, and the first derivative is a polynomial of degree $n - 1$.

The converse of (1) and (2) above can also be shown to be true. This implies that if a difference table is formed from a set of tabulated data with the independent variable equally spaced and the nth differences become constant, then a polynomial of degree n will fit the data exactly. Such a result neglects the practical problem of round-off error (see Sec. 2.13) preventing the attainment of true constant differences.

2.3. Newton's Interpolation Formulas

In the present section a number of different forms of the approximating polynomial $\phi_n(x)$ are presented. Equal spacing on the independent variable is still assumed. From the preceding discussion a number of comments are possible regarding the correspondence between $\phi_n(x)$ and $f(x)$. Since there are $n + 1$ tabulated data points, a polynomial of degree n, $\phi_n(x)$, can be constructed which coincides with the available data. If the function $y = f(x)$ is itself a polynomial of degree not in excess of n, $\phi_n(x)$ and $f(x)$ will coincide with each other exactly [rounding errors in forming $\phi_n(x)$ being ignored]. If, however, the degree of $f(x)$ exceeds n, $\phi_n(x)$ and $f(x)$ will agree only at the tabulated data points, but not between. In such a case

$$f(x) = \phi_n(x) + R(x)$$

where $R(x)$ is a function which has roots at the tabulated points, i.e., is zero at $x = x_0, x_1, \ldots, x_n$. In effect $R(x)$ may be thought of as the error which evolves when $\phi_n(x)$ is taken as a representation of $f(x)$ in the interval x_0 to x_n.

A word of caution is appropriate at this time. There are many analytic functions which cannot be adequately approximated by a polynomial under the restriction that the polynomial coincide with the function at equally spaced points in the independent variable. Examples of such functions include those with singularities or severe oscillations in the region of interest. Thus a polynomial fit of data should never be used blindly. The behavior of both the polynomial and the function should always be investigated over the region of interest before the polynomial is used to represent $f(x)$.

Since

$$E = 1 + \Delta$$
$$E^\alpha = (1 + \Delta)^\alpha \qquad \alpha = \text{constant}$$

the expansion of $(1 + \Delta)^\alpha$ leads to

$$E^\alpha = 1 + \alpha\Delta + \frac{\alpha(\alpha - 1)}{2!}\Delta^2 + \frac{\alpha(\alpha - 1)(\alpha - 2)}{3!}\Delta^3 + \cdots$$

For the particular case $\alpha = n$ = positive integer, the series terminates after $n + 1$ terms with the last term containing Δ^n. If $\alpha \neq$ an integer, then the series does not terminate but remains infinite. Upon applying both sides to the point $y(x_0)$ there results

$$\begin{aligned} E^\alpha y(x_0) &= y(x_0 + \alpha h) \\ &= \left[1 + \alpha\Delta + \frac{\alpha(\alpha - 1)\Delta^2}{2!} + \cdots \right. \\ &\quad \left. + \frac{\alpha(\alpha - 1)(\alpha - 2)\cdots(\alpha - n + 1)}{n!}\Delta^n + \cdots\right] y(x_0) \end{aligned}$$

or

$$\begin{aligned} y(x_0 + \alpha h) &= \left[1 + \alpha\Delta + \frac{\alpha(\alpha - 1)\Delta^2}{2!} + \cdots \right. \\ &\quad \left. + \frac{\alpha(\alpha - 1)(\alpha - 2)\cdots(\alpha - n + 1)}{n!}\Delta^n\right] y(x_0) + R(x) \end{aligned}$$

By calling the first part on the right side $\phi_n(x)$ this equation can be written as

$$y(x_0 + \alpha h) = \phi_n(x) + R(x)$$

For $\alpha = n$ = positive integer, $R(x) = 0$ since all differences above Δ^n are zero. Thus

$$y(x_0 + \alpha h) = \phi_n(x) \qquad \alpha = n = \text{positive integer}$$

where

$$\begin{aligned} \phi_n(x) &= \left[1 + \alpha\Delta + \frac{\alpha(\alpha - 1)\Delta^2}{2!} + \cdots \right. \\ &\quad \left. + \frac{\alpha(\alpha - 1)(\alpha - 2)\cdots(\alpha - n + 1)\Delta^n}{n!}\right] y(x_0) \qquad (2.3.1) \end{aligned}$$

$\phi_n(x)$ as given in (2.3.1) is an interpolating polynomial for $f(x)$ and is specifically called Newton's forward formula (NFF). Notice that (2.3.1) uses the successive values in the upper descending diagonal of a forward-difference table.

For $\alpha \neq n =$ positive integer, $R(x) \neq 0$, and $R(x)$ is the remainder, or error, term. It represents the error between $f(x)$ and $\phi_n(x)$ for values of $x \neq x_0, x_1, \ldots, x_n$. This corresponds to using fractional values of α.

In exactly the same manner, but starting with

$$E^{-1} = 1 - \nabla \qquad E^{\alpha} = (1 - \nabla)^{-\alpha}$$

there results
$$\begin{aligned} y(x_n + \alpha h) &= E^{\alpha} y(x_n) \\ &= \left[1 + \alpha\nabla + \frac{\alpha(\alpha+1)}{2!}\nabla^2 + \cdots \right. \\ &\quad \left. + \frac{\alpha(\alpha+1)\cdots(\alpha+n-1)}{n!}\nabla^n\right] y(x_n) + R(x) \end{aligned}$$

In this case

$$\begin{aligned} \phi_n(x) = \left[1 + \alpha\nabla + \frac{\alpha(\alpha+1)}{2!}\nabla^2 + \cdots \right. \\ \left. + \frac{\alpha(\alpha+1)\cdots(\alpha+n-1)\nabla^n}{n!}\right] y(x_n) \end{aligned} \qquad (2.3.2)$$

and $\phi_n(x)$ is called Newton's backward formula (NBF). This uses the successive values $y(x_n) = y_n, \nabla y_n, \nabla^2 y_n, \ldots$ in a backward-difference table.

To use formula (2.3.1), it can be seen that for $\alpha =$ positive fraction the value of $y(x)$ which results is between two of the tabulated points. Thus $\phi_n(x)$ is interpolating the given data with an error $R(x)$. For $-1 < \alpha < 0$, α a negative fraction, the value of $y(x)$ which results is outside the range of tabulated points and $\phi_n(x)$ is extrapolating the given data. Special care, however, must be used in the extrapolation. Since the interpolating polynomial has been chosen to fit in the interval $x_0 \leq x \leq x_n$, it is not to be expected to hold much beyond this interval. A general rule that one should not attempt to extrapolate more than one h spacing beyond x_0 or x_n is well worth remembering. For $\alpha = 0, 1, 2, \ldots, n$, $\phi_n(x)$ corresponds exactly to the values of $y_0, y_1, \ldots, y_n$ since $R(x) = 0$.

Actually the two interpolating polynomials are the same except for nomenclature as long as the same set of points $x_0, x_1, \ldots, x_n$ is used. Both polynomials may be written in shorthand notation by using the binomial coefficient [(2.1.6)]. Thus

$$\phi_n(x)_{\text{NFF}} = y(x_0 + \alpha h) = \sum_{k=0}^{n} \binom{\alpha}{k} \Delta^k y(x_0) = \sum_{k=0}^{n} \binom{\alpha}{k} \Delta^k y_0 \qquad (2.3.3)$$

and

$$\phi_n(x)_{\text{NBF}} = y(x_n + \alpha h) = \sum_{k=0}^{n} (-1)^k \binom{-\alpha}{k} \nabla^k y(x_n)$$

$$= \sum_{k=0}^{n} (-1)^k \binom{-\alpha}{k} \nabla^k y_n \quad (2.3.4)$$

Since the main function of the interpolation formulas is to calculate $f(x)$ between the given data points, an estimate of the error involved [the value of $R(x)$] is important. To aid in finding the analytical representation of $R(x)$, Rolle's theorem will first be stated.

If $f(x)$ is continuous in an interval $a < x < b$, $f'(x)$ is continuous for $a < x < b$, and *$f(a) = f(b) = 0$, then $f'(\xi) = 0$ for at least one ξ such that $a < \xi < b$.*

In order to find the remainder term for $f(x)$ in NFF, first assume that $f(x)$ has continuous derivatives up to order $n + 1$ in the interval x_0 to x_n. In this interval

$$f(x) = \phi_n(x) + R(x)$$

At the specific points $x_0, x_1, \ldots, x_n$, $R(x) = 0$, but for any other point let

$$R(x) \neq 0 = (x - x_0)(x - x_1) \cdots (x - x_n)G(x)$$

where $G(x)$ is unknown. Consider a new function $P(z)$ such that

$$P(z) = f(z) - \phi_n(z) - (z - x_0)(z - x_1) \cdots (z - x_n)G(x) \quad (2.3.5)$$

When $z = x_0, x_1, \ldots, x_n$, $P(z) = 0$, and when $z = x$, $P(x) = 0$ since the right-hand side is merely the definition of $f(x)$. Thus $P(z)$ possesses the property of having $n + 2$ roots corresponding to $z = x_0, x_1, \ldots, x_n, x$.

By Rolle's theorem $P'(z)$ must vanish at some point between each of the points at which $P(z)$ is zero. Thus there are $n + 1$ roots of $P'(z)$. If we extend this reasoning to $P''(z)$, there must be n distinct roots of $P''(z)$ in the interval x_0 to x_n.

Continuing further along this path, one finally arrives at the statement that $P^{[n+1]}(z)$† must vanish at least once in the interval x_0 to x_n. Call this point $z = \xi$. Upon differentiating (2.3.5) $n + 1$ times there results

$$P^{[n+1]}(z) = f^{[n+1]}(z) - G(x)(n + 1)!$$

For the specific point $z = \xi$

$$G(x) = \frac{f^{[n+1]}(\xi)}{(n + 1)!}$$

† The superscript in brackets is taken to mean differentiation.

Thus the remainder term in NFF is

$$R(x) = \frac{(x - x_0)(x - x_1) \cdots (x - x_n)}{(n + 1)!} f^{[n+1]}(\xi) \qquad (2.3.6)$$

where $x_0 < \xi < x_n$. If $f(x)$ is actually a polynomial of degree n, then $f^{[n+1]}(\xi) = 0$ and $R(x) = 0, f(x) = \phi_n(x)$. This, of course, was expected.

Since

$$x = x_0 + \alpha h$$

(2.3.6) can be rearranged to form

$$R(x)_{\text{NFF}} = \frac{h^{n+1} f^{[n+1]}(\xi)}{(n + 1)!} \alpha(\alpha - 1)(\alpha - 2) \cdots (\alpha - n) \qquad (2.3.7)$$

which is another version of the remainder term. On the assumption that $f^{[n+1]}(\xi)$ remains constant (2.3.7) shows that as h gets smaller or the spacing between $x_0, x_1, \ldots, x_n$ is decreased the error for interpolation becomes smaller. For certain functions, however, a variation in $f^{[n+1]}(\xi)$ may result in $R(x)$ increasing as h is decreased.

A real question arises, however, as to the practical limitations of (2.3.6) and (2.3.7) or whether or not it is possible actually to evaluate $R(x)$. If $f(x)$ is available only in the form of tabulated data, then there is no real way to determine $f^{[n+1]}(\xi)$ since nothing is known about $f(x)$. Even if $f(x)$ is given in analytical form, it is usually possible to estimate only the upper bound on $f^{[n+1]}(\xi)$. This is due to the fact that ξ is not a priori determined and is a function of x.

In exactly the same way the remainder term in NBF can be shown to be

$$R(x)_{\text{NBF}} = \frac{h^{n+1} f^{[n+1]}(\xi)}{(n + 1)!} \alpha(\alpha + 1)(\alpha + 2) \cdots (\alpha + n) \qquad (2.3.8)$$

2.4. Central-difference Interpolation Formulas

In much the same manner as the forward- and backward-difference operators were used to derive an interpolation formula, it is possible to use the central-difference operators to obtain further formulas. The results obtained will also hold only in the case of equally spaced data. As a first step note that

$$\Delta^\alpha = E^{\alpha/2} \delta^\alpha \qquad (2.4.1)$$

and thus that

$$E^{\frac{1}{2}} \delta y_0 = \delta y_{\frac{1}{2}} = \Delta y_0 \qquad (2.4.2)$$

Using
$$E^\alpha = 1 + \binom{\alpha}{1} \Delta + \binom{\alpha}{2} \Delta^2 + \binom{\alpha}{3} \Delta^3 + \cdots$$

where $\binom{\alpha}{k}$ are the binomial coefficients, multiply all terms from Δ^2 on by

$1 = (1 + \Delta)E^{-1}$. This leads to

$$E^\alpha = 1 + \binom{\alpha}{1}\Delta + \binom{\alpha}{2}\Delta^2E^{-1} + \left[\binom{\alpha}{2} + \binom{\alpha}{3}\right]\Delta^3E^{-1} + \left[\binom{\alpha}{3} + \binom{\alpha}{4}\right]\Delta^4E^{-1} + \cdots$$

It is a simple matter to show that

$$\binom{r}{k} + \binom{r}{k+1} = \binom{r+1}{k+1}$$

and thus

$$E^\alpha = 1 + \binom{\alpha}{1}\Delta + \binom{\alpha}{2}\Delta^2E^{-1} + \binom{\alpha+1}{3}\Delta^3E^{-1} + \binom{\alpha+1}{4}\Delta^4E^{-1} + \cdots$$

or

$$y(x_0 + \alpha h) = E^\alpha y_0 = \left[1 + \binom{\alpha}{1}\Delta + \binom{\alpha}{2}\Delta^2E^{-1} + \cdots\right]y_0 \tag{2.4.3}$$

But from (2.4.1), with $\alpha = 2$,

$$\Delta^2E^{-1} = \delta^2$$

or

$$\Delta^2E^{-1}y_0 = \delta^2y_0 \tag{2.4.4}$$

Further, with $\alpha = 3$,

$$\Delta^3E^{-1} = E^{\frac{1}{2}}\delta^3$$

and

$$\Delta^3E^{-1}y_0 = E^{\frac{1}{2}}\delta^3y_0$$

which becomes, upon application of (2.4.2),

$$E^{\frac{1}{2}}\delta^3y_0 = \delta^3y_{\frac{1}{2}} \tag{2.4.5}$$

Upon substituting (2.4.2), (2.4.4), and (2.4.5) into (2.4.3) there results

$$y(x_0 + \alpha h) = y_0 + \binom{\alpha}{1}\delta y_{\frac{1}{2}} + \binom{\alpha}{2}\delta^2y_0 + \binom{\alpha+1}{3}\delta^3y_{\frac{1}{2}} + \cdots$$

By multiplying all the terms from Δ^4 on up by $1 = (1 + \Delta)E^{-1}$ and proceeding as before to evaluate the central differences,

$$y(x_0 + \alpha h) = y_0 + \binom{\alpha}{1}\delta y_{\frac{1}{2}} + \binom{\alpha}{2}\delta^2y_0 + \binom{\alpha+1}{3}\delta^3y_{\frac{1}{2}} + \binom{\alpha+1}{4}\delta^4y_0 + \cdots$$

If we repeat the process of multiplication for Δ^6, Δ^8, etc., and evaluate the central differences, there finally results

$$y(x_0 + \alpha h) = y_0 + \binom{\alpha}{1} \delta y_{\frac{1}{2}} + \binom{\alpha}{2} \delta^2 y_0 + \binom{\alpha+1}{3} \delta^3 y_{\frac{1}{2}} + \binom{\alpha+1}{4} \delta^4 y_0 + \cdots + \binom{\alpha+r-1}{2r} \delta^{2r} y_0 + \binom{\alpha+r}{2r+1} \delta^{2r+1} y_{\frac{1}{2}} + R(x) \quad (2.4.6)$$

The interpolation polynomial of (2.4.6), resulting from $R(x) = 0$, is called "Gauss' forward formula" (GFF) and is written as

$$\phi_n(x) = y_0 + \binom{\alpha}{1} \delta y_{\frac{1}{2}} + \binom{\alpha}{2} \delta^2 y_0 + \binom{\alpha+1}{3} \delta^3 y_{\frac{1}{2}} + \binom{\alpha+1}{4} \delta^4 y_0 + \cdots + \binom{\alpha+r-1}{2r} \delta^{2r} y_0 + \binom{\alpha+r}{2r+1} \delta^{2r+1} y_{\frac{1}{2}} \quad (2.4.7)$$

The symbol r is used in this equation because the subscripts on $y(x)$ are taken as $\pm$ in a central-difference scheme. If the total number of differences used in (2.4.7) is even, $n = 2r$ and the final term involves $\delta^{2r} y_0$. n corresponds to the total of $n + 1$ tabulated values. The polynomial is exactly equal to $f(x)$ at the points $x = x_r, x_{-(r-1)}, \ldots, x_0, x_1, \ldots, x_{r-1}, x_r$. If the total number of differences used is odd, $n = 2r + 1$ and the final difference is $\delta^{2r+1} y_{\frac{1}{2}}$. The polynomial then corresponds exactly to $f(x)$ at the points $x = x_{-r}, x_{-(r-1)}, \ldots, x_0, x_1, \ldots, x_{r-1}, x_r, x_{r+1}$. The GFF is symmetrical with respect to a value of $\alpha = +0.25$, and the differences employed form a zigzag pattern in a central-difference table.

The same result can be obtained in an entirely different manner. Assume that the set of tabulated data is to fit a polynomial of the form

$$\begin{aligned}\phi_n(x) &= a_0 + a_1(x - x_0) + a_2(x - x_0)(x - x_1) \\ &+ a_3(x - x_0)(x - x_1)(x - x_{-1}) + a_4(x - x_0)(x - x_1)(x - x_{-1})(x - x_2) \\ &+ a_5(x - x_0)(x - x_1)(x - x_{-1})(x - x_2)(x - x_{-2}) + \cdots \quad (2.4.8)\end{aligned}$$

The a_i's are coefficients of the polynomial which are to be evaluated on the basis of making $y = f(x)$ and $\phi_n(x)$ agree at the tabulated points. From the character of the polynomial it can be seen that greater weight is to be given to the data around x_0.

At $x = x_0$, $y = y_0 = \phi_n(x)$, and (2.4.8) becomes

$$y_0 = a_0 + 0$$

At $x = x_1$, $y = y_1 = \phi_n(x)$, and (2.4.8) becomes

$$y_1 = y_0 + a_1(x_1 - x_0)$$

and thus

$$a_1 = \frac{y_1 - y_0}{x_1 - x_0} = \frac{y_1 - y_0}{h} = \frac{\Delta y_0}{h}$$

At $x = x_1$, $y = y_{-1}$, and (2.4.8) becomes

$$y_{-1} = y_0 + \frac{\Delta y_0}{h}(x_{-1} - x_0) + a_2(x_{-1} - x_0)(x_{-1} - x_1)$$

$$= y_0 + \frac{\Delta y_0}{h}(-h) + a_2(-h)(-2h)$$

and thus
$$a_2 = \frac{y_{-1} - 2y_0 + y_1}{2h^2} = \frac{\Delta^2 y_{-1}}{2h^2}$$

In exactly the same way

$$a_3 = \frac{\Delta^3 y_{-1}}{3!h^3} \qquad a_4 = \frac{\Delta^4 y_{-2}}{4!h^4}$$

Resubstituting into (2.4.8),

$$\phi_n(x) = y_0 + (x - x_0)\frac{\Delta y_0}{h} + (x - x_0)(x - x_1)\frac{\Delta^2 y_{-1}}{2!h^2}$$
$$+ (x - x_0)(x - x_1)(x - x_{-1})\frac{\Delta^3 y_{-1}}{3!h^3}$$
$$+ (x - x_0)(x - x_1)(x - x_{-1})(x - x_2)\frac{\Delta^4 y_{-2}}{4!h^4}$$
$$+ (x - x_0)(x - x_1)(x - x_{-1})(x - x_2)(x - x_{-2})\frac{\Delta^5 y_{-2}}{5!h^5} + \cdots$$

But since
$$x = x_0 + \alpha h$$

$$\phi_n(x) = y_0 + \alpha\,\Delta y_0 + \frac{\alpha(\alpha - 1)}{2!}\Delta^2 y_{-1} + \frac{\alpha(\alpha - 1)(\alpha + 1)}{3!}\Delta^3 y_{-1}$$
$$+ \frac{\alpha(\alpha - 1)(\alpha + 1)(\alpha - 2)}{4!}\Delta^4 y_{-2} + \cdots \tag{2.4.9}$$

We note further that

$$\Delta y_0 = \delta y_{\frac{1}{2}}$$
$$\Delta^2 y_{-1} = \delta^2 y_0$$
$$\Delta^3 y_{-1} = \delta^3 y_{\frac{1}{2}}$$
$$\Delta^4 y_{-2} = \delta^4 y_0$$

and
$$\frac{\alpha(\alpha - 1)(\alpha + 1)}{3!} = \binom{\alpha + 1}{3}$$
$$\frac{\alpha(\alpha - 1)(\alpha + 1)(\alpha - 2)}{4!} = \binom{\alpha + 1}{4}$$
. . . .

and (2.4.9) is transformed into GFF as given by (2.4.7). By expanding the binomial coefficients in (2.4.7) it is possible to write GFF in a more open form, namely,

$$\phi_n(x) = y_0 + \alpha\,\delta y_{\frac{1}{2}} + \frac{\alpha(\alpha - 1)}{2!}\,\delta^2 y_0 + \frac{\alpha(\alpha^2 - 1^2)}{3!}\,\delta^3 y_{\frac{1}{2}} + \frac{\alpha(\alpha^2 - 1^2)(\alpha - 2)}{4!}\,\delta^4 y_0 + \cdots + \frac{\alpha(\alpha^2 - 1^2)\cdots[\alpha^2 - (r-1)^2](\alpha - r)}{(2r)!}\,\delta^{2r} y_0 + \frac{\alpha(\alpha^2 - 1^2)\cdots(\alpha^2 - r^2)}{(2r+1)!}\,\delta^{2r+1} y_{\frac{1}{2}}$$

If the interpolation polynomial is written in the form

$$\phi_n(x) = a_0 + a_1(x - x_0) + a_2(x - x_0)(x - x_1) + a_3(x - x_0)(x - x_{-1})(x - x_1) + a_4(x - x_0)(x - x_{-1})(x - x_1)(x - x_2) + a_5(x - x_0)(x - x_{-1})(x - x_1)(x - x_{-2})(x - x_2) + \cdots$$

then evaluation of the coefficients in the same manner as just carried out leads to

$$\phi_n(x) = y_0 + \binom{\alpha}{1}\delta y_{-\frac{1}{2}} + \binom{\alpha+1}{2}\delta^2 y_0 + \binom{\alpha+1}{3}\delta^3 y_{-\frac{1}{2}} + \binom{\alpha+2}{4}\delta^4 y_0 + \cdots + \binom{\alpha+r}{2r}\delta^{2r} y_0 + \binom{\alpha+r}{2r+1}\delta^{2r+1} y_{-\frac{1}{2}} \qquad (2.4.10)$$

or
$$\phi_n(x) = y_0 + \alpha\,\delta y_{-\frac{1}{2}} + \frac{\alpha(\alpha + 1)}{2!}\,\delta^2 y_0 + \frac{\alpha(\alpha^2 - 1^2)}{3!}\,\delta^3 y_{-\frac{1}{2}} + \frac{\alpha(\alpha^2 - 1^2)(\alpha + 2)}{4!}\,\delta^4 y_0 + \cdots + \frac{\alpha(\alpha^2 - 1^2)\cdots[\alpha^2 - (r-1)^2](\alpha + r)}{(2r)!}\,\delta^{2r} y_0 + \frac{\alpha(\alpha^2 - 1^2)\cdots(\alpha^2 - r^2)}{(2r+1)!}\,\delta^{2r+1} y_{-\frac{1}{2}} \qquad (2.4.11)$$

In either form, (2.4.10) or (2.4.11), this interpolation polynomial is referred to as "Gauss' backward formula" (GBF). If the total number of differences used is even, $n = 2r$ and the final term involves $\delta^{2r}y_0$. This polynomial is then identical to GFF with $n = 2r$. If the total number of differences used is odd, then $n = 2r + 1$ and the final term involves $\delta^{2r+1}y_{-\frac{1}{2}}$. The polynomial then corresponds exactly to $f(x)$ at the points $x = x_{-(r+1)}, x_{-r}, x_{-(r-1)}, \ldots, x_0, x_1, \ldots, x_r$. The GBF is symmetrical with respect to a value of $\alpha = -0.25$, and the differences employed form a zigzag pattern in a central-difference table.

Since GFF is symmetrical around a point $x_0 + 0.25h$ and GBF is symmetrical around $x_0 - 0.25h$, the average of the two formulas will be symmetrical around x_0 corresponding to $\alpha = 0$. Adding (2.4.7) and

(2.4.10) and dividing by 2 leads to

$$\phi_n(x) = y_0 + \tfrac{1}{2}\left\{\binom{\alpha}{1}(\delta y_{\frac{1}{2}} + \delta y_{-\frac{1}{2}}) + \left[\binom{\alpha}{2} + \binom{\alpha+1}{2}\right]\delta^2 y_0 + \binom{\alpha+1}{3}(\delta^3 y_{\frac{1}{2}} + \delta^3 y_{-\frac{1}{2}}) + \left[\binom{\alpha+1}{4} + \binom{\alpha+2}{4}\right]\delta^4 y_0 + \cdots\right\}$$

Using the average operator μ such that

$$\mu\delta y_0 = \tfrac{1}{2}(\delta y_{\frac{1}{2}} + \delta y_{-\frac{1}{2}})$$
$$\mu\delta^2 y_0 = \tfrac{1}{2}(\delta^2 y_{\frac{1}{2}} + \delta^2 y_{-\frac{1}{2}})$$
$$\cdots\cdots\cdots\cdots\cdots$$
$$\mu\delta^i y_0 = \tfrac{1}{2}(\delta^i y_{\frac{1}{2}} + \delta^i y_{-\frac{1}{2}})$$

and also
$$\binom{\alpha+r-1}{2r} + \binom{\alpha+r}{2r} = \frac{\alpha}{r}\binom{\alpha+r-1}{2r-1}$$

transforms the above equation to

$$\phi_n(x) = y_0 + \binom{\alpha}{1}\mu\delta y_0 + \frac{\alpha}{2}\binom{\alpha}{1}\delta^2 y_0 + \binom{\alpha+1}{3}\mu\delta^3 y_0 + \frac{\alpha}{4}\binom{\alpha+1}{3}\delta^4 y_0 + \cdots + \frac{\alpha}{2r}\binom{\alpha+r-1}{2r-1}\delta^{2r}y_0 + \binom{\alpha+r}{2r}\mu\delta^{2r+1}y_0 \quad (2.4.12)$$

The interpolation polynomial of (2.4.12) is called the "Stirling formula" (SF). If the total number of differences is even, $n = 2r$ and the final term involves $\delta^{2r}y_0$. The polynomial is exactly equal to $f(x)$ at the points $x = x_{-r}, x_{-(r-1)}, \ldots, x_0, x_1, \ldots, x_{r-1}, x_r$ and is equal to GFF and GBF for $n = 2r$. If the total number of differences used is odd, $n = 2r + 1$ and the final term involves $\delta^{2r+1}y_0$. The polynomial is exactly equal to $f(x)$ at the points $x = x_{-r}, x_{-(r+1)}, \ldots, x_0, x_1, \ldots, x_{r-1}, x_r$ but is also influenced by the two outside points $x_{-(r-1)}$ and $x_{(r+1)}$. SF is symmetric with respect to a value of $\alpha = 0$, and the differences employed all line up on the horizontal line through x_0.

An expanded form of (2.4.12) would be

$$\phi_n(x) = y_0 + \alpha\mu\delta y_0 + \frac{\alpha^2}{2!}\delta^2 y_0 + \frac{\alpha(\alpha^2-1^2)}{3!}\mu\delta^3 y_0 + \frac{\alpha^2(\alpha^2-1^2)}{4!}\delta^4 y_0 + \cdots + \frac{\alpha^2(\alpha^2-1^2)\cdots[\alpha^2-(r-1)^2]}{(2r)!}\delta^{2r}y_0 + \frac{\alpha(\alpha^2-1^2)\cdots(\alpha^2-r^2)}{(2r+1)!}\mu\delta^{2r+1}y_0 \quad (2.4.13)$$

While the central-difference interpolation polynomials of Gauss and Stirling are interesting, they find little favor in modern-day usage.

Instead, the formulas of Bessel and Everett, coupled with a throwback feature (outlined shortly), are of computational importance. Starting with GBF, let $\alpha = \alpha - 1$, and multiply by E. This does not change the equality of the polynomial but the form becomes

$$\phi_n(x) = E\left[y_0 + \binom{\alpha - 1}{1} \delta y_{-\frac{1}{2}} + \binom{\alpha}{2} \delta^2 y_0 + \binom{\alpha}{3} \delta^3 y_{-\frac{1}{2}} + \binom{\alpha + 1}{4} \delta^4 y_0 + \cdots \right]$$

$$= y_1 + \binom{\alpha - 1}{1} \delta y_{-\frac{1}{2}} + \binom{\alpha}{2} \delta^2 y_1 + \binom{\alpha}{3} \delta^3 y_{-\frac{1}{2}} + \binom{\alpha + 1}{4} \delta^4 y_1 + \cdots$$

Averaging this formula with GFF and using the mean operator leads to

$$\phi_n(x) = \mu y_{\frac{1}{2}} + (\alpha - \tfrac{1}{2})\delta y_{\frac{1}{2}} + \binom{\alpha}{2} \mu\delta^2 y_{\frac{1}{2}} + \frac{\alpha - \frac{1}{2}}{3} \binom{\alpha}{2} \delta^3 y_{\frac{1}{2}} + \binom{\alpha + 1}{4} \mu\delta^4 y_{\frac{1}{2}} + \cdots + \binom{\alpha + r - 1}{2r} \mu\delta^{2r} y_{\frac{1}{2}} + \left(\frac{\alpha - \frac{1}{2}}{2r + 1}\right)\binom{\alpha + r - 1}{2r} \delta^{2r+1} y_{\frac{1}{2}} \quad (2.4.14)$$

Equation (2.4.14) is called "Bessel's polynomial interpolation formula" (BF) and may be written in expanded form as

$$\phi_n(x) = \mu y_{\frac{1}{2}} + (\alpha - \tfrac{1}{2})\, \delta y_{\frac{1}{2}} + \frac{\alpha(\alpha - 1)}{2!} \mu\delta^2 y_{\frac{1}{2}} + \frac{\alpha(\alpha - 1)(\alpha - \frac{1}{2})}{3!} \delta^3 y_{\frac{1}{2}} + \cdots + \frac{\alpha(\alpha^2 - 1^2) \cdots [\alpha^2 - (r - 1)^2](\alpha - r)}{(2r)!} \mu\delta^{2r} y_{\frac{1}{2}} + \frac{\alpha(\alpha^2 - 1^2) \cdots [\alpha^2 - (r - 1)^2](\alpha - r)(\alpha - \frac{1}{2})}{(2r + 1)!} \delta^{2r+1} y_{\frac{1}{2}} \quad (2.4.15)$$

If a change is made by defining

$$\alpha = s + \tfrac{1}{2}$$

then (2.4.15) takes the more symmetrical form

$$\phi_n(x) = \mu y_{\frac{1}{2}} + s\delta y_{\frac{1}{2}} + \frac{s^2 - \frac{1}{4}}{2!} \mu\delta^2 y_{\frac{1}{2}} + \frac{s(s^2 - \frac{1}{4})}{3!} \delta^3 y_{\frac{1}{2}} + \cdots + (s^2 - \tfrac{1}{4})(s^2 - \tfrac{9}{4}) \cdots \left[s^2 - \frac{(2r - 1)^2}{4} \right] \frac{\mu\delta^{2r} y_{\frac{1}{2}}}{(2r)!} + s(s^2 - \tfrac{1}{4})(s^2 - \tfrac{9}{4}) \cdots \left[s^2 - \frac{(2r - 1)^2}{4} \right] \frac{\delta^{2r+1} y_{\frac{1}{2}}}{(2r + 1)!} \quad (2.4.16)$$

If the total number of differences used in (2.4.14) is even or odd, the polynomial is exactly equal to $f(x)$ at the points $x = x_{-r}, x_{-(r-1)}, \ldots, x_0, x_1, \ldots, x_r, x_{r+1}$. The differences form a symmetrical pattern around $\alpha = 0.50$.

By using the relationship

$$\delta^{2r+1}y_{\frac{1}{2}} = \delta^{2r}y_1 - \delta^{2r}y_0$$

it is possible to eliminate all odd differences in any central-difference interpolation formula. This leaves a formula containing only even differences. In particular, when this is applied to GFF there results

$$\begin{aligned}\phi_n(x) &= \alpha y_1 + \binom{\alpha+1}{3}\delta^2 y_1 + \binom{\alpha+2}{5}\delta^4 y_1 + \binom{\alpha+3}{7}\delta^6 y_1 + \cdots \\ &\quad - \binom{\alpha-1}{1}y_0 - \binom{\alpha}{3}\delta^2 y_0 - \binom{\alpha+1}{5}\delta^4 y_0 - \binom{\alpha+2}{7}\delta^6 y_0 - \cdots\end{aligned} \tag{2.4.17}$$

In expanded form this can be written as

$$\begin{aligned}\phi_n(x) &= \alpha y_1 + \frac{\alpha(\alpha-1)(\alpha+1)}{3!}\delta^2 y_1 \\ &\quad + \frac{\alpha(\alpha-1)(\alpha-2)(\alpha+1)(\alpha+2)}{5!}\delta^4 y_1 + \cdots \\ &\quad + \frac{\alpha(\alpha-1)\cdots(\alpha-r)(\alpha+1)(\alpha+2)\cdots(\alpha+r-1)}{(2r+1)!}\delta^{2r}y_1 \\ &\quad - (\alpha-1)y_0 - \frac{\alpha(\alpha-1)(\alpha-2)}{3!}\delta^2 y_0 \\ &\quad - \frac{\alpha(\alpha-1)(\alpha-2)(\alpha-3)(\alpha+1)}{5!}\delta^4 y_0 - \cdots \\ &\quad - \frac{\alpha(\alpha-1)(\alpha-2)\cdots(\alpha-r-1)(\alpha+1)\cdots(\alpha+r-1)}{(2r+1)!}\delta^{2r}y_0\end{aligned} \tag{2.4.18}$$

In either form, (2.4.17) or (2.4.18), the interpolation formula is called "Everett's formula" (EF). It is identical to GFF when the latter is terminated at the $(2r+1)$st difference. It is important to note that because Everett's formula needs only $\delta^2 y_0, \delta^4 y_0, \delta^6 y_0, \ldots, \delta^2 y_1, \delta^4 y_1, \delta^6 y_1, \ldots$ considerable simplification can sometimes be achieved since only half the differences required by the other formulas are now needed.

The remainder, or error, term for each of the above interpolation formulas may be obtained in exactly the same manner as has been carried out for NFF. Listed below are the necessary results.

$\left.\begin{array}{l}\text{GFF}\\ \text{GBF}\end{array}\right\} n = \text{even}$

$$R(x) = \binom{\alpha + r}{2r + 1} h^{2r+1} f^{[2r+1]}(\xi) \qquad x_{-r} < \xi < x_r$$

GFF, n = odd

$$R(x) = \binom{\alpha + r}{2r + 2} h^{2r+2} f^{[2r+2]}(\xi) \qquad x_{-r} < \xi < x_{r+1}$$

GBF, n = odd

$$R(x) = \binom{\alpha + r + 1}{2r + 2} h^{2r+2} f^{[2r+2]}(\xi) \qquad x_{-(r+1)} < \xi < x_r$$

SF

If $n = 2r$ = even, then $R(x)$ is same as $R(x)$ for GFF and GBF for n even
If $n = 2r + 1$ = odd, then $R(x)$ is mean average of $R(x)$ for GFF and GBF for n odd

BF

If $n = 2r$ = even, then $R(x)$ is complicated function but can be obtained from GFF and GBF with averaging
If $n = 2r + 1$ = odd, then $R(x)$ is same as $R(x)$ for GFF terminated with an odd difference

EF

$R(x)$ is same as for GFF terminated with odd differences

2.5. Application of Throwback to Bessel's and Everett's Formulas

Consider BF as given in (2.4.15) and using the average operator.

$$\begin{aligned}\phi_n(x) &= \tfrac{1}{2}(y_0 + y_1) + (\alpha - \tfrac{1}{2})\delta y_{\frac{1}{2}} + \frac{\alpha(\alpha-1)}{2.2!}(\delta^2 y_0 + \delta^2 y_1) \\ &+ \frac{\alpha(\alpha-1)(\alpha-\frac{1}{2})}{3!}\delta^3 y_{\frac{1}{2}} + \frac{\alpha(\alpha-1)(\alpha-2)(\alpha+1)}{2.4!}(\delta^4 y_0 + \delta^4 y_1) \\ &+ \frac{\alpha(\alpha-1)(\alpha-2)(\alpha-\frac{1}{2})(\alpha+1)}{5!}\delta^5 y_{\frac{1}{2}} \\ &+ \frac{\alpha(\alpha-1)(\alpha-2)(\alpha-3)(\alpha+1)(\alpha+2)}{2.6!}(\delta^4 y_0 + \delta^6 y_1) + \cdots\end{aligned} \tag{2.5.1}$$

$$\begin{aligned}\phi_n(x) &= \tfrac{1}{2}(y_0 + y_1) + (\alpha - \tfrac{1}{2})\delta y_{\frac{1}{2}} + B^2(\delta^2 y_0 + \delta^2 y_1) + B^3\delta^3 y_{\frac{1}{2}} \\ &+ B^4(\delta^4 y_0 + \delta^4 y_1) + B^5\delta^5 y_{\frac{1}{2}} + B^6(\delta^6 y_0 + \delta^6 y_1) + \cdots\end{aligned} \tag{2.5.2}$$

The B^i's are merely the coefficients of the differences in (2.5.1). The ratio of B^4 to B^2 is then

$$\frac{B^4}{B^2} = \frac{(\alpha - 2)(\alpha + 1)}{12}$$

For $0 \leq \alpha \leq 1$, this ratio changes from $-\frac{1}{6}$ to $-\frac{1}{6}$ after passing through a maximum value of $-\frac{3}{16}$ at $\alpha = \frac{1}{2}$. Thus the ratio varies from -0.1660 to -0.1875 as α varies from 0 to 1.0. Because of this small variation, Comrie (7) suggested that a constant multiple of the fourth difference be thrown back and included with the second difference to form a modified second difference. The modified second difference is written as

$$[\delta^2 y_i] = \delta^2 y_i + C\delta^4 y_i \tag{2.5.3}$$

where C is the constant multiple of $\delta^4 y_i$ to be thrown back. If (2.5.2) is truncated after the third difference, this would mean that

$$\phi_n(x) = \tfrac{1}{2}(y_0 + y_1) + (\alpha - \tfrac{1}{2})\delta y_{\frac{1}{2}} + B^2([\delta^2 y_0] + [\delta^2 y_1]) + B^3\delta^3 y_{\frac{1}{2}} \tag{2.5.4}$$

with an error contribution in discarding the fourth difference of

$$\left[\frac{\alpha(\alpha - 1)(\alpha - 2)(\alpha + 1)}{2.4!} - \frac{\alpha(\alpha - 1)}{2.2!} C\right](\delta^4 y_0 + \delta^4 y_1)$$

or

$$\frac{\alpha(\alpha - 1)}{2}\left[\frac{(\alpha - 2)(\alpha + 1)}{12} - C\right]\frac{\delta^4 y_0 + \delta^4 y_1}{2} \tag{2.5.5}$$

The question, of course, is what value of C to use. By a relatively straightforward analysis Comrie showed that for

$$C = \frac{-3 - \sqrt{2}}{24} \approx 0.184$$

the absolute maximum positive and negative errors in the throwback were equal. For $0 \leq \alpha \leq 1$ the maximum value of the coefficient in (2.5.5) is ± 0.00045. If the value of $(\delta^4 y_0 + \delta^4 y_1)/2$ does not exceed 1,100 units in the last decimal place carried in the calculations, the maximum error is less than $\frac{1}{2}$ in the last place when (2.5.4) is used. As a result (2.5.4) may be used as an interpolation formula which is correct up to and including the fourth differences but requiring the computation of the coefficient of only the first, second, and third differences (the magnitude of $\delta^4 y_0$ and $\delta^4 y_1$ being assumed to be within the bounds above).

If desired, the technique can be extended to higher-order terms as well. It is possible to define a modified third difference which includes a throwback from the fifth difference, a modified fourth difference with throwback from the sixth difference, etc., in much the same way. Further, one can define a modified second difference in which the fourth and sixth differences are thrown back.

In much the same manner the throwback feature can be extended to Everett's interpolation formula. From (2.4.18), terminated after the fourth difference,

$$\begin{aligned}\phi_n(x) &= \alpha y_1 + \frac{\alpha(\alpha-1)(\alpha+1)}{3!}\,\delta^2 y_1 \\ &\quad + \frac{\alpha(\alpha-1)(\alpha-2)(\alpha+1)(\alpha+2)}{5!}\,\delta^4 y_1 - (\alpha-1)y_0 \\ &\quad - \frac{\alpha(\alpha-1)(\alpha-2)}{3!}\,\delta^2 y_0 - \frac{\alpha(\alpha-1)(\alpha-2)(\alpha-3)(\alpha+1)}{5!}\,\delta^4 y_0 \\ &= \alpha y_1 - (\alpha-1)y_0 + \frac{\alpha(\alpha-1)(\alpha+1)}{6} \\ &\qquad \left[\delta^2 y_1 + \frac{(\alpha-2)(\alpha+2)}{20}\,\delta^4 y_1\right] \\ &\quad - \frac{\alpha(\alpha-1)(\alpha-2)}{6}\left[\delta^2 y_0 + \frac{(\alpha-3)(\alpha+1)}{20}\,\delta^4 y_0\right] \qquad (2.5.6)\end{aligned}$$

For $0 \leq \alpha \leq 1$, both coefficients of the $\delta^4 y_i$ terms vary between -0.15 and -0.20. If one defines a modified second difference

$$[\delta^2 y_i] = \delta^2 y_i + C\delta^4 y_i \qquad i = 0, 1 \qquad (2.5.7)$$

the constant C will perform a throwback of both fourth differences on the second difference. Comrie has shown that as with Bessel's formula a value of $C = -0.184$ is satisfactory to minimize the error involved. In this case the error term will be given by

$$\begin{aligned}&\frac{\alpha(\alpha-1)(\alpha+1)}{6}\left[0.184 + \frac{(\alpha-2)(\alpha+2)}{20}\right]\delta^4 y_1 \\ &\quad - \frac{\alpha(\alpha-1)(\alpha-2)}{6}\left[0.184 + \frac{(\alpha-3)(\alpha+1)}{20}\right]\delta^4 y_0\end{aligned}$$

For $0 \leq \alpha \leq 1$ the coefficients of these fourth differences have a maximum value of about 0.007. In this case the use of (2.5.6) with (2.5.7) represents an interpolation polynomial which is correct up to the fifth differences. The technique can, as before, be extended to higher-order differences.

In terms of digital computation there is probably little advantage to using the throwback feature since it is relatively easy to generate as many terms as needed in any interpolation formula. However, the technique is sufficiently interesting so that it has been included here.

2.6. Use of the Various Interpolation Polynomials

The two Newton interpolation polynomials are mainly used near the ends of a set of tabulated data, i.e., between x_0 and x_1 or x_n and x_{n-1}. In this way as many of the data points as possible are employed. Actually only one of the two formulas is needed since an inversion of the data plus a renumbering of the subscripts shows that the two polynomials are identical. In contrast, the central-difference interpolation polynomials are used in the center of a set of tabulated data. These latter polynomials are more elegant than the Newton formulas and usually converge faster for an equal number of differences.

The two Gaussian polynomials are almost never used in practice. Stirling's polynomial is usually applied in the range $-0.25 \leq \alpha \leq +0.25$ and Bessel's polynomial in the range $0.25 \leq \alpha \leq 0.75$. In most cases the necessary interpolation accuracy can be obtained with four or five differences. However, it is impossible to make a precise statement as to which central-difference polynomial is the best to use.

In actually carrying out the interpolation on a digital computer the usual practice is to form a difference table as a first step in the computation. This is especially easy with address modification commands and index registers. In some cases, however, forming the entire difference table requires excessive storage. The necessary differences must then be calculated directly from the tabulated data. The program required is, of course, more complicated in this latter case.

It should be pointed out that the coefficients of the interpolation polynomials are tabulated for various ranges of α and r. In particular "Chambers' Six-figure Tables" (5) and "Tables of Higher Mathematical Functions" by Davis (8) are representative. It may be worthwhile, in special circumstances, to store the coefficients as taken from the tables within the computer memory before performing a calculation.

2.7. The Lagrangian Interpolation Polynomial for Unequal Intervals

The basis of the development of the previous interpolation polynomials has been data tabulated at equal interval spacing of the independent variable. Some of the same concepts can be further extended to the case where the spacing is not constant. In the present section the same $n + 1$ points as before will be assumed, but with $x_1 - x_0 \neq x_2 - x_1 \neq \cdots \neq x_n - x_{n-1}$. An interpolation polynomial is written in the form

$$\begin{aligned}\phi_n(x) = {} & a_0(x - x_1)(x - x_2) \cdots (x - x_n) \\ & + a_1(x - x_0)(x - x_2) \cdots (x - x_n) \\ & + a_2(x - x_0)(x - x_1)(x - x_2) \cdots (x - x_n) \\ & + \cdots\cdots\cdots\cdots\cdots\cdots\cdots\cdots \\ & + a_n(x - x_0)(x - x_1) \cdots (x - x_{n-1})\end{aligned} \tag{2.7.1}$$

with the coefficients $a_0, a_1, \ldots, a_n$ to be fitted to the tabulated data. Each term of (2.7.1) is seen to be a polynomial of degree n. At the point

$x = x_0$, $y = y_0 = \phi_n(x_0)$, and (2.7.1) becomes

$$y_0 = a_0(x_0 - x_1)(x_0 - x_2) \cdots (x_0 - x_n)$$

or

$$a_0 = \frac{y_0}{(x_0 - x_1)(x_0 - x_2) \cdots (x_0 - x_n)}$$

At the point $x = x_1$, $y = y_1 = \phi_n(x_1)$, and (2.7.1) becomes

$$y_1 = a_1(x_1 - x_0)(x_1 - x_2) \cdots (x_1 - x_n)$$

or

$$a_1 = \frac{y_1}{(x_1 - x_0)(x_1 - x_2) \cdots (x_1 - x_n)}$$

Continuing in the same manner for $x = x_2, x_3, \ldots, x_n$ leads to

$$\begin{aligned}\phi_n(x) = {} & \frac{(x - x_1)(x - x_2) \cdots (x - x_n)}{(x_0 - x_1)(x_0 - x_2) \cdots (x_0 - x_n)} y_0 \\ & + \frac{(x - x_0)(x - x_2) \cdots (x - x_n)}{(x_1 - x_0)(x_1 - x_2) \cdots (x_1 - x_n)} y_1 \\ & + \cdots\cdots\cdots\cdots \\ & + \frac{(x - x_0)(x - x_1) \cdots (x - x_{n-1})}{(x_n - x_0)(x_n - x_1) \cdots (x_n - x_{n-1})} y_n \end{aligned} \qquad (2.7.2)$$

In condensed form (2.7.2) may be written as

$$\phi_n(x) = \sum_{i=0}^{n} L_i(x) y_i \qquad (2.7.3)$$

where

$$L_i(x) = \prod_{\substack{j \neq i \\ j=0}}^{n} \frac{x - x_j}{x_i - x_j} \qquad (2.7.4)$$

The polynomial given by either (2.7.2) or (2.7.3) is called "Lagrange's interpolation formula." The $L_i(x)$'s are called the "Lagrangian coefficient functions" and are polynomials of degree n. This interpolation polynomial is exactly equal to $f(x)$ if $f(x)$ is a polynomial of degree n. If $f(x)$ is not a polynomial of degree n, $\phi_n(x) = f(x)$ only at the points x_0, $x_1, \ldots, x_n$. The coefficients $L_i(x)$ are equal to zero for all tabulated x's except x_i; at $x = x_i$, $L_i(x) = 1.0$. The error term associated with the use of Lagrange's formula between tabulated points is identical with NFF. Thus

$$R(x) = \frac{(x - x_0)(x - x_1)(x - x_2) \cdots (x - x_n)}{(n + 1)!} f^{[n+1]}(\xi) \qquad (2.7.5)$$

with $x_0 < \xi < x_n$.

An alternative way of writing the Lagrangian coefficients can be obtained by letting

$$\beta(x) = (x - x_0)(x - x_1)(x - x_2) \cdots (x - x_n)$$

Then it follows that

$$\begin{aligned}\frac{d}{dx}\beta(x) = \beta'(x) = \quad & (x - x_1)(x - x_2) \cdots (x - x_n) \\ & + (x - x_0)(x - x_2) \cdots (x - x_n) \\ & + \cdots\cdots\cdots\cdots \\ & + (x - x_0)(x - x_1) \cdots (x - x_{n-1})\end{aligned}$$

and, by setting $x = x_m$,

$$\beta'(x_m) = \prod_{\substack{k \neq m \\ k=0}}^{n} (x_m - x_k)$$

Thus (2.7.4) can be written as

$$L_i(x) = \frac{\beta(x)}{(x - x_i)\beta'(x_i)} \tag{2.7.6}$$

An advantage of the use of the Lagrangian interpolation polynomial is that a table of differences is not required. Coding of the computation on a machine is relatively simple, and the storage problem is not involved to any great extent. A serious disadvantage, however, is that a priori knowledge as to the degree of the polynomial to use to achieve a desired result is not available. In the case of the equal-interval polynomials, it is necessary only to add further terms to see whether or not the polynomial is adequate. Since the differences are available, an additional term can be easily constructed. In the case of Lagrange's polynomial the addition of one more term requires the complete recalculation of all the $L_i(x)$'s. A second serious problem is that the coefficients $L_i(x)$ are formed by performing subtractions of usually almost equal numbers. A significant loss of accuracy may result from such a process. As a check feature, it can be ascertained that the use of $f(x) = 1.0$ transforms (2.7.3) to

$$\sum_{i=0}^{n} L_i(x) = 1.0$$

Even with these disadvantages, there are many cases where this interpolation formula must be used.

Lagrange's interpolation formula can also be used with equal-interval data. It is intuitively obvious that under such a restriction the present polynomial should collapse to one of the previous formulas. To illustrate this point, the tabulated data may first be renumbered as follows:

$$\left.\begin{array}{ll} x_{-r} & y_{-r} \\ x_{-(r-1)} & y_{-(r-1)} \\ \cdots & \cdots \\ x_{-1} & y_{-1} \\ x_0 & y_0 \\ x_1 & y_1 \\ \cdots & \cdots \\ x_{r-1} & y_{r-1} \\ x_r & y_r \end{array}\right\} \quad n = 2r + 1$$

For equal spacing between the tabulated points

$$x_{i+1} - x_i = h \qquad \text{and} \qquad x = x_0 + hz$$

z corresponds to α as previously defined. However, since the subscripts on the tabulated points have been rearranged, it seems advisable to use z instead of α. Based upon this spacing,

$$\begin{aligned} x &= x_{-r} + h(z + r) \\ x &= x_{-(r-1)} + h(z + r - 1) \\ &\cdots \\ x &= x_{-2} + h(z + 2) \\ x &= x_{-1} + h(z + 1) \\ x &= x_0 + h(z) \\ x &= x_1 + h(z - 1) \\ x &= x_2 + h(z - 2) \\ &\cdots \\ x &= x_{r-1} + h(z - r - 1) \\ x &= x_r + h(z - r) \end{aligned} \tag{2.7.7}$$

and (2.7.3) can be written as

$$\phi_n(z) = \sum_{i=-r}^{i=+r} L_i(z) y_i \tag{2.7.8}$$

To illustrate, consider the case of three data points:

$$\begin{array}{ll} x_{-1},\ y_{-1} & x = x_{-1} + h(z + 1) \\ x_0,\ y_0 & x = x_0 + hz \\ x_{+1},\ y_{+1} & x = x_1 + h(z - 1) \end{array}$$

For these three points the Lagrangian coefficients become

$$L_{-1}(z) = \frac{(x - x_0)(x - x_1)}{(x_{-1} - x_0)(x_{-1} - x_1)} = \frac{(hz)[h(z - 1)]}{(-h)(-2h)} = \frac{z(z - 1)}{2}$$

$$L_0(z) = \frac{(x - x_{-1})(x - x_1)}{(x_0 - x_{-1})(x_0 - x_1)} = \frac{h(z + 1)h(z - 1)}{(h)(-h)}$$
$$= -(z + 1)(z - 1) = -(z^2 - 1^2)$$

$$L_1(z) = \frac{(x - x_{-1})(x - x_0)}{(x_1 - x_{-1})(x_1 - x_0)} = \frac{h(z + 1)hz}{(2h)(h)} = \frac{z(z + 1)}{2}$$

The remainder term is given by

$$R(x) = \frac{(x - x_{-1})(x - x_0)(x - x_1)}{3!} f^{[3]}(\xi)$$

or

$$R(z) = \frac{h^3(z + 1)z(z - 1)}{3!} f^{[3]}(\xi)$$

Finally,

$$f(z) = \frac{z(z - 1)}{2} y_{-1} - (z^2 - 1^2)y_0 + \frac{z(z + 1)}{2} y_1 + \frac{h^3(z + 1)z(z - 1)}{3!} f^{[3]}(\xi) \quad (2.7.9)$$

This procedure can obviously be extended to cover the general case of $n + 1$ tabulated points. In fact, the Lagrangian coefficients are tabulated extensively in the literature for the case of equal spacing on the independent variable as a function of r and z. The Tables of Lagrangian Interpolation Coefficients by the National Bureau of Standards (25) is an example of such a tabulation. The symmetry of the subscripts as given in the above example is employed.

By rearranging the subscripts to those used in NFF, this particular interpolation formula can be obtained:

x_0, y_0 $\qquad x = x_0 + \alpha h$

x_1, y_1 $\qquad x = x_1 + h(\alpha - 1)$

x_2, y_2 $\qquad x = x_2 + h(\alpha - 2)$

In the same way as the previous coefficients were obtained,

$$L_0(\alpha) = \frac{(x - x_1)(x - x_2)}{(x_0 - x_1)(x_0 - x_2)} = \frac{(\alpha - 1)(\alpha - 2)}{2}$$

$$L_1(\alpha) = \frac{(x - x_0)(x - x_2)}{(x_1 - x_2)(x_1 - x_2)} = -\alpha(\alpha - 2)$$

$$L_2(\alpha) = \frac{(x - x_0)(x - x_1)}{(x_2 - x_0)(x_2 - x_1)} = \frac{\alpha(\alpha - 1)}{2}$$

The Lagrangian interpolation formula becomes

$$\phi_2(\alpha) = \frac{(\alpha - 1)(\alpha - 2)}{2} y_0 - \alpha(\alpha - 2)y_1 + \frac{\alpha(\alpha - 1)}{2} y_2 \quad (2.7.10)$$

or, after algebraic juggling,

$$\begin{aligned}\phi_2(\alpha) &= y_0 + \alpha(y_1 - y_0) + \frac{\alpha(\alpha - 1)}{2}(y_2 - 2y_1 + y_0) \\ &= y_0 + \alpha\,\Delta y_0 + \frac{\alpha(\alpha - 1)}{2}\Delta^2 y_0\end{aligned}$$

This is merely NFF applied to a set of three equally spaced points.

2.8. Inverse Interpolation

Since interpolation is defined as the process of obtaining a value of $y = f(x)$ corresponding to a specific x from a tabulated set of data, inverse interpolation involves the determination of an x corresponding to a specific y from the same tabulated data. Associated with inverse interpolation is the problem of unequal spacing of the independent variable (y in this case). An obvious method for performing inverse interpolation is to use Lagrange's interpolation polynomial with the x and y interchanged in the previous formulation. This must, of course, be done with a certain degree of caution to make sure that a polynomial representation is possible.

If the spacing between the x data is a constant, it is possible to use one of the equal-interval interpolation polynomials for the inverse process. The NFF is used here as an illustration, but any of the others may be employed in the same manner. Writing NFF in the form

$$y = y_0 + \binom{\alpha}{1}\Delta y_0 + \binom{\alpha}{2}\Delta^2 y_0 + \cdots + \binom{\alpha}{n}\Delta^n y_0$$

or, for the particular value of $y = d$,

$$0 = -d + y_0 + \binom{\alpha}{1}\Delta y_0 + \binom{\alpha}{2}\Delta^2 y_0 + \cdots + \binom{\alpha}{n}\Delta^n y_0 \quad (2.8.1)$$

It can be seen that the problem is to find that value of α which will make the right side of (2.8.1) equal zero. In other words, the value of α desired is a root of the nth-degree polynomial. While efficient methods for root location will be presented in a later chapter, a simple procedure is outlined here. The method is one of successive approximation or iteration; it starts with an initial guess, $\alpha^{(0)}$, of the correct value of α and progressively generates a sequence $\alpha^{(1)}$, $\alpha^{(2)}$, ... This sequence converges to the desired root with

$$\lim_{i \to \infty} \alpha^{(i)} = \alpha$$

To start the calculation, (2.8.1) is truncated after the first difference.

$$d - y_0 = \alpha \Delta y_0$$

From this equation, an initial estimate of α is obtained.

$$\alpha^{(0)} = \frac{d - y_0}{\Delta y_0}$$

The next step is to use this $\alpha^{(0)}$ plus a higher difference form to obtain a better estimate $\alpha^{(1)}$. This may be done by

$$d - y_0 = \alpha^{(1)} \Delta y_0 + \frac{\alpha^{(0)}(\alpha^{(0)} - 1)}{2!} \Delta^2 y_0$$

wherein the second term involving $\alpha^{(0)}$ is used as a correction to the first term. The process is repeated successively to yield

$$d - y_0 = \alpha^{(2)} \Delta y_0 + \frac{\alpha^{(1)}(\alpha^{(1)} - 1)}{2!} \Delta^2 y_0 + \frac{\alpha^{(1)}(\alpha^{(1)} - 1)(\alpha^{(1)} - 2)}{3!} \Delta^3 y_0$$

$$d - y_0 = \alpha^{(3)} \Delta y_0 + \frac{\alpha^{(2)}(\alpha^{(2)} - 1)}{2!} \Delta^2 y_0 + \frac{\alpha^{(2)}(\alpha^{(2)} - 1)(\alpha^{(2)} - 2)}{3!} \Delta^3 y_0 + \frac{\alpha^{(2)}(\alpha^{(2)} - 1)(\alpha^{(2)} - 2)(\alpha^{(2)} - 3)}{4!} \Delta^4 y_0$$

. . . .

until $|\alpha^{(i+1)} - \alpha^{(i)}| < \epsilon$

where ϵ is the acceptable error in the calculation. In general, if the successive differences $\Delta^2 y_0$, $\Delta^3 y_0$, . . . decrease rapidly, the sequence $\alpha^{(2)}$, $\alpha^{(3)}$, . . . converges rapidly to the desired result.

2.9. Numerical Differentiation

Since $\phi_n(x)$ has been shown to approximate $y = f(x)$ in the interval (x_0,x_n), it would seem that differentiation of the approximating polynomial could be used to approximate $f'(x)$, $f''(x)$, ... Such a procedure is possible, but the numerical results must be carefully considered to ascertain their validity. A different representation of the data may frequently lead to better results (29).

To illustrate the basic process, differentiation formulas at a tabulated point will first be obtained in terms of the forward and backward differences at that point. Using (2.1.4) and (2.1.5),

$$hD = \log E = \log (1 + \Delta) = -\log (1 - \nabla)$$

Expanding the logarithmic terms in the series representation,

$$
\begin{aligned}
hD &= \Delta - \frac{\Delta^2}{2} + \frac{\Delta^3}{3} - \frac{\Delta^4}{4} + \frac{\Delta^5}{5} - \cdots \\
hD &= \nabla + \frac{\nabla^2}{2} + \frac{\nabla^3}{3} + \frac{\nabla^4}{4} + \frac{\nabla^5}{5} + \cdots
\end{aligned}
\qquad (2.9.1)
$$

and applying these to the point y_0,

$$
\begin{aligned}
Dy_0 = y_0' &= \frac{1}{h}\left(\Delta - \frac{\Delta^2}{2} + \frac{\Delta^3}{3} - \frac{\Delta^4}{4} + \frac{\Delta^5}{5} - \cdots\right) y_0 \\
Dy_0 = y_0' &= \frac{1}{h}\left(\nabla + \frac{\nabla^2}{2} + \frac{\nabla^3}{3} + \frac{\nabla^4}{4} + \frac{\nabla^5}{5} + \cdots\right) y_0
\end{aligned}
\qquad (2.9.2)
$$

If the series are truncated after n differences, these formulas correspond to differentiating NFF and NBF. The derivative is given at y_0 in terms of the components of a forward- or backward-difference table.

Extending the method to second differences,

$$(hD)^2 = [\log (1 + \Delta)]^2 = [- \log (1 - \nabla)]^2$$

or

$$
\begin{aligned}
(hD)^2 &= \Delta^2 - \Delta^3 + \tfrac{11}{12}\Delta^4 - \tfrac{5}{6}\Delta^5 + \tfrac{137}{180}\Delta^6 - \cdots \\
(hD)^2 &= \nabla^2 + \nabla^3 + \tfrac{11}{12}\nabla^4 + \tfrac{5}{6}\nabla^4 + \tfrac{137}{180}\nabla^6 + \cdots
\end{aligned}
$$

Applied to the point y_0,

$$D^2y_0 = y_0'' = \frac{1}{h^2}(\Delta^2 - \Delta^3 + \tfrac{11}{12}\Delta^4 - \tfrac{5}{6}\Delta^5 + \tfrac{137}{180}\Delta^6 - \cdots)y_0 \qquad (2.9.3)$$

$$D^2y_0 = y_0'' = \frac{1}{h^2}(\nabla^2 + \nabla^3 + \tfrac{11}{12}\nabla^4 + \tfrac{5}{6}\nabla^5 + \tfrac{137}{180}\nabla^6 + \cdots)y_0 \qquad (2.9.4)$$

This procedure can be extended, of course, to higher-order derivatives.

The difficulties associated with numerical differentiation can be outlined by considering (2.9.1). Since the interpolation polynomial is a representation of $f(x)$ and not $f'(x)$, there is a remainder, or error, term which goes along with (2.9.1). To minimize this error, the usual procedure is to use a small interval h. However, under such circumstances the formation of the successive differences will involve subtraction of nearly equal numbers, leading to a loss of significant figures. These less accurate numbers are then divided by the small h to form the desired derivative. Such a division by a small number will, however, serve to magnify the error. If, on the other hand, a large h is used, the error inherent in the remainder term becomes appreciable. When higher-order derivatives are desired, these competing error problems become more and more severe. As a result numerical differentiation should be performed with considerable caution. The author has seen cases where not only was the magnitude of the slope of the numerical process quite in error but even the sign was incorrect.

Central-difference differentiation formulas may be obtained in much the same manner as above. From (2.1.4)

$$\delta = 2 \sinh \frac{hD}{2}$$

or

$$hD = 2 \operatorname{arcsinh} \frac{\delta}{2}$$

Expanding arcsinh in its series representation,

$$\begin{aligned} hD &= 2\left[\frac{\delta}{2} - \frac{1}{2} \times \frac{1}{3}\left(\frac{\delta}{2}\right)^3 + \frac{1}{2} \times \frac{3}{4} \times \frac{1}{5}\left(\frac{\delta}{2}\right)^5 + \cdots\right] \\ &= \left(\delta - \frac{1^2}{2^2 3!}\,\delta^3 - \frac{1^2 \times 3^2}{2^4 5!}\,\delta^5 - \cdots\right) \end{aligned} \tag{2.9.5}$$

Multiplying the terms on the right side by $\mu(1 + \delta^2/4)^{-\frac{1}{2}} = 1.0$ yields, after condensation,

$$hD = \mu(\delta - \tfrac{1}{6}\delta^3 + \tfrac{1}{30}\delta^5 - \tfrac{1}{140}\delta^7 + \tfrac{1}{630}\delta^9 - \cdots)$$

or $$Dy_0 = y_0' = \frac{\mu}{h}(\delta - \tfrac{1}{6}\delta^3 + \tfrac{1}{30}\delta^5 - \tfrac{1}{140}\delta^7 + \tfrac{1}{630}\delta^9 - \cdots)y_0 \tag{2.9.6}$$

Extending the process to higher-order derivatives,

$$D^2y_0 = y_0'' = \frac{1}{h^2}\left(\delta^2 - \frac{\delta^4}{12} + \frac{\delta^6}{90} - \frac{\delta^8}{560} + \cdots\right)y_0$$

$$D^3y_0 = y_0''' = \frac{\mu}{h^3}(\delta^3 - \tfrac{1}{4}\delta^5 + \tfrac{7}{120}\delta^7 - \tfrac{41}{3{,}024}\delta^9 + \cdots)\,y_0$$

These equations are the same as those obtained by differentiating Stirling's interpolation formula. The odd derivatives involve the mean operator, but the even derivatives do not.

The formulas corresponding to differentiating Bessel's interpolation polynomial can be obtained directly from (2.9.5) applied to the point $y_{\frac{1}{2}}$,

$$Dy_{\frac{1}{2}} = y_{\frac{1}{2}}' = \frac{1}{h}(\delta - \tfrac{1}{24}\delta^3 + \tfrac{3}{640}\delta^5 - \tfrac{5}{7{,}168}\delta^7 + \cdots)\,y_{\frac{1}{2}}$$

Squaring (2.9.5) and multiplying the right side by $\mu(1 + \delta^2/4)^{-\frac{1}{2}} = 1.0$ yields

$$h(D)^2 = \mu\,(\delta^2 - \tfrac{5}{24}\delta^4 + \tfrac{259}{5{,}760}\delta^6 - \tfrac{3{,}229}{322{,}560}\delta^8 + \cdots)$$

or $$D^2y_{\frac{1}{2}} = y_{\frac{1}{2}}'' = \mu\,(\delta^2 - \tfrac{5}{24}\delta^4 + \tfrac{259}{5{,}760}\delta^6 - \cdots)\,y_{\frac{1}{2}}$$

Since

$$f(x) = \phi_n(x) + R(x)$$

differentiation leads to

$$f'(x) = \phi_n'(x) + R'(x)$$

If $R'(x)$ can be evaluated or estimated in some way, it will be possible to estimate a major source of error associated with the numerical differentiation. From

$$R(x) = \frac{(x - x_0)(x - x_1) \cdots (x - x_n)}{(n+1)!} f^{[n+1]}(\xi)$$

there results

$$R'(x) = \frac{(x - x_0)(x - x_1) \cdots (x - x_n)}{(n+1)!} \frac{d}{dx} [f^{[n+1]}](\xi) + \frac{f^{[n+1]}(\xi)}{(n+1)!} \frac{d}{dx} [(x - x_0)(x - x_1) \cdots (x - x_n)]$$

Since the variation of ξ with x is unknown, it is impossible to differentiate $f^{[n+1]}(\xi)$ or to evaluate $R'(x)$. If the differentiation is applied to one of the tabulated points, x_i, the first term in $R'(x)$ becomes zero, however. As a result

$$R'(x_i) = \sum_{\substack{k \neq i \\ k=0}}^{n} (x_i - x_k) \frac{f^{[n+1]}(\xi)}{(n+1)!} \qquad i = 0, 1, 2, \ldots, n$$

and the error can be estimated subject to the restrictions on $R(x)$ itself.

Instead of writing the differentiation formulas in terms of appropriate differences, it is possible to expand the differences and use the ordinate values themselves, i.e.,

$$y_0^{[r]} = F(y_0, y_1, \ldots, y_n)$$

Rather than carrying out this process, it is possible to start with the Lagrangian equal-interval polynomial given in terms of the ordinate values. From (2.7.9)

$$f(z) = \frac{z(z-1)}{2} y_{-1} - (z^2 - 1^2) y_0 + \frac{z(z+1)}{2} y_1 + \frac{h^3(z+1)z(z-1)}{3!} f^{[3]}(\xi)$$

and noting that

$$\frac{d\phi_n}{dx} \frac{dx}{dz} = h \frac{d\phi_n}{dx}$$

there results

$$h\phi_n'(x) = \frac{z-1}{2}\,y_{-1} + \frac{z}{2}\,y_{-1} - 2zy_0 + (z+1)y_0 + \frac{z}{2}\,y_1$$
$$= \frac{2z-1}{2}\,y_{-1} - 2zy_0 + \frac{2z+1}{2}\,y_1$$

and $R'(x) = (h^3/3!)f^{[3]}(\xi)(d/dx)[(z+1)z(z-1)]$ if z is an integer. By making $z = -1, 0, +1$ the following formulas are obtained:

$$z = -1 \qquad f'(x_{-1}) = \frac{1}{h}\left(-\tfrac{3}{2}y_{-1} + 2y_0 - \tfrac{1}{2}y_1\right) + \frac{h^2}{3!}f^{[3]}(\xi)$$
$$z = 0 \qquad f'(x_0) = \frac{1}{h}\left(-\frac{y_{-1}}{2} + \frac{y_1}{2}\right) - \frac{h^2}{6!}f^{[3]}(\xi) \qquad (2.9.7)$$
$$z = +1 \qquad f'(x_1) = \frac{1}{h}\left(\tfrac{1}{2}y_{-1} - 2y_0 + \tfrac{3}{2}y_1\right) + \frac{h^2}{3!}f^{[3]}(\xi)$$

Equation (2.9.7) is referred to as the "three-point Lagrangian differentiation formula." Note the symmetry of the coefficients of the three equations and the fact that the derivative at the central point exhibits the smallest error. Higher-order derivatives and n-point formulas can be obtained by extending the above material.

It is also possible to obtain formulas for the derivative at a point in terms of differences at another point. Starting with

$$hD = \Delta - \frac{\Delta^2}{2} + \frac{\Delta^3}{3} - \frac{\Delta^4}{4} + \frac{\Delta^5}{5} - \cdots$$

and then multiplying the right side by $(1+\Delta)E^{-1} = 1.0$ leads to

$$hD = \left(\Delta + \frac{\Delta^2}{2} - \frac{\Delta^3}{6} + \frac{\Delta^4}{12} - \frac{\Delta^5}{20} + \cdots\right)E^{-1}$$

Applying this to the point y_0 with $E^{-1}y_0 = y_{-1}$,

$$Dy_0 = y_0' = \frac{1}{h}\left(\Delta + \frac{\Delta^2}{2} - \frac{\Delta^3}{6} + \frac{\Delta^4}{12} - \frac{\Delta^5}{20} + \cdots\right)y_{-1}$$

Multiplying by $(1+\Delta)E^{-1}$ again produces

$$y_0' = \frac{1}{h}\left(\Delta + \tfrac{3}{2}\Delta^2 + \frac{\Delta^3}{3} - \frac{\Delta^4}{12} + \frac{\Delta^5}{30} - \cdots\right)y_{-2}$$

If the backward-difference operator is used, the following result:

$$y_0' = \frac{1}{h}\left(\nabla - \frac{\nabla^2}{2} + \frac{\nabla^3}{6} + \frac{\nabla^4}{12} + \frac{\nabla^5}{20} + \cdots\right)y_{+1}$$
$$y_0' = \frac{1}{h}\left(\nabla - \tfrac{3}{2}\nabla^2 + \frac{\nabla^3}{3} + \frac{\nabla^4}{12} + \frac{\nabla^5}{30} + \cdots\right)y_{+2}$$

These formulas evaluate the derivative of $f(x)$ at the point y_0 in terms of forward and backward differences at the point y_{-2}, y_{-1}, y_{+1}, or y_{+2}.

As a final approach consider

$$\delta = 2 \sinh \tfrac{1}{2}hD$$

which, squared, yields

$$\delta^2 = 4 \sinh^2 \tfrac{1}{2}hD$$

Expanding sinh in its series representation leads to

$$\delta^2 = (hD)^2 + \tfrac{1}{2}(hD)^4 + \tfrac{1}{360}(hD)^6 + \tfrac{1}{20,160}(hD)^8 + \cdots$$

or, applied to y_0,

$$\delta^2 y_0 = h^2 y_0^{[2]} + \tfrac{1}{2}h^4 y_0^{[4]} + \tfrac{1}{360}h^6 y_0^{[6]} + \tfrac{1}{20,160}h^8 y_0^{[8]} + \cdots \qquad (2.9.8)$$

Equation (2.9.8) relates the central difference at y_0 to a sequence of even-order derivatives of $f(x)$ at the point $y_0 = y(x_0)$.

The reader is, of course, aware of the fact that all the above material on differentiation applies only to the case of equally spaced data. For unequal spacing it is possible to differentiate Lagrange's formula, but this leads to extremely complicated expressions. In such a case it is best to turn to another type of approximation (29).

2.10. Numerical Integration with Equal-interval Data

For numerical integration the problem is to evaluate

$$\int_a^b f(x)\, dx$$

where $f(x)$ either is too complicated an analytical function to perform the integration directly or is given only in tabulated form. The numerical procedure is conceptually relatively simple. $\phi_n(x)$ is substituted for $f(x)$; the integral now can be evaluated analytically. a and b are usually finite but may be infinite. When b is infinite, the simplest approach is to replace (a,∞) by (a,N), where N is a large number. By evaluating this definite integral for various values of N ($N \to \infty$) the integral will converge to as many decimal places as desired, it being assumed, of course, that the integral is convergent.

Fortunately, numerical integration is not susceptible to the errors inherent in numerical differentiation. Because integration is essentially a smoothing process, relatively simple formulas yield high-accuracy answers. The reason for the smoothing effect is easy to point out in a qualitative way. The integral represents the area under the $f(x)$ versus x curve between the limits of $x = a$ and $x = b$. The polynomial approximation $\phi_n(x)$ oscillates above and below the true $f(x)$ curve, coinciding with $f(x)$ at the specified tabulated values of x. On the average, the area encompassed by the $\phi_n(x)$ curve above the $f(x)$ curve is equal to the area below the $f(x)$ curve. The difference between these two areas as compared with the total area is usually insignificant.

Replacing $f(x)$ with $\phi_n(x)$, as given by the Lagrangian interpolation polynomial, and integrating leads to

$$\int_a^b f(x)\,dx = H_0y_0 + H_1y_1 + H_2y_2 + \cdots + H_ny_n + E(x) \tag{2.10.1}$$

The H_i's, $0 \leq i \leq n$, are given by

$$H_i = \int_a^b \frac{(x - x_0)(x - x_1) \cdots (x - x_{i-1})(x - x_{i+1}) \cdots (x - x_n)}{(x_i - x_0)(x_0 - x_1) \cdots (x_i - x_{i-1})(x_i - x_{i+1}) \cdots (x_i - x_n)}\,dx \tag{2.10.2}$$

and $E(x)$ is the error resulting from the replacement of $f(x)$ with $\phi_n(x)$, that is,

$$E(x) = \int_a^b R(x)\,dx$$

From (2.10.2), it can be seen that the H_i's are dependent only on the values $x_0, x_1, \ldots, x_n$ and the limits of integration a and b. Once a and b are specified for a particular set of $x_0, x_1, \ldots, x_n$ the H_i's can be calculated independently of the particular function $f(x)$ under consideration. Thus the integral can be represented by a weighted linear combination of the tabulated values $y_0, y_1, \ldots, y_n$. The weighting-factor coefficients are given by the integral of the Lagrangian coefficients.

If the interval of integration is given by x_0 and $x_0 + nh$ (or by $b - a = nh$) with $h =$ constant, the coefficients of (2.10.1) take on a number of simple forms depending only on the choice of n. The material in the present section will outline the derivation of these coefficients for equally spaced data. For this particular arrangement the coefficients H_i are the celebrated Cotes numbers, which have been tabulated extensively (5).

As a first step in obtaining some specific integration formulas (2.1.4) and (2.1.5) yield

$$I = \int_{x_0}^{x_0+h} (\ \ )\,dx = (E - 1)D^{-1} = \frac{h\Delta}{\log(1 + \Delta)} \tag{2.10.3}$$

and

$$I_n = \int_{x_0}^{x_0+nh} (\ \ )\,dx = (E^n - 1)D^{-1} = \frac{h[(1 + \Delta)^n - 1]}{\log(1 + \Delta)}$$
$$= h\,\frac{(1 + \Delta)^n - 1}{\Delta}\,\frac{\Delta}{\log(1 + \Delta)} \tag{2.10.4}$$

We note that

$$\log(1+\Delta) = \Delta - \frac{\Delta^2}{2} + \frac{\Delta^3}{3} - \frac{\Delta^4}{4} + \cdots$$

and then (2.10.3) can be written as

$$I = h[1 + C_1\Delta + C_2\Delta^2 + C_3\Delta^3 + \cdots] \qquad (2.10.5)$$

The first few coefficients in (2.10.5) are given by

$$\begin{aligned} C_1 &= \tfrac{1}{2} & C_4 &= -\tfrac{19}{720} \\ C_2 &= -\tfrac{1}{12} & C_5 &= \tfrac{3}{160} \\ C_3 &= \tfrac{1}{24} & C_6 &= -\tfrac{863}{60{,}480} \end{aligned}$$

This is identical to the result obtained by integrating NFF between the limits x_0 and $x_0 + h$. We note further that

$$(1+\Delta)^n = 1 + n\Delta + \frac{n(n-1)}{2!}\Delta^2 + \frac{n(n-1)(n-2)}{3!}\Delta^3 + \cdots$$

and

$$\frac{(1+\Delta)^n - 1}{\Delta} = n + \frac{n(n-1)}{2!}\Delta + \frac{n(n-1)(n-2)}{3!}\Delta^2 + \cdots$$

and then (2.10.4) can be expanded to form

$$I_n = nh\left[1 + \frac{n}{2}\Delta + \frac{n(2n-3)}{12}\Delta^2 + \frac{n(n-2)^2}{24}\Delta^3 + \frac{n(6n^3 - 45n^2 + 110n - 90)}{720}\Delta^4 + \cdots\right] \qquad (2.10.6)$$

Equation (2.10.6) is equivalent to integrating NFF over the interval x_0 to $x_0 + nh$. Let $n = 1$ in (2.10.6), and truncate the series after the first difference. This yields, after expansion of the differences and application to y_0,

$$I_1 y_0 = I y_0 = \int_{x_0}^{x_0+h=x_1} \phi_n(x)\,dx = \frac{h}{2}(y_0 + y_1) \qquad (2.10.7)$$

Letting $n = 2$ in (2.10.6) and truncating after the second difference yields

$$I_2 y_0 = \int_{x_0}^{x_2} \phi_n(x)\,dx = 2h(1 + \Delta + \tfrac{1}{6}\Delta^2)y_0 = \frac{h}{3}(y_0 + 4y_1 + y_2) \qquad (2.10.8)$$

Equations (2.10.7) and (2.10.8) are the well-known trapezoidal and Simpson integration formulas, respectively. The trapezoidal rule fits a polynomial of degree 1 to two tabulated points. It is exact if $f(x)$ is a polynomial of degree 1. In the same way Simpson's rule is exact if $f(x)$ is a polynomial of degree 2. While this is not immediately apparent, Simpson's rule is also exact for $f(x)$ a polynomial of degree 3. From (2.10.6) it can be seen that for $n = 2$ the coefficient of Δ^3 is zero and thus the first term dropped involves Δ^4. These results may be used for the cases $n = 3, 5, 7, \ldots$ and $n = 4, 6, 8, \ldots$. For n odd (the trapezoidal rule as an example) the integration formula of (2.10.6) is exact if $f(x)$ is a polynomial of degree n. For n even (Simpson's rule as an example) the integration formula of (2.10.6) is exact if $f(x)$ is a polynomial of degree $n + 1$. As a further point of interest, n odd yields an even number of tabulated points and n even an odd number of points. The tabulated points are, of course, required to be equally spaced.

In the case where $f(x)$ is an arbitrary function, the replacement by $\phi_n(x)$ will lead to an error. This error may be obtained by integrating $R(x)$, but the following simple procedure leads to the same result. For NFF, with only first differences ($n = 1$), pick $f(x) = x^{n+1} = x^2$. Then $f^{[2]}(x) = 2$, and the following equation can be written,

$$\int_{x_0}^{x_1} f(x)\,dx = \frac{h}{2}(y_0 + y_1) + 2C = \int_{x_0}^{x_1} x^2\,dx$$

where C is to be determined. Carrying out the integration,

$$\frac{x_1^3}{3} - \frac{x_0^3}{3} = \frac{h}{2}(y_0 + y_1) + 2C$$

But since $x_1 = x_0 + h$ and $y_0 = x_0^2$, $y_1 = x_1^2$, an algebraic manipulation leads to

$$C = -\frac{h^3}{12}$$

Thus

$$E(x) = -\frac{h^3}{12} f^{[2]}(\xi)$$

These principles can be extended to cover the case $n \geq 2$. The results for $n = 1$ to 6 are listed below:

$n = 1$

$$\int_{x_0}^{x_1} f(x)\,dx = \frac{h}{2}(y_0 + y_1) - \frac{h^3}{12} f^{[2]}(\xi) \tag{2.10.9}$$

$n = 2$

$$\int_{x_0}^{x_2} f(x)\,dx = \frac{h}{3}(y_0 + 4y_1 + y_2) - \frac{h^5}{90} f^{[4]}(\xi) \tag{2.10.10}$$

$n = 3$

$$\int_{x_0}^{x_3} f(x)\,dx = \frac{3h}{8}(y_0 + 3y_1 + 3y_2 + y_3) - \frac{3h^5}{80} f^{[4]}(\xi) \qquad (2.10.11)$$

$n = 4$

$$\int_{x_0}^{x_4} f(x)\,dx = \frac{2h}{45}(7y_0 + 32y_1 + 12y_2 + 32y_3 + 7y_4) - \frac{8h^7}{945} f^{[6]}(\xi) \qquad (2.10.12)$$

$n = 5$

$$\int_{x_0}^{x_5} f(x)\,dx = \frac{5h}{288}(19y_0 + 75y_1 + 50y_2 + 50y_3 + 75y_4 + 19y_5) - \frac{275h^7}{12{,}096} f^{[6]}(\xi) \qquad (2.10.13)$$

$n = 6$

$$\int_{x_0}^{x_6} f(x)\,dx = \frac{h}{140}(41y_0 + 216y_1 + 27y_2 + 272y_3 + 27y_4 + 216y_5 + 41y_6) - \frac{9h^9}{1{,}400} f^{[8]}(\xi) \qquad (2.10.14)$$

Equation (2.10.11) is referred to as "Simpson's second," or "three-eighths rule." Weddle's rule results from the case $n = 6$ with a change in a coefficient from $\frac{41}{140}$ to $\frac{42}{140}$. This leads to

$$\int_{x_0}^{x_6} f(x)\,dx = \frac{3h}{10}(y_0 + 5y_1 + y_2 + 6y_3 + y_4 + 5y_5 + y_6) - \frac{h^7}{140} f^{[6]}(\xi) \qquad (2.10.15)$$

Weddle's rule can be shown to be exact for $f(x)$ a fifth-degree polynomial or lower. The set of integration formulas (2.10.9) to (2.10.14) and those for higher n are known as the "Newton-Cotes closed-end formulas." The term closed-end is used to indicate that the ordinate ends of the interval of integration, y_0 and y_n, are included as part of the formula.

The Lagrangian interpolation formula for equal-interval data can be used to obtain any one of (2.10.9) to (2.10.14). As an example, consider (2.7.10).

$$\phi_2(\alpha) = \frac{(\alpha - 1)(\alpha - 2)}{2} y_0 - \alpha(\alpha - 2)y_1 + \frac{\alpha(\alpha - 1)}{1} y_2$$

where $\quad x = x_0 + \alpha h \qquad dx = h\,d\alpha$

In terms of (2.10.1),

$$\int_{x_0}^{x_2} f(x)\,dx = h\int_0^2 \phi_2(\alpha)\,dx = H_0y_0 + H_1y_1 + H_2y_2$$

with

$$H_0 = h\int_0^2 \frac{(\alpha-1)(\alpha-2)}{2}\,d\alpha = \frac{h}{3}$$

$$H_1 = -h\int_0^2 \alpha(\alpha-2)\,d\alpha = \frac{4h}{3}$$

$$H_2 = h\int_0^2 \frac{\alpha(\alpha-1)}{2}\,d\alpha = \frac{h}{3}$$

Thus

$$\int_{x_0}^{x_2} f(x)\,dx = \frac{h}{3}(y_0 + 4y_1 + y_2)$$

which is Simpson's rule.

At this point the reader may well ask which formula of the ones listed and those not specifically derived should be used for a particular problem. The answer to this question is not always obvious, but certain rules of procedure may be generally specified. First, one should use the even formulas, $n = 2, 4, \ldots$, because of the smaller error terms compared with the corresponding odd formulas. Second, one would normally try to use as high an even formula as seems feasible; however, this can lead to certain difficulties. The basis for a high-order formula is the low error associated with it. But as has previously been pointed out, this premise is based on the supposition that while h^i decreases as i increases $f^{[\ \ ]}(\xi)$ remains essentially constant. In many cases this assumption may not hold, and in fact a higher-order formula may have a larger error than a lower-order one. Further, there is a tendency for the round-off error (see Sec. 2.13) to increase as higher-order formulas are used. As a result of these considerations the best procedure seems to be to use a low-order even formula combined with the application of subintervals and a possible extrapolation feature. These latter techniques will now be outlined.

The trapezoidal rule is written as

$$\int_{x_0}^{x_1} f(x)\,dx = \frac{h}{2}(y_0 + y_1) - \frac{h^3}{12}f^{[2]}(\xi)$$

with the implication that $x_0 = a$ and $x_1 = b$. In other words, a single application of this rule is used to evaluate the total area. The interval (a,b) can, however, be divided into m subintervals, $m \geq 1$, with the integration formula applied to each section. The sum of the subareas will then correspond to the total area. For the case $m = 2$ (two subintervals) the trapezoidal rule leads to

$$\int_a^b f(x)\,dx = h\left(\frac{y_0}{2} + y_1 + \frac{y_2}{2}\right) - \frac{2h^3}{12} f^{[2]}(\xi) \qquad (2.10.16)$$

where $x_0 = a$, $x_2 = b$, and $h = (b - a)/m = (b - a)/2$. Since there are two intervals, the error term is twice that for a single interval, although the h is cut in half. Generalizing to m subintervals,

$$\int_a^b f(x)\,dx = h\left(\frac{y_0}{2} + y_1 + y_2 + \cdots + y_{m-1} + \frac{y_m}{2}\right) - \frac{mh^3}{12} f^{[2]}(\xi) \qquad (2.10.17)$$

where $x_0 = a$, $x_m = b$, and $h = (b - a)/m$. In effect the interval (a,b) is approximated by m straight-line segments. From (2.10.17)

$$E(x) = \frac{mh^3}{12} f^{[2]}(\xi)$$

or, using $h = (b - a)/m$,

$$E(x) = \frac{(b - a)h^2}{12} f^{[2]}(\xi)$$

Thus the total error for m intervals is proportional to h^2, while for one interval, the local error, it is proportional to h^3.

Simpson's rule can be handled in the same way. For a single interval,

$$\int_a^b f(x)\,dx = \frac{h}{3}(y_0 + 4y_1 + y_2) - \frac{h^5}{90} f^{[4]}(\xi)$$

where $a = x_0$, $b = x_2$, and $h = (b - a)/2$. The error $(h^5/90)f^{[4]}(\xi)$ is associated with a total interval of $2h$ and thus would be $(h^5/180)f^{[4]}(\xi)$ when applied to interval h. For m subintervals, m = even number, there then results

$$\int_a^b f(x)\,dx = \frac{h}{3}[y_0 + 4(y_1 + y_3 + y_5 + \cdots + y_{m-1}) + 2(y_2 + y_4 + \cdots + y_{m-2}) + y_m] - \frac{mh^5}{180} f^{[4]}(\xi) \qquad (2.10.18)$$

The even ordinates are weighted with a 2, the odd ordinates with a 4, and the end values with a 1. The error term is more favorable than for the trapezoidal rule; the error associated with the m subintervals is

$$\frac{(b - a)h^4}{180} f^{[4]}(\xi)$$

The technique of subinterval integration can be extended to any of the other Newton-Cotes closed-end formulas. The coefficients in the resulting equations are not so simple as in (2.10.17) and (2.10.18), but this is not a problem in digital computation unless full machine accuracy is required. If the set of tabulated data is available, it is almost trivial to use any of the integration formulas on a computer. The coefficients are stored in memory and the successive values of $y_0, y_1, \ldots, y_n$ weighted by the appropriate coefficients. If the tabulated data are not available but a very complicated expression for $f(x)$ is known, a subroutine must be written for $f(x)$ at the specific points $x_0, x_1, \ldots$ from which to perform the major part of the calculation.

By performing the numerical integration with two different subinterval sizes it is possible to improve the answer obtained in either calculation. By using (2.10.17) or (2.10.18) it can be seen that the error associated with the use of m subintervals has the form

$$E = Ch^N$$

where N is the order on h and C is essentially a constant. C includes $f^{[N]}(\xi)$, which is taken to be a constant in subsequent discussion. If the integration is performed with h_1 as spacing, an error E_1 results; if h_2 is used, then E_2 results. The ratio of the two errors is given by

$$\frac{E_2}{E_1} = \left(\frac{h_2}{h_1}\right)^N$$

But the true value of the integral, I_T, is

$$I_T = I_1 - E_1 = I_2 - E_2$$

where I_1 and I_2 are the values obtained for the integral by using h_1 and h_2, respectively. Thus

$$E_2 = (I_2 - I_1) + E_1 = (I_2 - I_1) + E_2\left(\frac{h_1}{h_2}\right)^N$$

or

$$-E_2 = \frac{I_2 - I_1}{(h_1/h_2)^N - 1}$$

Finally,

$$I_T = I_2 - E_2 = I_2 + \frac{I_2 - I_1}{(h_1/h_2)^N - 1}$$

If $2h_2 = h_1$, this equation reduces to

$$I_T = I_2 + \frac{I_2 - I_1}{2^N - 1} \qquad (2.10.19)$$

For the trapezoidal rule (2.10.17) $N = 2$, and $2^N - 1 = 3$. For Simpson's rule (2.10.18) $N = 4$, and $2^N - 1 = 15$. Substituting in (2.10.19) leads to

$$I_T = I_2 + \tfrac{1}{3}(I_2 - I_1) \tag{2.10.20}$$

for the trapezoidal rule and

$$I_T = I_2 + \tfrac{1}{15}(I_2 - I_1) \tag{2.10.21}$$

for Simpson's rule. These formulas show that the value of I_T may be approximated by using the two calculated values I_2 and I_1 in the form given. In many calculations this procedure will considerably improve the estimate for the value of the integral.

In addition to the Newton-Cotes closed-end integration formulas, it is also possible to derive the Newton-Cotes open-end integration formulas. These have the form

$$\int_{x_0}^{x_0+nh} f(x)\,dx = H_1y_1 + H_2y_2 + \cdots + H_{n-1}y_{n-1}$$

and do not contain the values of the dependent variable corresponding to the end points of the integration, that is, y_0 and y_n. To illustrate the derivation, take $n = 4$ in (2.10.6), but truncate the series after the third difference. This yields

$$I_4 = \int_{x_0}^{x_4} f(x)\,dx = 4h(1 + 2\Delta + \tfrac{5}{3}\Delta^2 + \tfrac{2}{3}\Delta^3)y_0$$

or, upon expanding the various differences,

$$I_4 = \frac{4h}{3}(2y_1 - y_2 + 2y_3)$$

In this formula the end points y_0 and y_4 are not used. Tabulated below are the first five of the Newton-Cotes open-end integration formulas with error term attached.

$$I_2 = \int_{x_0}^{x_2} f(x)\,dx = 2hy_1 + \frac{h^3}{3}f^{[2]}(\xi) \tag{2.10.22}$$

$$I_3 = \int_{x_0}^{x_3} f(x)\,dx = \frac{3h}{2}(y_1 + y_2) + \frac{3h^3}{4}f^{[2]}(\xi) \tag{2.10.23}$$

$$I_4 = \int_{x_0}^{x_4} f(x)\,dx = \frac{4h}{3}(2y_1 - y_2 + 2y_3) + \frac{14h^5}{45}f^{[4]}(\xi) \tag{2.10.24}$$

$$I_5 = \int_{x_0}^{x_5} f(x)\,dx = \frac{5h}{24}(11y_1 + y_2 + y_3 + 11y_4) + \frac{95h^5}{144}f^{[4]}(\xi) \tag{2.10.25}$$

$$I_6 = \int_{x_0}^{x_6} f(x)\,dx = \frac{3h}{10}(11y_1 - 14y_2 + 26y_3 - 14y_4 + 11y_5) + \frac{41h^7}{140}f^{[6]}(\xi) \tag{2.10.26}$$

These formulas find little use in integration procedures but are employed extensively in the numerical solution of ordinary differential equations.

It is also possible to derive an endless number of other integration formulas by using various operators. As an example, (2.10.6) with $n = 2$ can be written as

$$I_2 = \int_{x_0}^{x_2} f(x)\,dx = 2h\left(1 + \Delta + \frac{\Delta^2}{6} - \frac{\Delta^4}{180} + \cdots\right)y_0$$
$$= \frac{h}{3}(y_0 + 4y_1 + y_2) - \frac{h}{90}(\Delta^4 + \cdots)y_0$$

This formula corresponds to Simpson's rule with correction terms added. Equation (2.10.5) becomes, with $n = -1$,

$$I_{-1} = \int_{x_0-h}^{x_0} f(x)\,dx = h\left(1 - \frac{\Delta}{2} + \tfrac{5}{12}\Delta^2 - \tfrac{3}{8}\Delta^3 + \cdots\right)y_0$$

which amounts to integration over an extrapolated interval. By using NBF as a representation for $f(x)$ between the limits x_n and $x_n + h$,

$$\int_{x_n}^{x_n+h} f(x)\,dx = h\left(1 + \frac{\nabla}{2} + \tfrac{5}{12}\nabla^2 + \tfrac{3}{8}\nabla^3 + \cdots\right)y_n \qquad (2.10.27)$$

The use of the backward-difference operator in the same context as (2.10.5) leads to

$$\int_{x_n-h}^{x_n} f(x)\,dx = h\left(1 - \frac{\nabla}{2} - \frac{\nabla^2}{12} - \frac{\nabla^3}{24} - \tfrac{19}{720}\nabla^4 - \cdots\right)y_n \qquad (2.10.28)$$

This is the inverse of (2.10.5). Using Bessel's interpolation formula to approximate $f(x)$ leads to equations of the form

$$\int_{x_0}^{x_1} f(x)\,dx = \frac{h}{2}\left[y_0 + y_1 - \tfrac{1}{12}(\delta^2 y_0 + \delta^2 y_1) + \tfrac{11}{720}(\delta^4 y_0 + \delta^4 y_1) - \cdots\right]$$

Other and more detailed formulas of this type can be derived when necessary.

2.11. Gaussian Quadrature with Unequally Spaced Data

When $f(x)$ is available only in the form of equally spaced tabulated data, the previous formulas are recommended for numerical integration. If $f(x)$ is given in analytical form but is too complicated for a direct integration, the Gaussian approach to be described is highly recommended. Further, it is suggested as a means of determining when or where to take experimental data. Rather than choosing equal-interval points, Gauss inquired into the possibility of choosing certain specific values of $x_0, x_1, \ldots, x_n$, not equally spaced, which could be used in (2.10.1). As will be seen, the technique is simple to use, is more accurate than any of the well-known equal-interval formulas for a fixed number of x_i, and is ideally suited for digital computation.

Before outlining Gauss' procedure, it is necessary to review certain properties of orthogonal functions. The interested reader can delve further into this subject in a number of excellent references (Chap. 1, 30). Only the important results will be presented here. Two real functions $g_n(x)$ and $g_m(x)$ are said to be orthogonal over an interval (a,b) with respect to a weighting function $w(x)$ if

$$\int_a^b w(x)g_n(x)g_m(x)\,dx = 0 \qquad n \neq m \tag{2.11.1}$$

A number of important functions fit this category, among which are the Bessel functions. If $w(x) = x$, $g_n(x) = J_i(\lambda_n x)$, and $g_m(x) = J_i(\lambda_m x)$, then the above integral is equal to zero. $J_i(\lambda_n x)$ is the Bessel function of the ith order, and λ_n is a root of this function. With $w(x) = 1.0$, $\sin nx$ and $\cos nx$ are orthogonal in the interval $a = -\pi$ and $b = +\pi$. This leads to the Fourier series expansion of an arbitrary function.

If the choice $n = m$ is made in (2.11.1),

$$\int_a^b w(x)\overline{g_n(x)}^2\,dx = C_n \qquad n = m \tag{2.11.2}$$

where C_n is a function independent of x. By a proper choice of the constants involved in $g_n(x)$ and $w(x)$,

$$\int_a^b w(x)\overline{g_n(x)}^2\,dx = 1.0 \qquad n = m \tag{2.11.3}$$

The function $g_n(x)$ is now said to be normalized with respect to the weighting function $w(x)$.

Of particular interest to the present discussion are the Legendre polynomials, or functions, of the first kind and degree n which are solutions of Legendre's equation

$$(1 - x^2)y'' - 2xy' + n(n + 1)y = 0$$

The Legendre polynomials are indicated symbolically as $P_n(x)$, with the first five given by

$$\begin{aligned}
P_0(x) &= 1.0 \\
P_1(x) &= x \\
P_2(x) &= \tfrac{1}{2}(3x^2 - 1) \\
P_3(x) &= \tfrac{1}{2}(5x^3 - 3x) \\
P_4(x) &= \tfrac{1}{8}(35x^4 - 30x^2 + 3)
\end{aligned}$$

The roots of these polynomials are tabulated in the literature with n distinct roots of $P_n(x)$ in the interval $x = -1$ to $x = +1$.

Using the Rodrigues formula

$$P_n(x) = \frac{1}{2^n n!} \frac{d^n}{dx^n} (x^2 - 1)^n$$

it is a simple matter to show that the Legendre polynomials are orthogonal in the interval -1 to $+1$ with respect to the weighting function $w(x) = 1.0$. Thus

$$\int_{-1}^{+1} P_n(x)P_m(x)\, dx = 0 \qquad n \neq m;\ n, m = 0, 1, 2, \ldots \tag{2.11.4}$$

and

$$\int_{-1}^{+1} \overline{P_n(x)}^2\, dx = \frac{2}{2n + 1} \qquad n = m;\ n, m = 0, 1, 2, \ldots \tag{2.11.5}$$

Since $P_n(x)$ is a polynomial, the orthogonal feature of (2.11.4) can be stated by saying that $P_n(x)$ is orthogonal to any polynomial of degree less than n, that is,

$$\int_{-1}^{+1} P_n(x)x^m\, dx = 0 \qquad m = 0, 1, 2, \ldots, n - 1 \tag{2.11.6}$$

Gauss considered the following problem: How may the integral of (2.10.1) be expressed in the form

$$\int_a^b f(x)\, dx = H_1 y(x_1) + H_2 y(x_2) + \cdots + H_n y(x_n) \tag{2.11.7}$$

such that it is exact for $f(x)$ as high a degree polynomial as possible? Not only the coefficients $H_1, H_2, \ldots, H_n$ are to be determined, but also the values of $x_1, x_2, \ldots, x_n$. For $n = 1, 2, \ldots, n$ there are $2n$ unknowns $H_1, H_2, \ldots, H_n, x_1, x_2, \ldots, x_n$ or $2n$ coefficients to be determined, indicating that the highest-order polynomial corresponding to $f(x)$ is probably $2n - 1$.

For the points $x_1, x_2, \ldots, x_n$† (not equally spaced) there exists one polynomial of degree $n - 1$ which fits the n points. In terms of the Lagrangian interpolation polynomial this may be expressed as

$$\phi_{n-1}(x) = \sum_{i=1}^{n} L_i(x) y_i$$

where, as in (2.7.6),

$$L_i(x) = \frac{\beta(x)}{(x - x_i)\beta'(x_i)}$$

$\phi_{n-1}(x)$ is exactly equal to $f(x)$ if $f(x)$ is a polynomial of degree $n - 1$ or less. If, however, $f(x)$ is taken as an arbitrary polynomial of degree

† Note that the point x_0 has been deleted in this discussion.

$2n - 1$ or less, it is possible to write

$$f(x) = \phi_{n-1}(x) + \beta(x)z_{n-1}(x)$$

where $z_{n-1}(x)$ is an arbitrary polynomial of degree $n - 1$ and $\beta(x)$ is of degree n. Integrating both sides between a and b,

$$\int_a^b f(x)\,dx = \int_a^b \phi_{n-1}(x)\,dx + \int_a^b \beta(x)z_{n-1}(x)\,dx$$

there results

$$\int_a^b f(x)\,dx = \sum_{i=1}^{n} H_i y(x_i) + E_{n-1} \tag{2.11.8}$$

In (2.11.8),

$$H_i = \int_a^b L_i(x)\,dx \tag{2.11.9}$$

and

$$E_{n-1} = \int_a^b \beta(x)z_{n-1}(x)\,dx \tag{2.11.10}$$

E_{n-1} may be thought of as the error term associated with representing the integral of $f(x)$ by means of the discrete set of values given by the summation in (2.11.8). If $E_{n-1} = 0$, then this representation is exact for $f(x)$ a polynomial of degree $2n - 1$ or less. If we call $a = -1$ and $b = +1$, (2.11.10) can be written as

$$E_{n-1}(x) = \int_{-1}^{+1} \beta(x)x^m\,dx \qquad m = 0, 1, 2, \ldots, n-1$$

Comparison with (2.11.6) shows that a sufficient condition for $E_{n-1}(x) = 0$ is that $\beta(x)$ be taken as the Legendre polynomial $P_n(x)$. Further, this implies that the x_i's in (2.11.8) are the roots of the Legendre polynomial. As a result, the choice of a value of n automatically determines x_1, x_2, $\ldots$, x_n in (2.11.8), and the H_i's in the same equation are given uniquely by (2.11.9).

It is important to realize that, while only n ordinate values are used, the representation of (2.11.7) behaves as if $2n$ ordinate values are used as long as the x_i's are roots of the Legendre polynomial. For n ordinates (2.11.7) is exact for any polynomial of degree $2n - 1$ or less. This contrasts with the equally spaced formulas which are exact for a polynomial of degree $n - 1$ under the same conditions. In general, this accounts for the high accuracy of the Gaussian integration scheme.

By means of the transformation

$$\lambda = \frac{2x - (a + b)}{b - a} \tag{2.11.11}$$

any finite interval of integration (a,b) may be changed to $(-1,+1)$.

Equation (2.11.7) becomes

$$\int_a^b f(x)\,dx = \frac{b-a}{2}\int_{-1}^{+1} f(\lambda)\,d\lambda$$
$$= \frac{b-a}{2}[H_1 y(\lambda_1) + H_2 y(\lambda_2) + \cdots + H_n y(\lambda_n)] \quad (2.11.12)$$

In this form the integration process is referred to as the "Legendre-Gauss quadrature formula." A paper by Davis and Rabinowitz (9) tabulates the values of λ_i and H_i for $n = 2, 3, 4, \ldots, 46$. The first few values are given in Table 2.1. Note that the λ_i's are symmetrically placed with respect to the mid-point of the integration interval.

TABLE 2.1

$\pm\lambda_i$		H_i
	$n = 2$	
0.5773502691		1.000000000
	$n = 3$	
0.7745966692		$\frac{5}{9}$
0.0000000000		$\frac{8}{9}$
	$n = 4$	
0.8611363115		0.3478548451
0.3399810435		0.6521451548
	$n = 5$	
0.9061709459		0.2369268850
0.5384693101		0.4786286704
0.0000000000		0.5688888888

The actual evaluation of the integral in (2.11.12) is quite simple to carry out. For a given integration interval (a,b), on the assumption that these are not $(-1,+1)$ at the start, (2.11.11) is first used to transform to $(-1,+1)$. A convenient choice of n is then made, and on this basis Table 2.1 immediately specifies the corresponding λ_i and H_i. Based upon the now determined values of λ_i the necessary $y(\lambda_i)$ can then be evaluated. To illustrate this latter point, consider that $f(x) = xe^{-x}$ and that $n = 2$ has been chosen. From the table $\lambda_1 = +0.5773502691$, and from (2.11.11) the corresponding x_1 can be determined. $y(\lambda_1)$ then equals $x_1e^{-x_1}$. The same approach is used for $\lambda_2 = -0.5773502691$ to yield $x_2e^{-x_2}$. Thus all the terms in (2.11.12) are known, and the value of the integral follows by direct substitution.

As a simple illustration of how this method proves quite useful in a practical situation, consider that a distillation column is operating under pseudo-steady-state conditions. Over the next 12-hour period it is desired to take samples of the distillate composition x_D such that an average composition can be calculated for this time period. The obvious approach is to take a sample at the end of every hour, and from these data the evaluation of an integral expression leads to the average composition. Gauss' method, however, says to pick an n (the total number of samples to be used) and from Table 2.1 determine the appropriate λ_i. From the λ_i's it follows that (2.11.11) tells when (the independent variable x is now time) to take the samples in the specified 12-hour period. The average composition can now be calculated from these experimental values and the appropriate H_i. For the same accuracy this procedure will use many fewer samples than the obvious approach.

By including a weighting factor $w(x)$ [in the previous procedure $w(x) = 1.0$], the following integral and its representation may be written:

$$\int_a^b w(x)f(x)\,dx = H_1y(x_1) + H_2y(x_2) + \cdots + H_ny(x_n) \qquad (2.11.13)$$

It can be shown that if the Laguerre polynomials $L_n(x)$ are defined by

$$L_n(x) = e^x \frac{d^n}{dx^n}(x^ne^{-x})$$

as a solution of the differential equation

$$xy'' + (1 - x)y' + ny = 0$$

then

$$\int_0^\infty e^{-x}L_n(x)L_m(x)\,dx = 0 \qquad n \neq m$$

In other words, the Laguerre polynomials are orthogonal in the interval $(0, \infty)$ with respect to the weighting factor e^{-x}. The Laguerre polynomials are given by

$$\begin{aligned} L_0(x) &= 1 \\ L_1(x) &= -x + 1 \\ L_2(x) &= x^2 - 4x + 2 \\ L_3(x) &= -x^3 + 9x^2 - 19x + 6 \\ &\cdots\cdots\cdots\cdots \\ L_{n+1} &= (1 + 2n - x)L_n - n^2L_{n-1} \end{aligned}$$

In much the same way as for the Legendre-Gauss quadrature, it can be shown that, if x_i is the root of $L_n(x) = 0$, (2.11.13) is exact for all polynomials of degree $2n - 1$ or less with $w(x) = e^{-x}$ and $a = 0$, $b = +\infty$. Table 2.2 presents some of the tabulated values of the roots of $L_n(x)$ and the corresponding H_i's for various n's. The *National Bureau of Standards Applied Mathematics Series*† presents an extended table of these values. The procedure itself is referred to as the "Laguerre-Gauss quadrature."

† Vol. 37.

TABLE 2.2

x_i		H_i
	$n = 2$	
0.5857864376		0.8535533905
3.4142135623		0.1464466094
	$n = 3$	
0.4157745567		0.7110930099
2.2942803602		0.2785177335
6.2899450829		0.0103892565
	$n = 4$	
0.3225476896		0.6031541043
1.7457611011		0.3574186924
4.5366202969		0.0138887908
9.3950709123		0.0005392947
	$n = 5$	
0.2635603197		0.5217556105
1.4134030591		0.3986668110
3.5964257710		0.0175942449
7.0858100058		0.0036117586
12.6408008442		0.0000233699

If it is desired to evaluate the integral with limits of $\pm\infty$ and with a weighting factor of $w(x) = e^{-x^2}$, the quadrature formula

$$\int_{-\infty}^{+\infty} e^{-x^2} f(x)\,dx = H_1 y(x_1) + H_2 y(x_2) + \cdots H_n y(x_n) \quad (2.11.14)$$

can be used with the Hermite polynomials $\bar{H}_n(x)$ playing the dominant role. The Hermite polynomials are defined by the equation

$$\bar{H}_n(x) = (-1)^n e^{x^2} \frac{d^n}{dx^n} (e^{-x^2})$$

and satisfy the differential equation

$$y'' - 2xy' + 2ny = 0$$

The $\bar{H}_n(x)$'s are given by

$$\begin{aligned}
\bar{H}_0(x) &= 1 \\
\bar{H}_1(x) &= 2x \\
\bar{H}_2(x) &= 4x^2 - 2 \\
\bar{H}_3(x) &= 8x^3 - 12x \\
&\cdots\cdots\cdots\cdots \\
\bar{H}_{n+1} &= 2x\bar{H}_n + 2n\bar{H}_{n-1}
\end{aligned}$$

and are orthogonal in the interval $(-\infty, +\infty)$ with respect to the weighting factor $w(x) = e^{-x^2}$. Thus

$$\int_{-\infty}^{+\infty} e^{-x^2}\bar{H}_n(x)\bar{H}_m(x)\,dx = 0 \qquad n \neq m$$

Once again, if the x_i's are roots of $\bar{H}_n(x) = 0$, then (2.11.14) is exact for $f(x)$ a polynomial of degree $2n - 1$ or less. The procedure is called the "Hermite-Gauss quadrature," and some of the lower-order x_i's and H_i's are given in Table 2.3.

TABLE 2.3

$\pm x_i$		H_i
	$n = 2$	
0.7071067811		0.8862269254
	$n = 3$	
1.2247448713		0.2954089751
0.0000000000		1.1816359006
	$n = 4$	
1.6506801238		0.0813128354
0.5246476232		0.80491409000
	$n = 5$	
2.0201828704		0.0199532420
0.9585724646		0.3936193231
0.0000000000		0.9453087204

An important variation of the Gauss quadrature is given by the Chebyshev quadrature. In this case it is desired to represent the integral with limits $(-1,+1)$ in the form

$$\int_{-1}^{+1} f(x)\,dx = H[y(x_1) + y(x_2) + \cdots + y(x_n)] \qquad (2.11.15)$$

Note that (2.11.15) uses a single value of the coefficient H as the weighting factor. The advantages of such a procedure from a computational point of view are apparent. A further feature is that any errors, computational or experimental, associated with the $y(x_i)$'s are given equal weight. In all the previous methods the errors are weighted differently. As shown by Chebyshev, (2.11.15) is exact for $f(x)$ a polynomial of degree n or less if the x_i's are roots of the polynomials $C_n(x)$ given by

$$\begin{aligned}
C_0(x) &= 1\\
C_1(x) &= x\\
C_2(x) &= x^2 - \tfrac{1}{3}\\
C_3(x) &= x^3 - \frac{x}{2}\\
C_4(x) &= x^4 - \tfrac{2}{3}x^2 + \tfrac{1}{45}\\
&\cdots\cdots\cdots\cdots
\end{aligned}$$

The constant value of H is merely $H = 2/n$. Some of the necessary roots are given in Table 2.4. One of the defects of this quadrature formula is that complex roots occur for $n = 8$ and $n \geq 10$. Thus the quadrature does not exist in these cases, and the nine-point quadrature formula is the highest possible.

TABLE 2.4

$n = 2$	$\pm x_i = 0.5773502691$
$n = 3$	$-x_1 = 0.7071067812$
	$x_2 = 0.0000000000$
	$+x_3 = -x_1$
$n = 4$	$-x_1 = 0.7946544723$
	$-x_2 = 0.1875924741$
	$+x_3 = -x_2$
	$+x_4 = -x_1$
$n = 5$	$-x_1 = 0.8324974870$
	$-x_2 = 0.3745414096$
	$x_3 = 0.0000000000$
	$x_4 = -x_2$
	$x_5 = -x_1$

If a weighting function of $w(x) = 1/\sqrt{1 - x^2}$ is used in the interval $(-1,+1)$, the orthogonal Chebyshev polynomials $T_n(x)$ lead to the interesting Chebyshev-Gauss quadrature. These polynomials are defined as

$$T_n(x) = \cos (n \cos^{-1} x)$$

and possess the orthogonality property

$$\int_{-1}^{+1} \frac{x^m T_n(x)}{\sqrt{1 - x^2}}\, dx = 0 \qquad n \neq m;\ m = 0, 1, 2, \ldots, n - 1$$

In the same way as previously,

$$\int_{-1}^{+1} \frac{f(x)\, dx}{\sqrt{1 - x^2}} = H_1 y(x_1) + H_2 y(x_2) + \cdots + H_n y(x_n) \qquad (2.11.16)$$

where the x_i's are the roots of $T_n(x) = 0$. The roots are given simply by

$$x_i = \cos \frac{(2i - 1)\pi}{2n} \qquad i = 1, 2, \ldots, n$$

and the coefficients of (2.11.16) become

$$H_i = H = \frac{\pi}{n}$$

As a result the Chebyshev-Gauss quadrature formula is

$$\int_{-1}^{+1} \frac{f(x)\,dx}{\sqrt{1-x^2}} = \frac{\pi}{n}\,[y(x_1) + y(x_2) + \cdots + y(x_n)]$$

This formula is exact if $f(x)$ is of degree $2n - 1$ or less. Further important considerations of the Chebyshev polynomials will be pointed out in a later chapter (Chap. 7).

As a final point the reader will note that the end points of the integration interval have not been included in any of the quadrature formulas. By specifying that $x_1 = a$ and $x_n = b$ the problem of using a quadrature formula is to locate $x_2, x_3, \ldots, x_{n-1}$. This might be thought of as a closed-end Gaussian integration formula. If the roots of $(1 - x^2)P'_{n-1}(x)$ are used,

$$\int_{-1}^{+1} f(x)\,dx = H_1 y(a) + H_2 y(x_2) + H_3 y(x_3) + \cdots + H_{n-1} y(x_{n-1}) + H_n y(b) \qquad (2.11.17)$$

is found to be exact for $f(x)$ a polynomial of degree $2n - 3$ or less. This is referred to as "Lobatto's quadrature formula." The analogous case wherein only one limit is predetermined is called the "Radau quadrature."

The work of Ralston (21) in which the integration interval (a,b) is first broken into a number of subintervals is of interest. A specially derived quadrature formula is then applied to each subinterval with the property that the H_i's are forced to be equal but of opposite signs at the extremities of the subinterval. When this formula is summed up for the total integration interval, all the end-point values drop out except for those at a and b. Thus the integration formula has the form

$$\int_a^b f(x)\,dx = H_0[y(b) - y(a)] + \sum_{i=1}^{n} H_i y(x_i) \qquad (2.11.18)$$

While the only cases actually worked out correspond to $b - a = h$ and $b - a = 2h$, the results show that (2.11.18) usually gives a lower error than the analogous Gaussian quadrature formulas for the same number of x_i's.

Because of the high accuracy of the Gaussian type of quadrature as compared with the corresponding Newton-Cotes formulas, all computers are nowadays equipped with standard Gaussian integration routines. The user supplies such items as the n to use, a subroutine to calculate $f(x)$ given an x, and the limits of the integration. These are fitted into the master integration routine, which may be a 16-point ($n = 16$) Legendre-Gauss quadrature to perform the calculation.

It is very difficult to estimate the truncation error involved in the use of the quadrature formulas, and thus no consideration has been given to this point herein. However, just as the equal-interval case, it perhaps is best to use a low-order formula and subintervals to cover the total interval. The round-off error is likely to be of the same order of magnitude for the quadrature formulas when compared with the corresponding Newton-Cotes formulas. However, for low-order formulas this error is probably insignificant.

2.12. Concluding Remarks

In the present chapter the more important methods have been outlined for replacing a set of equally or nonequally spaced data with a suitable approximating polynomial. In all cases the functionality of the data involved only a single variable. It is for this situation that the method has the greatest applicability; the extension to the multiple-variable problem is more complex. Details are given by Thacher and Milne (26).

As has been pointed out, interpolation by polynomial fitting should be applied only after a close inquiry into the behavior of the function $f(x)$. It is impossible, in certain cases, to fit the function with this type of approximation. This is especially true if the function exhibits singularities or is highly oscillatory in the region of interest. A general statement applied to a known $f(x)$ is that if the Taylor series expansion converges in the region of interest then the polynomial fit can be used. However, when $f(x)$ is an unknown function, such a statement has no real meaning.

A further point to be kept in mind is that it is not necessary to fit a function with a single polynomial over the entire interval of interest. A piecewise approximation, using a number of different polynomials for each subinterval, may be more accurate to use, may be faster to evaluate because the degree of the polynomial will be smaller, and will require only a moderate increase in storage requirements. In a later chapter methods will also be developed for economizing (or decreasing) the degree of the polynomial (Chap. 7) used for the approximation.

As a means of effecting differentiation, the polynomial representation has been shown to be very susceptible to excessive errors. The competitive feature in terms of a small spacing h versus a large h is extremely difficult to bypass. Only when the function is well behaved can the derivatives be calculated with any accuracy.

The same problems carry over to numerical integration. Once again the function $f(x)$ should be examined before a blind application of the techniques described is made. Functions which have singularities or which oscillate excessively in the integration interval can lead to erroneous answers for the value of the integral. When the function is well behaved, multiple integration can usually be performed by repeated application of any of the single integration procedures.

Because of the comparatively high accuracy of the Gaussian type of quadrature formulas, these are specifically recommended as being better to use than the Newton-Cotes type of formulas. A further feature of these former formulas, as applied to integrals involving experimental data, is that the points at which the data should be collected are predetermined by the roots of the respective orthogonal polynomials. Instead of taking data at equally spaced periods and then using the Newton-Cotes procedure, it is possible to take the data at a much more infrequent interval (but at predetermined points) to achieve the same accuracy in the result.

The idea occurs, of course, that the process of polynomial fitting in which the polynomial is forced to agree with the function at the tabulated points but not between may not be the best procedure. Other procedures exist (see Chap. 7) which do not use this criteria of "goodness of fit" but instead may minimize the squares of the difference of the error function over the entire interval of interest.

2.13. The Generation and Accumulation of Computational Errors

In assessing the results of any serious digital computation it is very important to be able to judge the accuracy of the answers from the computation. Since present-day computers perform a large number of arithmetic operations per unit time, a small error generated in the initial stages of a calculation may propagate through the remainder of the calculation and produce an answer which either is completely meaningless or, perhaps even worse, is of the right order of magnitude but still incorrect. It is not possible to overstress the need for error analysis in any computation scheme; this analysis is probably as important as the main computation itself. One of the main features of the "debugging" of a computer program lies in the extra calculations which are performed in an effort to ascertain the validity of the intermediate and final answers. It would thus seem desirable to present, at this point, a brief discussion of the type of errors which may be encountered.

In discussing the source of errors in a digital computation accidental mistakes made by the computer will not be considered. These can be treated only by statistical means, and generally the computer has substantial internal checking features to detect such random errors. The statement is frequently made: The computer never makes a mistake. In terms of mistakes per arithmetic operation this is close to the truth.

There are a number of different types of errors which may occur in the course of a numerical computation. These include the round-off error, the truncation error, the inherited error, and the accumulated error. Each will be discussed briefly. Before this discussion however, it should be pointed out that there are a number of different ways of specifying the magnitude of an error in a number. Calling y the true value of a number and $\bar{y}$ the approximate value or representation of the number,

$$\text{Absolute error} = y - \bar{y}$$

The relative error is defined by

$$\text{Relative error} = \frac{y - \bar{y}}{y}$$

In considering the number representation $\bar{y}$ every digit, except zeros which are used to locate the decimal point, which is correct is called a significant digit.

Round-off Error. Round-off is the replacing of a number of more than r digits with an r-digit number which has minimum absolute error or is best in some way. This is sometimes referred to as digitalizing a number. The *rth* digit may or may not be changed in rounding; this depends on the magnitude of the $(r + 1)$st digit. This is different from lopping of a number in which the $(r + 1)$st, $(r + 2)$nd, . . . digits are discarded and the *rth* digit is always left untouched.

Rounding of numbers is a necessary evil in machine computation because of the fixed digit capacity of the memory and arithmetic units. When two r-digit numbers are multiplied, the result is a $2r$-digit number; when division occurs, the result is a number with infinite digits. In both cases the answer must be placed back into storage with only r digits. An attempt to get around this problem is the multiple-precision handling of numbers or arithmetic.

In decimal notation the usual rounding procedure is given by the following set of rules:

1. If the $(r + 1)$st digit is 0, 1, 2, 3, 4, the rth digit is left unchanged.
2. If the $(r + 1)$st digit is 6, 7, 8, 9, the rth digit is increased by 1.
3. If the $(r + 1)$st digit is 5, the rth digit is either increased by 1 or left unchanged so that the result leaves the rth digit even.

In binary notation the above rounding process corresponds to adding a binary 1 to the $(r + 1)$st binary bit and allowing the resulting carry to propagate. The $(r + 1)$st bit is then lopped off. As an alternative method, the rth binary bit can be replaced with a 1 irrespective of the $(r + 1)$st bit. This introduces more round-off error than the first method, i.e., its variance is larger, but it is more easily implemented since the $(r + 1)$st digit is not needed and no additions are required. If full or almost full machine accuracy is important, then either the first method should be used or multiple-precision handling of the numbers.

In deciding which method of rounding is better the basis used is to assume that the errors created are random in nature. When a large number of roundings are used in a calculation, the errors are not truly random. However, a true random rounding has been devised by Forsythe. This procedure has created so much interest that the details have been reprinted recently (10). The process consists in the addition to the rth digit of a random number either obtained from a random-number table or generated within the computer. This seems to work quite well in minimizing the over-all rounding error in a computation.

Truncation Error. This is the error committed by using a mathematical formula which is an approximation to the true formula. Another way of stating the same thing is that a finite series of terms is used to represent an infinite series. The error, or remainder, term in any of the interpolation formulas fits this category. Thus $R(x)$ is the truncation error associated with truncating the finite series after the nth difference. This is an error inherent in the mathematical procedure and is not affected by the use of multiple-precision arithmetic. Decreasing the value of h [assuming that $f^{[\ \ ]}(\xi)$ remains constant] will decrease the truncation error. In summary the truncation error is a direct function of the interval size, the numerical method, and the particular system under consideration.

Inherited Error. This is the initial error at the nth step in the calculation resulting from all previous calculations.

Accumulated Error. This is the total error at the end of the nth step of the calculation. This becomes the inherited error for the $(n + 1)$st step.

Of primary concern in many calculations is the question of what happens to an error generated on the nth step. It may build up continuously, i.e., propagate with increasing magnitude, or may oscillate with decreasing or increasing amplitude. If the error propagates and builds up, it plus the errors from other steps may soon make the main calculation worthless. On the other hand, if the error damps out, it is to be expected that the calculation will provide a valid answer. While it may not be possible to calculate the local error inherent in a single stage of the calculation, it is frequently possible to decide what happens to the propagation. An attempt will be made in subsequent discussion to carry out such an analysis whenever feasible.

2.14. Numerical Examples

Example 2.1. For the definite integral

$$I_{ab} = \int_a^b \frac{dx}{1 + 10x^2} \tag{2.14.1}$$

it is desired to evaluate I_{ab} by various different techniques and for a variety of different

TABLE 2.5. CALCULATED VALUES OF I_{ab} [EQ. (2.14.1)] FOR $a = 0$, $b = 1.0$
Known $I_{ab} = 0.3998760$

Method	I_{ab}	Integration interval	No. of quadrature points
Trapezoidal	0.3993742	0.250	
	0.3996614	0.125	
	0.3997384	0.100	
	0.3998415	0.050	
	0.3998746	0.010	
	0.3998756	0.005	
Simpson	0.3939708	0.250	
	0.3997571	0.125	
	0.3998591	0.100	
	0.3998759	0.050	
	0.3998760	0.010	
	0.3998761	0.005	
Weddle	0.4002483	0.166 · · ·	
	0.3999071	0.0833 · · ·	
	0.3998760	0.04166 · · ·	
	0.3998760	0.02083 · · ·	
	0.3998760	0.0052083 · · ·	
Chebyshev	0.4148935	....	2
	0.4099338	....	3
	0.4033534	....	4
	0.4013780	....	5
	0.3994608	....	6
	0.3998881	....	2†
	0.3998745	....	6†
Legendre-Gauss	0.4148935	....	2
	0.3998872	....	6
	0.3998760	....	6†

† With five subintervals.

a's and b's. Since $f(x) = 1/(1 + 10x^2)$ is a very rapidly decreasing function from $x = 0$ to $x \approx 1.0$ and then levels off for $x > 1.0$ it would be expected that the main difficulty of computing I_{ab} should be in the region $x < 1.0$.

To minimize the quantity of results only the cases tabulated are considered:

a	b	Known value of I_{ab}
0	1.0	0.3998760
0	10.0	0.4867327
0	1,000.0	0.4966294
1	10.0	0.0868567

TABLE 2.6. CALCULATED VALUES OF I_{ab} [EQ. (2.14.1)] FOR $a = 0$, $b = 10.0$
Known $I_{ab} = 0.4867327$

Method	I_{ab}	Integration interval	No. of quadrature points
Trapezoidal	1.3050155	2.50	
	0.7413442	1.25	
	0.6445829	1.00	
	0.5057647	0.50	
	0.4867326	0.10	
	0.4867327	0.05	
Simpson	0.8992147	2.50	
	0.5534537	1.25	
	0.5024899	1.00	
	0.4594920	0.50	
	0.4867168	0.10	
	0.4867327	0.05	
Weddle	0.6085014	1.666 · · ·	
	0.4600136	0.833 · · ·	
	0.4644537	0.4166 · · ·	
	0.4860497	0.2083 · · ·	
	0.4867332	0.052083 · · ·	
Chebyshev	0.1175348	....	2
	0.2418363	....	4
	0.3466254	....	6
Legendre-Gauss	0.1175347	....	2
	0.3377256	....	4
	0.4866645	....	6

The known values of I_{ab} above were obtained by evaluating

$$\frac{1}{\sqrt{10}}\left[\arctan\frac{x}{\sqrt{10}}\right]_a^b$$

which results from the analytical integration of (2.14.1). In performing the numerical integration the following methods are to be used:

	Equation
Trapezoidal rule	(2.10.7)
Simpson's rule	(2.10.8)
Weddle's rule	(2.10.16)
Chebyshev quadrature	(2.11.15)
Legendre-Gauss quadrature	(2.11.12)

Tables 2.5 to 2.8 present some of the calculated results. As a general conclusion the quadrature formulas give greater accuracy for an equivalent number of points than the equal-interval formulas. The difference between the various methods, however, is apparent only beyond four or five significant figures. The trapezoidal rule is obviously less efficient than any of the others.

TABLE 2.7. CALCULATED VALUES OF I_{ab} [EQ. (2.14.1)] FOR $a = 0$, $b = 1{,}000.0$
Known $I_{ab} = 0.4966294$

Method	I_{ab}	Integration interval	No. of quadrature points
Trapezoidal	125.0005	250	
	62.501216	125	
	50.001544	100	
	25.003190	50	
	5.016339	10	
	2.532712	5	
	0.6544962	1	
Simpson	83.334000	250	
	41.668100	125	
	33.335105	100	
	16.670404	50	
	3.352410	10	
	1.704836	5	
	0.5123862	1	
Weddle	50.001116	166.6 · · ·	
	12.504769	41.6 · · ·	
	1.6012434	5.2083 · · ·	
Chebyshev	0.0012000	....	2
	0.0026250	....	4
	0.0041539	....	6
Legendre-Gauss	0.0012000	....	2
	0.0040000	....	4
	0.0083994	....	6

The results point out that a priori inspection of the function being integrated is very important in terms of an efficient procedure. If the area near $x = 0$ is to be evaluated, a large number of intervals (small values of h) are required; if the area near $x = 0$ is not involved, a much smaller number of intervals may be used to achieve an equivalent accuracy. Thus, if we consider $a = 0$, $b = 1{,}000.0$, the use of 192 equally distributed intervals with Weddle's rule yields a value of $I_{ab} = 1.6012434$ versus the correct 0.4966294. If, instead, the major number of intervals are used to cover $x = 0$ to $x = 1.0$, then only 15 total intervals yield four-digit agreement.

The utility of the extrapolation technique using two different subinterval sizes can also be ascertained from these data. For the case $a = 0$, $b = 1.0$ the formula for the trapezoidal rule (2.10.20) is

$$I_T = I_2 + \tfrac{1}{3}(I_2 - I_1)$$

For $I_2 = 0.3998756$ (interval of 0.005) and $I_1 = 0.3998746$ (interval of 0.010) this formula yields

$$I_T = 0.3998760$$

which is exact. If, however, $I_2 = 0.3996614$ (interval of 0.125) and $I_1 = 0.3993742$ (interval of 0.250) are used,

$$I_T = 0.3997572$$

TABLE 2.8. CALCULATED VALUES OF I_{ab} [EQ. (2.14.1)] FOR $a = 1.0$, $b = 10.0$
Known $I_{ab} = 0.0868567$

Method	I_{ab}	Integration interval	No. of quadrature points
Trapezoidal	0.1119404	1.50	
	0.0940663	0.75	
	0.0869941	0.10	
	0.0868911	0.05	
Simpson	0.0950520	1.50	
	0.0881083	0.75	
	0.0868573	0.10	
	0.0868568	0.50	
Weddle	0.0925093	1.50	
	0.0875004	0.75	
	0.0868578	0.1875	
Chebyshev	0.0596612	......	2
	0.0686712	......	3
	0.0778161	......	4
	0.0804799	......	5
	0.0836431	......	6
	0.0868592	......	6†
Legendre-Gauss	0.0596612	......	2
	0.0833308	......	4
	0.0865370	......	6
	0.0868567	......	6†

† With four subintervals.

This value is closer than either I_2 or I_1 but is still far from the correct value. This simple calculation points out the need to extrapolate from almost correct answers.

Since $f(x)$ is a known analytical function in the present case, it is possible to estimate an upper bound on the truncation error involved in using the approximation formulas. For the trapezoidal rule this error is $(-h^3/12)f^{[2]}(\xi)$; if we use $h = 0.10$ and $x = 1.0$, the largest possible truncation error is 3.7×10^{-5}. Thus, to cover the interval $a = 0$ to $b = 1.0$, this error becomes 3.7×10^{-4}. By using Table 2.5 and the calculated value of 0.3997384 corresponding to $h = 0.1$ the actual computation error is seen to be 1.4×10^{-4}. This is well within the upper-bound value.

There is at least one further point of interest in the present example. If the integral were indefinite in the sense that $b = \infty$, it can be ascertained that the evaluation of this area would not present any serious computational difficulties. Since the calculation is relatively simple to perform for $b > 10$, all that would be required would be to use $b = 10{,}000$, $100{,}000$, etc., until the total area obtained were constant within the number of specified decimal places.

Example 2.2. A hypothetical wet material has been postulated whose drying rate in contact with hot air leads to an equation of the form

$$x = x_0 e^{-t/\Theta}$$

where x = lb H_2O/lb dry solid at any time
x_0 = lb H_2O/lb dry solid at start of drying
Θ = constant = 1 hr
t = time, hr

Further, the rate of drying is given by

$$N = \frac{L_s}{A}\left(-\frac{dx}{dt}\right)$$

where L_s/A = lb solid/unit area of drying surface, and the time to dry the solid from x_0 to x_1 by

$$t_T = \frac{L_s}{A}\int_{x_0}^{x_1}\frac{dx}{N}$$

For $L_s/A = 1.0$, $x_0 = 1.0$, and $x_1 = 0.16$ it is desired to calculate N and t_T by various techniques. Note that the answers are known exactly because of the form chosen for $x(t)$. In particular,

$x(0.5) = 0.606531$ $N(0) = 1.0$
$x(1.5) = 0.223130$ $N(1.0) = 0.367879$
$x(2.5) = 0.082085$ $N(2.0) = 0.135335$
$x(3.5) = 0.030197$ $N(3.0) = 0.049787$
$x(4.5) = 0.011109$ $N(4.0) = 0.018316$

$$t_T = \int_{1.0}^{0.16}\frac{dx}{N} = 1.832581$$

To investigate the numerical behavior of this system, only the period up to $t = 4$ hr is considered and a coarse breakdown of time intervals used, that is, $t = 0, 1, 2, 3,$ and 4 hr. On this basis a difference table of e^{-t} versus x can be constructed.

t	x	Δ	Δ^2	Δ^3	Δ^4
$t_0 = 0$	*1.0*				
		−0.632121			
$t_1 = 1$	0.367879		*0.399577*		
		−0.232544		*−0.252581*	
$t_2 = 2$	0.135335		0.146996		*0.159662*
		−0.085548		−0.092919	
$t_3 = 3$	0.049787		0.054077		
		−0.031471			
$t_4 = 4$	0.018316				

It is now desired to form various interpolation polynomials which can be used to calculate $x(t)$ for values of t other than the integers given in the difference table. The polynomial can be checked by calculating $x(t)$ at $t = 0.05$, 1.5, 2.5, 3.5, and 4.5 and comparing with the known values previously listed. To start, NFF is used in the form

$$\phi_n(t) = \sum_{k=0}^{n}\binom{\alpha}{k}\Delta^k x(t_0) \tag{2.3.3}$$

or, with $n = 4$,

$$\phi_4(t) = \left[1 + \alpha\Delta + \frac{\alpha(\alpha-1)}{2!}\Delta^2 + \frac{\alpha(\alpha-1)(\alpha-2)}{3!}\Delta^3 + \frac{\alpha(\alpha-1)(\alpha-2)(\alpha-3)}{4!}\Delta^4\right]x(t_0)$$

Since $t = t_0 + \alpha h$
and $t_0 = 0 \qquad h = 1$
there results $\alpha = t$

Thus using the italicized values in the difference table leads to

$$\phi_4(t) = 1 - 0.632121t + 0.199789t(t-1) - 0.042097t(t-1)(t-2) + 0.006653t(t-1)(t-2)(t-3) \qquad (2.14.2)$$

For the desired values of t, (2.14.2) yields the following:

$$\left.\begin{aligned} \phi_4(0.5) &= 0.610805 \\ \phi_4(1.5) &= 0.221189 \\ \phi_4(2.5) &= 0.083737 \\ \phi_4(3.5) &= 0.026867 \\ \phi_4(4.5) &= 0.037510 \end{aligned}\right\} \quad \text{NFF}$$

For a central-difference interpolation formula a convenient choice is Stirling's as given in (2.4.13).

$$\phi_4(t) = \left[1 + \alpha\mu\delta + \frac{\alpha^2\delta^2}{2!} + \frac{\alpha(\alpha^2-1)}{3!}\mu\delta^3 + \frac{\alpha^2(\alpha^2-1)}{4!}\delta^4\right]x(t_0)$$

Since $h = 1$, $t_0 = 2$ in this nomenclature,

$$\alpha = \frac{t - t_0}{h} = t - 2$$

and using the appropriate values in the difference table,

$$\phi_4(t) = 0.135335 - 0.159046\alpha + 0.073498\alpha^2 - 0.028792\alpha(\alpha^2-1) + 0.006653\alpha^2(\alpha^2-1) \qquad (2.14.3)$$

Equation (2.14.3) leads to the following answers:

$$\left.\begin{aligned} \phi_4(0.5) &= 0.611971 \\ \phi_4(1.5) &= 0.221188 \\ \phi_4(2.5) &= 0.084861 \\ \phi_4(3.5) &= 0.026863 \\ \phi_4(4.5) &= 0.037489 \end{aligned}\right\} \quad \text{SF}$$

Lagrange's interpolation formula may also be used in the form (2.7.3). However, since the data are given at equal intervals, only one point will be calculated. Without writing the entire equation down, it suffices to show merely the first term; i.e., for $t = 1.5$,

$$\phi_4(t) = \frac{(1.5-1.0)(1.5-2.0)(1.5-3.0)(1.5-4.0)}{(0-1.0)(0-2.0)(0-3.0)(0-4.0)}(1.0) + \cdots$$
$$= 0.221179 \qquad \text{Lagrange's}$$

At the point $t = 1.5$, it can be seen that all three interpolation formulas yield about the same error, namely, about 1.95×10^{-3}. Even with the coarse spacing used the error is small. At other points NFF usually gives slightly better values than SF; thus, at $t = 0.5$, NFF has an error of 4.27×10^{-3} and SF of 5.44×10^{-3}. The truncation-error bound given by (2.3.6) for NFF

$$R(t) = \frac{(t - t_0)(t - t_1) \cdots (t - t_4)}{5!} f^{[5]}(\xi)$$

can also be calculated where $t_0 < \xi < t_4$. Since $f(t) = e^{-t}$, $|f^{[5]}(t)| = e^{-t} \leq 1.0$ and the maximum error possible is given by

$$|R(t)| = \frac{|(t - t_0)(t - t_1) \cdots (t - t_4)|}{120}$$

Thus

$$|R(t = 0.5)| = 27.34 \times 10^{-3}$$

The actual error obtained in using NFF at $t = 0.5$ is seen to be well within the calculated bound.

Values of N may be obtained by differentiating NFF and SF. From NFF

$$\phi_4'(t) = \frac{1}{h}\left[\Delta + \frac{(2\alpha - 1)\Delta^2}{2!} + \frac{3\alpha^2 + 6\alpha + 2}{3!}\Delta^3 + \frac{4\alpha^3 - 18\alpha^2 + 22\alpha - 6}{4!}\Delta^4\right] x(t_0)$$

which becomes, for $t = 0$ and $t = 1.0$ $(h = 1.0)$,

$$\phi_4'(t_0) = \left(\Delta - \frac{\Delta^2}{2} + \frac{\Delta^3}{3} - \frac{\Delta^4}{4}\right) x(t_0)$$

$$\phi_4'(t_1) = \left(\Delta + \frac{\Delta^2}{2} - \frac{\Delta^3}{6} + \frac{\Delta^4}{12}\right) x(t_0)$$

Substituting the indicated differences,

$$\left.\begin{aligned} \phi_4'(t_0) &= -0.956020 \\ \phi_4'(t_1) &= -0.377014 \end{aligned}\right\} \quad \text{NFF}$$

Differentiating SF and applying to the point t_2,

$$\begin{aligned} \phi_4'(t_0) &= (\mu\delta - \tfrac{1}{6}\mu\delta^3)x(t_0) \\ &= -0.130254 \qquad \text{SF, } x(t = 2.0) \end{aligned}$$

Using NFF or NBF for the points t_3 and t_4 (just as above) yields

$$\left.\begin{aligned} \phi_4'(t_3) &= -0.056128 \\ \phi_4'(t_4) &= +0.004509 \end{aligned}\right\} \quad \text{NFF}$$

A comparison of these values with the known N given above (the sign on N must be changed for this comparison) indicates the large amount of error which has resulted. At $t = 0$ the error is 43.9×10^{-3}, while at $t = 4$ the slope even has an incorrect sign. The calculated values tend to oscillate around the exact values. This serves to point out that differentiation is basically a less accurate process than interpolation. If higher-order derivatives were calculated, the errors would become progressively larger. Thus, without giving the details, the error in the second derivative at $t = 0$ is 201.48×10^{-3}.

The value of t_T, the time to dry the material to a water content of $x = 0.16$, can be numerically evaluated from

$$t_T = -\int_{1.0}^{0.16} \frac{dx}{x} = \int_a^b f(x)\,dx$$

Table 2.9 presents the results of such calculations using the trapezoidal, Simpson's, and Weddle's rules plus the Legendre-Gauss quadrature. As in Example 2.1, the trapezoidal rule is the worst method. The quadrature method is the best, with Simpson's and Weddle's rules being essentially equivalent. To illustrate the extrapolation feature, Simpson's rule is chosen now. The appropriate formula is

$$I_T = I_2 + \tfrac{1}{15}(I_2 - I_1)$$

which, for $I_1 = 1.9805$ and $I_2 = 1.9007$, yields

$$I_T = 1.8947$$

If $I_1 = 1.9007$ and $I_2 = 1.8412$, the result is

$$I_T = 1.8395$$

As before, the extrapolation works best when approximate values are used which are already close to the exact value.

TABLE 2.9. CALCULATION OF t_T BY NUMERICAL INTEGRATION
Exact value of $t_T = 1.832581$

Method	t_T	Interval size	Number of points
Trapezoidal..................	3.0450	0.84 (1 interval)	
	2.2466	0.42	
	2.0402	0.28	
	1.9567	0.21	
	1.8909	0.14	
Simpson....................	1.9805	0.42	
	1.9007	0.21	
	1.8412	0.14	
Weddle.....................	1.8433	0.14	
	1.8329	0.07	
Legendre-Gauss.............	1.8298	....	4

Example 2.3. In the two preceding examples analytical answers were available to check the numerical calculations. The present example does not have this feature, with the answers not a priori known. It is desired to fractionate a binary mixture of A and B in a batch column having seven theoretical plates and an external reflux ratio of 2.5. The relative volatility α is a function of liquid concentration expressed as

$$\alpha = 10 - 8.95x \qquad (2.14.4)$$

An initial charge of 100 moles, 50 per cent A, is to be used at the start of the distillation. Assuming equal molal overflow, no holdup in the column, and a maximum tolerable bottoms composition of 5 per cent A, determine the composition of the overhead and bottoms products after completion of the fractionation.

Table 2.10. Difference Table for x_L versus $\dfrac{1}{x_D - x_L}$

x_L	$1/(x_D - x_L)$	Δ	Δ^2	Δ^3	Δ^4	Δ^5	Δ^6	Δ^7	Δ^8	Δ^9
0.50	1.10496829									
		0.04976989								
0.10	1.15473819		0.01739772							
		0.06716761		−0.00738963						
0.15	1.22190580		0.01000808		0.00859946					
		0.07717569		0.00120983		−0.00773698				
0.20	1.29908149		0.01121791		0.00086248		0.00793007			
		0.08839360		0.00207230		0.00019309		−0.00819337		
0.25	1.38747509		0.01329021		0.00105557		−0.00026330		0.00939219	
		0.10168381		0.00312787		−0.00007021		0.00119881		−0.01173992
0.30	1.48915890		0.01641808		0.00098535		0.00093551		−0.00234774	
		0.11810189		0.00411323		0.00086530		−0.00114892		
0.35	1.60726079		0.02053131		0.00185065		−0.00021341			
		0.13863321		0.00596388		0.00065188				
0.40	1.74589400		0.02649519		0.00250253					
		0.16512839		0.00846641						
0.45	1.91102239		0.03496160							
		0.20008999								
0.50	2.11111239									

TABLE 2.11. CALCULATED VALUES OF $\frac{1}{x_D - x_L}$ USING DIFFERENT INTERPOLATION POLYNOMIALS

x_L	Newton	Bessel	Lagrange
0.0500000	1.1049683	1.1049683	1.1049683
0.0625000	1.1142052	1.1142051	1.1142049
0.0750000	1.1261236	1.1261235	1.1261232
0.0875000	1.1398225	1.1398224	1.1398223
0.1000000	1.1547382	1.1547382	1.1547381
0.1125000	1.1705387	1.1705388	1.1705387
0.1250000	1.1870455	1.1870456	1.1870455
0.1375000	1.2041763	1.2041763	1.2041763
0.1500000	1.2219058	1.2219058	1.2219057
0.1625000	1.2402393	1.2402393	1.2402392
0.1750000	1.2591965	1.2591964	1.2591963
0.1875000	1.2788020	1.2788019	1.2788018
0.2000000	1.2990815	1.2990815	1.2990814
0.2125000	1.3200608	1.3200609	1.3200608
0.2250000	1.3417665	1.3417666	1.3417665
0.2375000	1.3642272	1.3642273	1.3642271
0.2500000	1.3874751	1.3874751	1.3874749
0.2625000	1.4115474	1.4115473	1.4115472
0.2750000	1.4364863	1.4364863	1.4364861
0.2875000	1.4623395	1.4623394	1.4623393
0.3000000	1.4891589	1.4891589	1.4891587
0.3125000	1.5170005	1.5170005	1.5170004
0.3250000	1.5459232	1.5459232	1.5459231
0.3375000	1.5759884	1.5759884	1.5759884
0.3500000	1.6072608	1.6072608	1.6072607
0.3625000	1.6398086	1.6398086	1.6398086
0.3750000	1.6737062	1.6737062	1.6737061
0.3875000	1.7090356	1.7090365	1.7090364
0.4000000	1.7458940	1.7458940	1.7458939
0.4125000	1.7843880	1.7843880	1.7843879
0.4250000	1.8246442	1.8246442	1.8246442
0.4375000	1.8668044	1.8668044	1.8668044
0.4500000	1.9110224	1.9110224	1.9110223
0.4625000	1.9574531	1.9574530	1.9574531
0.4750000	2.0062341	2.0062341	2.0062343
0.4875000	2.0574553	2.0574553	2.0574554
0.5000000	2.1111124	2.1111124	2.1111123

TABLE 2.12. VALUE OF THE INTEGRAL OF (2.14.6) FOR THE LIMITS OF $x_L = 0.05$ AND $x_L = 0.50$

Trapezoidal rule:	
10 points	0.671228
19 points	0.670642
37 points	0.670494
Extrapolation on error formula	0.670445
Simpson's rule:	
19 points	0.670446
37 points	0.670446
Extrapolation on error formula	0.670446
Weddle's rule:	
7 points	0.670495
19 points	0.670445
37 points	0.670445
Extrapolation on error formula	0.670445

If we call D the moles of distillate and L the moles of liquid in the still, a total and partial material balance on the entire distillation column yields

$$-dD = dL \tag{2.14.5}$$

$$\frac{dD}{L} = -\frac{dL}{L} = \frac{dx_L}{x_L - x_D} \tag{2.14.6}$$

Integration of (2.14.6) from the known initial conditions of $L_0 = 100$ moles and $x_{L0} = 0.50$ to $L = L$ and $x_L = 0.05$ will yield the necessary information. This integration, however, cannot be performed analytically because of the unknown functionality of $1/(x_L - x_D)$. By using the operating line equation

$$y_{n+1} = \frac{O}{V}x_n + \frac{D}{V}x_D \tag{2.14.7}$$

where O is the liquid flow down the column, the equilibrium relation

$$y_n = \frac{\alpha x_n}{1 + (\alpha - 1)x_n} \tag{2.14.8}$$

and (2.14.4) it is possible to assume a value of x_L and calculate the corresponding x_D. By assuming various values of x_L a table of x_L versus $1/(x_L - x_D)$ may be obtained and (2.14.6) integrated within the appropriate limits.

The calculation using (2.14.4), (2.14.7), and (2.14.8) can be put into difference form as shown in Table 2.10. An increment of $\Delta x_L = 0.05$ was used with the data given as x_L versus $1/(x_D - x_L)$. Once the tabulated data are available, it is possible to fit them with an interpolation polynomial and generate further data if desired. Table 2.11 presents the result of using NFF, BF, and Lagrange's polynomial; the data show the values generated by the interpolation polynomials at the fitted points and three interpolated values between the fitted points. As can be seen, the increment spacing of $\Delta x_L = 0.05$ is sufficiently small so that all three methods yield essentially identical results.

The determination of the integral

$$\int_L^{L_0} \frac{dL}{L} = \ln \frac{L_0}{L} = \int_{0.05}^{0.50} \frac{dx_L}{x_D - x_L}$$

can be performed by using various integration methods. The results of such calculation are shown in Table 2.12; only the equal-interval methods have been used. These indicate that the value of the integral is 0.670446. As in previous examples the trapezoidal rule is decidedly inferior to the others. It is thus possible to calculate directly

Moles of component A taken overhead = 47.4425
Moles of component B taken overhead = 1.4093
Mole % A in overhead = 97.1151

This problem was coded for the IBM 704 in FORTRAN and required approximately 13 sec, excluding output. The calculations were performed in the floating-point mode.

BIBLIOGRAPHY

1. Abramowitz, M., and I. A. Stegun: *J. SIAM*, **4**: 207 (1956).
2. Acton, F. S., and L. Lapidus: *Ind. Eng. Chem.*, **47**: 706 (1955).
3. Bennet, C. O., C. J. Brasket, and J. W. Tierney: *J. AICHE*, **6**: 67 (1960).
4. Carr, J. W.: *Communs. ACM*, **2**(5): 10 (1959).
5. "Chambers' Six-figure Mathematical Tables," W. & R. Chambers, Ltd., Edinburgh, 1949.
6. Comrie, A. J.: "Chambers' Six-figure Mathematical Tables," W. & R. Chambers, Ltd., Edinburgh, 1949.
7. Comrie, L. J.: "Interpolation and Allied Tables," H. M. Stationery Office, London, 1949.
8. Davis, H. T.: "Tables of the Higher Mathematical Functions. I and II," Principia Press, Bloomington, Ind., 1933, 1935.
9. Davis, P. J., and P. Rabinowitz: *J. Research Natl. Bur. Standards*, **56**: 35 (1956).
10. Forsythe, G. E.: *SIAM Rev.*, **1**: 66 (1959).
11. Gorn, S.: On the Study of Computational Errors, *Aberdeen Proving Ground Rept.* 816, 1952.
12. Gregory, R. T.: *Am. Math. Soc.*, **64**: 79 (1957).
13. Halton, J. H., and D. C. Handscomb: *J. Assoc. Comput. Mach.*, **4**: 329 (1957).
14. Hammer, P. C.: "On Numerical Approximation," p. 99, University of Wisconsin Press, Madison, Wis., 1959.
15. Hammer, P. C., and A. H. Stroud: *Math. Tables Aids Comput.*, **12**: 272 (1958).
16. Kunz, K. S.: *Math. Tables Aids Comput.*, **10**: 87 (1956).
17. Lowan, A. N., N. Davids, and A. Levenson: *Bull. Am. Math. Soc.*, **48**: 739 (1942).
18. Metropolis, N., and R. L. Ashenhurst: *IRE Trans. on Electronic Computers*, **EC7**: 265 (1958).
19. Miles, J. W.: *Quart. Appl. Math.*, **14**: 97 (1956).
20. Morrison, D.: *J. Assoc. Comput. Mach.*, **6**: 219 (1959).
21. Ralston, A.: *J. Assoc. Comput. Mach.*, **6**: 384 (1959).
22. Schmittroth, L. A.: *Communs. ACM*, **3**: 17 (1960).
23. Shaw, R. F.: *Rev. Sci. Instr.*, **21**: 687 (1950).
24. Stroud, A. H.: *Math. Tables Aids Comput.*, **11**: 257 (1957).
25. "Tables of Lagrangian Interpolation Coefficients," National Bureau of Standards, Columbia University Press, New York, 1944.
26. Thacher, H. C., Jr., and W. E. Milne: *J. SIAM*, **8**: 33 (1960).
27. Wedey, W. G.: *J. Assoc. Comput. Mach.*, **7**: 129 (1960).
28. Whitaker, S., and R. L. Pigford: *Ind. Eng. Chem.*, **52**: 185 (1960).
29. Wynn, P.: *Quart. J. Mech. Appl. Math.*, **9**: 249 (1956).

CHAPTER 3

FUNCTIONAL EQUATIONS 1. ORDINARY DIFFERENTIAL EQUATIONS

Of increasing concern to the chemical engineer is the proper description of dynamic or transient staged and/or lumped-parameter processes. Ordinary differential equations are used to represent the behavior of such processes; when combined with chemical-reaction or suitable equilibrium relationships, the equations are highly nonlinear. Because of the need to integrate these systems plus others too numerous to mention, numerical techniques must usually be employed.

3.1. nth-order Ordinary Differential Equations

For one independent variable x and one dependent variable $y = y(x)$ the implicit form of an nth-order ordinary differential equation may be written as

$$F(x,y,y^{[1]},y^{[2]},y^{[3]}, \ . \ . \ . \ ,y^{[n]}) = 0$$

where $y^{[r]} = d^ry/dx^r$. In explicit form this equation becomes

$$y^{[n]} + g_1y^{[n-1]} + g_2y^{[n-2]} + \cdots + g_ny = p(x,y) \qquad (3.1.1)$$

with the g_r's as constants and/or functions of x and y. It is always possible to convert an nth-order differential equation into n first-order differential equations. By letting

$$\begin{aligned} w_1 &= y^{[1]} \\ w_2 &= y^{[2]} \\ w_3 &= y^{[3]} \\ &\cdots\cdots \\ w_{n-1} &= y^{[n-1]} \end{aligned}$$

(3.1.1) converts to

$$\begin{aligned} w_1 &= y^{[1]} \\ w_2 &= w_1{}^{[1]} \\ w_3 &= w_2{}^{[1]} \\ &\cdots\cdots\cdot \\ w_{n-1} &= w_{n-2}^{[1]} \\ f(x,y,w_1,w_2, \ . \ . \ . \ ,w_{n-1}) &= w_{n-1}^{[1]} \end{aligned}$$

This is a set of n simultaneous first-order equations. As a concrete illustration, the third-order equation

$$y^{[3]} + g_1 y^{[2]} + g_2 y^{[1]} + g_3 y = 0$$

can be changed by defining

$$w_1 = y^{[1]} \qquad w_2 = y^{[2]}$$

so that

$$\begin{aligned} w_1 &= y^{[1]} \qquad w_2 = w_1{}^{[1]} \\ -(g_1 w_2 + g_2 w_1 + g_3 y) &= w_2{}^{[1]} \end{aligned}$$

The possibility of solving (3.1.1) analytically is largely dependent on the nature of the coefficients $g_1, g_2, \ldots, g_n$ and the nonhomogeneous term p. When these are constants, an analytical solution can always be obtained; when they are functions of x, it is usually possible to obtain an analytical solution. When, however, some of the coefficients and p are functions of y, the equation is nonlinear and an explicit analytical solution is almost impossible to obtain. Under such conditions numerical techniques must be used to obtain a solution.

In all numerical approaches the solution is given by values of the dependent variable y at discrete values of x starting from a specified x_0. In other words y is calculated at $x_1, x_2, x_3, \ldots$ with the usual case $x_i - x_{i-1} = h =$ constant. h is called the integration step, or interval, or the grid spacing. The question of the means of obtaining these values of y with a maximum accuracy, a minimum number of computer instructions and storage, and a minimum amount of calculation time consistent with stability of the answer has been the source of extensive investigations. Stability is taken to mean that errors committed in an early stage of the calculation damp out as the calculation proceeds.

Associated with any nth-order differential equation there must be specified n values of y. These are the boundary conditions or the initial values. As an example, the specification

$$\left.\begin{aligned} y &= y_0 = \text{constant} \\ y^{[1]} &= y_{00} = \text{constant} \\ y^{[2]} &= y_{000} = \text{constant} \end{aligned}\right\} \qquad x = x_0$$

is suitable as initial values for a third-order equation. The system comprised of an nth-order differential equation plus associated initial conditions at $x = x_0$ is termed an initial-value problem. In many cases, however, certain of the assigned values of y are given at $x = x_0$ and the remainder at another point x_p. Thus the three values

$$\left.\begin{aligned} y &= y_0 = \text{constant} \\ y^{[1]} &= y_{00} = \text{constant} \end{aligned}\right\} \qquad x = x_0$$
$$y = y_p = \text{constant} \qquad x = x_p$$

also define the necessary conditions for a third-order equation. The system comprised of an nth-order differential equation plus associated conditions specified at more than one value of x is termed a boundary-value problem. Obviously a boundary-value problem can occur only with equations of second order or higher. The numerical solution of an initial-value problem is usually termed a marching solution and that for a boundary-value problem a jury solution. The reason for this terminology will become obvious in subsequent discussion.

The techniques used for solving initial-value and boundary-value problems are discussed separately. For the initial-value situation, these are illustrated in terms of a single first-order differential equation; the extension to an nth-order equation follows in a direct manner. The special case of certain types of second-order equations is also discussed.

3.2. The Numerical Solution of First-order ODE

A first-order ODE plus initial condition can be written as

$$\begin{aligned} \frac{dy}{dx} &= y' = f(x,y) \qquad x > x_0 \\ y &= y_0 \qquad\qquad\quad x = x_0 \end{aligned} \tag{3.2.1}$$

Starting with the known value of y_0 at x_0, the numerical procedure is to calculate y_1 at x_1, y_2 at x_2, ... This is continued as far as necessary in x space. Integrating both sides of (3.2.1) leads to

$$y_n - y_0 = \int_{x_0}^{x_n} f(x,y)\, dx = \int_{x_0}^{x_n} y'\, dx \tag{3.2.2}$$

or

$$y_{n+1} - y_n = \int_{x_n}^{x_{n+1}} f(x,y)\, dx = \int_{x_n}^{x_{n+1}} y'\, dx \tag{3.2.3}$$

In either form, the discrete difference on the left side of the equation can be determined if y' or $f(x,y)$ is approximated on the right side by an interpolation polynomial; the integral can then be explicitly evaluated, since a polynomial can always be integrated. The interpolation polynomial must, however, be written in terms of the first derivatives of y, instead of y itself, as has previously been done.

For purposes of codification and ease of usage, it is possible to define five different processes for solving the initial-value system of (3.2.1). These are listed, with equal spacing of the independent variable always assumed.

Type I Process

$$y_{n+1} - y_n = F[h, f(x_n, y_n)] \qquad n = 0, 1, 2, \ldots \qquad (3.2.4)$$

This process starts with the known value of y_0 and, using h and $f(x_0,y_0)$ in some suitable manner, calculates y_1. The process is repeated, with y_1, h, and $f(x_1,y_1)$ used to give y_2, and is continued in this same manner for as many steps as desired. The terminology of a marching solution becomes clear for this process, since one goes from point to point in a direct and orderly sequence.

Type II Process

$$y_{n+1} - y_{n-k} = F[h, f(x_n, y_n), f(x_{n-1}, y_{n-1}), \ldots, f(x_{n-r}, y_{n-r})]$$
$$k, r = \text{integers} > 0 \qquad (3.2.5)$$

In order to evaluate y_{n+1}, (3.2.5) uses the known value of y_{n-k}, h, and $f(x_n,y_n)$, $f(x_{n-1},y_{n-1})$, . . . , $f(x_{n-r},y_{n-r})$ in some suitable arrangement. In this process it is not possible to calculate y_1 from y_0; this implies that y_1, y_2, . . . (the total number depend on k and r) must be calculated by another integration process before (3.2.5) can be used. As will be seen, formulas of the type given by (3.2.5) are obtained from Newton-Cotes open-end integration formulas.

Type III Process

$$y_{n+1} - y_{n-k} = F[h, f(x_{n+1}, y_{n+1}), f(x_n, y_n), \ldots, f(x_{n-r}, y_{n-r})]$$
$$k, r = \text{integers} > 0 \qquad (3.2.6)$$

This process is the same as the type II process except that $f(x_{n+1},y_{n+1})$ is included on the right side. Since y_{n+1} is to be calculated, this means that the unknown function occurs on both sides of the equation. Under such conditions an iterative scheme must be used in which a value of y_{n+1} is estimated, substituted into $f(x_{n+1},y_{n+1})$, and (3.2.6) used to calculate an improved value of y_{n+1}. This new value is then used in $f(x_{n+1},y_{n+1})$, to yield a better y_{n+1}. This is continued in a cyclic manner until the equation is satisfied within the necessary accuracy. An initial estimate for y_{n+1} is frequently furnished by using a type II process formula. As will be seen, formulas of the type given by (3.2.6) are obtained from Newton-Cotes closed-end integration formulas.

Type IV Process

$$y_{n+1} - y_n = F[h, f(x_{n+1}, y_{n+1}), f(x_n, y_n)] \qquad n = 0, 1, 2, \ldots \qquad (3.2.7)$$

This process is much like the type III process except that the value of y_1 can be calculated directly from the known y_0.

Type V Process

$$y_{n+1} - y_n = F[h, f(x_{n+\frac{1}{2}}, y_{n+\frac{1}{2}})] \qquad n = 0, 1, 2, \ldots \tag{3.2.8}$$

Here y_{n+1} is calculated by a suitable combination of h, $f(x_{n+\frac{1}{2}}, y_{n+\frac{1}{2}})$, and y_n. This presupposes some alternative scheme for evaluating $f(x_{n+\frac{1}{2}}, y_{n+\frac{1}{2}})$.

In actual practice these five approaches may be used in combination with each other to speed up the integration. Examples will shortly be given of the more important explicit forms of each. Before detailing these methods, however, it is important to emphasize a distinction between types I to V. In the case of type I and type IV a new point y_{n+1} can be calculated by using information at only a single other point y_n. Thus, these are referred to as single-step processes. By contrast, the types II, III, and V processes all require information at more than one point to calculate y_{n+1}. Thus, these are referred to as multiple-step processes.

In terms of machine computation there are a number of advantages associated with the use of the single-step methods. Two of these are listed below:

1. Of paramount importance is the fact that multiple-step methods employing data at more than one point require a second formula to get started in the calculation. In distinct contrast the single-step formulas start themselves. Thus computer instructions and storage requirements are usually minimized in the single-step process.

2. The usual practice in carrying out the numerical integration is to start with a very small grid space h and then gradually to increase this value as the calculation proceeds. Such grid-space changing can be easily accomplished with single-step methods but may require excessive programming or computation time with a multiple-step method.

Other comparisons can be made, some of which are favorable to the multiple-step process, but these will be discussed at the appropriate time when they can be fully appreciated.

The reader's attention is called to Example 3.4, where the integrating of ODE by a completely different method is outlined.

3.3. Single-step Methods for Initial-value Problems

With the formulation of (3.2.2),

$$y_n - y_0 = \int_{x_0}^{x_n} f(x,y)\, dx = \int_{x_0}^{x_n} y'\, dx \tag{3.3.1}$$

where x_0 and x_n are any two points in x-coordinate spaces, the difficulty of evaluating (3.3.1) numerically resides in computing the integral on the right-hand side. This can be accomplished by replacing y' with $\phi_n'(x)$, where $\phi_n'(x)$ is an interpolation polynomial passing through the $n + 1$ equally spaced points y_0' at x_0, y_1' at x_1, . . . , y_n' at x_n. This is exactly the situation considered in Chap. 2, except that in all the interpolation formulas $y_i' = f(x_i,y_i)$ replace the y_i's, $i = 0, 1, 2, \ldots, n$. Any of the specific integration formulas may be used immediately. In the particular case of the single-step methods the integral limits in (3.3.1) are changed to x_n and x_{n+1} as given in (3.2.3).

The simplest single-step integration scheme is called "Euler's method." By using (2.10.5), but truncated before the first difference, there results

$$y_{n+1} - y_n = hf(x_n,y_n) \qquad n = 0, 1, 2, \ldots$$

or

$$y_{n+1} = y_n + hf(x_n,y_n) \qquad n = 0, 1, 2, \ldots ; O(h^2)$$

with the local truncation error shown as being of order h^2. This error follows from the first term dropped in (2.10.5). To use the Euler method, the system

$$\left.\begin{aligned} y &= y_0 \qquad x = x_0 \\ y_n' &= f(x_n,y_n) \\ y_{n+1} &= y_n + hf(x_n,y_n) \end{aligned}\right\} \qquad n = 0, 1, 2, \ldots ; O(h^2) \tag{3.3.2}$$

is constructed. Starting with the known initial condition $y = y_0$ at $x = x_0$, substitution into the first-order differential equation yields y_0' or $f(x_0,y_0)$. By using this value in the Euler equation with a specified h, the value of y_1 at x_1 can be calculated directly. The cycle is then repeated by calculating y_1' or $f(x_1,y_1)$ followed by y_2. In a systematic manner the successive values of y_3, y_4, . . . are thus evaluated.

The geometric meaning of Euler's method is quite simple. By using the point y_n at x_n and the known slope at that point $y_n' = f(x_n,y_n)$, a straight-line extrapolation is made over the interval h to yield y_{n+1}. That this procedure could involve considerable error is quite obvious, and this point is indicated by the order of the truncation error. Extremely small grid or integration intervals must ordinarily be used to obtain even a moderate amount of accuracy. Programming for machine computation is, however, very simple, and $y' = f(x,y)$ is computed only once every integration step. The method is seen to be a type I process.

Because of the large truncation error Euler's method finds little usage in practice. If, however, this method can be used to provide an initial estimate of the true value of y_{n+1} and a second independent integration formula then used to improve the value of y_{n+1}, a much more suitable procedure results. As an illustration, the trapezoidal rule (2.10.9), which is a closed-end integration formula, can be used as the correcting equation. The integrating system now becomes

$$\begin{aligned} y &= y_0 \qquad x = x_0 \\ y'_n &= f(x_n,y_n) \\ \bar{y}_{n+1} &= y_n + hf(x_n,y_n) && O(h^2) \qquad (3.3.3) \\ y_{n+1} &= y_n + \frac{h}{2}[f(x_{n+1},\bar{y}_{n+1}) + f(x_n,y_n)] && O(h^3) \end{aligned}$$

Equation (3.3.3) is often called the "modified Euler's method" or "Heun's first method." The approximate value $\bar{y}_{n+1}$ calculated from the simple Euler equation is used in the trapezoidal equation to obtain a better y_{n+1}. Usually the trapezoidal equation must be iterated a number of times to obtain the desired accuracy in y_{n+1}.

In geometric terms this system uses the average slope at x_n and x_{n+1} to calculate a value of y_{n+1}. The order of the truncation error is h^3, and it is almost as easy to program as Euler's method. The value of y' or $f(x,y)$ must be evaluated at least twice per integration step. The method is seen to be a type IV process and finds extensive use in many calculations because of its simplicity and moderately low error.

A second variation on the simple Euler scheme is based upon the following type V process:

$$\begin{aligned} y &= y_0 \qquad x = x_0 \\ y'_n &= f(x_n,y_n) \\ \bar{y}_{n+\frac{1}{2}} &= y_n + \frac{h}{2}f(x_n,y_n) \\ y_{n+1} &= y_n + hf(x_{n+\frac{1}{2}},\bar{y}_{n+\frac{1}{2}}) \qquad O(h^3) \end{aligned} \qquad (3.3.4)$$

This process uses Euler's equation applied to a grid interval of $h/2$ to obtain $\bar{y}_{n+1}$. This differs from (3.3.3) in that the final formula is an open-ended integration formula and no iteration is required. The open-ended formula can be obtained by integrating any central-difference interpolation formula between the limits of $x_n - h$ and $x_n + h$, truncating the result before the first difference and shifting h to $h/2$. While the truncation error in this process is the same as in (3.3.3), the value of y' or $f(x,y)$ need be evaluated only twice.

There also exists a class of formulas called the "Runge-Kutta single-step integration process." This method is in considerable favor nowadays because of the low truncation error. However, this error is achieved at the expense of more complicated formulas. Since the derivation of the necessary equations is very long, only the final resultant equations will be presented here. Specifically, the so-called third-order and fourth-order Runge-Kutta integration processes are listed below:

Third-order process

$$\left.\begin{aligned} k_1 &= hf(x_n,y_n) \\ k_2 &= hf\left(x_n + \frac{h}{2}, y_n + \frac{k_1}{2}\right) \\ k_3 &= hf(x_n + h, y_n + 2k_2 - k_1) \\ y_{n+1} &= y_n + \tfrac{1}{6}(k_1 + 4k_2 + k_3) \end{aligned}\right\} \quad n = 0, 1, 2, \ldots ; O(h^4) \qquad (3.3.5)$$

Fourth-order process

$$\left.\begin{aligned} k_1 &= hf(x_n,y_n) \\ k_2 &= hf\left(x_n + \frac{h}{2}, y_n + \frac{k_1}{2}\right) \\ k_3 &= hf\left(x_n + \frac{h}{2}, y_n + \frac{k_2}{2}\right) \\ k_4 &= hf(x_n + h, y_n + k_3) \\ y_{n+1} &= y_n + \tfrac{1}{6}(k_1 + 2k_2 + 2k_3 + k_4) \end{aligned}\right\} \quad n = 0, 1, 2, \ldots ; O(h^5) \qquad (3.3.6)$$

The use of these formulas is quite simple. Starting with $y = y_0$, $x = x_0$, and a specific h, the third-order process calculates k_1, k_2, and k_3 successively. Note that k_1 must be known before k_2 can be evaluated and k_2 before k_3. The terminology $f(x_n + h/2, y_n + k_1/2)$ means that $f(x,y)$ is evaluated at $x = x_n + h/2$ and $y = y_n + k_1/2$. The resultant k_1, k_2, and k_3 are then substituted in the last equation to yield y_1 at x_1. The process repeats itself to form y_2 at x_2, y_3 at x_3, ...

The truncation error associated with either process is much better than for any of the previous single-step methods, and the over-all scheme may be considered a version of the type V process. The fourth-order system has frequently been called the "Runge-Kutta-Simpson method," since the application to the case $f(x,y) = f(x)$ reduces to Simpson's rule.

There are a number of defects associated with the use of the Runge-Kutta process. Working storage for the various k_i's must be provided, $f(x,y)$ must be evaluated a number of times per grid step, and it is difficult to estimate the errors (both truncation and round-off) involved in a calculation. If a large number of simultaneous equations are being solved, the first two defects can become quite serious; this is especially true if $f(x,y)$ is complicated, since the computation time will then be very large. In an attempt to keep the round-off errors to a minimum, it is not unusual to calculate $f(x,y)$ in a double-precision routine, even though this extends the computation time.

A modification of the standard fourth-order Runge-Kutta scheme has been proposed by Gill (26) which minimizes the storage problem and minimizes the growth of the round-off errors. Conte (15) has applied the same approach for the third-order process. The Gill modification uses the following set of equations:

$$
\begin{aligned}
k_1 &= hf(x_n,y_n) \\
k_2 &= hf\left(x_n + \frac{h}{2}, y_n + \frac{k_1}{2}\right) \\
k_3 &= hf\left[x_n + \frac{h}{2}, y_n + \left(-\frac{1}{2} + \frac{1}{\sqrt{2}}\right)k_1 + \left(1 - \frac{1}{\sqrt{2}}\right)k_2\right] \\
k_4 &= hf\left[x_n + h, y_n + \left(-\frac{1}{\sqrt{2}}\right)k_2 + \left(1 + \frac{1}{\sqrt{2}}\right)k_3\right] \\
y_{n+1} &= y_n + \frac{1}{6}(k_1 + k_4) + \frac{1}{3}\left(1 - \frac{1}{\sqrt{2}}\right)k_2 + \frac{1}{3}\left(1 + \frac{1}{\sqrt{2}}\right)k_3
\end{aligned}
\tag{3.3.7}
$$

The calculation proceeds by sequentially calculating the j_i's, k_i's, and q_i's listed below.

$$
\begin{array}{lll}
j_0 = y_n & & k_1 = hf(x_n,j_0) \\
j_1 = j_0 + \tfrac{1}{2}k_1 & q_1 = k_1 & k_2 = hf\left(x_n + \frac{h}{2}, j_1\right) \\
j_2 = j_1 + \left(1 - \frac{1}{\sqrt{2}}\right)(k_2 - q_1) & q_2 = (2 - \sqrt{2})k_2 + \left(-2 + \frac{3}{\sqrt{2}}\right)q_1 & \\
& & k_3 = hf\left(x_n + \frac{h}{2}, j_2\right) \\
j_3 = j_2 + \left(1 + \frac{1}{\sqrt{2}}\right)(k_3 - q_2) & q_3 = (2 + \sqrt{2})k_3 + \left(-2 - \frac{3}{\sqrt{2}}\right)q_2 & \\
& & k_4 = hf(x_n + h, j_3)
\end{array}
$$

$$y_{n+1} = j_4 = j_3 + \tfrac{1}{6}k_4 - \tfrac{1}{3}q_3$$

It is fair to say that the fourth-order Runge-Kutta-Gill system is probably the most widely used single-step integration formula.

The main hypothesis in all the previous methods has been the replacement in (3.2.3) of $f(x,y)$ with an equal-interval interpolation polynomial followed by direct integration. Extending this concept to the use of an unequally spaced interpolation polynomial or Gaussian quadrature would seem to be a logical step. Upon rewriting (3.2.3) as

$$y(x_n + h) - y(x_n) = \int_{x_n}^{x_{n+h}} f(x,y)\,dx$$

the limits must first be transformed to $(-1,+1)$. This can be done by the new variable λ,

$$\lambda = \frac{2x - (a + b)}{b - a}$$

leading to [see (2.11.12)]

$$x = x_n + \frac{h(\lambda + 1)}{2} \tag{3.3.8}$$

and
$$\int_{x_n}^{x_n+h} f(x,y)\,dx = \frac{b-a}{2}\int_{-1}^{+1} f(\lambda,y)\,d\lambda = \frac{h}{2}\int_{-1}^{+1} f(\lambda,y)\,d\lambda$$

In terms of the two-point Gaussian formula ($n = 2$) this may be written as

$$y(x_n + h) - y(x_n) = \int_{x_n}^{x_n+h} f(x,y)\,dx = \frac{h}{2}[H_a f(\lambda_a,y_a) + H_b f(\lambda_b,y_b)] \tag{3.3.9}$$

From Table 2.1,

$$\lambda_a = +0.5773502691 \qquad \lambda_b = -0.5773502691$$
$$H_a = H_b = 1.0000$$

and thus (3.3.8) leads to

$$x_a = x_n + (0.7886751345)h \qquad x_b = x_n + (0.2113248654)h$$

If there is some way to calculate y_a at x_a and y_b at x_b, (3.3.9) can be used to evaluate $y(x_n + h) = y_{n+1}$ by an almost trivial calculation. These values can be obtained by using the fourth-order Runge-Kutta process, proceeding from x_n, y_n to x_a, y_a and then to x_b, y_b. The local truncation error in either process is at least $O(h^5)$. Such a procedure requires the use of the Runge-Kutta process only twice, plus a single application of (3.3.9).

Stoller and Morrison (42) have extended this concept by using the Radau quadrature formula instead of the Gauss formula. This quadrature formula uses the point x_n plus two interior points. In the same way as above,

$$y(x_n + h) - y(x_n) = \frac{h}{2}[H_n f(\lambda_n,y_n) + H_a f(\lambda_a,y_a) + H_b f(\lambda_b,y_b)]$$

with
$$\lambda_a = 2\left(\frac{3}{5} - \frac{\sqrt{6}}{10}\right) - 1 \qquad \lambda_b = 2\left(\frac{3}{5} + \frac{\sqrt{6}}{10}\right) - 1$$
$$H_n = \tfrac{2}{9} \qquad H_a = \frac{8}{9} + \frac{\sqrt{6}}{18} \qquad H_b = \frac{8}{9} - \frac{\sqrt{6}}{18}$$

Equation (3.3.8) yields, in this case,

$$x_a = x_n + \left(\frac{3}{5} - \frac{\sqrt{6}}{10}\right)h \qquad x_b = x_n + \left(\frac{3}{5} + \frac{\sqrt{6}}{10}\right)h$$

and all the necessary information is available. The truncation error is now of order $O(h^6)$ with only a minute amount of extra computation. As shown by Stoller and Morrison, either technique described above gives a much better accuracy with less computation than the straight use of the fourth-order Runge-Kutta process.

3.4. Error Propagation and the Monitoring of Single-step Methods

In using any of the single-step methods there are at least three different types of errors which may be encountered. These include:

1. The local truncation error of the integration formula itself. This is the error shown with each equation and results from the use of an approximate equation to represent the real function.

2. The round-off error involved in the arithmetic implementation of the integration formula.

3. The inherited error made in proceeding from y_0 to $y_1, \ldots, y_n$. In other words, y_n will not be exact because of errors committed in reaching x_n.

Of paramount importance in the computation is the question of the stability of the single-step procedures. That is to say, if an error is committed in calculating y_{n+1}, will it propagate with increasing magnitude through the remainder of the calculation or will it damp itself out? In the former case, an unstable solution, the errors will wash out or invalidate the computation results. If the system is stable, the errors will damp themselves out, leading to a valid answer. Thus it is important to try to devise some criteria of automatic error analysis which can be used to detect the effect of error propagation and to maintain the magnitude of the errors within preassigned bounds as the computation marches from point to point.

To illustrate the necessary procedure, the simplest single-step method will be considered. The extension to other single-step methods will follow directly. The exact value of y_n or y_{n+1} will be designated as u_n or u_{n+1}. For Euler's method these latter values are related by

$$u_{n+1} = u_n + hu'_n + T_{E,n+1} \tag{3.4.1}$$

where $T_{E,n+1}$ = local truncation error associated with Euler's method and is $O(h^2)$. If we define an absolute error ϵ_n† by means of

$$\epsilon_n = y_n - u_n$$

the subtraction of (3.4.1) and (3.3.2) leads to

$$y_{n+1} - u_{n+1} = y_n - u_n + h(y'_n - u'_n) - T_{E,n+1}$$

or

$$\epsilon_{n+1} = \epsilon_n + h(y'_n - u'_n) - T_{E,n+1} = \epsilon_n + h[f(x_n,y_n) - f(x_n,u_n)] - T_{E,n+1}$$

† This error term is frequently written in reverse order.

If the round-off error is included, then this would add a term $R_{E,n+1}$ on the right side of the last equation:

$$\epsilon_{n+1} = \epsilon_n + h[f(x_n,y_n) - f(x_n,u_n)] - T_{E,n+1} + R_{E,n+1}$$

Note that in this development it has been assumed that $T_{E,n+1}$ and $R_{E,n+1}$ are functions of n. The mean-value theorem states that

$$\begin{aligned} f(x_n,y_n) - f(x_n,u_n) &= \left.\frac{\partial f}{\partial y}\right)_{\alpha,x_n} (y_n - u_n) \qquad y_n < \alpha < u_n \\ &= \left.\frac{\partial f}{\partial y}\right)_{\alpha,x_n} \epsilon_n \end{aligned}$$

where $\left.\partial f/\partial y\right)_{\alpha,x_n}$ is called the local relaxation length. When substituted into the error equation, the mean-value theorem yields

$$\epsilon_{n+1} = \epsilon_n + h \left.\frac{\partial f}{\partial y}\right)_{\alpha,x_n} \epsilon_n - T_{E,n+1} + R_{E,n+1}$$

or

$$\epsilon_{n+1} - \left[1 + h \left.\frac{\partial f}{\partial y}\right)_{\alpha,x_n}\right] \epsilon_n = -T_{E,n+1} + R_{E,n+1} \qquad n = 0, 1, 2, \ldots \tag{3.4.2}$$

Equation (3.4.2) is a first-order nonhomogeneous difference equation. The solution of this difference equation will show how an error committed at any integration step in the calculation will propagate through the remaining steps. Calling

$$1 + h \left.\frac{\partial f}{\partial y}\right)_{\alpha,x_n} = \beta_n$$

we find

$$\epsilon_{n+1} - \beta_n \epsilon_n = -T_{E,n+1} + R_{E,n+1} \tag{3.4.3}$$

which can be solved by iteration. For $n = 0$ and $y_0 = u_0$ (no error in the initial value), $\epsilon_0 = 0$, and thus

$$\epsilon_1 = -T_{E,1} + R_{E,1}$$

For $n = 1$

$$\epsilon_2 = \beta_1\epsilon_1 - T_{E,2} + R_{E,2} = \beta_1(-T_{E,1} + R_{E,1}) - T_{E,2} + R_{E,2}$$

This can be continued for $n = 2, 3, 4, \ldots$ until a general solution for ϵ_n is ascertained. Instead, however, it is just as instructive to take the simplified case of

$$\begin{aligned} T_{E,n+1} &= T_E = \text{constant} \\ R_{E,n+1} &= R_E = \text{constant} \\ \beta_n &= \beta = \text{constant} \end{aligned}$$

In the last term the constant value of β implies that $\left.\partial f/\partial y\right)_{\alpha,x_n}$ = constant which will be designated as λ. Under these simplifying assumptions (3.4.3) becomes

$$\epsilon_{n+1} - \beta\epsilon_n = -T_E + R_E$$

and this can be solved directly to yield

$$\epsilon_n = C_1\beta^n + \frac{-T_E + R_E}{1 - \beta}$$

C_1 is an arbitrary constant which can be evaluated from $\epsilon_0 = 0$ when $n = 0$. This leads to

$$\epsilon_n = \frac{-T_E + R_E}{1 - \beta}(1 - \beta^n)$$

or

$$\epsilon_n = \frac{-T_E + R_E}{h\lambda}[(1 + h\lambda)^n - 1] \qquad (3.4.4)$$

If $\lambda > 0$, the term $1 + h\lambda = \beta > 1.0$ and ϵ_n will increase with increasing n. Under these circumstances an error generated at any step will propagate with larger and larger magnitude as the calculation proceeds. The solution will be unstable. If $\lambda < 0$ = negative, and a proper choice of h, the term $1 + h\lambda = \beta < 1.0$ and ϵ_n will decrease with increasing n. The solution will be stable. Thus the criterion has been developed for Euler's method that for $\lambda > 0$ the solution is unstable, while for $\lambda < 0$ (with an appropriate h) it will be stable.

The question now arises as to how to devise an automatic monitoring scheme to prevent the error from exceeding either a prescribed lower or a prescribed upper bound. The extrapolation scheme outlined in Sec. 2.10 can be used to advantage in the present case. Suppose that the calculation is carried from point y_n to y_{n+1} first with an interval h_1 and then with an interval h_2. By using h_1 a value $y_{n+1}^{(1)}$ is calculated and with h_2 a value $y_{n+1}^{(2)}$. For the integrating formula under consideration the total truncation error will be of the form

$$\epsilon_{n+1} = Ch^N$$

where N is the order of the truncation error and C is a constant. As a result

$$\epsilon_{n+1}^{(1)} = Ch_1^N$$
$$\epsilon_{n+1}^{(2)} = Ch_2^N$$

or

$$\epsilon_{n+1}^{(1)} = \epsilon_{n+1}^{(2)}\left(\frac{h_1}{h_2}\right)^N$$

Expanding ϵ_{n+1} in terms of y_{n+1} and μ_{n+1},

$$y_{n+1}^{(1)} - u_{n+1} = (y_{n+1}^{(2)} - u_{n+1})\left(\frac{h_1}{h_2}\right)^N$$

or

$$u_{n+1} = \frac{(h_1/h_2)^N y_{n+1}^{(2)} - y_{n+1}^{(1)}}{(h_1/h_2)^N - 1}$$

For the case $2h_2 = h_1$, this becomes

$$u_{n+1} = \frac{2^N y_{n+1}^{(2)} - y_{n+1}^{(1)}}{2^N - 1} \tag{3.4.5}$$

and

$$\epsilon_{n+1}^{(2)} = y_{n+1}^{(2)} - u_{n+1} = \frac{y_{n+1}^{(1)} - y_{n+1}^{(2)}}{2^N - 1} \tag{3.4.6}$$

Equation (3.4.5) can be used for an estimate of the true value of u_{n+1} and (3.4.6) for an estimate of the error in the calculated value $y_{n+1}^{(2)}$.

For Euler's method the local truncation error is $O(h^2)$, and as in Sec. 2.10 the total error is of order 1 less, or $O(h)$. Thus $N = 1$ for Euler's method, and for the modified Euler scheme $N = 2$. In the latter case, (3.4.5) and (3.4.6) become

$$u_{n+1} = \frac{4y_{n+1}^{(2)} - y_{n+1}^{(1)}}{3} \qquad \epsilon_{n+1}^{(2)} = \frac{y_{n+1}^{(1)} - y_{n+1}^{(2)}}{3}$$

An automatic error-monitoring procedure is now possible. $y_{n+1}^{(2)}$ can be used as the desired answer at x_{n+1} with $\epsilon_{n+1}^{(2)}$ monitored for an error estimate. In contrast, the corrected value u_{n+1} can be used as an initial value for the calculation of $y_{n+2}^{(1)}$ and $y_{n+2}^{(2)}$. However, if the correction or the monitoring is performed at each integration interval, over three times as much computation is required than in using the single-step process without correction. Further there will be additional storage requirements. The technique can, of course, be extended to any of the single-step methods. Thus the fourth-order Runge-Kutta process has a local truncation error of $O(h^5)$ and an over-all truncation error of $O(h^4)$; $N = 4$, and

$$\epsilon_{n+1}^{(2)} = \frac{y_{n+1}^{(1)} - y_{n+1}^{(2)}}{15}$$

Since this extrapolation process only assumes a truncation error, the round-off error is neglected. The usual procedure is to use as large an h as possible to minimize the round-off but still maintain the truncation below an upper bound. This may be accomplished by defining a relative error term

$$E_{n+1} = \left|\frac{\epsilon_{n+1}^{(2)}}{u_{n+1}}\right|$$

and a lower bound L_1 and an upper bound L_2. If $E_{n+1} > L_2$, the integration interval is too large and must be decreased; if $E_{n+1} < L_1$, the interval is too small and can be increased. By performing the calculation for E_{n+1} every p integration steps in the calculation the error can be monitored without the excessive loss of time involved in performing the comparison at every integration step.

An alternative means of monitoring the single-step procedure is to reverse direction at each step of the advancing solution and compute the previous ordinate. This can easily be accomplished by using $-h$ instead of $+h$. Call and Reeves (10) have applied this reversal process to the Runge-Kutta procedures. If we call y_n^* the value obtained from y_{n+1} and $-h$, the third-order Runge-Kutta leads to a truncation error of

$$E = \frac{y_n - y_n^*}{2}$$

This may be monitored between two limits to adjust for the proper integration-step size. For the fourth-order Runge-Kutta this technique does not work, because the truncation error in one direction exactly cancels that generated by passing in the reverse direction.

3.5. Multiple-step Methods for Initial-value Problems

As previously pointed out, the multiple-step methods require the use of y_n, y_{n-1}, y_{n-2}, . . . to calculate y_{n+1}. An open-end integration formula is ordinarily used to predict the approximate value of $\bar{y}_{n+1}$ (type II process) and a closed-end formula uses this $\bar{y}_{n+1}$ to generate a more accurate y_{n+1} (type III process). The closed-end formula may be iterated to obtain as accurate an answer as desired.

The simplest multiple-step integration process is the mid-point method described by Lotkin (34). This procedure requires the values of y_n and y_{n-1} to calculate y_{n+1}. Writing the backward version of Euler's formula leads to

$$y_n - y_{n-1} = hf(x_n,y_n) \qquad O(h^2)$$

Euler's formula with a grid spacing of $h/2$ can be written as

$$y_{n+1/2} = y_n + \frac{h}{2}f(x_n,y_n)$$

which, when combined with the first equation, yields

$$y_{n+\frac{1}{2}} = y_n + \tfrac{1}{2}(y_n - y_{n-1}) \qquad O(h^2)$$

In addition, the last formula of (3.3.4) can be used to form the system

$$\begin{aligned} y &= y_0 \qquad x = x_0 \\ y'_n &= f(x_n,y_n) \\ \bar{y}_{n+\frac{1}{2}} &= y_n + \tfrac{1}{2}(y_n - y_{n-1}) \qquad O(h^2) \\ y_{n+1} &= y_n + hf(x_{n+\frac{1}{2}},\bar{y}_{n+\frac{1}{2}}) \qquad O(h^3) \end{aligned} \tag{3.5.1}$$

The local truncation error for the mid-point-slope method is the same as in the modified Euler method, but $f(x,y)$ need be evaluated only once.

The best-known multiple-step integration processes are due to Milne (Chap. 1, 31). Milne's method I requires that y_n, y_{n-1}, y_{n-2}, and y_{n-3} be known to calculate y_{n+1}. Based upon the open-end formula (2.10.24), $\bar{y}_{n+1}$ is first predicted. This value is then corrected to yield an improved y_{n+1} by means of the closed-end formula (2.10.10). The closed-end formula is seen to be Simpson's rule. The actual predictor and corrector equations are

Milne method I

$$\begin{aligned} \bar{y}_{n+1} &= y_{n-3} \\ &\quad + \frac{4h}{3}[2f(x_n,y_n) - f(x_{n-1},y_{n-1}) + 2f(x_{n-2},y_{n-2})] \qquad O(h^5) \\ y_{n+1} &= y_{n-1} \\ &\quad + \frac{h}{3}[f(x_{n+1},\bar{y}_{n+1}) + 4f(x_n,y_n) + f(x_{n-1},y_{n-1})] \qquad O(h^5) \end{aligned} \tag{3.5.2}$$

The local truncation error in each formula is of order $O(h^5)$, but the corrector has a lower actual error than the predictor. In the case of the predictor, the local truncation error is

$$\tfrac{14}{45}h^5y^{[5]}(\xi_1) \qquad x_{n-3} < \xi_1 < x_{n+1}$$

and for the corrector

$$-\frac{h^5}{90}y^{[5]}(\xi_2) \qquad x_{n-1} < \xi_2 < x_{n+1}$$

Because y' is used in the interpolation formula instead of y, the derivative in the error term is one order higher than in (2.10.24) and (2.10.10). If $y^{[5]}(\xi_1) = y^{[5]}(\xi_2)$, the error in the corrector is one twenty-eighth of that in the predictor.

Milne's method II requires six starting values and uses (2.10.26) as predictor and (2.10.12) as corrector. These are

Milne method II

$$\begin{aligned}\bar{y}_{n+1} &= y_{n-5} + \frac{3h}{10}[11f(x_n,y_n) - 14f(x_{n-1},y_{n-1}) + 26f(x_{n-2},y_{n-2}) \\ &\qquad - 14f(x_{n-3},y_{n-3}) + 11f(x_{n-4},y_{n-4})] \qquad O(h^7) \\ y_{n+1} &= y_{n-3} + \frac{2h}{45}[7f(x_{n+1},\bar{y}_{n+1}) + 32f(x_n,y_n) + 12f(x_{n-1},y_{n-1}) \\ &\qquad + 32f(x_{n-2},y_{n-2}) + 7f(x_{n-3},y_{n-3})] \qquad O(h^7)\end{aligned} \tag{3.5.3}$$

The local truncation error for both equations is of order $O(h^7)$, and as in method I the corrector has less error than the predictor. The local truncation error of the predictor is

$$\tfrac{41}{140}h^7y^{[7]}(\xi_1) \qquad x_{n-5} < \xi_1 < x_{n+1}$$

and for the corrector

$$-\tfrac{8}{945}h^7y^{[7]}(\xi_2) \qquad x_{n-3} < \xi_2 < x_{n+1}$$

The method of Adams-Moulton completes the list of frequently used name multiple-step integration processes. The predictor is obtained by integrating over x_n to x_{n+1} with NBF fitted to the points x_n, x_{n-1}, . . . and truncated after the third difference. The corrector is obtained in the same way, but with NBF fitted to the points x_{n+1}, x_n, x_{n-1}, ... The specific equations are

Adams-Moulton

$$\begin{aligned}\bar{y}_{n+1} &= y_n + \frac{h}{24}[55f(x_n,y_n) - 59f(x_{n-1},y_{n-1}) \\ &\qquad + 37f(x_{n-2},y_{n-2}) - 9f(x_{n-3},y_{n-3})] \qquad O(h^5) \\ y_{n+1} &= y_n + \frac{h}{24}[9f(x_{n+1},\bar{y}_{n+1}) + 19f(x_n,y_n) \\ &\qquad - 5f(x_{n-1},y_{n-1}) + f(x_{n-2},y_{n-2})] \qquad O(h^5)\end{aligned} \tag{3.5.4}$$

The specific local truncation errors are

$$\tfrac{251}{720}h^5y^{[5]}(\xi_1) \qquad x_{n-3} < \xi_1 < x_{n+1}$$

for the predictor and

$$-\tfrac{19}{720}h^5y^{[5]}(\xi_2) \qquad x_{n-2} < \xi_2 < x_{n+1}$$

for the corrector.

Since all the multiple-step methods require some starting values before they can be used, a means must be devised for calculating these values.

The usual procedure is to use one of the single-step formulas such as the modified Euler or Runge-Kutta with a small grid interval to generate the necessary values.

A serious problem involved in the use of the multiple-step methods is the difficulty of changing the grid interval as the calculation proceeds. Doubling the interval is relatively simple except that $2r$ instead of r values of y must be stored so that the increased value of h can be used (r is an integer). Cutting the interval in half, however, is more difficult. Based upon the stored values of $y_n, y_{n-1}, y_{n-2}, \ldots$, an interpolation formula can be employed to calculate $y_{n-\frac{1}{2}}, y_{n-\frac{3}{2}}, y_{n-\frac{5}{2}}, \ldots$ and then $h/2$ used. A detailed outline of such a procedure has been given by Keitel (31). Alternatively, the entire computation can be restarted with $h/2$ used.

3.6. Error Propagation and the Monitoring of Multiple-step Methods

As in the case of the single-step integration methods, it is necessary to inquire into the stability of the multiple-step methods. Of further importance, however, is the question of the rate of convergence of the iterating corrector equation, which is a unique feature of the multiple-step methods. These factors can most easily be discussed with the Milne method I used as an illustration.

Consider (3.5.2), in which a predicted value $\bar{y}_{n+1}$ is used to calculate y_{n+1}. Following this sequence the value of y_{n+1} is used to iterate an improved estimate $y_{n+1}^{(1)}$, then $y_{n+1}^{(2)}$, and so on. The mean-value theorem states that

$$f(x_{n+1},y_{n+1}) - f(x_{n+1},\bar{y}_{n+1}) = \left.\frac{\partial f}{\partial y}\right)_{\alpha,x_{n+1}} (y_{n+1} - \bar{y}_{n+1}) \qquad y_{n+1} < \alpha < \bar{y}_{n+1}$$
$$= \lambda_{n+1}(y_{n+1} - \bar{y}_{n+1})$$

If we define a correction factor γ by

$$\gamma = y_{n+1} - \bar{y}_{n+1}$$

the mean-value theorem may be written as

$$\gamma' = \lambda_{n+1}\gamma$$

or, for the special case of $\lambda_{n+1} = \lambda = \text{constant}$,

$$\gamma' = \lambda\gamma \tag{3.6.1}$$

The corrector formula is

$$y_{n+1} = y_{n-1} + \frac{h}{3}[f(x_{n+1},\bar{y}_{n+1}) + 4f(x_n,y_n) + f(x_{n-1},y_{n-1})]$$

or

$$y_{n+1}^{(1)} = y_{n-1} + \frac{h}{3}[f(x_{n+1},y_{n+1}) + 4f(x_n,y_n) + f(x_{n-1},y_{n-1})]$$

and, upon subtracting the two equations,

$$y_{n+1}^{(1)} - y_{n+1} = \frac{h}{3}\left[f(x_{n+1},y_{n+1}) - f(x_{n+1},\bar{y}_{n+1})\right]$$

From (3.6.1) this last equation may be given as

$$y_{n+1}^{(1)} - y_{n+1} = \frac{h}{3}\gamma' = \frac{h\lambda}{3}\gamma$$

The convergence factor Θ being defined by

$$\Theta = \frac{h\lambda}{3}$$

there results

$$y_{n+1}^{(1)} - y_{n+1} = \Theta\gamma$$

Repeating the entire procedure with $y_{n+1}^{(1)}$, in the corrector formula to estimate $y_{n+1}^{(2)}$ leads to

$$y_{n+1}^{(2)} - y_{n+1}^{(1)} = \Theta^2\gamma$$

and after $r + 1$ iterations

$$y_{n+1}^{(r+1)} - y_{n+1}^{(r)} = \Theta^r\gamma \qquad (3.6.2)$$

Equation (3.6.2) is a formula which shows how the consecutive iterations develop as a function of the initial iterate γ and the convergence factor Θ. For the case $|\Theta| < 1.0$, the right side of (3.6.2) converges to zero and the entire process will converge. If $|\Theta| > 1.0$, the process will not converge and the successive iterates will deviate further and further from each other.

The most appropriate choice of Θ is $|\Theta| \ll 1.0$, so that the convergence will be very quick. If possible, the optimum condition would be the case where a single application of the corrector formula with $\bar{y}_{n+1}$ yields the final value y_{n+1} with the maximum necessary accuracy. From the definition of Θ, a small value of h is seen to be compatible with an attempt to use the corrector formula only once.

On the basis of the requirements on the convergence factor, it is possible to obtain an automatic error-monitoring scheme. If we let u_{n+1} be the exact value of y_{n+1} and assume that there is no error in y_n, y_{n-1}, y_{n-2}, and y_{n-3}, Milne's method I equations can be written as

$$u_{n+1} = y_{n-3} + \frac{4h}{3}\left[2f(x_n,y_n) - f(x_{n-1},y_{n-1}) + 2f(x_{n-2},y_{n-2})\right] + \tfrac{14}{45}h^5y^{[5]}(\xi_1)$$

$$u_{n+1} = y_{n-1} + \frac{h}{3}\left[f(x_{n+1},u_{n+1}) + 4f(x_n,y_n) + f(x_{n-1},y_{n-1})\right] - \tfrac{1}{90}h^5y^{[5]}(\xi_2)$$

on the assumption of no round-off error. Subtracting from the Milne method I equations leads to

$$u_{n+1} - \bar{y}_{n+1} = \tfrac{14}{45}h^5 y^{[5]}(\xi_1) \tag{3.6.3}$$

$$u_{n+1} - y_{n+1} = \frac{h}{3}\,[f(x_{n+1},u_{n+1}) - f(x_{n+1},y_{n+1})] - \frac{h^5}{90}\,y^{[5]}(\xi_2) \tag{3.6.4}$$

If we use the mean-value theorem and $\partial f/\partial y)_{\alpha,x_{n+1}} = \lambda_{n+1} = \lambda$, (3.6.4) becomes

$$u_{n+1} - y_{n+1} = \frac{h\lambda}{3}\,(u_{n+1} - y_{n+1}) - \tfrac{1}{90}h^5 y^{[5]}(\xi_2)$$

or $$(u_{n+1} - y_{n+1})(1 - \Theta) = -\frac{h^5}{90}\,y^{[5]}(\xi_2)$$

where Θ = convergence factor. Since a necessary condition for convergence is $|\Theta| < 1$ and preferably $|\Theta| \ll 1.0$, Θ can be neglected relative to 1.0. Thus

$$u_{n+1} - y_{n+1} = -\frac{h^5}{90}\,y^{[5]}(\xi_2)$$

On the assumption that $y^{[5]}(\xi_1) = y^{[5]}(\xi_2)$, this last equation, when compared with (3.6.3), leads to

$$u_{n+1} - \bar{y}_{n+1} = -28(u_{n+1} - y_{n+1})$$

or, after some algebraic manipulation,

$$u_{n+1} - y_{n+1} = -\tfrac{1}{29}(y_{n+1} - \bar{y}_{n+1}) = -\frac{\gamma}{29} \qquad \gamma = y_{n+1} - \bar{y}_{n+1} \tag{3.6.5}$$

The left-hand side of (3.6.5) represents the local truncation error in calculating y_{n+1} by Milne's method I if we assume that the convergence factor is small enough to provide rapid convergence. An automatic error-monitoring scheme, based upon the relative error

$$E = \frac{|\gamma/29|}{u_{n+1}}$$

follows in the same way as described for the single-step processes. This procedure provides, of course, an estimate of the truncation error and not the round-off and inherited errors. It is also apparent that the value of u_{n+1} calculated from (3.6.5) is a better value at x_{n+1} than y_{n+1}.

In exactly the same way the local truncation error per step in Milne's method II can be approximated by $-\gamma/35$ and in the Adams-Moulton method by $-\gamma/14$.

Actually there is a way to improve this procedure, namely, by improving the predicted value $\bar{y}_{n+1}$ to be used initially in the corrector formula (29). Since $\bar{y}_{n+1}$ has an error of $\frac{14}{45}h^5y^{[5]}(\xi_1)$ and y_{n+1} an error of $-(h^5/90)y^{[5]}(\xi_2)$, the assumption $y^{[5]}(\xi_1) = y^{[5]}(\xi_2)$ leads to

$$y_{n+1} - \bar{y}_{n+1} = \tfrac{29}{90}h^5y^{[5]}(\xi)$$

If we assume further that $\bar{y}_{n+1} - y_{n+1} \approx \bar{y}_n - y_n$, it can be seen that

$$y_n - \bar{y}_n = \tfrac{29}{90}h^5y^{[5]}(\xi)$$

and

$$\tfrac{28}{90}h^5y^{[5]}(\xi) = \tfrac{28}{29}(y_n - \bar{y}_n)$$

But since $u_{n+1} = \bar{y}_{n+1} + \frac{28}{90}h^5y^{[5]}(\xi) = \bar{y}_{n+1} + \frac{28}{29}(y_n - \bar{y}_n)$
an improved value of $\bar{y}_{n+1}$ is obtained by

$$\bar{\bar{y}}_{n+1} = \bar{y}_{n+1} + \tfrac{28}{29}(y_n - \bar{y}_n)$$

This value of $\bar{\bar{y}}_{n+1}$ is used as an improved initial estimate for the corrector formula. Thus the best over-all procedure is to predict the value $\bar{y}_{n+1}$ by using the predictor equation, to improve this value to yield $\bar{\bar{y}}_{n+1}$, to apply the corrector equation to yield y_{n+1}, and finally, without any iteration, to use (3.6.5) to get the best value at x_{n+1}.

The necessary stability criteria can be developed for the multiple-step processes in the same manner as previously described for the single-step processes. As will be seen, however, the difference equation for error propagation is now of higher order than the original differential equations; this means that extraneous solutions are included, leading to instability problems. The Milne method I will be used for illustration again. The corrector formula can be written as

$$u_{n+1} = u_{n-1} + \frac{h}{3}(u'_{n-1} + 4u'_n + u'_{n-1}) + T_E$$

where T_E, the local truncation error, is assumed constant and given by

$$T_E = -\frac{h^5}{90}y^{[5]}(\xi) \qquad x_{n-1} < \xi < x_{n+1}$$

The error terminology $\epsilon_n = y_n - u_n$ being used, the subtraction of this equation from the corrector formula leads to

$$\epsilon_{n+1} = \epsilon_{n-1} + \frac{h}{3}(\epsilon'_{n+1} + 4\epsilon'_n + \epsilon'_{n-1}) - T_E$$

From the mean-value theorem, however,

$$\epsilon'_n = \lambda_n\epsilon_n$$

which, when substituted, yields

$$\epsilon_{n+1} = \epsilon_{n-1} + \frac{h}{3}(\lambda_{n+1}\epsilon_{n+1} + 4\lambda_n\epsilon_n + \lambda_{n-1}\epsilon_{n-1}) - T_E$$

or
$$\left(1 - \frac{h\lambda_{n+1}}{3}\right)\epsilon_{n+1} - \left(\frac{4h\lambda_n}{3}\right)\epsilon_n - \left(1 + \frac{h\lambda_{n-1}}{3}\right)\epsilon_{n-1} = -T_E$$

If $\lambda_{n+1} = \lambda_n = \lambda =$ constant, this may be written as

$$\epsilon_{n+1} + A\epsilon_n + B\epsilon_{n-1} = D \tag{3.6.6}$$

where
$$A = \frac{-4\Theta}{1-\Theta} \qquad B = -\frac{1+\Theta}{1-\Theta}$$
$$D = \frac{-T_E}{1-\Theta} \qquad \Theta = \frac{h\lambda}{3} = \text{convergence factor}$$

Equation (3.6.6) is a second-order nonhomogeneous difference equation expressing the propagation of an error at one step to the subsequent steps. The homogeneous solution is given by

$$\epsilon_{n_{\text{hom}}} = c_1\eta_1{}^n + c_2\eta_2{}^n$$

where c_1 and c_2 are arbitrary constants and η_1 and η_2 are roots of the characteristic equation

$$\eta^2 + A\eta + B = 0$$

Explicitly,

$$\eta_1 = -\frac{A}{2} + \frac{1}{2}\sqrt{A^2 - 4B} \qquad \eta_2 = -\frac{A}{2} - \frac{1}{2}\sqrt{A^2 - 4B}$$

or
$$\eta_1 = \frac{2\Theta}{1-\Theta} + \frac{\sqrt{1+3\Theta^2}}{1-\Theta} \qquad \eta_2 = \frac{2\Theta}{1-\Theta} - \frac{\sqrt{1+3\Theta^2}}{1-\Theta} \tag{3.6.7}$$

The particular solution of (3.6.6) is given by $\epsilon_{n_{\text{par}}} = K =$ constant such that

$$K + AK + B = D \qquad \text{or} \qquad K = \frac{D}{1+A+B} = \frac{T_E}{6\Theta}$$

The general solution thus becomes

$$\epsilon_n = c_1\eta_1{}^n + c_2\eta_2{}^n + \frac{T_E}{6\Theta} \tag{3.6.8}$$

The two arbitrary constants can be determined by stating that

$\epsilon_0 = 0$	$n = 0$	no error in starting point
$\epsilon_1 = d_1$	$n = 1$	y_1 has error d_1

Substitution of these conditions leads to

$$0 = c_1 + c_2 + \frac{T_E}{6\Theta}$$

$$d_1 = c_1\eta_1 + c_2\eta_2 + \frac{T_E}{6\Theta}$$

From these two simultaneous equations, the value of c_1 and c_2 can be determined.

Since η_1 and η_2 are only functions of Θ, the stability of (3.6.8) can be determined by investigating the two roots. For convergence, it is necessary that $|\Theta| \ll 1$, and thus $\Theta > 0$ yields $\eta_1 > 1.0$; (3.6.8) will propagate any error with increasing magnitude as n increases. For $\Theta < 0$, $\eta_2 > -1$ and the propagation will still occur in the same way. Independent of the finite value of Θ, the Milne method I is seen to be unstable. All that can be done is to make Θ very small (h very small) to minimize this instability.

The problem, of course, results from the fact that even though a first-order equation is being solved the corrector equation yields an error equation which is second-order. Thus a second extraneous factor evolves from the use of Milne's method I corrector formula.

In a general case the number of added terms is equal to the number of added initial conditions above one which are required to start using a multiple-step process; in the case of Milne method I, only y_{n-1} is needed in addition to y_n in the corrector formula.

Since the multiple-step procedures have the advantage of requiring the calculation of $f(x,y)$ only twice per step, it is natural that attempts have been made to remove the instability feature. In particular, Milne (36) has recently suggested that, after $r + 1$ steps in the use of Milne's method I, the value of y_{r+1} be recomputed by the use of the three-eighths integration rule (2.10.11),

$$y^*_{r+1} = y_{r-2} + \frac{3h}{8}\,[f(x_{r+1},y_{r+1}) + 3f(x_r,y_r) + 3f(x_{r-1},y_{r-1}) + f(x_{r-2},y_{r-2})] \tag{3.6.9}$$

This value is then averaged with the previously calculated y_{r+1} to yield a new estimate y^{**}_{r+1},

$$y^{**}_{r+1} = \frac{y_{r+1} + y^*_{r+1}}{2} \tag{3.6.10}$$

With the requirement that $r > 2$ this scheme was shown to lead to a completely stable system. As an illustration, the system

$$y' = -y \qquad y_0 = 1,\ x_0 = 0$$

was subjected to computational analysis. With the normal Milne method I instability quickly occurs. However, the above correction was found to yield a stable solution for any $r < 40$ for a full range of $h\lambda$'s. Note that this means that the three-eighths rule was required only at every fortieth integration interval. Thus the infrequent use of the above equation changes an unstable solution to a stable one. The extra computation effort and time required would seem to be relatively trivial.

At approximately the same time as Milne, Hamming (29) outlined a method for obtaining predictor-corrector multiple-step integration equations which are stable. Since the corrector is the cause of the instability, a generalized corrector

$$y_{n+1} = ay_n + by_{n-1} + cy_{n-2} + h[df(x_{n+1},y_{n+1}) + ef(x_n,y_n) + gf(x_{n-1},y_{n-1})]$$

was examined. This corrector includes only the data points required by Milne's method I; that is, $a = c = 0$, $b = 1$, $d = g = \frac{1}{3}$, $e = \frac{4}{3}$ would correspond to the unstable corrector. It was found that the case of $a = \frac{9}{8}$, $b = 0$, $c = -\frac{1}{8}$, $d = \frac{3}{8}$, $e = \frac{3}{4}$, and $g = -\frac{3}{8}$ lead to a corrector which was stable. The truncation error is $-\frac{9}{360}h^5y^{[5]}(\xi)$. If the discussion of (3.6.5) and the following material are used, the system would be

$$\bar{y}_{n+1} = y_{n-3} + \frac{4h}{3}[2f(x_n,y_n) - f(x_{n-1},y_{n-1}) + 2f(x_{n-2},y_{n-2})]$$

as a first prediction. From the error terms this can be improved by

$$\bar{\bar{y}}_{n+1} = \bar{y}_{n+1} + \tfrac{112}{121}(y_n - \bar{y}_n)$$

and then corrected with

$$y_{n+1} = \tfrac{1}{8}\{9y_n - y_{n-2} + 3h[f(x_{n+1},\bar{\bar{y}}_{n+1}) + 2f(x_n,y_n) - f(x_{n-1},y_{n-1})]\}$$

If desired, the value of γ is $\frac{9}{121}$ and thus y_{n+1} can be further improved by

$$y_{n+1}^{(1)} = y_{n+1} - \tfrac{9}{121}(y_{n+1} - \bar{y}_{n+1})$$

as in using (3.6.5).

3.7. Initial-value Problems for Special Second-order Equations

While a second-order differential equation with initial values may be integrated by decomposing into two first-order equations, certain types of equations are better handled by other means. If the first derivative is missing,

$$\begin{aligned} y'' &= f(x,y) \\ y &= y_0 \qquad x = x_0 \\ y' &= y_{00} \qquad x = x_0 \end{aligned} \tag{3.7.1}$$

there is no real reason to calculate the first derivative. A technique which does not require the evaluation of y' would seem to be most appropriate. Actually the system of (3.7.1) is not an unusual one. Any linear second-order differential equation of the form

$$y'' + g_1(x)y' + g_2(x)y = h(x)$$

may be transformed to (3.7.1) by the change of variable

$$y(x) = v(x) \exp\left[-\tfrac{1}{2}\int g_1(x)\,dx\right]$$

The new equation has the form

$$v'' + \tfrac{1}{4}[4g_2(x) - 2g_1'(x) - \overline{g_1(x)}^2]v = h(x) \exp\left[\tfrac{1}{2}\int g_1(x)\,dx\right]$$

or

$$v'' = f(x,v)$$

In the present approach the differentiated form of a central-difference interpolation polynomial is used; this contrasts with the previous use of an integrated polynomial. From (2.9.6) and the next equation

$$D^2 = \frac{1}{h^2}\left(\delta^2 - \frac{\delta^4}{12} + \frac{\delta^6}{90} - \frac{\delta^8}{560} + \cdots\right) = \frac{\delta^2}{h^2}\left(1 - \frac{\delta^2}{12} + \frac{\delta^4}{90} - \frac{\delta^6}{560} + \cdots\right)$$

or

$$\delta^2 D^{-2} = h^2\left(1 - \frac{\delta^2}{12} + \frac{\delta^4}{90} - \frac{\delta^6}{560} + \cdots\right)^{-1}$$

For any function $g(x)$

$$\delta^2 D^{-2} g''(x) = \delta^2 g(x)$$

which, when combined with the previous equation plus some algebraic manipulation, leads to

$$\delta^2 g(x) = h^2\left(1 + \frac{\delta^2}{12} - \frac{\delta^4}{240} + \frac{31\delta^6}{60{,}480} - \cdots\right) g''(x)$$

or

$$g_{n+1} - 2g_n + g_{n-1} = h^2(g_n'' + \tfrac{1}{12}\delta^2 g_n'' - \tfrac{1}{240}\delta^4 g_n'' + \cdots) \qquad (3.7.2)$$

Expanding the right-hand side of (3.7.2) after truncating before the fourth difference,

$$g_{n+1} - 2g_n + g_{n-1} = \frac{h^2}{12}\,(g_{n+1}'' + 10g_n'' + g_{n-1}'') \qquad (3.7.3)$$

with an error in the first neglected difference. Applied to the differential equation of (3.7.1), (3.7.3) becomes

$$y_{n+1} - 2y_n + y_{n-1} = \frac{h^2}{12}\,[f(x_{n+1},\bar{y}_{n+1}) + 10f(x_n,y_n) + f(x_{n-1},y_{n-1})]$$

This is a closed-end integration formula which uses the values y_n and y_{n-1} and an initial estimate of $\bar{y}_{n+1}$ to obtain the new y_{n+1}. Note that the calculation of y' is bypassed completely and never has to be used.

There are two schools of thought on the means of actually using this procedure. Since the first truncated term involves the fourth difference multiplied by h^2, the local truncation error is of order $O(h^6)$. The use of a small h will then produce a small error, but a large number of applications of the equation will be required to move far into the x space. Fox (20) suggests an alternative procedure. A large value of h is used, yielding as a first approximation $y_{n+1}^{(1)}$. Based upon $y_{n+1}^{(1)}$ and the other previously calculated values, the first neglected difference is computed and used as a correction term to yield $y_{n+1}^{(2)}$. The process is then repeated until $y_{n+1}^{(r)}$ has attained the desired accuracy. This method seems to work extremely well. Further details of an analogous procedure for boundary-value problems will shortly be presented.

3.8. Initial-value *n*th-order Differential Equations

As previously stated, any initial-value nth order differential equation can be decomposed into n first-order equations. Thus

$$y^{[n]} + g_1 y^{[n-1]} + g_2 y^{[n-2]} + \cdots + g_n y = p$$

with

$$\left.\begin{aligned} y &= y_0 \\ y' &= y_{00} \\ &\cdots\cdots \\ y^{[n-1]} &= y_{00\ldots 0} \end{aligned}\right\} \quad x = x_0$$

can be written as

$$\begin{aligned} w_1' &= f_1(x,w_1,w_2, \ldots ,w_n) \\ w_2' &= f_2(x,w_1,w_2, \ldots ,w_n) \\ &\cdots\cdots\cdots\cdots\cdots\cdots \\ w_n' &= f_n(x,w_1,w_2, \ldots ,w_n) \end{aligned}$$

with

$$\left.\begin{aligned} w_1 &= w_{10} \\ w_2 &= w_{20} \\ &\cdots\cdots \\ w_n &= w_{n0} \end{aligned}\right\} \quad x = x_0$$

The Euler single-step process can be used as an illustration of how the n first-order equations are integrated. At the initial point $x = x_0$, all the $f_1, f_2, \ldots, f_n$ can be calculated from the initial conditions. The $w_1(x_1), w_2(x_1), \ldots, w_n(x_1)$ follow directly from the Euler system in the form

$$\begin{aligned} w_1(x_1) &= w_1(x_0) + hf_1[x_0,w_1(x_0),w_2(x_0), \ldots ,w_n(x_0)] \\ w_2(x_1) &= w_2(x_0) + hf_2[x_0,w_1(x_0),w_2(x_0), \ldots ,w_n(x_0)] \\ &\cdots\cdots\cdots\cdots\cdots\cdots\cdots\cdots\cdots \\ w_n(x_1) &= w_n(x_0) + hf_n[x_0,w_1(x_0),w_2(x_0), \ldots ,w_n(x_0)] \end{aligned}$$

This process is repeated as many times as required into x space. The same type of procedure can be applied with any of the multiple-step processes. Usually at least one iteration will be required with the corrector formula to achieve the desired result. Obviously the computational time may be quite large when n is large.

3.9. Boundary-value Ordinary Differential Equations

The second-order differential equation plus boundary conditions

$$\begin{aligned} y'' + g_1(x,y)y' + g_2(x,y)y &= p(x,y) \\ y = y_0 \qquad & x = x_0 \\ y = y_{N+1} \qquad & x = x_{N+1} \end{aligned} \tag{3.9.1}$$

may be used to illustrate the important methods of solving boundary value problems.

One possible approach to the numerical solution of (3.9.1) is to try to use one of the initial-value integration procedures and integrate from $x = x_0$ to $x = x_{N+1}$. The check on the calculation is that the value of y_{N+1} must agree with the known boundary value at that point. Since this is a second-order equation, it is necessary to assume the value of y' at $x = x_0$ to start the integration. By suitable trial and error or iteration a value of $y'(x_0)$ can sometimes be found which yields the correct y_{N+1} at $x = x_{N+1}$. If g_1, g_2, and p in (3.9.1) are only functions of x (linear system), this procedure has a good chance of success. For $\bar{y}(x)$ one solution of the differential equation and $\bar{\bar{y}}(x)$ another solution, the superposition principle for linear systems leads to

$$y(x) = c_1\bar{y}(x) + c_2\bar{\bar{y}}(x)$$

with c_1 and c_2 as arbitrary constants. Upon applying the boundary conditions

$$\begin{aligned} y_0 &= c_1\bar{y}(x_0) + c_2\bar{\bar{y}}(x_0) \\ y_{N+1} &= c_1\bar{y}(x_{N+1}) + c_2\bar{\bar{y}}(x_{N+1}) \end{aligned}$$

two equations with two unknowns c_1 and c_2 are obtained. The two solutions $\bar{y}(x)$ and $\bar{\bar{y}}(x)$ may be obtained by assuming two initial derivatives for $y'(x_0)$. Integrating each case with the known $y = y_0$ at $x = x_0$ leads to the two solutions. An alternative procedure is to assume $y'(x_0)$ and $y'(x_{N+1})$ and to integrate first in one direction and then in the other.

Unfortunately this procedure cannot be used in the nonlinear case. Instead, the following modification is sometimes used: Three estimates of $y'(x_0)$ are made, and by using an initial-value integration the corresponding three values $y^{(1)}(x_{N+1})$, $y^{(2)}(x_{N+1})$, and $y^{(3)}(x_{N+1})$ are calculated. None of these, except in an unusual case, is equal to the correct $y(x_{N+1})$. The grid interval in these first calculations can be taken rather large since accuracy is not desired at this point. Having three values of $y'(x_0)$ and the three corresponding $y(x_{N+1})$, parabolic interpolation is used to approximate that value of $y'(x_0)$ which yields the boundary condition $y(x_{N+1})$. The derivative so obtained is only a rough estimate but does tend to indicate narrow bounds on the true value. The entire process can now be repeated with a smaller grid interval used and assumed values of the derivative within the known bounds. Further repetition can be used to finally obtain the desired accuracy. The set of points $y_1, y_2, \ldots, y_N$ obtained in the last computation are then the numerical solution of (3.9.1).

There is, of course, no a priori reason to expect that convergence of the over-all iteration process will occur. In many systems the calculated value of $y(x_{N+1})$ is very sensitive to the assumed $y'(x_0)$. It may be impossible to obtain a value of $y(x_{N+1})$ with the desired accuracy without specifying $y'(x_0)$ to a large number of digits. In other words, accuracy at one point does not necessarily imply the same accuracy at other points. A few rough calculations will, however, indicate whether or not the technique has a chance of succeeding.

A second approach to the numerical solution of (3.9.1) uses a finite-difference substitution and the inclusion of the boundary conditions at the start. Let the interval x_0 to x_{N+1} be divided into $N + 1$ equally spaced intervals of width h; this leads to N internal points $x_1, x_2, \ldots, x_N$. A difference-equation representation may then be substituted for the differential equation at each of the internal points. This leads to N equations with N unknowns $y_1, y_2, \ldots, y_N$ with the boundary values y_0 and y_{N+1} included explicitly. Solution of the simultaneous equations yields the desired numerical values of $y(x)$. If the terms g_1, g_2, and p are functions of x only, the set of simultaneous equations can be evaluated by the methods of Chap. 5. The main error in solving the simultaneous equations is round-off, and there are no stability questions. If the coefficients g_1 and g_2 and/or p are functions of y, the set of simultaneous equations are nonlinear and are quite difficult to solve.

To illustrate these points, consider the linear system first, that is, (3.9.1), with $g_1(x,y) = g_1(x)$, $g_2(x,y) = g_2(x)$, and $p(x,y) = p(x)$. In such a system the first derivative may be removed by the change of variable in Sec. 3.7. Thus the system to be considered can be written as

$$\begin{gathered} y'' + g(x)y = p(x) \\ y = y_0 \qquad x = x_0 \\ y = y_{N+1} \qquad x = x_{N+1} \end{gathered} \tag{3.9.2}$$

The boundary conditions after the transformation of variables are not actually the same as the original, but in the present context this will not cause any difficulties. The differential equation may be written as

$$y'' = p(x) - g(x)y$$

and substituted into (3.7.2) for the second derivative term. This yields

$$y_{n+1} - 2y_n + y_{n-1} = h^2[(p_n - g_ny_n) + \tfrac{1}{12}\delta^2(p_n - g_ny_n) - \tfrac{1}{240}\delta^4(p_n - g_ny_n) + \cdots] \quad (3.9.3)$$

Truncating the right side before the second-order difference leads to

$$y_{n+1} - 2\left(1 - \frac{h^2}{2}g_n\right)y_n + y_{n-1} = h^2p_n \quad (3.9.4)$$

with truncation error $O(h^4)$. Truncating after the second-order difference leads to

$$y_{n+1} - 2y_n + y_{n-1} = h^2(p_n - g_ny_n) + \frac{h^2}{12}\delta^2p_n - \frac{h^2}{12}(g_{n+1}y_{n+1} - 2g_ny_n + g_{n-1}y_{n-1})$$

or

$$\left(1 + \frac{h^2}{12}g_{n+1}\right)y_{n+1} - 2(1 - \tfrac{5}{12}h^2g_n)y_n + \left(1 + \frac{h^2}{12}g_{n-1}\right)y_{n-1} = h^2(p_n + \tfrac{1}{12}\delta^2p_n) = \frac{h^2}{12}(p_{n+1} + 10p_n + p_{n-1}) \quad (3.9.5)$$

with truncation error $O(h^6)$. Breaking the interval x_0 to x_{N+1} into $N + 1$ equal intervals of width h such that $x_1, x_2, \ldots, x_N$ are the interior points, either (3.9.4) or (3.9.5) can be applied at each of the interior points. Since y_0 and y_{N+1} are known values, this leads to the following systems of simultaneous equations:

For (3.9.4)

$$\begin{aligned}
-2\left(1 - \frac{h^2}{2}g_1\right)y_1 + y_2 &= h^2p_1 - y_0 \\
y_1 - 2\left(1 - \frac{h^2}{2}g_2\right)y_2 + y_3 &= h^2p_2 \\
y_2 - 2\left(1 - \frac{h^2}{2}g_3\right)y_3 + y_4 &= h^2p_3 \\
\cdots\cdots\cdots\cdots\cdots\cdots& \\
y_{N-2} - 2\left(1 - \frac{h^2}{2}g_{N-1}\right)y_{N-1} + y_N &= h^2p_{N-1} \\
y_{N-1} - 2\left(1 - \frac{h^2}{2}g_N\right)y_N &= h^2p_N - y_{N+1}
\end{aligned} \quad (3.9.6)$$

For (3.9.5)

$$
\begin{aligned}
&-2(1 - \tfrac{5}{12}h^2 g_1)y_1 + \left(1 + \frac{h^2}{12} g_2\right) y_2 \\
&\qquad = \frac{h^2}{12}(p_0 + 10p_1 + p_2) - \left(1 + \frac{h^2}{12} g_0\right) y_0 \\
&\left(1 + \frac{h^2}{12} g_1\right) y_1 - 2(1 - \tfrac{5}{12}h^2 g_2)y_2 + \left(1 + \frac{h^2}{12} g_3\right) y_3 \\
&\qquad = \frac{h^2}{12}(p_1 + 10p_2 + p_3) \\
&\left(1 + \frac{h^2}{12} g_2\right) y_2 - 2(1 - \tfrac{5}{12}h^2 g_3)y_3 + \left(1 + \frac{h^2}{12} g_4\right) y_4 \\
&\qquad = \frac{h^2}{12}(p_2 + 10p_3 + p_4) \qquad (3.9.7) \\
&\cdots\cdots\cdots\cdots\cdots\cdots\cdots\cdots\cdots\cdots \\
&\left(1 + \frac{h^2}{12} g_{N-2}\right) y_{N-2} - 2(1 - \tfrac{5}{12}h^2 g_{N-1})y_{N-1} + \left(1 + \frac{h^2}{12} g_N\right) y_N \\
&\qquad = \frac{h^2}{12}(p_{N-2} + 10p_{N-1} + p_N) \\
&\left(1 + \frac{h^2}{12} g_{N-1}\right) y_{N-1} - 2(1 - \tfrac{5}{12}h^2 g_N)y_N \\
&\qquad = \frac{h^2}{12}(p_{N-1} + 10p_N + p_{N+1}) - \left(1 + \frac{h^2}{12} g_{N+1}\right) y_{N+1}
\end{aligned}
$$

In either form there are N simultaneous equations and N unknowns. Actually (3.9.7) is almost as easy to use as (3.9.6), the difference being largely in the calculation of the coefficients.

There are a number of problems associated with the implementation of (3.9.6) or (3.9.7). In order to minimize the truncation error, the value of h required may be quite small. This means that N will be quite large; the storage and computational-time requirements for solving such large systems of simultaneous equations may become completely impractical. To attempt to remove this problem, a possible path might be to include the fourth-order difference in (3.9.3). This would allow a larger h (or a smaller number of simultaneous equations) to be used. However, now the formulas corresponding to (3.9.6) to (3.9.7) include the values of y_{n+2}, y_{n+1}, y_n, y_{n-1}, and y_{n-2}. When these are applied to the point x_1, the value y_{-1} is developed; when they are applied to the point x_N, the value y_{N+2} results. Neither y_{-1} nor y_{N+2} exists, since they extend one grid space beyond the boundaries; there are now $N + 2$ unknowns and only N equations. Two equations may be added by using an interpolation polynomial to relate y_{-1} to y_0, y_1, y_2, . . . and to relate y_{N+2} to y_{N+1}, y_N, y_{N-1}, ... In this way $N + 2$ equations and unknowns result. These various manipulations require extra programming, but this is not necessarily a serious problem.

An alternative approach which uses a large h has been outlined by Fox (20). A first approximate solution is obtained by using (3.9.6) or (3.9.7) with a large enough h so that the number of simultaneous equations can be easily solved. The first neglected differences in (3.9.3) are then used, and a correction is calculated to the first set of answers. If this correction is significant, a further correction is calculated. This is continued until the desired accuracy is obtained. To take (3.9.6) as an example, the first approximate values would be $y_1^{(0)}$, $y_2^{(0)}$, . . . , $y_N^{(0)}$. By differencing these values a set of δ^2 can be calculated. With the first correction defined by $\epsilon_n^{(1)}$ the system of equations given by (3.9.6) with $\epsilon_n^{(1)}$ replacing the y_n's and with the right side equal to $-\delta^2 y_n^{(0)}$ can be solved for the $\epsilon_n^{(1)}$'s. The boundary values $\epsilon_0^{(1)}$ and $\epsilon_{N+1}^{(1)}$ are zero, since these values are known. The process can be continued as desired by forming the second differences on $\epsilon_n^{(1)}$ and calculating $\epsilon_n^{(2)}$ as before (the system of equations now has the $-\delta^2\epsilon_n^{(1)}$ replacing the previous $-\delta^2 y_n^{(0)}$ and $\epsilon_n^{(2)}$ replacing $\epsilon_n^{(1)}$). In this way a large h can be used and the truncation error successively wiped out. The process can be readily mechanized for a computer, and since it involves only the solution of small sets of simultaneous equations, it is a very attractive technique. One further point needs to be mentioned. In generating the differences it is necessary to have values outside the interval x_0 to x_{N+1}. These can be obtained by using (3.9.6) applied to x_0 and x_{N+1}.

This entire discussion has been based on the use of (3.9.2) instead of (3.9.1). Sometimes the change of variable may lead to a differential equation of the form of (3.9.2), which possess undesirable properties. In such a case or if (3.9.1) is nonlinear, (3.9.1) must be used in its primary form with both the first and second derivatives replaced by difference approximations. The mechanics of such a substitution is self-evident. The solution of the simultaneous equations when (3.9.1) is nonlinear involves an iteration type of process for which no general discussion can be given here (see Chap. 7, however).

In many physical situations the boundary conditions will involve the gradient of y with respect to x. Such a boundary condition may be expressed as

$$a_1 y' + a_2 y = a_3 \qquad x = x_0 \text{ and/or } x = x_{N+1} \tag{3.9.8}$$

Equation (3.9.8) reduces to the previous boundary condition when $a_1 = 0$. Since there exist a number of finite-difference formulas for representing a first derivative at a point in terms of forward or backward differences, (3.9.8) can be handled in a straightforward manner. As an example, from (2.9.1),

$$hy_0' = \left(\Delta - \frac{\Delta^2}{2} + \frac{\Delta^3}{3} - \frac{\Delta^4}{4} + \cdots\right) y_0$$

or

$$hy_0' = F(y_0, y_1, y_2, y_3, \ldots)$$

can be used to replace the derivative in (3.9.8) at $x = x_0$. The same type of equation in terms of backward differences can be used at $x = x_{N+1}$. Since y_0 and y_{N+1} are unknown, the addition of these two equations leads to $N + 2$ equations and $N + 2$ unknowns. The only problem here is to maintain approximately the same truncation error in the two added equations as in the other difference equations.

Since there are no questions of stability associated with the boundary-value solution, it would seem an inviting approach to replace a first-order initial-value system with a second-order boundary-value system. This has been discussed by Allen and Severn (1) and by Fox (Chap. 1, 13). For the system

$$y' + g(x)y = p(x) \qquad y = y_0 \qquad x = x_0 \tag{3.9.9}$$

Differentiating yields

$$y'' + g'(x)y + g(x)y' = p'(x)$$

The first derivative can be removed by substituting (3.9.9).

$$y'' + [g'(x) - \overline{g(x)}^2]y = p'(x) - g(x)p(x)$$

The boundary conditions now become

$$y = y_0 \qquad x = x_0$$
$$y' + g(x)y = p(x) \qquad x = x_{N+1}$$

In this way the original initial-value problem of (3.9.9) is replaced with a boundary-value system. Details of the computational comparisons for the two systems are given by Fox.

3.10. Numerical Examples

Example 3.1. Consider the transient operation of a single, continuous stirred-tank reactor with a first-order exothermic reaction. On the assumption that a cooling coil is used to remove the heat generated by the chemical reaction, the dynamic or transient mass balance is given by

$$V \frac{dc}{dt} = Fc_0 - Fc - Vke^{-E/RT}c \tag{3.10.1}$$

and the corresponding heat balance by

$$V\rho c_p \frac{dT}{dt} = F\rho c_p(T_0 - T) - \Delta H\, Vke^{-E/RT}c - U(T - T') \tag{3.10.2}$$

The derivation of these equations has been presented in the literature (3) and will not be repeated here. For nomenclature see below. The physical problem may now be stated:

Given the initial temperature T_∞ and concentration c_∞ in the reactor,

$$\left.\begin{aligned} T &= T_\infty \\ c &= c_\infty \end{aligned}\right\} \quad t = 0$$

and a feed temperature and concentration T_0 and c_0 which are initiated at time zero, calculate the transient response of the reactor.

The system is initial-value and consists of two first-order coupled nonlinear ODE. The numerical values chosen for the parameters are

V = reactor volume = 2,000 cm^3
F = feed-flow rate = 10 cm^3/sec
k = reaction constant = 7.86×10^{12}
E = energy of activation = 22,500
ρ = density of solution = 1 g/cm^3
c_p = heat capacity of solution = 1 cal/(g)(°C)
ΔH = heat of reaction = $-10{,}000$ cal/mole
U = heat-transfer coefficient for cooling coil = 1.356 cal/(°C)(sec)
T' = average cooling-water temperature = 350°K
$T_0 = T_\infty$ = 300.0°K
$c_0 = c_\infty = 5.0 \times 10^{-3}$ mole/liter

The methods of solution are the fourth-order Runge-Kutta process and Milne method I, with the modified Euler employed for starting values.

As a first step (3.10.1) and (3.10.2) can be simplified by defining

$$\alpha_1 = \frac{Fc_0}{V} \qquad \alpha_2 = \frac{FT_0}{V} + \frac{UT'}{V\rho c_p}$$

$$\beta_1 = \frac{F}{V} \qquad \beta_2 = \frac{F}{V} + \frac{U}{V\rho c_p}$$

$$\gamma_1 = k \qquad \gamma_2 = \frac{(-\Delta H)k}{\rho c_p}$$

which leads to

$$\frac{dc}{dt} = \alpha_1 - c(\beta_1 + \gamma_1 e^{-E/RT}) \tag{3.10.3}$$

$$\frac{dT}{dt} = \alpha_2 - \beta_2 T + \gamma_2 c e^{-E/RT} \tag{3.10.4}$$

To provide a check on the transient calculations, the final equilibrium values for the reactor can be calculated. At equilibrium, $dc/dt = dT/dt = 0$, and (3.10.3) and (3.10.4) become

$$0 = \alpha_1 - c_E(\beta_1 + \gamma_1 e^{-E/RT})$$
$$0 = \alpha_2 - \beta_2 T_E + \gamma_2 c_E e^{-E/RT}$$

where c_E and T_E indicate equilibrium values. Substituting c_E from the first equation into the second yields

$$T_E = \frac{1}{\beta_1\beta_2}\left[\alpha_2\beta_1 + (\alpha_2\gamma_1 + \alpha_1\gamma_2 - \beta_2\gamma_1 T_E)e^{-E/RT_E}\right]$$

This last equation contains one unknown, the equilibrium temperature T_E, and may be solved by iteration. Guessing at $T_E^{(0)}$ and substituting into the right side of the equation yields $T_E^{(1)}$ on the left side. This new value is substituted back in the right side to yield $T_E^{(2)}$, etc. When $|T_E^{(r+1)} - T_E^{(r)}| < \epsilon$, an accuracy value, T_E is known and c_E can be calculated directly. For the parameters under consideration and $\epsilon = 10^{-7}$

$$T_E = 305.436°\text{K} \qquad c_E = 4.45053 \times 10^{-3} \text{ mole/liter}$$

To solve the transient equations by the fourth-order Runge-Kutta method, (3.3.6) is expanded to handle two dependent variables as follows:

$$\frac{dc}{dt} = J(c,T) \qquad \frac{dT}{dt} = G(c,T) \tag{3.10.5}$$

$$\begin{aligned}
k_0 &= \Delta t\, J(c_n,T_n) & m_0 &= \Delta t\, G(c_n,T_n)\\
k_1 &= \Delta t\, J\left(c_n + \frac{k_0}{2}, T_n + \frac{m_0}{2}\right) & m_1 &= \Delta t\, G\left(c_n + \frac{k_0}{2}, T_n + \frac{m_0}{2}\right)\\
k_2 &= \Delta t\, J\left(c_n + \frac{k_1}{2}, T_n + \frac{m_1}{2}\right) & m_2 &= \Delta t\, G\left(c_n + \frac{k_1}{2}, T_n + \frac{m_1}{2}\right)\\
k_3 &= \Delta t\, J(c_n + k_2, \quad T_n + m_2) & m_3 &= \Delta t\, G(c_n + k_2, \quad T_n + m_2)\\
c_{n+1} &= c_n + \tfrac{1}{6}(k_0 + 2k_1 + 2k_2 + k_3) & T_{n+1} &= T_n + \tfrac{1}{6}(m_0 + 2m_1 + 2m_2 + m_3)
\end{aligned}$$

The computation cycle thus becomes one of starting with c_n, T_n and calculating k_0, m_0, k_1, m_1, . . . until finally c_{n+1}, T_{n+1} are available.

TABLE 3.1. TRANSIENT T AND c VALUES FOR STIRRED REACTOR
Runge-Kutta fourth-order method

t, sec	$\Delta t = 20$ sec		$\Delta t = 10$ sec	
	$c \times 10^3$	T	$c \times 10^3$	T
0	5.000	300.000	5.000	300.000
100	4.863	301.589	4.863	301.589
200	4.760	302.685	4.760	302.685
300	4.681	303.456	4.681	303.456
400	4.622	304.004	4.622	304.004
500	4.578	304.397	4.578	304.397
600	4.545	304.681	4.545	304.681
700	4.520	304.887	4.520	304.887
800	4.502	305.036	4.502	305.036
900	4.488	305.145	4.488	305.145
1,000	4.478	305.224	4.478	305.224
1,100	4.471	305.281		
1,500	4.456	305.393		
2,000	4.452	305.426		

Equilibrium $\quad T_E = 305.436$

$c_E = 4.45053 \times 10^{-3}$

The numerical results of such a calculation are given in Table 3.1 for $\Delta t = 20$ and 10 sec. The data are identical for the digits shown and smoothly approach the equilibrium values. A further calculation using $\Delta t = 5$ sec (data not shown) also yielded identical values. Thus the results for $\Delta t = 20$ sec may be considered as correct.

As a second method of numerical integration Milne's method I was used, with the modified Euler method generating the necessary three starting values. The modified Euler method may be written as [see (3.3.3)]

$$\left.\begin{aligned} \bar{c}_{n+1} &= c_n + \Delta t\, J(c_n,T_n) \\ \bar{T}_{n+1} &= T_n + \Delta t\, G(c_n,T_n) \end{aligned}\right\} \quad \text{predict}$$

$$\left.\begin{aligned} c_{n+1} &= c_n + \frac{\Delta t}{2}\,[J(c_n,T_n) + J(\bar{c}_{n+1},\bar{T}_{n+1})] \\ T_{n+1} &= T_n + \frac{\Delta t}{2}\,[G(c_n,T_n) + G(\bar{c}_{n+1},\bar{T}_{n+1})] \end{aligned}\right\} \quad \text{correct and iterate} \qquad (3.10.6)$$

The nomenclature of (3.10.5) is assumed. Starting with c_∞ and T_∞, (3.10.6) is used to calculate c_1, c_2, c_3, T_1, T_2, and T_3. The iteration involved in using the second set of (3.10.6) was fixed at full machine word accuracy. Milne's method I equations [(3.5.2) and (3.6.5)] may be written as

$$\left.\begin{aligned} \bar{c}_{n+1} &= c_{n-3} + \frac{4\,\Delta t}{3}\,[2J(c_n,T_n) - J(c_{n-1},T_{n-1}) + 2J(c_{n-2},T_{n-2})] \\ \bar{T}_{n+1} &= T_{n-3} + \frac{4\,\Delta t}{3}\,[2G(c_n,T_n) - G(c_{n-1},T_{n-1}) + 2G(c_{n-2},T_{n-2})] \end{aligned}\right\} \quad \text{predict}$$

$$\left.\begin{aligned} \bar{\bar{c}}_{n+1} &= \bar{c}_{n+1} + \tfrac{28}{29}\,(c_n - \bar{c}_n) \\ \bar{\bar{T}}_{n+1} &= \bar{T}_{n+1} + \tfrac{28}{29}\,(T_n - \bar{T}_n) \end{aligned}\right\} \quad \text{correct predicted values} \qquad (3.10.7)$$

$$\left.\begin{aligned} c_{n+1} &= c_{n-1} + \frac{\Delta t}{3}\,[J(\bar{\bar{c}}_{n+1},\bar{\bar{T}}_{n+1}) + 4J(c_n,T_n) + J(c_{n-1},T_{n-1})] \\ T_{n+1} &= T_{n-1} + \frac{\Delta t}{3}\,[G(\bar{\bar{c}}_{n+1},\bar{\bar{T}}_{n+1}) + 4G(c_n,T_n) + G(c_{n-1},T_{n-1})] \end{aligned}\right\} \quad \text{corrector}$$

$$\left.\begin{aligned} c^*_{n+1} &= c_{n+1} - \tfrac{1}{29}\,(c_{n+1} - \bar{c}_{n+1}) \\ T^*_{n+1} &= T_{n+1} - \tfrac{1}{29}\,(T_{n+1} - \bar{T}_{n+1}) \end{aligned}\right\} \quad \text{correct corrector}$$

A measure of the truncation error [see (3.6.5)] results from consideration of $-\gamma_c/29$ and $-\gamma_T/29$, where $\gamma_c = c_{n+1} - \bar{c}_{n+1}$ and $\gamma_T = T_{n+1} - \bar{T}_{n+1}$. No iteration was used, however, in (3.10.7).

A selected number of numerical results are tabulated in Tables 3.2 and 3.3. In all cases the iteration error in the modified Euler calculation was set at 10^{-10}; this equals the maximum number of significant figures attainable on the digital computer employed. These values of the initial temperatures and concentrations were thus quite accurate to ensure a high degree of accuracy in succeeding calculations. An examination of the results for $\Delta t = 20$ sec shows that the calculation agrees with the previous Runge-Kutta computation and also that the truncation error is extremely small. In fact, for $\Delta t = 10$ sec (data not shown) the truncation error for both the temperature and the concentration is less than can be detected in the total word length of the computer.

With an interval of $\Delta t = 60$ sec, however, the Milne method I leads to instability as oscillation sets in at some point in the calculation. It is interesting to note that until the instability occurs the results are correct to about five significant figures. In Table 3.3 a comparison is made of the calculation with and without the correction on the predictor value. As seen, correcting the predictor does improve the accuracy, i.e., cuts down the truncation error, but only by a relatively small amount. The

TABLE 3.2. TRANSIENT T AND c VALUES FOR STIRRED REACTOR

Milne method I with modified Euler to start†

t	$\Delta t = 60$ sec				$\Delta t = 20$ sec			
	$c \times 10^3$	T	$-\gamma_c/29 \times 10^8$	$-\gamma_T/29 \times 10^4$	$c \times 10^3$	T	$-\gamma_c/29 \times 10^8$	$-\gamma_T/29 \times 10^4$
0	5.000	300.000	0	0	5.000	300.000	0	0
180	4.777	302.505	0	0	4.777	302.496	0.001	0.014
300	4.681	303.462	1.249	2.344	4.681	303.456	0.003	0.010
480	4.586	304.329	0.097	0.707	4.586	304.329	0.009	0.013
600	4.545	304.681	0.260	0.686	4.545	304.681	0.013	0.014
780	4.505	305.014	0.571	0.659	4.505	305.010	0.025	0.014
900	4.488	305.149	0.850	0.707	4.488	305.145	0.035	0.017
1,080	4.472	305.268	1.422	0.772	4.472	305.271	0.057	0.017
1,200	4.465	305.320	1.952	0.793	4.465	305.323	0.077	0.014
1,380	4.459	305.376	3.036	0.786	4.459	305.373	0.119	0.010
1,500	4.457	305.397	4.000	0.755	4.456	305.393	0.159	0.007
1,680	Oscillation				4.453	305.411	0.243	0.003
1,800	↓				4.453	305.419	0.320	0.010

† Data include correction of predicted value.

TABLE 3.3. TRANSIENT T AND c VALUES FOR STIRRED REACTOR

Milne method I with modified Euler to start

t	Δt = 60 sec; correct prediction				Δt = 60 sec; prediction not corrected			
	$c \times 10^3$	T	$-\gamma_c/29 \times 10^8$	$-\gamma_T/29 \times 10^4$	$c \times 10^3$	T	$-\gamma_c/29 \times 10^8$	$-\gamma_T/29 \times 10^4$
0	5.000	300.000	0	0	5.000	300.000	0	0
180	4.777	302.505	0	0	4.777	302.505	0	0
300	4.681	303.462	1.249	2.344	4.681	303.462	1.252	2.314
480	4.586	304.329	0.097	0.707	4.586	304.329	0.143	0.731
600	4.545	304.681	0.260	0.686	4.545	304.684	0.354	0.731
780	4.505	305.014	0.571	0.659	4.505	305.014	0.873	0.734
900	4.488	305.149	0.850	0.707	4.488	305.149	1.243	0.803
1,080	4.472	305.268	1.422	0.772	4.472	305.268	2.109	0.889
1,200	4.465	305.320	1.952	0.793	4.465	305.319	2.985	0.914
1,380	4.459	305.376	3.036	0.786	4.460	305.378	4.999	0.866
1,500	4.457	305.397	4.000	0.755	4.457	305.398	6.838	0.783

Oscillation
↓

correction does, however, become more noticeable at larger values of time. There is thus a serious question in the present case as to the need for these added correction calculations in light of the extra computation time required.

These calculations were performed on the IBM 650 using the Bell I interpretive floating-point mode. Approximately 8 sec was required in the Milne method I program to advance one Δt. It was impossible to estimate the Runge-Kutta timing because of the means of output of data.

Example 3.2. Based upon a given reaction and catalyst and under given conditions, the tube diameter is the major design variable which determines the maximum temperature attained in a tubular catalyst bed. The critical bed diameter is that diameter which permits the maximum allowable temperature to be attained without destroying the catalyst or shifting the equilibrium. A means of estimating the critical bed diameter for an exothermic reaction can be obtained by starting with a steady-state heat balance on a radial slice within the reactor. Catalyst conduction being neglected, this heat balance yields

$$\Delta H\bar{r} + k_g \left(\frac{\partial^2 T}{\partial r^2} + \frac{1}{r}\frac{\partial T}{\partial r} \right) - G_0 c_p \frac{\partial T}{\partial x} = 0 \tag{3.10.8}$$

where T = temperature
$\Delta H\bar{r}$ = volumetric rate of heat release
k_g = thermal conductivity of fluid phase
r = radial distance from center of bed
x = axial distance from bed entrance
G_0 = superficial mass velocity
c_p = specific heat of fluid stream

Now consider the temperature profile along the axis of the reactor bed. As x increases, the temperature rises to a maximum and then declines to that at the end of the bed. At the maximum point

$$\frac{\partial T}{\partial x} = 0$$

Further, there will be a maximum temperature at all other radial positions. However, the maximum with the largest magnitude is on the center line and is called the peak temperature as indicated by

$$\left. \frac{\partial T}{\partial x} \right|_{x = x_p} = 0$$

If the assumption is made that the maxima for all radial profiles occur at the same peak point x_p, the flow term in (3.10.8) can be dropped. Thus

$$\left[\Delta H\bar{r} + k_g \left(\frac{\partial^2 T}{\partial r^2} + \frac{1}{r}\frac{\partial T}{\partial r} \right) \right]_p = 0$$

or

$$\left[\Delta H\bar{r} + k_g \left(\frac{d^2 T}{dr^2} + \frac{1}{r}\frac{dT}{dr} \right) \right]_p = 0 \tag{3.10.9}$$

Equation (3.10.9) is a second-order ODE which can be solved after $\Delta H\bar{r}$ is explicitly defined. For ease in computation $\Delta H\bar{r}$ can be assumed linear in T, that is,

$$\Delta H\bar{r} = a + bT$$

so that (3.10.9) becomes

$$\frac{d^2 T}{dr^2} + \frac{1}{r}\frac{dT}{dr} + \frac{a + bT}{k_g} = 0 \tag{3.10.10}$$

The boundary conditions which fit the physical situation are

$$\begin{aligned} \frac{dT}{dr} &= 0 \qquad r = 0 \qquad \text{bed centerline} \\ T &= T_w \qquad r = R \qquad \text{wall temperature} \end{aligned} \tag{3.10.11}$$

A convenient set of numbers for the various parameters is

$$\begin{aligned} D &= 2 \text{ ft} \\ T_w &= 200°\text{F} \\ k_g &= 200 \text{ Btu/(hr)(ft)(°F)} \\ a &= 400 \text{ Btu/(hr)(ft}^3) \\ b &= 600 \text{ Btu/(hr)(ft}^3)(°\text{F}) \end{aligned}$$

By using (3.10.9) and (3.10.11) the radial temperature distribution at the axial position of the peak temperature can be calculated. The equations under consideration form a boundary-value problem involving a linear second-order ODE.

Actually the system as defined can be solved analytically since (3.10.9) is a form of Bessel's equation. The solution is given by

$$T = \left(T_w + \frac{a}{b}\right) \frac{J_0(r\sqrt{3})}{J_0(R\sqrt{3})} - \frac{a}{b}$$

and for the parameters used

$$T = \frac{(3.1728 \times 10^5) J_0(r\sqrt{3}) - 400}{600}$$

For the particular value of $r = 0$, center of tube,

$$T = 528.1°\text{F}$$

The numerical solution is obtained here by using the Runge-Kutta, Runge-Kutta-Gill, and Milne method I methods. Since the system is linear, use can be made of this fact to simplify the calculations. In this way the problem can be solved as initial-value. The particular integral and the complementary functions are first solved and then the correct solution obtained by superposition. Let $u(r)$ be the solution of the homogeneous equation

$$\frac{d^2u}{dr^2} + \frac{1}{r}\frac{du}{dr} + \frac{b}{k_g}u = 0$$

and boundary conditions

$$\begin{aligned} u' &= 0 \qquad r = 0 \\ u &= 1.0 \qquad r = 0 \end{aligned}$$

and let $v(r)$ be the solution of the full equation

$$\frac{d^2v}{dr^2} + \frac{1}{r}\frac{dv}{dr} + \frac{b}{k_g}v = -\frac{a}{k_g}$$

with boundary conditions

$$\begin{aligned} v' &= 0 \qquad r = 0 \\ v &= 1.0 \qquad r = 0 \end{aligned}$$

From the principle of superposition it follows that

$$T(r) = v(r) + Ku(r)$$

where K is a constant to be determined by the boundary value

$$T = T_w \qquad r = R$$

or

$$v(R) + Ku(R) = T_w$$

Table 3.4 presents the results of such a calculation (the radial temperature distribution) using the Runge-Kutta-Gill method with $\Delta r = 0.01$. As can be seen, the calculated value of $T(r = 0)$ obtained by superposition agrees with the known 528.1°K at the centerline. Further data are presented in Table 3.5, in which the same procedure was employed with the fourth-order Runge-Kutta method and Milne method I using the Runge-Kutta-Gill to start. Integration intervals of $\Delta r = 0.01$ were used again, and the Milne method I results agree with the Runge-Kutta-Gill. The Runge-Kutta shows a small deviation from the other two methods, indicating the increased accuracy of the Gill version.

TABLE 3.4. RADIAL TEMPERATURE DISTRIBUTION IN FIXED-BED REACTOR
Runge-Kutta-Gill with $\Delta r = 0.01$

r	u	u'	v	v'	T	T'
0	1.0	0	1.0	0	528.1970	0
0.2	0.970199	0.295515	0.950333	0.492525	512.4369	156.2872
0.4	0.883530	0.564699	0.805884	0.941164	466.6004	298.6486
0.6	0.747669	0.783826	0.579448	1.306378	394.7481	414.5374
0.8	0.574604	0.934117	0.291007	1.556861	303.2204	494.0204
1.0	0.379430	1.003554	0.034284	1.672589	200.0000	530.7430

TABLE 3.5. RADIAL TEMPERATURE DISTRIBUTION IN A FIXED-BED REACTOR
Various integration methods

r	T		
	Runge-Kutta-Gill	Runge-Kutta	Milne method I
0	528.1970	527.7944	528.1971
0.2	512.4369	512.1799	512.4369
0.4	466.6004	466.4762	466.6004
0.6	394.7481	394.7228	394.7481
0.8	303.2204	303.2399	303.2205
1.0	200.0000	200.0000	200.0000

It is, of course, obvious that the method used here is applicable only because the rate of heat release was assumed to be a simple linear function of temperature [(3.10.10)]. In the more general case it would be necessary to solve the full nonlinear boundary-value problem. In the next example an illustration of the means of solving such a system is presented.

These computations were performed on the IBM 650 in machine language. The Runge-Kutta method required about 8 sec per Δr step, the Runge-Kutta-Gill about 8 sec, and the Milne method I about 5 sec. For this problem the Milne method I seems the most efficient.

Example 3.3. The physical problem of this example involves the isothermal flow of chemical reactant through a homogeneous tubular reactor. The reactor operates under steady-state conditions with a finite amount of backmixing. A material balance on the reactant leads to

$$\frac{1}{\text{Pe}}\frac{d^2f}{dz^2} - \frac{df}{dz} - Rf^n = 0 \qquad 0 < z < 1.0 \tag{3.10.12}$$

where f = fraction of reactant remaining $= f(z)$
z = dimensionless axial-distance parameter obtained by dividing axial distance by reactor length L
L = reactor length
Pe = Peclet no. $= uL/D$
u = linear velocity of fluid
D = effective axial-diffusion coefficient
R = constant involving reaction constant
n = integer depending on chemical reaction

The effect of backmixing is included in the first term of the equation. For Pe $= \infty$ (or $D = 0$) the fluid would be in plug flow, and for Pe $= 0$ ($D = \infty$) the fluid would be completely mixed. The boundary conditions associated with (3.10.12) are given by

$$\begin{aligned} 1 &= f - \frac{1}{\text{Pe}}\frac{df}{dz} && z = 0 && \text{inlet to reactor} \\ \frac{df}{dz} &= 0 && z = 1 && \text{outlet of reactor} \end{aligned} \tag{3.10.13}$$

Note that the case $n = 1.0$ specifies a first-order chemical reaction; the system of equations is then linear, and an analytical solution can be obtained with little difficulty. A choice of

$$\text{Pe} = 1.0$$
$$R = 2.0$$

is made here for convenience, and the problem under examination is to calculate f as a function of z.

In performing the integration of (3.10.12) and (3.10.13) the technique is a relatively simple one conceptually. At $z = 0$ a guess is made of the value of $f(0)$; based upon this guess and the first of (3.10.13), $f'(0)$ can be calculated. The integration of the second-order ODE can now be carried out till $z = 1.0$ is reached. At this point the second condition of (3.10.13), $f'(1) = 0$, must be met. If this condition is not met, a new guess at $f(0)$ is made and the computation repeated, etc. In the present case the machine used to perform the calculations was the IBM 704, and because of its great speed a large number of $f(0)$'s could be examined very quickly (the time to calculate the entire functionality from $z = 0$ to $z = 1.0$ was about 2 sec). Thus it is not necessary to interpolate the values of $f(0)$ and $f'(1)$ as indicated in the text to locate the correct value of $f(0)$. To actually perform the integration of (3.10.12), a change of variable is first made. Letting

$$y = f'$$

converts (3.10.12) to the two first-order equations

$$f' = y \qquad \frac{1}{\text{Pe}}y' - y - Rf^n = 0$$

which can be handled by methods already discussed.

To ensure that the computations were working correctly, the case $n = 1$ was first chosen. The analytical solution for (3.10.12) is then

$$f = Ae^{2z} + Be^{-z}$$

where A and B are arbitrary constants. When these constants are evaluated by using (3.10.13), there results

$$f(0) = 0.518987$$

Table 3.6 presents the result of using this value of $f(0)$ with the Runge-Kutta-Gill integration process and a $\Delta z = 0.01$. The computation is now merely an initial-value one. As can be seen, the final slope at $z = 1.0$ is 8.001×1^{-4}, which is essentially zero as required by the outlet boundary condition. A closer value to zero could be obtained by using more digits in the value of $f(0)$. It should be pointed out that in the examples for Chap. 5 the present problem is also worked out, but using a completely different approach.

TABLE 3.6. ISOTHERMAL TUBULAR REACTOR WITH FIRST-ORDER REACTION
Runge-Kutta-Gill with $\Delta z = 0.01$

z	f	f'
0	0.518987	−0.481013
0.1	0.473606	−0.427224
0.2	0.433431	−0.376780
0.3	0.398163	−0.328968
0.4	0.367574	−0.283060
0.5	0.341513	−0.238286
0.6	0.319907	−0.193825
0.7	0.302768	−0.148771
0.8	0.290206	−0.102113
0.9	0.282438	-0.526997×10^{-1}
1.0	0.279803	-0.800178×10^{-3}

It having been decided that the method of attack yields valid answers for the linear case $n = 1$, the nonlinear case $n = 2$ can then be examined. The Runge-Kutta-Gill and Adams-Moulton methods were employed. Table 3.7 gives the results of the hunt procedure for locating $f(0)$ using the Runge-Kutta-Gill method with an integration interval of $\Delta z = 0.01$. The technique consisted in taking large jumps in the numerical values assumed for $f(0)$. When the resulting $f'(1)$ changed sign, this was taken as an indication of the location of the approximate neighborhood of the final desired value. A new set of $f(0)$'s was then used within this approximate location until another change of sign occurred. The procedure was continued until the desired accuracy in the answer was achieved. As can be seen, a value of $f(0) = 0.636737$ finally yields a slope of 4.71080×10^{-4} at $z = 1.0$; a better answer could probably be obtained by further hunting in the fifth, sixth, . . . decimal places, but this value was felt to be adequate for the present illustration.

TABLE 3.7. ISOTHERMAL TUBULAR REACTOR WITH SECOND-ORDER REACTION
Runge-Kutta-Gill with $\Delta z = 0.01$

Assumed $f(0)$	*Calculated* $f'(1.0)$
$< +0.560$	Some $f(z)$ in region $0 \le z \le 1$ became negative
0.570	-0.579773
0.580	-0.504007
0.618987	-0.172099
0.668987	$+0.347158$
0.628987	-0.770576×10^{-1}
0.633987	-0.279402×10^{-1}
0.638987	$+0.222622 \times 10^{-1}$
0.635987	-0.799088×10^{-2}
0.636487	-0.297613×10^{-2}
0.636987	$+0.204939 \times 10^{-2}$
0.636687	-0.967893×10^{-3}
0.636737	-0.471080×10^{-3}
0.636787	$+0.370184 \times 10^{-4}$

Table 3.8 presents further calculations using the initial value of $f(0) = 0.636737$ and the Adams-Moulton multiple-step process using the Runge-Kutta-Gill for starting values. The estimated truncation error is calculated from

$$E_{n+1} = \frac{|\bar{f}_{n+1} - f_{n+1}|}{14}$$

As can be seen, the two methods agree when values of f are compared, within at least one part in the sixth decimal place. The truncation error for $\Delta z = 0.01$ is negligible, but becomes significant when $\Delta z = 0.10$ is used. This points out what is probably the most efficient way to run this calculation by using Adams-Moulton. If an error of 0.1×10^{-5} could be tolerated, a Δz of 0.10 would be used to start the calculation. When z approaches a value of 0.8, however, the monitoring of E_{n+1} would show that the specified error is being exceeded and Δz would be decreased. The calculation would then be continued to the end unless the error once again became too large.

These calculations were performed on the IBM 704 computer in floating-point mode. A single calculation from $f(0)$ to $f(1)$ took at most about 2 sec.

Example 3.4. The one-dimensional transient-heat conduction equation may be written as

$$\rho c_p \frac{\partial T}{\partial t} = \frac{\partial}{\partial x}\left(k \frac{\partial T}{\partial x}\right) \tag{3.10.14}$$

where ρ and c_p, the density and heat capacity of the solid, are assumed constant but k, the thermal conductivity, is assumed a function of T, the body temperature. t is the time variable and x the space variable. By a suitable change of variables this partial

TABLE 3.8. ISOTHERMAL TUBULAR REACTOR WITH SECOND-ORDER REACTION
Runge-Kutta-Gill and Adams-Moulton with $\Delta z = 0.10$ and 0.01

Runge-Kutta-Gill			Adams-Moulton, fixed Δz			
			$\Delta z = 0.10$, $f'(1.0) = -0.4675 \times 10^{-3}$		$\Delta z = 0.01$, $f'(1.0) = -0.4711 \times 10^{-3}$	
t	f	f'	f	E_{n+1}	f	E_{n+1}
0	0.636737	−0.363263	0.636737	0	0.636737	0
0.2	0.572475	−0.281823	0.572475	0	0.572475	0
0.4	0.523278	−0.211384	0.523277	0.5026×10^{-5}	0.523278	0
0.6	0.487636	−0.145232	0.487634	0.5500×10^{-5}	0.487636	0
0.8	0.465311	−0.077159	0.465310	0.1014×10^{-4}	0.465311	0.8621×10^{-9}
1.0	0.457342	−0.000471	0.457341	0.2150×10^{-2}	0.457342	0.1765×10^{-7}

differential equation may be converted to an ODE consistent with some requirements on the boundary conditions. For

$$s = \frac{x}{\alpha\sqrt{2t}}$$

where $\alpha^2 = k_0/\rho c_p$, Eq. (3.10.14) becomes

$$-k_0 s \frac{dT}{ds} = \frac{d}{ds}\left(k \frac{dT}{ds}\right)$$

and if the thermal conductivity is given by a linear relationship of the form

$$k = k_0(1 + bT)$$

there results

$$(1 + bT)\frac{d^2T}{ds^2} + b\left(\frac{dT}{ds}\right)^2 + s\frac{dT}{ds} = 0 \tag{3.10.15}$$

For a semi-infinite body initially at temperature T_0 and with a constant surface temperature $T = 0$, the necessary boundary conditions for Eq. (3.10.15) are

$$\begin{aligned} T &= T_0 \qquad s \to \infty \\ T &= 0 \qquad s = 0 \end{aligned} \tag{3.10.16}$$

The first condition in (3.10.16) indicates the semi-infinite extent of the solid. For a given set of parameters, $b = 0.001$ and $T_0 = 400°F$, it is desired to calculate the temperature distribution in the solid (T/T_0 versus s). Note that once this curve is known a cross plot of T/T_0 versus x at various t's can be constructed.

The modified Euler, fourth-order Runge-Kutta, and combined Runge-Kutta and Gaussian quadrature of (3.3.9) are used for this problem. Since (3.10.15) and (3.10.16) comprise a nonlinear boundary-value system, the hunt approach of Example

3.3 can be used. However, to illustrate a more sophisticated technique, an interpolation scheme was used to obtain the correct initial slope at $s = 0$. Defining $w = dT/ds = T'$, (3.10.15) can be split into

$$T' = w \qquad w' = -\frac{bw^2 + sw}{1 + bT} \tag{3.10.17}$$

which comprise two first-order equations. If an initial guess is made at w or T' such that

$$\begin{array}{lll} T = 0 & s = 0 & \text{known} \\ w = T' = w^{(0)} & s = 0 & \text{first guess} \end{array}$$

the integration can be performed in initial-value form. The solution is carried out to $s \to \infty$ (or from a practical point of view until $T/T_0 \to$ constant). This calculated value of T at $s \to \infty$, called $T_\infty^{(0)}$, is then compared with the specified T_0; if $T_\infty^{(0)}/T_0$ is equal to 1.0, the initial slope $w^{(0)}$ and $T_\infty^{(0)}$ are correct. If $T_\infty^{(0)}/T_0 \neq 1.0$, a new guess at $w = T'$ must be made and the process repeated. To mechanize the procedure, the following scheme is adopted:

1. Assume two different values of $w = T'$ designated as $w^{(0)}$ and $w^{(1)}$.
2. Based upon these values, integrate (3.10.17) with the known condition $T = 0$, $s = 0$ to obtain $T_\infty^{(0)}/T_0$ and $T_\infty^{(1)}/T_0$.
3. Using linear interpolation, calculate the value $w^{(2)}$ which should make $T_\infty^{(2)}/T_0 = 1.0$.
4. Based upon $w^{(2)}$, calculate $T_\infty^{(2)}/T_0$.
5. If $T_\infty^{(2)}/T_0$ is not equal to 1.0, repeat the linear interpolation, using $w^{(1)}$, $w^{(2)}$ and $T_\infty^{(1)}/T_0$, $T_\infty^{(2)}/T_0$ to obtain $w^{(3)}$.
6. Keep repeating the process until $T_\infty^{(n)}/T_0 = 1.0$ within, say, five decimal places.

TABLE 3.9. TEMPERATURE DISTRIBUTION IN SOLID
Linear interpolation for initial slope; $\Delta s = 0.05$

Modified Euler		Fourth-order Runge-Kutta	
$w^{(n)}$	$T_\infty^{(n)}/T_0$	$w^{(n)}$	$T_\infty^{(n)}/T_0$
280.0	0.829084	280.0	0.827664
440.0	1.267806	450.0	1.292945
342.3237	1.002566	342.9664	1.002682
341.3698	0.999938	341.9773	0.999967
341.3835		341.9892	

This procedure was used to obtain the correct initial slope by means of the modified Euler and fourth-order Runge-Kutta methods. The numerical results are given in Table 3.9 for a $\Delta s = 0.05$. Only three interpolations are required for either method to yield a value of $T_\infty^{(n)}/T_0$ differing from 1.0 only in the fifth decimal place. These values could be refined further, but there seems little reason to do so; the value of initial slope, $w = 341.9892$ at $s = 0$, given by the Runge-Kutta method was then used in all subsequent calculations.

With this value of the initial slope the calculations shown in Table 3.10 were next obtained. As can be seen, the modified Euler method yields the most unreliable

TABLE 3.10. TEMPERATURE DISTRIBUTION IN SOLID
Initial slope of w = 341.9892

	s								
	0.1	0.2	0.6	1.0	1.6	2.0	2.6	3.0	6.0
Modified Euler, Δs = 0.05	33.5755	65.7890	178.522	263.339	342.794	371.369	391.807	397.157	400.720
Modified Euler, Δs = 0.10	33.5645	65.7725	178.525	263.388	342.927	371.546	392.022	397.382	400.947
Runge-Kutta, Δs = 0.025	33.5791	65.7945	178.525	263.322	342.750	371.311	391.735	397.082	400.644
Runge-Kutta, Δs = 0.05	33.5791	65.7945	178.525	263.322	342.750	371.311	391.735	397.082	400.644
Runge-Kutta, Δs = 0.10	33.5791	65.7945	178.525	263.322	342.750	371.311	391.735	397.082	400.644
Runge-Kutta, Δs = 0.20	....	65.7947	178.525	263.322	342.749	371.309	391.733	397.080	400.645
Gauss quadrature, Δs = 0.10	33.5791	65.7945	178.525	263.322	342.750	371.311	391.735	397.082	
Gauss quadrature, Δs = 0.20	....	65.7945	178.525	263.322	342.750	371.311	391.735	397.082	400.644

values. The fourth-order Runge-Kutta and Gaussian quadratures are comparable, with differences only in the sixth decimal place. However, the quadrature method holds up better for the larger Δs values, where the Runge-Kutta begins to show deviations. The differences are, however, small between any of the various methods.

This problem was carried out on the IBM 650 operating in the Bell I interpretive floating-point mode. The modified Euler method required about 4 sec per Δs step, the Runge-Kutta about 6 sec, and the Gaussian quadrature about 24 sec. Thus the Runge-Kutta seems to have an advantage in this case when accuracy and machine time are considered.

Example 3.5. While the material contained here does not constitute a numerical example, the ideas are sufficiently different from those discussed in the text to suggest their being allotted a separate place. By this time the reader realizes that in actual operation the particular numerical integration process can be used as a subroutine within the digital computer; if the subroutine is sufficiently flexible, all that is needed is to specify the particular form of the ODE to be integrated, the initial values, and perhaps some error criteria. In this way a single trajectory of $y(x)$ in x-space can be calculated.

There currently is considerable interest in the feasibility of interconnecting an analog and digital computer through appropriate analog-digital converters such that the integration can be performed at tremendous speeds. This can result even though both the analog and digital computers are relatively "small." Lapidus and Shapiro† have outlined the necessary techniques and certain of these are presented here.

† L. Lapidus and S. Shapiro, Simulation of Chemical Processes on a Combined Analog-Digital Computer, presented at the Combined Analog Digital Computer Systems Symposium, Philadelphia, 1960; The Hybrid Analog-Digital Computer, presented at the AIChE meeting, Cleveland, Ohio, 1961.

Consider that we are interested in integrating the simultaneous nonlinear ODE of (3.10.3) and (3.10.4) and that there are available a small analog computer, a small digital computer (IBM 650), and a suitable converter system. This latter system is constructed so that any analog voltage may be converted to its digital number equivalent and any digital number may be converted to an equivalent analog voltage. Further, by appropriate connections between the analog and the converter and the digital and the converter and by certain commands within the logic structure of the digital it is possible, under complete control of the digital, to send any number or word from digital storage to any point within the analog, and vice versa. The speed of these conversions is important; for currently available equipment this may be in the microsecond range, although millisecond conversions are easier and cheaper to attain.

To return to the system of equations under consideration, they first are rewritten in the following form suitable for normal analog computation:

$$c = -\int_0^\tau (\alpha_1 - \beta_1 c - \gamma_1 c e^{-E/RT})\, dt \tag{3.10.18}$$

$$T = -\int_0^\tau (\alpha_2 - \beta_2 T + \gamma_2 c e^{-E/RT})\, dt \tag{3.10.19}$$

One integrator within the analog is used for the concentration c and another for the temperature T. Both the inputs and outputs of each integrator are connected to the converter system and thus to the digital computer. At time $t = 0$ the digital computer sends T_∞ and c_∞ to the initial-condition point of the appropriate integrators and $c_\infty e^{-E/RT_\infty}$ to the inputs of both. These values actually go through suitable potentiometers within the analog to multiply by the constants γ_1 and γ_2; the constant voltages α_1 and α_2 are assumed to be generated within the analog, and the feedback loops for $\beta_1 c$ and $\beta_2 T$ are connected. These latter points need not concern us here, since they are important only in terms of scaling the analog voltages. At the same time as these voltages are sent to the analog, the analog is turned on and allowed to integrate for τ sec; depending on the speed of the integrators and the parameters of the equations τ could be 1 msec or 1 min. At the end of this time period the digital computer samples and converts the values of c and T at the integrator outputs (call these c_1 and T_1), calculates a new value of $c_1 e^{-E/RT_1}$, immediately sends this value back to the inputs of the integrators, and also stores the values of c_1 and T_1 in memory. Depending on converter and digital-computer speeds this sequence of operations may take 1 to 100 msec. The analog continues to operate, and at the end of another τ sec the sampling, etc., is repeated. This simple loop is continued until equilibrium in the analog is finally achieved. At this point the stored values of c and T as a function of integer multiples of τ are printed out, and the integration is complete.

Even though this sequence of operations has been described only in a qualitative manner, there are a number of interesting points which are apparent. Only a minimal amount of analog equipment is required, and the nonlinear function generation is accomplished with high accuracy within the digital. This latter point is very important, since nonlinear function generation is the weakest link in the use of an analog computer and one of the strongest in a digital. Since the integration is done by the analog and not by a series of arithmetic approximations within the digital, it is further apparent that each machine is essentially performing those chores for which it is best suited. Regarding the over-all computation time of this calculation it is probably fair to say that it is limited by the speed of the integrators. This is not always true, since the speed of the digital in calculating the exponential and storing number is involved, but as a general rule of thumb this statement is correct.

As a further point the reader will note that the integrators are operating in a sample-and-hold condition over any τ sec with regard to the value of $ce^{-E/RT}$. In other words, the true continuous function is being approximated by a series of step functions. Actually this discrepancy may be removed if desired. Since the discrete series of values of $ce^{-E/RT}$ may be stored within the digital as they are calculated, it is a simple matter for the digital to calculate an approximate slope value at each τ, that is,

$$\frac{d(ce^{-E/RT})}{dt} = \frac{c_{T+1}e^{-E/RT_{T+1}} - c_T e^{-E/RT_T}}{\tau}$$

When these values (as they are calculated) are sent to the input of a third integrator, the output of same is a continuous function which may be used to input the c and T integrators.

Perhaps one of the more important points of this discussion lies in the fact that while one continuous stirred-tank reactor has been used for illustration many dynamics systems of interest to the chemical engineer can be modeled on the basis of a series of such reactors. As an illustration see Example 6.2, which deals with the very complicated fixed-bed catalytic reactor. However, to solve this latter system, only the equipment mentioned here is required. In other words a very simple extension of the technique outlined can be used to solve problems which are probably impossible or uneconomical by analog or digital computers alone.

BIBLIOGRAPHY

1. Allen, D. N., and R. T. Severn: *Quart. J. Mech. Appl. Math.*, **4**: 199 (1951).
2. Alonso, R.: *J. Assoc. Comput. Mach.*, **7**: 176 (1960).
3. Amundson, N. R., and O. Bilous: *J. AIChE*, **1**: 513 (1955).
4. Anderson, W. H., R. B. Ball, and J. R. Voss: *J. Assoc. Comput. Mach.*, **7**: 61 (1960).
5. Beutler, J. A.: *Chem. Eng. Progr.*, **50**: 569 (1954).
6. Beutler, J. A., and J. G. Knudsen: *Chem. Eng. Progr. Symposium Ser.*, **49**(5): 115 (1953).
7. Bieberbach, J.: *J. Appl. Math. Phys.*, **11**: 233 (1951).
8. Billingsley, D. S., W. S. McLaughlin, N. E. Welch, and C. D. Holland: *Ind. Eng. Chem.*, **50**: 74 (1958).
9. Borwein, D., and A. R. Mitchell: *Z. angew. Math. u. Phys.*, **10**: 221 (1959). (In English.)
10. Call, D. H., and R. F. Reeves: *Communs. ACM*, **1**(9): 7 (1958).
11. Carr, J. W.: *J. Assoc. Comput. Mach.*, **5**: 39 (1958).
12. Chang, K. T.: *J. SIAM*, **7**: 468 (1959).
13. Clenshaw, C. W.: *Proc. Cambridge Phil. Soc.*, **53**: 134 (1957).
14. Clenshaw, C W., and F. W. J. Olver: *Math. Tables Wash.*, **5**: 34 (1951).
15. Conte, S. D., and R. F. Reeves: *J. Assoc. Comput. Mach.*, **3**: 22 (1956).
16. Dahlquist, G.: *Math. Scand.*, **4**: 33 (1956).
17. Dennis, S. C. R., and G. Poots: *Proc. Cambridge Phil. Soc.*, **51**: 422 (1955).
18. De Vogelaere, R.: *J. Appl. Math. Phys.*, **8**: 151 (1957).
19. Fox, L.: *Quart. J. Mech. Appl. Math.*, **4**: 199 (1951).
20. Fox, L.: *Math. Tables Aids Comput.*, **7**: 14 (1953).
21. Fox, L.: *Quart. J. Mech.*, **7**: 367 (1954).
22. Fox, L.: "The Numerical Solution of Two-point Boundary Problems," Oxford University Press, New York, 1957.
23. Fox, L., and A. R. Mitchell: *Quart. J. Mech. Appl. Math.*, **10**: 232 (1957).

24. Galler, B. A., and D. P. Rosenberg: *J. Assoc. Comput. Mach.*, **7**: 57 (1960).
25. Gee, R. E., W. H. Linton, R. E. Maier, and J. W. Raines: *Chem. Eng. Progr.*, **50**: 497 (1954).
26. Gill, S.: *Proc. Cambridge Phil. Soc.*, **47**: 96 (1951).
27. Goodman, T. R., and G. N. Lance: *Math. Tables Aids Comput.*, **10**: 82 (1956).
28. Gray, H. J., Jr.: *J. Assoc. Comput. Mach.*, **3**: 212 (1956).
29. Hamming, R. W.: *J. Assoc. Comput. Mach.*, **6**: 37 (1959).
30. Hull, T. E., and A. C. R. Newbery: *J. SIAM*, **7**: 402 (1959).
31. Keitel, G. H.: *J. Assoc. Comput. Mach.*, **3**: 212 (1956).
32. Lax, P. D., and R. D. Richtmyer: *Communs. Pure Appl. Math.*, **9**: 267 (1956).
33. Lotkin, M.: *Proc. Am. Math. Soc.*, **5**: 869 (1954).
34. Lotkin, M.: *J. Assoc. Comp. Mach.*, **3**: 208 (1956).
35. Martin, D. W.: *Computer J.*, **1**: 118 (1958).
36. Milne, W. E., and R. R. Reynolds: *J. Assoc. Comput. Mach.*, **6**: 196 (1959), **1**: 46 (1960).
37. Mitchell, A. R., and J. W. Craggs: *J. Assoc. Comput. Mach.*, **7**: 127 (1953).
38. Morrison, D.: *J. Assoc. Comput. Mach.*, **6**: 219 (1959).
39. Radok, J. R. M.: *J. SIAM*, **7**: 425 (1959).
40. Richardson, L. F., and J. A. Gaunt: *Trans. Roy. Soc. (London)*, **226**: 300 (1927).
41. Salzer, H. E.: *J. Franklin Inst.*, **263**: 401 (1957).
42. Stoller, L., and D. Morrison: *Math. Tables Aids Comput.*, **12**: 269 (1958).
43. Wilf, H. S.: *J. Assoc. Comput. Mach.*, **6**: 363 (1959).
44. Yesberg, D., and A. I. Johnson: *Can. J. Chem. Eng.*, **38**: 49 (1960).
45. Zondek, B., and J. W. Sheldon: *Math. Tables Aids Comput.*, **13**: 52 (1959).

CHAPTER 4

FUNCTIONAL EQUATIONS 2. PARTIAL DIFFERENTIAL EQUATIONS

Partial differential equations occur in a wide variety of areas of interest to chemical engineers. These include flow and/or chemical reaction in packed beds, heat or mass transfer in various geometric bodies, and the dynamic behavior of distributed systems such as heat exchangers and fixed-bed reactors. In the present chapter certain standard partial differential equations are considered and the numerical methods of solution outlined. Consideration is given to stability and convergence of the various methods, and the possible extension to more complicated cases is discussed.

4.1. The Classification of Partial Differential Equations

To ease the burden of the presentation, the following second-order linear PDE is taken for consideration,

$$A(x,y)\frac{\partial^2 z}{\partial x^2} + B(x,y)\frac{\partial^2 z}{\partial x\,\partial y} + C(x,y)\frac{\partial^2 z}{\partial y^2} = F\left(x,y,z,\frac{\partial z}{\partial x},\frac{\partial z}{\partial y}\right) \tag{4.1.1}$$

or

$$A(x,y)z_{xx} + B(x,y)z_{xy} + C(x,y)z_{yy} = F(x,y,z,z_x,z_y)$$

where $z_{xx} = \partial^2 z/\partial x^2$, $z_{xy} = \partial^2 z/\partial x\,\partial y$, ... $A(x,y)$, $B(x,y)$, and $C(x,y)$ are assumed to be continuous functions of x and y possessing continuous partial derivatives. The distinction of homogeneous, nonhomogeneous, and variable-coefficient PDE follows in the same way as for ODE. A simplified form of (4.1.1) is obtained when $F = 0$,

$$A(x,y)z_{xx} + B(x,y)z_{xy} + C(x,y)z_{yy} = 0 \tag{4.1.2}$$

Equation (4.1.2) can always be reduced to one of three standard canonical forms by a suitable change of variables; these forms are the elliptic, parabolic, and hyperbolic PDE. The means of classifying a PDE as one of the three forms results from the magnitude of the coefficients in (4.1.2). Thus,

$B(x,y)^2 - 4A(x,y)C(x,y) < 0$ elliptic PDE at point x, y
$B(x,y)^2 - 4A(x,y)C(x,y) = 0$ parabolic PDE at point x, y
$B(x,y)^2 - 4A(x,y)C(x,y) > 0$ hyperbolic PDE at point x, y

If the coefficients A, B, and C are constants independent of x and y, the canonical equations are completely elliptic, parabolic, or hyperbolic.

To illustrate how the three canonical PDE occur, consider (4.1.2) with A, B, and C as constants (this latter assumption is only for convenience). First define two new variables

$$\xi = y + a_1 x \qquad \eta = y + a_2 x \tag{4.1.3}$$

where

$$a_1 = \frac{-B + \sqrt{B^2 - 4AC}}{2A} \qquad a_2 = \frac{-B - \sqrt{B^2 - 4AC}}{2A} \tag{4.1.4}$$

Since (4.1.2) is a linear PDE

$$z = f(y + ax)$$

can be taken as a solution. Now z may be considered as a function of the two new variables ξ and η, or $z = z(\xi,\eta)$ operating through the intermediate variables x and y. From the total differential for z there results

$$\begin{aligned} z_x &= a_1 z_\xi + a_2 z_\eta \\ z_{xy} &= a_1 z_{\xi\xi} + (a_1 + a_2) z_{\xi\eta} + a_2 z_{\eta\eta} \\ z_{xx} &= a_1^2 z_{\xi\xi} + 2a_1 a_2 z_{\xi\eta} + a_2^2 z_{\eta\eta} \\ z_{yy} &= z_{\xi\xi} + 2z_{\xi\eta} + z_{\eta\eta} \end{aligned}$$

and (4.1.2) becomes

$$(Aa_1^2 + Ba_1 + C)z_{\xi\xi} + (2Aa_1a_2 + Ba_1 + Ba_2 + 2C)z_{\xi\eta} + (Aa_2^2 + Ba_2 + C)z_{\eta\eta} = 0 \tag{4.1.5}$$

Consider next the quadratic function

$$Aa_i^2 + Ba_i + C = 0 \qquad i = 1, 2$$

which has two roots, a_1 and a_2, real and unequal, real and equal, or complex conjugates. The correct set of roots depends, of course, on the value of $B^2 - 4AC$. If $B^2 - 4AC > 0$, the roots a_1 and a_2 will be real and unequal [given by (4.1.4)] and the coefficients of the first and third terms of (4.1.5) are zero. Thus (4.1.5) becomes

$$z_{\xi\eta} = 0 \tag{4.1.6}$$

This is the canonical form of a hyperbolic PDE. In the more general case of (4.1.1) the canonical form can be written as

$$z_{\xi\eta} = f(\xi,\eta,z,z_\xi,z_\eta)$$

If $B^2 - 4AC = 0$, $a_1 = a_2$ are both real numbers and ξ and η are no longer independent. If we let a_1 be the single root, $a_1 = -B/2A$, a_2 can be arbitrary as long as $a_1 \neq a_2$. Upon substituting in (4.1.5) there results

$$z_{\eta\eta} = 0 \tag{4.1.7}$$

This is the canonical form of a parabolic PDE. In the more general case it can be written as

$$z_{\eta\eta} = f(\xi,\eta,z,z_\xi,z_\eta)$$

If $B^2 - 4AC < 0$, a_1 and a_2 are complex conjugates with the form

$$a_1 = b_1 + ib_2$$
$$a_2 = b_1 - ib_2$$

and (4.1.5) becomes

$$z_{\xi\xi} + z_{\eta\eta} = 0 \tag{4.1.8}$$

This is the canonical form of an elliptic PDE. In the more general case it may be written as

$$z_{\xi\xi} + z_{\eta\eta} = f(\xi,\eta,z,z_\xi,z_\eta)$$

Some classic examples of linear PDE are Laplace's equation in two dimensions,

$$z_{xx} + z_{yy} = 0$$

which is already in canonical elliptic form, the one-dimensional diffusion, or heat-flow, equation

$$z_{xx} = z_y$$

which is already in canonical parabolic form, and the one-dimensional wave equation

$$z_{xx} = z_{yy}$$

The wave equation becomes

$$z_{\xi\eta} = 0$$

when put into canonical hyperbolic form.

While the second-order linear PDE has been used above to develop the idea of canonical classification, the same concepts may be used for nth-order PDE. However, since most applications involve, at most, only second-order equations, it is felt unnecessary to explore these higher-order systems.

The three canonical forms may be further tied together in terms of the so-called characteristics of a PDE. By defining

$$r = z_x \qquad s = z_y$$
$$t = z_{xx} \qquad u = z_{yy} \qquad v = z_{xy}$$

(4.1.1) can be written as

$$A(x,y)t + B(x,y)v + C(x,y)u = F(z,r,s)$$

If r and s are considered as functions of x and y, that is, $r = r(x,y)$ and $s = s(x,y)$, there follows directly

$$dr = \frac{\partial r}{\partial x} dx + \frac{\partial r}{\partial y} dy = t\,dx + v\,dy$$

and

$$ds = \frac{\partial s}{\partial x} dx + \frac{\partial s}{\partial y} dy = v\,dx + u\,dy$$

These three equations can be rearranged into the form

$$\begin{aligned} A(x,y)t + B(x,y)v + C(x,y)u &= F(z,r,s) \\ dx\,t + \quad dy\,v \qquad\qquad &= dr \\ dx\,v + \quad dy\,u &= ds \end{aligned} \tag{4.1.9}$$

For a curve Γ in xy space (the projection of the curve in x, y, z space) and assuming that z, r, and s are known at all points on the curve, (4.1.9) may be thought of as three simultaneous equations in the three unknowns t, u, and v. Such a system can have a unique solution on the curve Γ if the determinant of the coefficients (see Chap. 5)

$$\Delta = \det \begin{vmatrix} A & B & C \\ dx & dy & 0 \\ 0 & dx & dy \end{vmatrix}$$

is not zero. If $\Delta = 0$, there are an infinite set of solutions. Upon expanding the determinant there results

$$\Delta = A\left(\frac{dy}{dx}\right)^2 - B\frac{dy}{dx} + C$$

where A, B, and C are taken as constants for simplicity of manipulation. This is a quadratic function of the form previously considered except that dy/dx replaces the a_i. For $\Delta = 0$ and $B^2 - 4AC > 0$ there exist two real slopes $dy/dx)_1$ and $dy/dx)_2$. For $\Delta = 0$ and $B^2 - 4AC = 0$ there exists one real slope $dy/dx)_1$, and for $B^2 - 4AC < 0$ no real slopes exist. The values given by the slopes dy/dx are called the characteristic directions of the PDE, and the curves generated by the slopes in the xy plane are called the characteristic curves of the PDE. A hyperbolic PDE has two characteristic curves, a parabolic PDE has one, and an elliptic PDE has none. For the case

$$\left.\frac{dy}{dx}\right)_1 = C_1 = f_1(x,y) \qquad \left.\frac{dy}{dx}\right)_2 = C_2 = f_2(x,y)$$

the change of variables

$$\xi = f_1(x,y) \qquad \eta = f_2(x,y)$$

leads to the canonical form of the hyperbolic PDE. For the change of variables

$$\xi = f_1(x,y) \qquad \eta \neq f_2(x,y)$$

and

$$\xi + iy = f_1(x,y) \qquad \xi - iy = f_2(x,y)$$

the canonical form of the parabolic and elliptic PDE result, respectively.

The boundary conditions associated with the three canonical forms of the second-order linear PDE may be classified also, but only in a broad sense. For hyperbolic and parabolic PDE the boundary conditions are usually of the initial-value type and are open in the sense that only part of the xy domain is specified in advance. The integration proceeds into an open-ended domain. For elliptic PDE the boundary conditions are usually of the boundary-value type, the integration proceeding from the closed boundary into the enclosed domain. Specific examples of these boundary conditions will be presented shortly.

In addition to the three types of canonical PDE already described, it is quite possible to have a mixed type of PDE. Because of the changes in $A(x,y)$, $B(x,y)$, and $C(x,y)$, an equation may be hyperbolic for one set of x and y, parabolic for another set, and elliptic for a further set. Under these conditions the numerical solution may become quite difficult.

4.2. Finite-difference Approximations

Finite-difference representations for partial derivatives are the most frequent approach to the numerical integration of PDE. The partial derivatives are replaced by difference quotients in the independent variables and the result used for an approximation of the derivatives. In general the domain over which the PDE holds is equal to the number of independent variables. For the special case of only two independent variables x and y, the domain is two-dimensional and can be represented on a plane surface (see Fig. 4.1). The techniques to be described can be best visualized by covering the domain with a network of rectangular spacings. The spacing between any two adjacent vertical lines (the x direction) is taken as h, a constant, and between any two horizontal points (the y direction) as k, a constant. The value of the dependent variable z, $z = z(x,y)$, is specified at any point within the domain. In particular, if one point on the rectangular grid spacing is given the coordinates x_r, y_s, then the four points around it have the coordinates

$$x_{r+h},\ y_s \qquad x_{r-h},\ y_s \qquad x_r,\ y_{s+k} \qquad x_r,\ y_{s-k}$$

All these values are shown in Fig. 4.1.

The method of replacing the partial derivatives by finite differences follows directly from the material of Chap. 2. In that chapter representations were obtained for various-order derivatives of a single variable, i.e., by differentiation of the various interpolation formulas or the

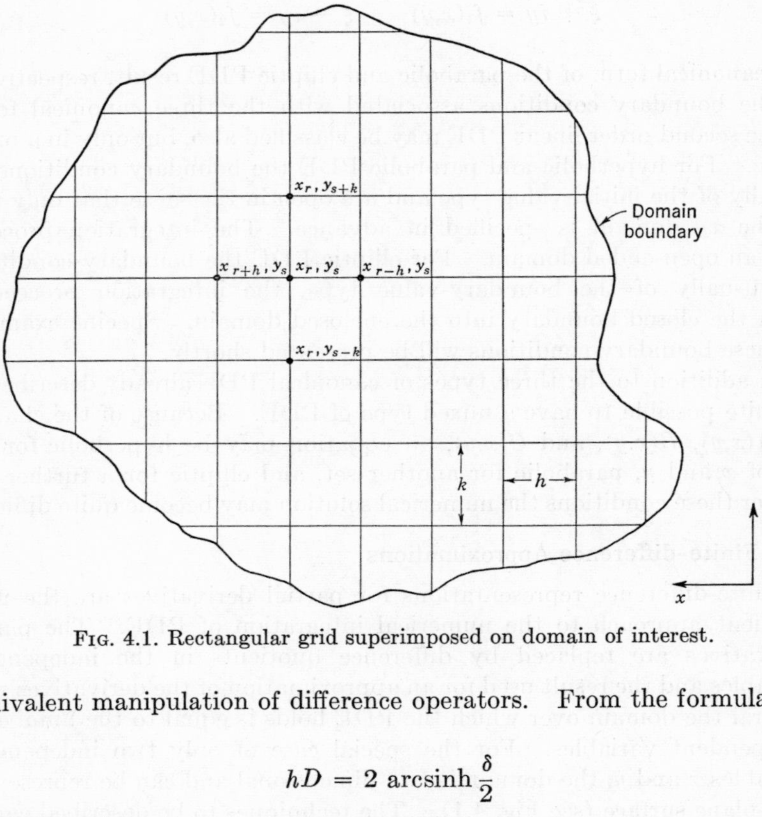

FIG. 4.1. Rectangular grid superimposed on domain of interest.

equivalent manipulation of difference operators. From the formula

$$hD = 2 \operatorname{arcsinh} \frac{\delta}{2}$$

applied to the point $x = x_r$ there results

$$\frac{dz_r}{dx} = \frac{\mu}{h}\left(\delta - \frac{\delta^3}{6} + \frac{\delta^5}{30} - \cdots\right) z_r \tag{4.2.1}$$

where $z = z(x)$ and $z_r = z(x_r)$. In the same way the formulas

$$h^2D^2 = \left(2 \operatorname{arcsinh} \frac{\delta}{2}\right)^2 \qquad \text{and} \qquad h^4D^4 = \left(2 \operatorname{arcsinh} \frac{\delta}{2}\right)^4$$

lead to

$$\frac{d^2z_r}{dx^2} = \frac{1}{h^2}\left(\delta^2 - \frac{\delta^4}{12} + \frac{\delta^6}{90} - \cdots\right) z_r \tag{4.2.2}$$

and

$$\frac{d^4z_r}{dx^4} = \frac{1}{h^4}\left(\delta^4 - \frac{\delta^6}{6} + \tfrac{7}{240}\delta^8 - \cdots\right) z_r \tag{4.2.3}$$

respectively. Differentiation of NFF or the expansion of

$$hD = \log (1 + \Delta)$$

leads to

$$\frac{dz_r}{dx} = \frac{1}{h}\left(\Delta - \frac{\Delta^2}{2} + \frac{\Delta^3}{3} - \cdot \cdot \cdot\right) z_r \tag{4.2.4}$$

Each of these formulas may be truncated after a suitable number of terms to yield a difference representation for the derivative. Equations (4.2.1) and (4.2.4) truncated after the first differences and then the second differences yield, respectively,

$$\frac{dz_r}{dx} = \frac{z_{r+1} - z_{r-1}}{2h} + O(h^2) \tag{4.2.5}$$

$$\frac{dz_r}{dx} = \frac{z_{r+1} - z_r}{h} + O(h) \tag{4.2.6}$$

$$\frac{dz_r}{dx} = \frac{-z_{r+2} + 8z_{r+1} - 8z_{r-1} + z_{r-2}}{12h} + O(h^4) \tag{4.2.7}$$

$$\frac{dz_r}{dx} = \frac{-z_{r+2} + 4z_{r+1} - 3z_r}{2h} + O(h^2) \tag{4.2.8}$$

Equation (4.2.2) truncated after the first and second differences and (4.2.3) truncated after the first difference yield, respectively,

$$\frac{d^2z_r}{dx^2} = \frac{z_{r+1} - 2z_r + z_{r-1}}{h^2} + O(h^2) \tag{4.2.9}$$

$$\frac{d^2z_r}{dx^2} = \frac{-z_{r+2} + 16z_{r+1} - 30z_r + 16z_{r-1} - z_{r-2}}{12h^2} + O(h^4) \tag{4.2.10}$$

$$\frac{d^4z_r}{dx^4} = \frac{z_{r+2} - 4z_{r+1} + 6z_r - 4z_{r-1} + z_{r-2}}{h^4} + O(h^2) \tag{4.2.11}$$

The order of the truncation error is shown along with each equation.

The computational molecule or stencil is frequently used as a visual representation of equations of the type of (4.2.5) to (4.2.11). As examples, (4.2.6) and (4.2.9) are represented in the form

$$\frac{dz_r}{dx} = \frac{1}{h} \; (+1)\!-\!(-1)\!-\!(0) \; z_r$$ computational molecule

or $$\frac{dz_r}{dx} = \frac{1}{h} \; \boxed{+1 \mid -1 \mid 0} \; z_r$$ computational stencil

and $$\frac{d^2z_r}{dx^2} = \frac{1}{h^2} \; (+1)\!-\!(-2)\!-\!(+1) \; z_r$$ computational molecule

or $$\frac{d^2z_r}{dx^2} = \frac{1}{h^2} \; \boxed{+1 \mid -2 \mid +1} \; z_r$$ computational stencil

In the case of the computational molecule the coefficients of the difference equation are given within the connected circles, with the highest-order coefficient on the left end and the lowest-order coefficient on the right end.   The center coefficient of the array is assumed to correspond to the value of z given at the right end of the brackets.   The computational stencil uses boxes instead of circles.   These symbolic diagrams may be thought of as linear operators on z_r which form the respective difference representation.

The extension of this approach to partial derivatives follows in a direct manner.   For $z = z(x,y)$ the designation of

$$z_{r,s} = z(x_r, y_s)$$

is used.   The subscripts are taken as locating the coordinates of the point $z(x_r, y_s)$ on the rectangular grid spacing of Fig. 4.1.   Since $\partial z / \partial x$ really means $\partial z / \partial x \Big)_y$, y held constant, (4.2.6) can be written as

$$\frac{\partial z_{r,s}}{\partial x} = \frac{1}{h} \left(z_{r+1,s} - z_{r,s} \right)$$

or in computational-molecule form as

$$\frac{\partial z_{r,s}}{\partial x} = \frac{1}{h} \; \boxed{+1}\!\!-\!\!\boxed{-1}\!\!-\!\!\boxed{0} \; z_{r,s}$$

The computational molecule has only horizontal elements, since s (or the y variation) is held constant.   In the same way

$$\frac{\partial z_{r,s}}{\partial y} = \frac{1}{k} \; \boxed{\begin{matrix} +1 \\ -1 \\ 0 \end{matrix}} \; z_{r,s}$$

for a derivative in the s direction.   Mixed derivatives are easily obtained by row times column multiplication.   As an example, for $h = k$, (4.2.5) leads to

$$\frac{\partial^2 z_{r,s}}{\partial x \, \partial y} = \frac{\partial}{\partial x} \left(\frac{\partial z_{r,s}}{\partial y} \right) = \frac{1}{2h} \; \boxed{+1}\!\!-\!\!\boxed{0}\!\!-\!\!\boxed{-1} \; \frac{1}{2h} \; \boxed{\begin{matrix} +1 \\ 0 \\ -1 \end{matrix}} \; z_{r,s}$$

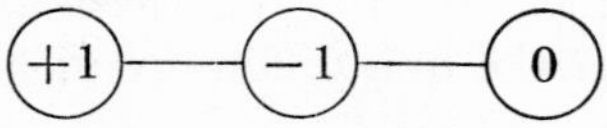

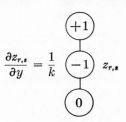

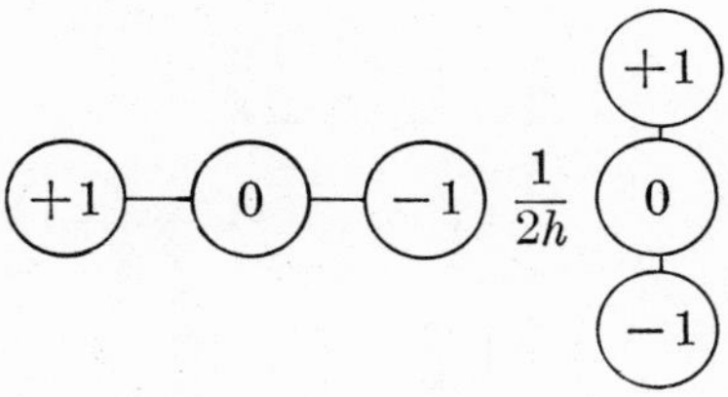

Multiplying the single row into each element of the column produces

$$\frac{\partial^2 z_{r,s}}{\partial x\,\partial y} = \frac{1}{4h^2}$$

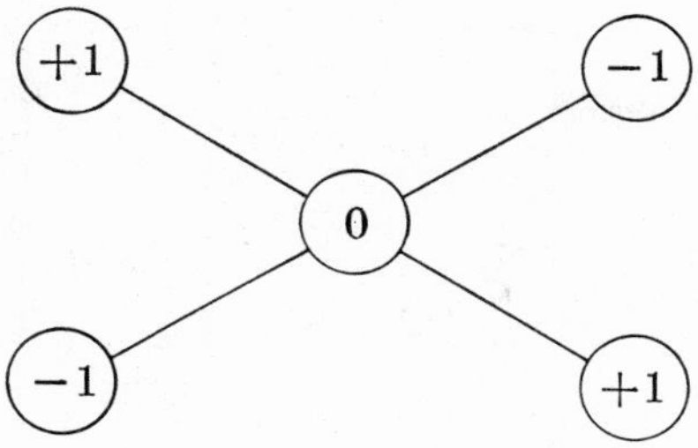

$$z_{r,s}$$

with all extraneous zero terms except the center one omitted.

To conclude this section, the most commonly used computational molecules are listed below. These follow directly from (4.2.5) to (4.2.11).

$\frac{\partial z_{r,s}}{\partial x} = \frac{1}{2h}$ (+1)——(0)——(−1) $z_{r,s} + O(h^2)$ (4.2.12)

$\frac{\partial z_{r,s}}{\partial x} = \frac{1}{h}$ (+1)——(−1)——(0) $z_{r,s} + O(h)$ (4,2.13)

$\frac{\partial z_{r,s}}{\partial x} = \frac{1}{2h}$ (−1)——(+4)——(−3)——(0)——(0) $z_{r,s}$
$+ O(h^2)$ (4.2.14)

$\frac{\partial z_{r,s}}{\partial x} = \frac{1}{12h}$ (−1)——(+8)——(0)——(−8)——(+1) $z_{r,s}$
$+ O(h^4)$ (4.2.15)

$\frac{\partial^2 z_{r,s}}{\partial x^2} = \frac{1}{h^2}$ (+1)——(−2)——(+1) $z_{r,s} + O(h^2)$ (4.2.16)

$\frac{\partial^2 z_{r,s}}{\partial x^2} = \frac{1}{12h^2}$ (−1)——(+16)——(−30)——(+16)——(−1) $z_{r,s}$
$+ O(h^4)$ (4.2.17)

$\frac{\partial^4 z_{r,s}}{\partial x^4} = \frac{1}{h^4}$ (+1)——(−4)——(+6)——(−4)——(+1) $z_{r,s}$
$+ O(h^2)$ (4.2.18)

$$\frac{\partial^2 z_{r,s}}{\partial x\,\partial y} = \frac{1}{4h^2}$$

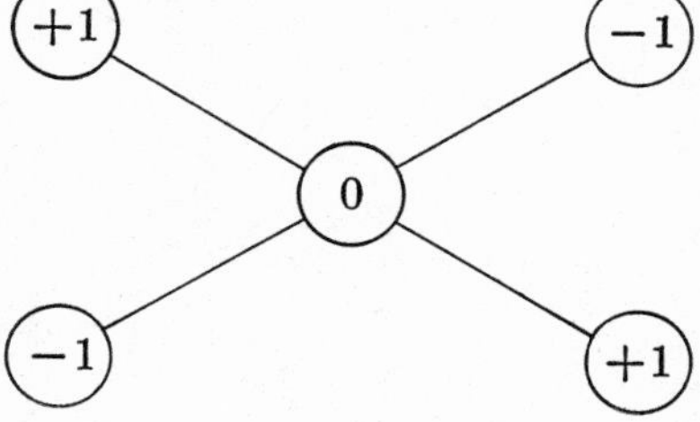

$z_{r,s} + O(h^2) \qquad h = k$

(4.2.19)

The molecules corresponding to (4.2.12) to (4.2.18), but in terms of y instead of x, are merely identical vertical arrangements, with k replacing h.

4.3. Approximating Elliptic PDE

As an illustration of the numerical techniques used for the solution of an elliptic PDE, Laplace's equation in two dimensions will be considered.

$$\frac{\partial^2 z}{\partial x^2} + \frac{\partial^2 z}{\partial y^2} = 0 \tag{4.3.1}$$

This equation represents the steady-state case of heat flow, or diffusion, through a two-dimensional body.

On the assumption that (4.3.1) holds in a region R surrounded by a boundary B, it is desired to evaluate $z(x,y)$ within R based upon the known boundary condition on B. For simplicity in the initial discussions the boundary B is taken as square and of width L in both x and y directions. There are three possible ways of specifying the values of z on the boundary B. The function itself may be defined with the form

$$\begin{aligned} z &= f_1(y) \qquad & x &= 0 \\ z &= f_2(y) \qquad & x &= L \\ z &= g_1(x) \qquad & y &= 0 \\ z &= g_2(x) \qquad & y &= L \end{aligned} \tag{4.3.2}$$

where f_1, f_2, g_1, and g_2 indicate arbitrary functions. The solution of (4.3.1) and (4.3.2) is called a "Dirichlet problem."

A second type of boundary condition is often used, with the derivative or gradient of z specified.

$$\begin{aligned} \frac{\partial z}{\partial x} &= f_1(y) \qquad & x &= 0 \\ \frac{\partial z}{\partial x} &= f_2(y) \qquad & x &= L \\ \frac{\partial z}{\partial y} &= g_1(x) \qquad & y &= 0 \\ \frac{\partial z}{\partial y} &= g_2(x) \qquad & y &= L \end{aligned} \tag{4.3.3}$$

Equations (4.3.1) and (4.3.3) form a Neumann problem. In the more general case a mixed type of boundary condition of the form

$$a_1 \frac{\partial z}{\partial x} + a_2 z = a_3 \qquad b_1 \frac{\partial z}{\partial y} + b_2 z = b_3$$

may be specified. For particular choices of the a_1, a_2, a_3 and b_1, b_2, b_3 these reduce to (4.3.2) or (4.3.3).

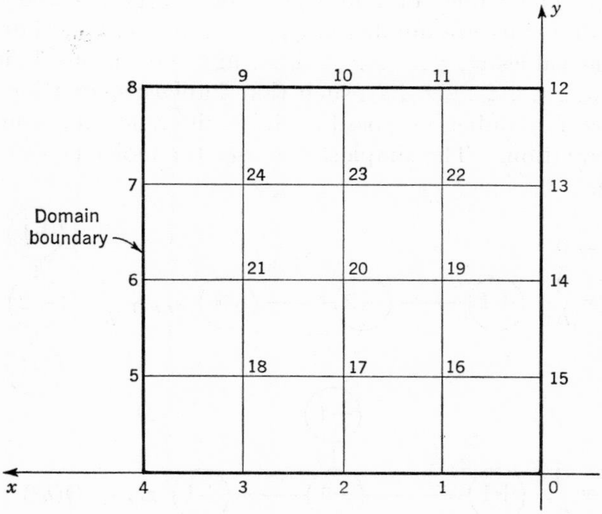

FIG. 4.2. Square-grid representation for Laplace's equation.

For any of the boundary conditions listed the system is defined on the boundary B, with Laplace's equation to be satisfied within the area encompassed by B. This may be considered as a boundary-value problem. In certain specific situations the physical problem may actually define z and the gradient on only two sides (82). This would correspond to an initial-value problem, but such a situation is quite rare in practice.

When the PDE system to solve has been decided on, i.e., (4.3.1) plus boundary conditions, it is necessary to answer a number of questions. On the assumption that an analytical solution cannot be obtained,† the first question is how to set up a system of difference equations which

† The analytic solution of Laplace's equation can, of course, be obtained. However, for purposes of illustration only numerical techniques will be used. The extension to PDE which cannot be analytically solved will follow by using the same principles.

approximate the PDE and boundary conditions. Next it is necessary to determine a means of solving the system of difference equations and finally to determine the error between the solution of the difference equations and the exact solution of the PDE. Each of these points will be discussed in turn.

Figure 4.2 shows a square mesh ($h = k$) placed over the region, or domain, R and coinciding with the boundary B. The lower right point has the coordinates x_0, y_0, and the value of z is $z(x_0,y_0)$ or, for ease of writing, z_0. The values of z at the boundary points and the interior mesh or node points are numbered $z_1, z_2, \ldots, z_{23}, z_{24}$. For a Dirichlet problem the values $z_0, z_1, \ldots, z_{14}, z_{15}$ are known, and it is desired to calculate $z_{16}, z_{17}, \ldots, z_{23}, z_{24}$ such that Laplace's equation is satisfied.

There are a number of possible finite-difference representations for Laplace's equation. The simplest one uses the molecule of (4.2.16) with error $O(h^2)$.

$$\frac{\partial^2 z}{\partial x^2}+\frac{\partial^2 z}{\partial y^2}=0$$

$$=\frac{1}{h^2}\left(\begin{matrix} (+1) & \text{———} & (-2) & \text{———} & (+1) \end{matrix} \right) z_{r,s} + \frac{1}{h^2}\left(\begin{matrix} (+1) \\ | \\ (-2) \\ | \\ (+1) \end{matrix} \right) z_{r,s} + O(h^2)$$

$$=\frac{1}{h^2}\left(\begin{matrix} & & (+1) & & \\ & & | & & \\ (+1) & \text{———} & (-4) & \text{———} & (+1) \\ & & | & & \\ & & (+1) & & \end{matrix} \right) z_{r,s} + O(h^2) \qquad (4.3.4)$$

In expanded form this becomes

$$\frac{\partial^2 z}{\partial x^2}+\frac{\partial^2 z}{\partial y^2}=0=\frac{1}{h^2}\left(z_{r,s+1}+z_{r,s-1}+z_{r+1,s}+z_{r-1,s}-4z_{r,s}\right)+O(h^2)$$

where the subscript $r + 1$ is taken equivalent to $r + h$, etc. As pointed out by Greenspan (42), (4.3.4) is the "best" five-point-difference analog representation for Laplace's equation when equally spaced intervals ($h = k$) are used. The term "best" means that there is no other five-point formula which has a better error term than (4.3.4). In the same sense the equation

$$\frac{2}{1+P^2}\left(z_{r+1,s}+z_{r-1,s}\right)+\frac{2P^2}{1+P^2}\left(z_{r,s+1}+z_{r,s-1}\right)-4z_{r,s}=0$$

with $P = h/k$ is the "best" formula for unequal spacing. When $P = 1$ is used, (4.3.4) results.

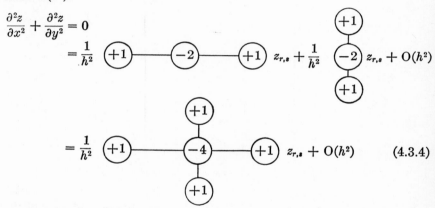

A second finite-difference approximation uses the molecule of (4.2.17) with error $O(h^4)$.

$$\frac{\partial^2 z}{\partial x^2} + \frac{\partial^2 z}{\partial y^2} = 0$$

$$= \frac{1}{12h^2} \left(\boxed{-1} \text{---} \boxed{+16} \text{---} \boxed{-30} \text{---} \boxed{+16} \text{---} \boxed{-1} \right) z_{r,s}$$

$$+ \frac{1}{12h^2} \begin{pmatrix} \boxed{-1} \\ | \\ \boxed{+16} \\ | \\ \boxed{-30} \\ | \\ \boxed{+16} \\ | \\ \boxed{-1} \end{pmatrix} z_{r,s} + O(h^4)$$

$$= \frac{1}{12h^2} \begin{array}{ccccccccc} & & & & \boxed{-1} & & & & \\ & & & & | & & & & \\ & & & & \boxed{+16} & & & & \\ & & & & | & & & & \\ \boxed{-1} & \text{---} & \boxed{+16} & \text{---} & \boxed{-60} & \text{---} & \boxed{+16} & \text{---} & \boxed{-1} \\ & & & & | & & & & \\ & & & & \boxed{+16} & & & & \\ & & & & | & & & & \\ & & & & \boxed{-1} & & & & \end{array} z_{r,s} + O(h^4) \qquad (4.3.5)$$

While the truncation error of (4.3.5) is smaller than that for (4.3.4), the computational problems involved in using (4.3.5) are severe. This point will be detailed shortly. As a result a finite-difference formula of error $O(h^4)$ but with none of the computational difficulties of (4.3.5) is highly desired. Such an equation can be obtained by first differentiating Laplace's equation twice.

$$\frac{\partial^4 z}{\partial y^2\,\partial x^2} + \frac{\partial^4 z}{\partial y^4} = 0 \qquad \frac{\partial^4 z}{\partial x^4} + \frac{\partial^4 z}{\partial x^2\,\partial y^2} = 0$$

Thus,

$$\frac{\partial^4 z}{\partial x^2\,\partial y^2} = -\frac{\partial^4 z}{\partial x^4} = -\frac{\partial^4 z}{\partial y^4}$$

and

$$\frac{\partial^4 z}{\partial x^4} + \frac{\partial^4 z}{\partial y^4} = -2\frac{\partial^4 z}{\partial x^2\,\partial y^2} = -2\frac{\partial^2}{\partial x^2}\left(\frac{\partial^2 z}{\partial y^2}\right)$$

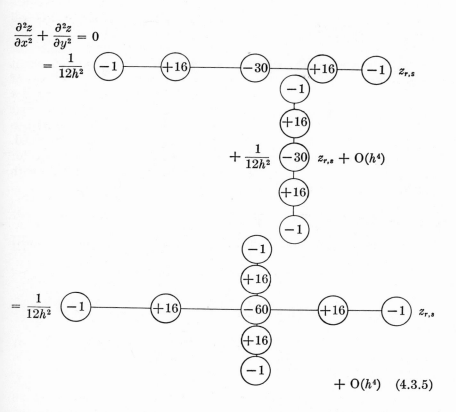

If we use (4.2.16), the right-hand term may be represented as

$$-2\frac{\partial^2}{\partial x^2}\left(\frac{\partial^2 z}{\partial y^2}\right) = -\frac{2}{h^4}\begin{array}{ccc}(+1) & \text{—} (-2) \text{—} & (+1)\end{array} \quad \begin{array}{c}(+1)\\ | \\ (-2)\\ | \\ (+1)\end{array} z_{r,s}$$

$$= -\frac{2}{h^4}\begin{array}{ccccc}(+1) & \text{—} & (-2) & \text{—} & (+1)\\ | & & | & & | \\ (-2) & \text{—} & (+4) & \text{—} & (-2)\\ | & & | & & | \\ (+1) & \text{—} & (-2) & \text{—} & (+1)\end{array} z_{r,s}$$

But from (4.2.3) there results

$$\frac{\partial^4 z}{\partial x^4} + \frac{\partial^4 z}{\partial y^4} = \frac{1}{h^4}(\delta_x{}^4 + \delta_y{}^4)z_{r,s}$$

where δ_x means the operator with respect to x and δ_y the operator with respect to y. Thus,

$$\delta_x{}^4 + \delta_y{}^4 = -2\begin{array}{ccccc}(+1) & \text{—} & (-2) & \text{—} & (+1)\\ | & & | & & | \\ (-2) & \text{—} & (+4) & \text{—} & (-2)\\ | & & | & & | \\ (+1) & \text{—} & (-2) & \text{—} & (+1)\end{array} z_{r,s}$$

Upon using (4.2.2),

$$\frac{\partial^2 z}{\partial x^2} + \frac{\partial^2 z}{\partial y^2} = \frac{1}{h^2}\left[\delta_x{}^2 + \delta_y{}^2 - \frac{1}{12}(\delta_x{}^4 + \delta_y{}^4)\right] z_{r,s} + O(h^4) \tag{4.3.6}$$

and noting, from (4.3.4), that

$$\frac{1}{h^2}(\delta_x{}^2 + \delta_y{}^2) = \frac{1}{h^2}\begin{array}{ccccc} & & (+1) & & \\ & & | & & \\ (+1) & \text{—} & (-4) & \text{—} & (+1)\\ & & | & & \\ & & (+1) & & \end{array} z_{r,s}$$

and

$$-\frac{1}{12h^2}(\delta_x{}^4 + \delta_y{}^4) = +\frac{1}{6h^2}\begin{array}{ccccc}(+1) & \text{—} & (-2) & \text{—} & (+1)\\ | & & | & & | \\ (-2) & \text{—} & (+4) & \text{—} & (-2)\\ | & & | & & | \\ (+1) & \text{—} & (-2) & \text{—} & (+1)\end{array} z_{r,s}$$

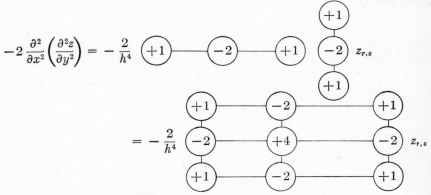

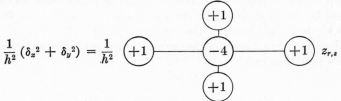

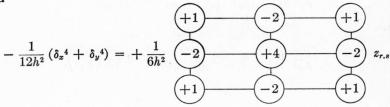

(4.3.6) becomes

$$\frac{\partial^2 z}{\partial x^2} + \frac{\partial^2 z}{\partial y^2} = 0 = \frac{1}{6h^2} \begin{Bmatrix} +1 & +4 & +1 \\ +4 & -20 & +4 \\ +1 & +4 & +1 \end{Bmatrix} z_{r,s} + O(h^4) \qquad (4.3.7)$$

As shown by Greenspan (39, 43), (4.3.7) is the "best" nine-point difference analog of Laplace's equation. In addition it has some important computational advantages over (4.3.5).

Equation (4.3.4) can be applied to Fig. 4.2 in a relatively simple way. For the point 20, (4.3.4) becomes

$$z_{19} + z_{21} + z_{17} + z_{23} - 4z_{20} = 0$$

with all the z's unknown and to be determined. For the point 16

$$z_{15} + z_{17} + z_{19} + z_1 - 4z_{16} = 0$$

or

$$z_{17} + z_{19} - 4z_{16} = -z_1 - z_{15}$$

with the z on the right side known by the boundary conditions. Equation (4.3.4) applied to all the points $z_{16}, z_{17}, \ldots, z_{23}, z_{24}$ results in a set of nonhomogeneous simultaneous algebraic equations. There are N equations with N unknowns $z_{16}, z_{17}, \ldots, z_{23}, z_{24}$ corresponding to the number of internal mesh points. To minimize the truncation error resulting from approximating Laplace's equation with (4.3.4), h would be taken quite small; this leads to a very large value of N. As a result there may be too many simultaneous equations to be solved directly even on the largest digital computer. Iteration procedures must thus be used, and these will be described in the next section.

The use of (4.3.7) leads to much the same set of simultaneous equations as for (4.3.4). Since the truncation error is smaller, however, it is recommended that (4.3.7) be used whenever possible. When (4.3.5) is used, the application to points in the mesh just inside the boundary (such as 16) leads to the involvement of fictitious points outside the boundary. As a result (4.3.5) is generally not recommended for use unless absolutely necessary. As will be seen shortly, the same problem may result when the gradient in z is given at the boundary.

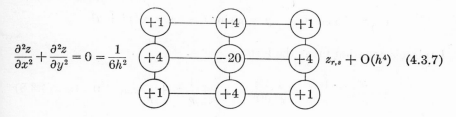

Of particular importance to chemical engineers are PDE expressed in cylindrical and spherical coordinates. In most practical problems the assumption of symmetry in polar coordinates is made, and this simplifies the finite-difference representation. If we let

$$x = \rho \cos \Theta \qquad y = \rho \sin \Theta \qquad \rho = \sqrt{x^2 + y^2}$$

Laplace's equation takes the form

$$\frac{\partial^2 z}{\partial \rho^2} + \frac{1}{\rho}\frac{\partial z}{\partial \rho} + \frac{1}{\rho^2}\frac{\partial^2 z}{\partial \Theta^2} = z_{\rho\rho} + \frac{1}{\rho} z_\rho + \frac{1}{\rho^2} z_{\Theta\Theta} = 0 \tag{4.3.8}$$

For symmetry about the origin, $z_{\Theta\Theta} = 0$,

$$z_{\rho\rho} + \frac{1}{\rho} z_\rho = 0 \tag{4.3.9}$$

In the same way a spherical-coordinate transformation with symmetry about the origin converts Laplace's equation to

$$z_{\rho\rho} + \frac{2}{\rho} z_\rho = 0 \tag{4.3.10}$$

The finite-difference approximations to these two PDE can be developed easily with the aid of Fig. 4.3, where $h = \Delta\rho$ and $k = \Delta\Theta$. Using (4.2.16)

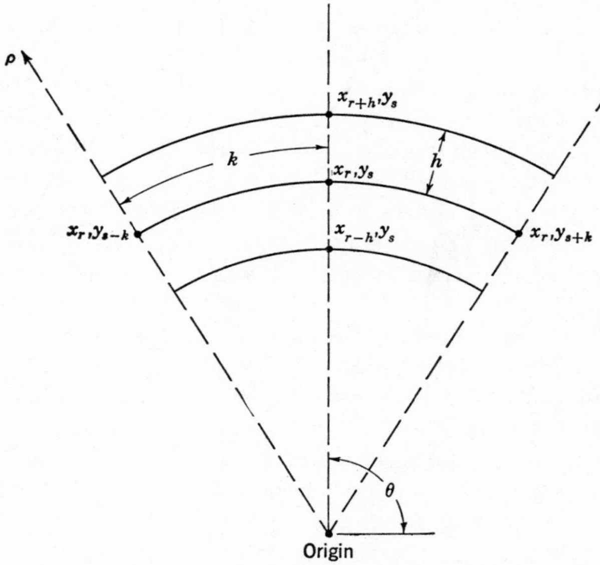

FIG. 4.3. Grid spacing for cylindrical or spherical coordinates.

and (4.2.12) (with equal truncation error) leads to (with subscript s used for ρ and r for Θ)

$$z_{\rho\rho} = \frac{1}{h^2} \begin{array}{c} (+1) \\ | \\ (-2) \\ | \\ (+1) \end{array} z_{r,s} + O(h^2)$$

and

$$\frac{1}{\rho} z_\rho = \frac{1}{2\rho h} \begin{array}{c} (+1) \\ | \\ (0) \\ | \\ (-1) \end{array} z_{r,s} + O(h^2)$$

respectively. Calling $\rho = rh$,

$$\frac{1}{\rho} z_\rho = \frac{1}{2rh^2} \begin{array}{c} (+1) \\ | \\ (0) \\ | \\ (-1) \end{array} z_{r,s}$$

where $r = 0$ at the origin. In the same way

$$\frac{1}{\rho^2} z_{\Theta\Theta} = \frac{1}{(rh)^2} \frac{1}{k^2} \; (+1) — (-2) — (+1) \; z_{r,s} + O(k^2)$$

By grouping terms, (4.3.8) becomes

$$z_{\rho\rho} + \frac{1}{\rho} z_\rho + \frac{1}{\rho^2} z_{\Theta\Theta} = \frac{1}{h^2} \begin{array}{ccccc} & & \left(1 + \frac{1}{2r}\right) & & \\ & & | & & \\ \left(\frac{1}{(rk)^2}\right) & — & \left(-2\left[1 + \frac{1}{(rk)^2}\right]\right) & — & \left(\frac{1}{(rk)^2}\right) \\ & & | & & \\ & & \left(1 - \frac{1}{2r}\right) & & \end{array} z_{r,s}$$

In the case of axial symmetry (4.3.9) becomes

$$z_{\rho\rho} + \frac{1}{\rho} z_\rho = \frac{1}{h^2} \begin{array}{c} \left(1 + \frac{1}{2r}\right) \\ | \\ (-2) \\ | \\ \left(1 - \frac{1}{2r}\right) \end{array} z_{r,s} + O(h^2)$$

and, at $\rho = 0$ or $r = 0$, the origin, $\partial z/\partial \rho = 0$. But if $\partial z/\partial \rho = 0$,

$$z_{1,s} = z_{-1,s}$$

and
$$\left(z_{\rho\rho} + \frac{1}{\rho} z_\rho\right)_{\text{origin}} = \frac{4}{h^2}(z_{1,s} - z_{0,s}) + O(h^2)$$

The finite-difference representation for (4.3.10) follows in an obvious and direct manner.

It should be noted that the latter difference approximations were applied to linear PDE with variable coefficients. Any PDE with variable coefficients can be handled in the same way.

4.4. Solution of the Difference Equations for Elliptic PDE

Once the difference-equation representation for the elliptic PDE is known, i.e., (4.3.4) or (4.3.7) for Laplace's equation, the next problem is to solve the set of resulting simultaneous equations in a suitable, efficient manner. The method of relaxation in the Southwell sense (Chap. 1, 3) is not appropriate, but relaxation as an iterative process is quite suitable. With (4.3.4) as an illustration, the system to be solved is

$$\begin{aligned} z_{r+1,s} + z_{r-1,s} + z_{r,s+1} + z_{r,s-1} - 4z_{r,s} &= 0 \qquad \text{inside } R \\ z_{r,s} &= b_{r,s} \qquad \text{on boundary } B \end{aligned}$$

for a Dirichlet problem. The $b_{r,s}$'s are the known boundary values; the solution involves a jury technique. Let N be the number of internal mesh points on a row and $N + 1$ the number of intervals in a row (as before, the domain of interest is a square). The simplest iterative method of solving this set of equations is due to Richardson, with the above system written as

$$z_{r,s}^{(n+1)} = \begin{cases} \frac{1}{4}(z_{r+1,s}^{(n)} + z_{r-1,s}^{(n)} + z_{r,s+1}^{(n)} + z_{r,s-1}^{(n)}) & \text{inside } R \\ b_{r,s} & \text{on boundary } B \end{cases} \tag{4.4.1}$$

The nomenclature $z_{r,s}^{(n)}$ and $z_{r,s}^{(n+1)}$ refers to the nth and $(n + 1)$st approximation in the iteration pattern. Starting with assumed values $z_{r,s}^{(0)}$ on the interior mesh points and the known values of the boundary points, (4.4.1) is used to sweep all the interior points and calculate a new set of points $z_{r,s}^{(1)}$. This sequence is merely a cyclic single-step process and is repeated over and over to calculate successively the $z_{r,s}^{(2)}, z_{r,s}^{(3)}, \ldots$. In each case the new set of points $z_{r,s}^{(n+1)}$ is calculated from the last set $z_{r,s}^{(n)}$. In terms of storage requirements two complete sets of interior values, $2N^2$, plus the boundary values and program storage are required. Finally, there results

$$|z_{r,s}^{(n+1)} - z_{r,s}^{(n)}| \leq \epsilon$$

over all r and s, where ϵ is a predetermined error value. When this condition is met, the iteration has converged to the solution of the finite-difference approximation of Laplace's equation plus boundary values. This is true for the specific value of h used to form the mesh. An alternative way to write (4.4.1) is

$$z_{r,s}^{(n+1)} = \begin{cases} z_{r,s}^{(n)} + \alpha(z_{r+1,s}^{(n)} + z_{r-1,s}^{(n)} + z_{r,s+1}^{(n)} + z_{r,s-1}^{(n)} - 4z_{r,s}^{(n)}) \\ \qquad\qquad \text{inside } R \\ b_{r,s} \qquad\qquad \text{on boundary } B \end{cases} \tag{4.4.2}$$

The parameter α has been added to the original formulation. Note that the case $\alpha = \frac{1}{4}$ reduces (4.4.2) to (4.4.1), or Richardson's method.

The Richardson process is simple to program for digital computation and converges to the solution of the difference equation. However, convergence of the iteration process is very slow. Liebmann's method or the Gauss-Seidel method detailed in Chap. 5 represents a distinct improvement in that as soon as a new value is calculated it is used in the iteration pattern. The difference formulation becomes

$$z_{r,s}^{(n+1)} = \begin{cases} z_{r,s}^{(n)} + \alpha(z_{r+1,s}^{(n)} + z_{r-1,s}^{(n+1)} + z_{r,s+1}^{(n)} + z_{r,s-1}^{(n+1)} - 4z_{r,s}^{(n)}) \\ \qquad\qquad \text{inside } R \\ b_{r,s} \qquad\qquad \text{on boundary } B \end{cases} \tag{4.4.3}$$

or, with the specific value of $\alpha = \frac{1}{4}$,

$$z_{r,s}^{(n+1)} = \begin{cases} \frac{1}{4}(z_{r+1,s}^{(n)} + z_{r-1,s}^{(n+1)} + z_{r,s+1}^{(n)} + z_{r,s-1}^{(n+1)}) & \text{inside } R \\ b_{s,r} & \text{on boundary } B \end{cases}$$

If the computation starts at the lower right corner of Fig. 4.2, moves along the first row until new values for the entire first row are calculated, and then jumps to the right end of the second row, etc., $z_{r-1,s}^{(n+1)}$ and $z_{r,s-1}^{(n+1)}$ are known before the need to calculate $z_{r,s}^{(n+1)}$ arises. In other words as soon as a new value is calculated, it is immediately substituted for the previous value at the same mesh point. In this way the storage requirements for the internal mesh points are reduced to N^2. Each iteration cycle in the Liebmann method reduces the errors at any stage of the iteration by an amount approximately equal to two iteration cycles in Richardson's method.

As usual in any calculation of this type the use of h, $h/2$, $h/4$, . . . is used to help estimate the error involved in the calculation. This error will, of course, be truncation with essentially zero round-off because of the iterative method of solution. In this context of a decreasing h it can be shown that the number of iterations required for convergence varies approximately as $1/h^2$. Thus, as h is decreased, the number of iterations goes up rather rapidly.

In order further to speed up the rate of convergence of the iteration cycles Frankel (33) and Young (92) have suggested that there may be a value of α, the relaxation factor, other than $\alpha = \frac{1}{4}$, which is optimum for speed of convergence. As shown by both writers, the value of α calculated from solving the quadratic

$$\alpha^2 t^2 - 4\alpha + 1 = 0$$

for the smallest root is truly an optimum value. In the quadratic

$$t = 2 \cos \frac{\pi}{N + 1}$$

for the square Dirichlet problem under consideration. α is a fixed number, $\frac{1}{4} \leq \alpha \leq \frac{1}{2}$, which is retained through all the iterations.

The serious question in the use of this method is how to choose the optimum α when Laplace's equation is not applied to a square or plain rectangle. An obvious approach is to try a number of different α's and compare the rates of convergence until a maximum is located. Such a hunt procedure is naturally very time-consuming.

The procedure in the form outlined is called the "extrapolated Liebmann," or "successive-overrelaxation method." Of extreme importance is the fact that with essentially no extra work involved over the Liebmann method the number of iterations required for convergence varies approximately as $1/h$ instead of $1/h^2$. On this basis, and even if the exact optimum α is not used, the overrelaxation method is the preferred one.

There exists at least one further important method for solving the Dirichlet form of Laplace's equation which is due to Peaceman and Rachford (67). The transient version of Laplace's equation (a parabolic PDE) is solved and the limiting case of large time (as $t \to \infty$) is taken as the solution of Laplace's equation. Note that this procedure is a most interesting one, since it solves a more difficult problem than the original one. Each stage of the iteration is regarded as a time step of the unsteady state problem. The method involves the use of an iteration parameter ρ and the simultaneous modification of the values on one whole row or column of internal mesh points. First a row is altered, and then a column, i.e., two iterations per cycle. This differs from the previous methods, which modified only one mesh point at a time. Since details of this calculation will be presented later, it suffices now merely to list the pertinent formulas of the method. These are

$$\begin{aligned} z_{r+1,s}^{(2n+1)} - (2+\rho)z_{r,s}^{(2n+1)} + z_{r-1,s}^{(2n+1)} &= -z_{r,s+1}^{(2n)} + (2-\rho)z_{r,s}^{(2n)} - z_{r,s-1}^{(2n)} \\ z_{r,s+1}^{(2n+2)} - (2+\rho)z_{r,s}^{(2n+2)} + z_{r,s-1}^{(2n+2)} &= -z_{r+1,s}^{(2n+1)} + (2-\rho)z_{r,s}^{(2n+1)} - z_{r-1,s}^{(2n+1)} \end{aligned} \tag{4.4.4}$$

where the superscript n is used to indicate the time variable or the iteration step. An appropriate choice for ρ (on the assumption of Laplace's equation in a square) is given by the sequence of values

$$\rho_k = 4\sin^2\frac{k\pi}{2(N+1)} \qquad k = 1, \ldots, N$$

with each succeeding ρ_k used for one complete iteration cycle. If the number of ρ_k's are allowed to increase as h decreases (when h decreases, N must increase), the number of iterations required to achieve a specified convergence by the Peaceman-Rachford method is proportional to $|\log h|^{-1}$. This is much better than in the case of successive overrelaxation; the corresponding programming, however, is more complicated.

Just as in the case of the successive-overrelaxation method a problem arises in the Peaceman-Rachford scheme when a square or simple rectangle is not involved. Now it is necessary to estimate the ρ_k's. Further details of the method are given in Sec. 4.7 and such references as Varga (89).

Conceptually, at least, these procedures can be extended to cover the nine-point formula (4.3.7). Obviously the truncation error will be more satisfactory but the programming more complex. In either case, (4.3.4) or (4.3.7), the best method of solving the simultaneous equations is the successive-overrelaxation or the Peaceman-Rachford method. There is considerable question at this time as to which is the more appropriate to use in a specific case.

It is possible to show that the iterative solution of the difference-equation representation of Laplace's equation converges in the limit as n becomes large, i.e. that for a fixed h and k

$$\lim_{n\to\infty} z_{r,s}^{(n)} = \text{finite value of } z_{r,s}$$

Thus the system of linear equations, (4.3.4) and (4.3.7), possess a unique solution. In the same sense it can be shown that as h approaches zero this unique solution approaches the exact analytical solution of Laplace's equation [Greenspan (42)]. This means that

$$\lim_{h \to 0} z_{r,s} = z(x_r, y_s)$$

at the interior points. Unfortunately, such convergence and uniqueness proofs cannot be obtained for nonlinear elliptic PDE, and the final solution obtained must be examined carefully to see whether or not it is physically valid.

The methods discussed for the Dirichlet problem can be extended directly to handle the Neumann problem as long as the boundary remains square. To illustrate, consider that

$$\frac{\partial z}{\partial x} = b = \text{constant} \qquad x = L$$

is used as a boundary condition. This may be represented by

$$\frac{\partial z_{r,s}}{\partial x} = \frac{z_{r+1,s} - z_{r,s}}{h} = b \tag{4.4.5}$$

with O(h) or by

$$\frac{\partial z_{r,s}}{\partial x} = \frac{z_{r+1,s} - z_{r-1,s}}{2h} = b \tag{4.4.6}$$

with O(h^2). Rearranging (4.4.5) yields

$$z_{r+1,s} = bh + z_{r,s}$$

or, for $r + 1 = L$,

$$z_{L,s} = bh + z_{L-h,s}$$

This expression relates the value of z on the boundary and some s line to the value of z one mesh point in from the boundary and on the same s line. This allows the unknown value of $z_{L,s}$ (say, z_6 in Fig. 4.2) to be replaced with $z_{L-1,s}$ (say, z_{21} in Fig. 4.2). As a result, the unknown $z_{L,s}$ can be removed from the problem or given in terms of $z_{L-1,s}$, and the problem becomes essentially the same as for the Dirichlet system, i.e., the same number of equations and unknowns. Equations (4.3.4) can be used as before, with a modification required only on the outermost mesh points. If $b = 0$, the gradient at $x = L$ is zero and $z_{L,s} = z_{L-1,s}$.

However, if (4.3.4) is used for the internal points and (4.4.5) on the boundary, there is a mismatch in the truncation errors. Equation (4.3.4) is O(h^2) and (4.4.5) is O(h). This mismatch can be removed by using (4.4.6) in the form

$$z_{r+1,s} = 2bh + z_{r-1,s}$$

or, for $r = L$,

$$z_{L+h,s} = 2bh + z_{L-h,s} \tag{4.4.7}$$

$z_{L+h,s}$ is an imaginary point placed one h space beyond the boundary and on the same line as $z_{L-h,s}$. If we call this point z_{25}, (4.4.7) becomes

$$z_{25} = 2bh + z_{21}$$

where $z_{L-h,s} = z_{21}$ in Fig. 4.2. Applying (4.3.4) to point 6 in Fig. 4.2,

$$z_{21} + z_5 + z_7 + z_{25} = 4z_6$$

or

$$z_{21} + z_5 + z_7 + (2bh + z_{21}) = 4z_6$$

with the imaginary point eliminated. In this procedure the region of definition has been extended by introducing the imaginary points, with the points on the actual boundary treated as regular interior points of the extended region.

4.5. The Influence of Curved Boundaries

In a more general situation the boundary B will be curved and not square or rectangular; the mesh points will not necessarily coincide with the boundary. Figure 4.4 illustrates a typical curved boundary with a

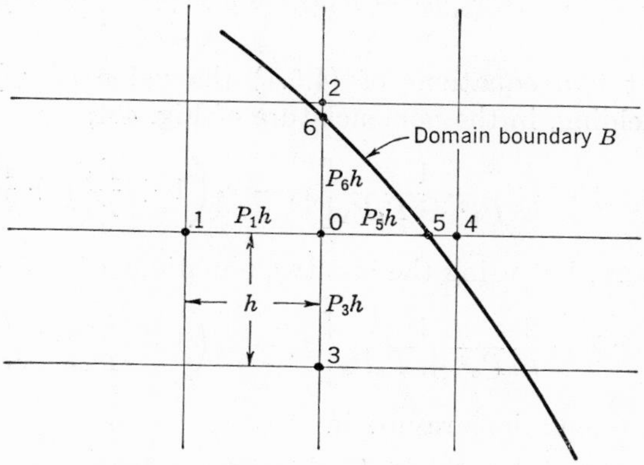

FIG. 4.4. Curved boundary and Dirichlet problem.

square mesh placed over it. The P_1h, P_2h, P_3h, and P_4h represent the distances from the point 0 to the boundary or adjacent point. As shown, $P_5, P_6 < 1.0$, and $P_1, P_3 = 1.0$. In the succeeding discussion P_1, P_3 can also be taken as less than 1 for generality.

First consider Fig. 4.4 in the light of a Dirichlet problem. z_5 and z_6 are given, and z_2 and z_4 are imaginary points outside the boundary (called irregular points). Expanding $z(x_0 + \alpha, y_0)$ and $z(x_0, y_0 + \beta)$ in a Taylor series about the point x_0, y_0 leads to

$$z(x_0 + \alpha, y_0) = z(x_0,y_0) + \alpha z_x(x_0,y_0) + \frac{\alpha^2}{2!} z_{xx}(x_0,y_0) + \frac{\alpha^3}{3!} z_{xxx}(x_0,y_0) + \cdots$$

$$z(x_0, y_0 + \beta) = z(x_0,y_0) + \beta z_y(x_0,y_0) + \frac{\beta^2}{2!} z_{yy}(x_0,y_0) + \frac{\beta^3}{3!} z_{yyy}(x_0,y_0) + \cdots$$

If we let $\alpha = +P_5h$ and then $\alpha = -P_1h$ in the first equation, $\beta = +P_6h$ and then $\beta = -P_3h$ in the second equation, truncating each after the second derivative yields [with $O(h^2)$]

$$\begin{aligned}
z(x_0 + P_5h, y_0) &= z(x_0,y_0) + P_5hz_x(x_0,y_0) + \frac{(P_5h)^2}{2} z_{xx}(x_0,y_0) \\
z(x_0 - P_1h, y_0) &= z(x_0,y_0) - P_1hz_x(x_0,y_0) + \frac{(P_1h)^2}{2} z_{xx}(x_0,y_0) \\
z(x_0, y_0 + P_6h) &= z(x_0,y_0) + P_6hz_y(x_0,y_0) + \frac{(P_6h)^2}{2} z_{yy}(x_0,y_0) \\
z(x_0, y_0 - P_3h) &= z(x_0,y_0) - P_3hz_y(x_0,y_0) + \frac{(P_3h)^2}{2} z_{yy}(x_0,y_0)
\end{aligned} \tag{4.5.1}$$

From the first two equations of (4.5.1) the value of $z_x(x_0,y_0)$ can be eliminated, yielding, in the nomenclature of Fig. 4.4,

$$z_{xx}(x_0,y_0) = \frac{2}{h^2}\frac{1}{P_5^2 + P_5P_1}\left[z_5 - z_0\left(1 + \frac{P_5}{P_1}\right) + \frac{P_5}{P_1} z_1\right]$$

In the same way, but using the last two equations of (4.5.1),

$$z_{yy}(x_0,y_0) = \frac{2}{h^2}\frac{1}{P_6^2 + P_6P_3}\left[z_6 - z_0\left(1 + \frac{P_6}{P_3}\right) + \frac{P_6}{P_3} z_3\right]$$

Adding the two equations results in

$$\left.z_{xx} + z_{yy}\right)_{x_0,y_0} = \frac{2}{h^2}\left\{\frac{1}{P_5^2 + P_5P_1}\left[z_5 - z_0\left(1 + \frac{P_5}{P_1}\right) + \frac{P_5}{P_1} z_1\right] + \frac{1}{P_6^2 + P_6P_3}\left[z_6 - z_0\left(1 + \frac{P_6}{P_3}\right) + \frac{P_6}{P_3} z_3\right]\right\} \tag{4.5.2}$$

For the special case $P_1 = P_3 = 1.0$, (4.5.2) reduces to

$$\left.z_{xx} + z_{yy}\right)_{x_0,y_0} = \frac{2}{h^2}\left[\frac{1}{P_5 + 1} z_1 + \frac{1}{P_6 + 1} z_3 + \frac{1}{P_5(P_5 + 1)} z_5 + \frac{1}{P_6(P_6 + 1)} z_6 - \frac{P_6 + P_5}{P_5P_6} z_0\right] + O(h^2)$$

For $P_5 = P_6 = 1.0$ this reduces to the case of a square boundary, i.e.,

$$\left. z_{xx} + z_{yy} \right)_{x_0,y_0} = \frac{1}{h^2}(z_1 + z_3 + z_5 + z_6 - 4z_0)$$

Cross multiplying plus some algebraic manipulation on (4.5.2) leads to

$$P_5P_6(P_6 + 1)z_1 + P_5P_6(P_5 + 1)z_3 + P_6(P_6 + 1)z_5 + P_5(P_5 + 1)z_6 - (P_5 + 1)(P_6 + 1)(P_6 + P_5)z_0 = 0 \quad (4.5.3)$$

Equation (4.5.3) is an equation much like (4.3.4) except that the boundary values are included plus the coefficients P_1, P_3, P_5, and P_6. The process of solving Laplace's equation now becomes one of using (4.3.4)

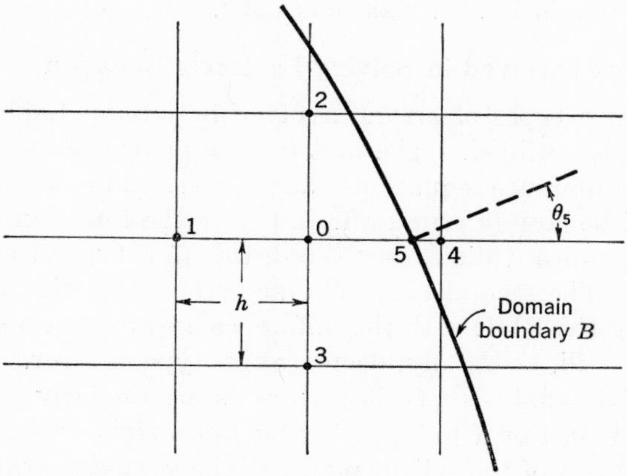

FIG. 4.5. Curved boundary and Neumann problem.

for all points not adjacent to a boundary and (4.5.3), with appropriate values of P_1, P_3, P_5, and P_6, for points adjacent to the boundary. All other details are as given for the square-boundary case.

When the system is a Neumann problem, a similar but more complicated procedure can be used. Figure 4.5 can be used for illustration with $\partial z/\partial n = f(x,y)$ specified on the boundary. $\partial z/\partial n$ is the normal gradient of z to the boundary and at an angle Θ_5 to the horizontal. At the point 5

$$\left.\frac{\partial z}{\partial n}\right)_5 = \left.\frac{\partial z}{\partial x}\right)_5 \cos \Theta_5 + \left.\frac{\partial z}{\partial y}\right)_5 \sin \Theta_5 \quad (4.5.4)$$

If it is assumed that $z(x,y)$ can be fitted by a polynomial in x and y, that is,

$$z(x,y) = a_0 + a_1x + a_2x^2 + a_3y + a_4y^2 + a_5xy$$

the derivatives in (4.5.4) can be evaluated explicitly. The coefficients of the polynomial are also related to the values z_0, z_1, z_2, z_3, and z_4. As an illustration, for $x = y = 0$ (corresponding to the point x_0, y_0),

$$z(x_0,y_0) = z_0 = a_0$$

For $y = 0$ but x a variable,

$$a_1 = \frac{z_4 - z_1}{2h}$$

and so on. With all the a_i's known in terms of z_0, z_1, z_2, z_3, and z_4, (4.5.4) can be written in terms of these same values. By writing (4.3.4) around the point z_0 and using (4.5.4) to eliminate z_4 an equation results which involves only the known boundary values. The problem is now in the form used previously. For a detailed discussion of the errors associated with curved boundaries, see Laasonen (53).

4.6. The Errors Involved in Solving Laplace's Equation

There are two types of errors involved in solving Laplace's equation by the methods outlined. The first type of error results in the solution of the finite-difference equations themselves. For square boundaries this error will be largely round-off, and since the iteration can be carried to as many significant digits as desired, this first type of error is usually insignificant. The second type of error is the truncation error resulting from replacing the PDE with the difference approximation. Decreasing the grid space will, as usually, decrease this type of error. A qualitative or quantitative analysis of the errors is particularly difficult if the boundary is curved or if finite-difference approximations are used at the boundary. A few of the salient points of the simplest error analysis will, however, prove instructive.

Let $\epsilon_{r,s}^{(n)}$ be the error in the nth iteration step at the internal mesh point x_r, y_s such that

$$\epsilon_{r,s}^{(n)} = z_{r,s}^{(n)} - z_{r,s}$$

and $z_{r,s} = \lim_{n \to \infty} z_{r,s}^{(n)}$ = convergent limit at the point x_r, x_s. Substituting into the difference formula for Richardson's process, (4.4.1), yields

$$\epsilon_{r,s}^{(n+1)} = \begin{cases} \frac{1}{4}(\epsilon_{r+1,s}^{(n)} + \epsilon_{r-1,s}^{(n)} + \epsilon_{r,s+1}^{(n)} + \epsilon_{r,s-1}^{(n)}) & \text{inside } R \\ 0 & \text{on boundary } B \end{cases}$$

In a simpler notation this may be written as

$$\epsilon^{(n+1)} = \left(1 + \frac{K}{4}\right) \epsilon^{(n)}$$

where K is a linear symbolic operator such that

$$Kz_{r,s} = z_{r+1,s} + z_{r-1,s} + z_{r,s+1} + z_{r,s-1} - 4z_{r,s} = 0$$

For convergence of the iteration process the necessary and sufficient condition is that

$$\left| 1 + \frac{K}{4} \right| < 1.0$$

so that the error decreases at each iteration step. After convergence, the maximum error in the final answers can be estimated from Milne (Chap. 1, 31) to be

$$\epsilon_{\max} \leq \frac{R^2\gamma}{4h^2}$$

when (4.3.4) is used and

$$\epsilon_{\max} \leq \frac{R^2\gamma}{24h^2}$$

when (4.3.7) is used. γ is the maximum residual in the final iteration step, and R is the radius of the smallest circle which encloses the domain under investigation. The residual is merely the difference between the left and right side of the particular equation, i.e., (4.4.2), when the calculated values of the z_i's are substituted.

The truncation error associated with replacing the PDE with the finite-difference equation can be estimated from a Taylor series expansion of $z(x,y)$. If we let $P_5 = 1.0$ in the first equation of (4.5.1), $P_1 = 1.0$ in the second, $P_6 = 1.0$ in the third, and $P_3 = 1.0$ in the fourth equation, there results

$$z(x_0 + h,\, y_0) = z(x_0,y_0) + hz_x(x_0,y_0) + \frac{h^2}{2!} z_{xx}(x_0,y_0) + \frac{h^3}{3!} z_{xxx}(x_0,y_0) + \frac{h^4}{4!} z_{xxxx}(\xi_1,y_0)$$

$$z(x_0 - h,\, y_0) = z(x_0,y_0) - hz_x(x_0,y_0) + \frac{h^2}{2!} z_{xx}(x_0,y_0) - \frac{h^3}{3!} z_{xxx}(x_0,y_0) + \frac{h^4}{4!} z_{xxxx}(\xi_2,y_0)$$

$$z(x_0,\, y_0 + h) = z(x_0,y_0) + hz_y(x_0,y_0) + \frac{h^2}{2!} z_{yy}(x_0,y_0) + \frac{h^3}{3!} z_{yyy}(x_0,y_0) + \frac{h^4}{4!} z_{yyyy}(x_0,\xi_3)$$

$$z(x_0,\, y_0 - h) = z(x_0,y_0) - hz_y(x_x,y_x) + \frac{h^2}{2!} z_{yy}(x_0,y_0) - \frac{h^3}{3!} z_{yyy}(x_0,y_0) + \frac{h^4}{4!} z_{yyyy}(x_0,\xi_4)$$

where

$$x_0 < \xi_1 < x_0 + h$$
$$x_0 - h < \xi_2 < x_0$$
$$y_0 < \xi_3 < y_0 + h$$
$$y_0 - h < \xi_4 < y_0$$

Adding the first two equations and then the second two and grouping,

$$(z_{xx} + z_{yy})_{x_0,y_0} = \frac{1}{h^2}\Big\{[z(x_0 + h, y_0) - 2z(x_0,y_0) + z(x_0 - h, y_0)] + [z(x_0, y_0 + h) - 2z(x_0,y_0) + z(x_0, y_0 - h)] - \frac{h^4}{4!}[z_{xxxx}(\xi_1,y_0) + z_{xxxx}(\xi_2,y_0) + z_{yyyy}(x_0,\xi_3) + z_{yyyy}(x_0,\xi_4)]\Big\}$$

If the difference equation of (4.3.4) is used, the above equation indicates that the truncation error associated with replacing Laplace's equation at x_0, y_0 is

$$z_{\text{TE}}(x_0,y_0) = -\frac{h^4}{4!}[z_{xxxx}(\xi_1,y_0) + z_{xxxx}(\xi_2,y_0) + z_{yyyy}(x_0,\xi_3) + z_{yyyy}(x_0,\xi_4)]$$

From the formidable nature of this expression, it is apparent that there is little that can be done actually to evaluate the truncation error. However, the work of Keller (51) presents a detailed analysis of this problem.

The finite-difference representations for elliptic PDE have been illustrated with the special case of Laplace's equation. The methods and techniques can be extended directly to cover other elliptic PDE with such complications as variable coefficients and nonlinearities. However, as soon as the linear PDE is discarded, it becomes impossible to discuss a priori the various features of convergence and error analysis. The techniques illustrated will still work, but a systematic investigation must be carried out on each equation to ensure that the system behaves as expected.

It is important to note that in the solution of the elliptic equation the question of stability of the numerical solution has not arisen. This is because of the iterative nature of the solution and is a feature not common to other types of PDE.

4.7. Approximating Parabolic and Hyperbolic PDE

Since many of the basic features of the numerical integration of both parabolic and hyperbolic PDE are similar, they are considered together in this section. The classic parabolic PDE is the one-dimensional heat-flow, or diffusion, equation

$$\alpha \frac{\partial^2 z}{\partial x^2} = \frac{\partial z}{\partial t} \qquad 0 < x < 1.0,\ t > 0,\ \alpha = \text{constant} > 0 \tag{4.7.1}$$

where $z = z(x,t)$, α is a positive constant, t is time, x is distance, and the interval on x is restricted to (0,1). This last stipulation on the range of x is merely for convenience in the discussion and can readily be extended to (a,b). Since (4.7.1) is second-order in the space variable and first-order in the time variable, it is necessary to specify two conditions for z at some x and one condition for z at some t. These may be written as

$$\begin{aligned} z(0,t) &= f_0(t) \qquad x = 0,\ t \geq 0 \\ z(1,t) &= f_1(t) \qquad x = 1,\ t \geq 0 \end{aligned} \tag{4.7.2}$$

and

$$z(x,0) = g_0(x) \qquad t = 0,\ 0 < x < 1 \tag{4.7.3}$$

The general functions $f_0(t)$, $f_1(t)$, and $g_0(x)$ are simple analytical functions in most applications.

The classic hyperbolic PDE is the wave equation

$$\frac{\partial^2 z}{\partial x^2} = \frac{\partial^2 z}{\partial t^2} \qquad 0 < x < 1.0,\ t > 0 \tag{4.7.4}$$

with the same connotations as in (4.7.1). Since (4.7.4) is second-order in both independent variables, two boundary and two initial conditions are required. These may be written as

$$\begin{aligned} z(0,t) &= f_0(t) \qquad x = 0,\ t \geq 0 \\ z(1,t) &= f_1(t) \qquad x = 1,\ t \geq 0 \end{aligned} \tag{4.7.5}$$

and

$$\begin{aligned} z(x,0) &= g_0(x) \qquad t = 0,\ 0 < x < 1 \\ \frac{\partial z}{\partial t}(x,0) &= g_1(x) \qquad t = 0,\ 0 < x < 1 \end{aligned} \tag{4.7.6}$$

It is possible to replace the boundary conditions of (4.7.2) and (4.7.5) with a more general gradient criterion. This might take the form

$$a_1 \frac{\partial z}{\partial x} + a_2 z = a_3 \qquad x = 0 \text{ or } x = 1,\ t > 0 \tag{4.7.7}$$

and, upon a proper choice of the a_1, a_2 and a_3 reduce to almost any boundary condition which the chemical engineer will encounter.

In both classes of PDE the boundary is defined on three sides of an xt domain but unbounded on the fourth side. For $f_0(t)$ and $f_1(t)$ as constants and $g_0(x)$ as a constant, say, zero, the domain and boundary of the PDE can be specified as in Fig. 4.6. The problem becomes one of determining $z(x,t)$ in the region R subject to the conditions on B. To accomplish this, a rectangular mesh is placed over the region with an h-interval spacing in the x direction and a k-interval spacing in the t direction. A mesh point x_r, t_s is equivalent to

$$z(x_r,t_s) = z(rh,sk) = z_{r,s}$$

If we let N = number of internal points in any single row,

$$(N + 1)h = 1.0$$

or if we call $M = N + 1$ = number of intervals in x direction, $Mh = 1.0$.

The simplest finite-difference representation for the parabolic PDE of

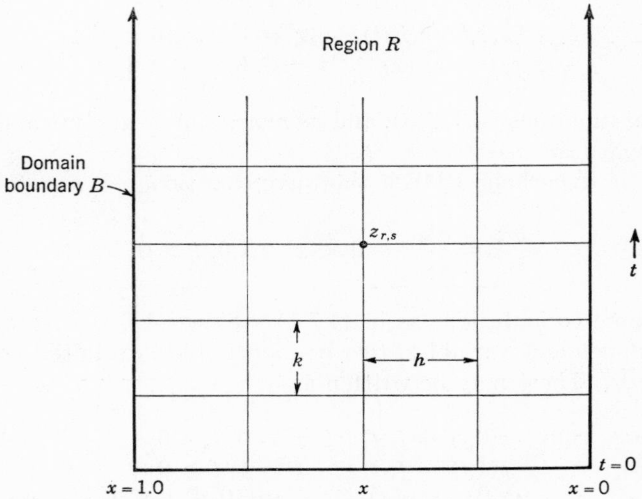

FIG. 4.6. Mesh spacing for parabolic and hyperbolic PDE.

(4.7.1) uses a central-difference formula for z_{xx} and a forward difference for z_t. From (4.2.13) and (4.2.16)

$$\alpha z_{xx} - z_t = 0 = \alpha \frac{z_{r+1,s} - 2z_{r,s} + z_{r-1,s}}{h^2} - \frac{z_{r,s+1} - z_{r,s}}{k}$$

or
$$z_{r,s+1} = z_{r,s} + \frac{\alpha k}{h^2}(z_{r+1,s} - 2z_{r,s} + z_{r-1,s}) + O(h^2) + O(k)$$

Calling $\beta = \alpha k/h^2$,

$$z_{r,s+1} = \beta z_{r+1,s} + (1 - 2\beta)z_{r,s} + \beta z_{r-1,s} \qquad \text{explicit} \qquad (4.7.8)$$

where $1 \leq r \leq N$ and $s \geq 1$. Equation (4.7.8) is called the explicit, or forward-difference, representation for (4.7.1) and has a computational molecule

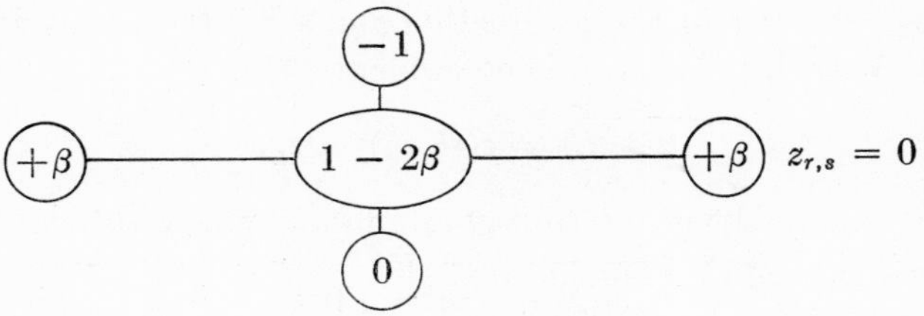

In the particular case in which $\beta = \frac{1}{2}$, (4.7.8) reduces to the familiar Schmidt formula

$$z_{r,s+1} = \tfrac{1}{2}(z_{r+1,s} + z_{r-1,s}) \tag{4.7.9}$$

The boundary and initial conditions (4.7.2) and (4.7.3) become

$$\begin{aligned} z_{0,s} &= f_0(sk) && s \geq 0 \\ z_{M,s} &= f_1(sk) && s \geq 0 \\ z_{r,0} &= g_0(rh) && 0 < r < M \end{aligned} \tag{4.7.10}$$

The manner of solving (4.7.8) and (4.7.10) for $z_{r,s}$ at the mesh points of Fig. 4.6 is quite straightforward. The initial and boundary conditions (4.7.10) determine the values of $z_{r,s}$ at all the boundary points. Equation (4.7.8) may be used to calculate all the $z_{r,1}$'s on the first row by using merely the values at $z_{r,0}$. This can easily be seen from the computational molecule, in which a value $z_{r,s+1}$ follows from the values at the s level only. Once the entire row of $z_{r,1}$'s are known, the $z_{r,2}$'s can be calculated by using (4.7.8), the known boundary values, and the $z_{r,1}$'s. This can be continued as far into the time domain as desired. Note that this procedure is merely a line-by-line calculation, with the unknown z at the $s + 1$ step calculated explicitly from those on the s step. The digital program for this process is relatively simple, and the storage requirements are modest.

It should be pointed out that one problem exists in calculating the first row $z_{r,1}$. A discontinuity exists in the corner points $z_{0,0}$ and $z_{M,0}$, since approaching these points from the x direction or the t direction leads to different values. This is usually compensated for by using the arithmetic averages at the corner corresponding to $x \to 0$ and $t \to 0$. Fortunately, the actual numerical value used at the corners is quickly "washed out" in subsequent calculations and thus is not too important.

There are some severe computational restrictions involved in the use of the explicit formula (4.7.8). While these will be detailed in the next section, it can be stated here that problems of stability of the computation and excessive computing time minimize the usefulness of (4.7.8). To remove these difficulties, a number of implicit finite-difference formulas have been developed. These formulas are obtained by replacing z_{xx} with a difference approximation applied to the $s + 1$ row or by the average of the $s + 1$ and s rows instead of the s row as in the explicit approach. Replacing z_{xx} with a difference approximation on the $s + 1$ row yields

$$\alpha z_{xx} - z_t = 0 = \alpha \frac{z_{r+1,s+1} - 2z_{r,s+1} + z_{r-1,s+1}}{h^2} - \frac{z_{r,s+1} - z_{r,s}}{k}$$

or, rearranging,

$$\left(2 + \frac{1}{\beta}\right) z_{r,s+1} = z_{r+1,s+1} + \frac{1}{\beta} z_{r,s} + z_{r-1,s+1} + O(h^2) + O(k)$$

Laasonen 4-point implicit form (4.7.11)

Equation (4.7.11) is called "Laasonen's four-point implicit form" and has the computational molecule

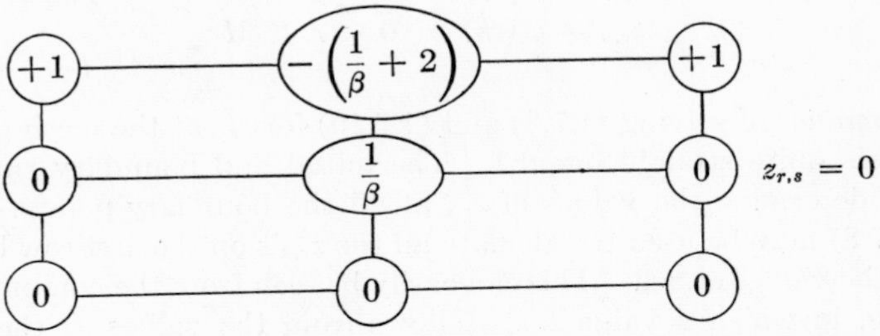

This system is also called the "backward-difference formulation," since it may be derived by considering the $s + 1$ point and approximating the time derivative with a backward-difference approximation. Averaging z_{xx} on the $s + 1$ and s rows was suggested by Crank and Nicholson (17). This leads to

$$\alpha z_{xx} - z_t = 0 = \frac{\alpha}{2h^2} [(z_{r+1,s+1} - z_{r,s+1} + z_{r-1,s+1}) + (z_{r+1,s} - 2z_{r,s} + z_{r-1,s})] - \frac{z_{r,s+1} - z_{r,s}}{k}$$

or

$$z_{r+1,s+1} - 2\left(1 + \frac{1}{\beta}\right) z_{r,s+1} + z_{r-1,s+1} + z_{r+1,s} - 2\left(1 - \frac{1}{\beta}\right) z_{r,s} + z_{r-1,s} + O(h^2) + O(k) = 0$$

Crank-Nicholson 6-point implicit form (4.7.12)

In computational-molecule form (4.7.12) may be represented as

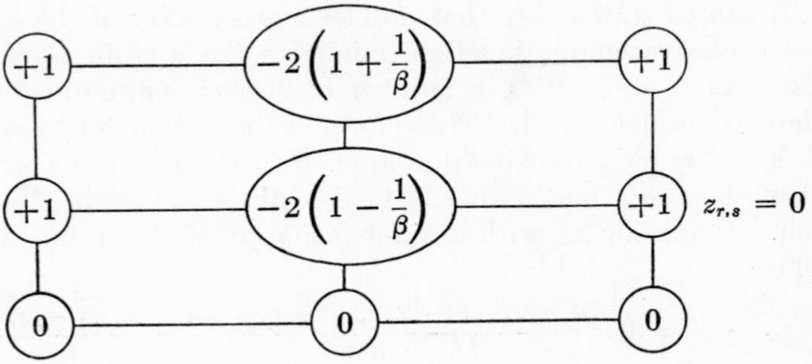

Actually these formulas are merely special cases of the more general implicit equation

$$\frac{\alpha}{h^2}[\Theta(z_{r+1,s+1} - 2z_{r,s+1} + z_{r-1,s+1}) + (1 - \Theta)(z_{r+1,s} - 2z_{r,s} + z_{r-1,s})] = \frac{z_{r,s+1} - z_{r,s}}{k} \quad (4.7.13)$$

For $\Theta = 0$, (4.7.13) reduces to the explicit equation (4.7.8), for $\Theta = \frac{1}{2}$ to the implicit equation (4.7.12), and for $\Theta = 1.0$ to the implicit equation (4.7.11). Douglas (19) has also presented a higher-order implicit formula, but it will not be discussed here.

While the computational program for the explicit formula is quite direct and follows from the recurrent line-by-line use of (4.7.8), the implicit formulas are more complicated to use. With (4.7.11) as an example, it can be seen that a single application of the formula yields a relation between three unknown values on the $s + 1$ row (except when next to the boundary) in terms of one known value on the s row. If, however, (4.7.11) is applied at each point on the s row (a total of N times) a set of N simultaneous linear equations result with N unknowns. The unknowns are the interior points on the $s + 1$ row. Included in the set of simultaneous equations are the N known values on the s row plus the known boundary conditions on the s and $s + 1$ rows. Thus a set of simultaneous algebraic equations must be solved at each row as one passes further and further into the time domain. The implicit methods thus require a more complicated computer program. As will be pointed out shortly, however, the implicit method while seemingly more difficult and complex has certain advantages that far outweigh this defect.

The solution of the set of simultaneous algebraic equations may be obtained in a number of ways. Thus the Laasonen implicit equation can be written in the form

$$z_{r+1,s+1} - \left(2 + \frac{1}{\beta}\right) z_{r,s+1} + z_{r-1,s+1} + \frac{1}{\beta} z_{r,s} = 0$$

and the successive-overrelaxation iteration scheme applied in the form

$$z_{r,s+1}^{(n+1)} = z_{r,s+1}^{(n)} + \Delta\left[z_{r+1,s+1}^{(n)} - \left(2 + \frac{1}{\beta}\right) z_{r,s+1}^{(n)} + z_{r-1,s+1}^{(n+1)} + \frac{1}{\beta} z_{r,s}^{(n)}\right]$$

n here indicates the iterative step, with Δ the relaxation factor. The iteration is, of course, carried out a single row at a time. However, the arrangement of the simultaneous equations (only three unknowns in each equation) suggests the method of Thomas detailed in Chap. 5. The author's experience indicates that this latter method, which does not involve any iteration, is faster than and as accurate as the overrelaxation method.

The reader may ask the logical question at this point as to why the time derivative z_t was replaced with a difference approximation of $O(k)$ and not of $O(k^2)$ to match the replacement of z_{xx}. In the latter case this would mean using (4.2.12) or

$$\frac{\partial z}{\partial t} = \frac{z_{r,s+1} - z_{r,s-1}}{2h}$$

As will be pointed out shortly, this difference approximation in the parabolic system always leads to unstable solutions. Thus it is not used in practice.

An explicit finite-difference representation for the hyperbolic PDE of (4.7.4) to (4.7.6) results from the replacement of both derivatives of (4.7.4) with the simplest central-difference formula

$$z_{xx} - z_{tt} = 0 = \frac{z_{r+1,s} - 2z_{r,s} + z_{r-1,s}}{h^2} - \frac{z_{r,s+1} - 2z_{r,s} + z_{r,s-1}}{k^2}$$

Letting $\gamma = k/h$,

$$z_{r,s+1} = \gamma^2 z_{r+1,s} + 2(1 - \gamma^2)z_{r,s} + \gamma^2 z_{r-1,s} - z_{r,s-1} + O(h^2) + O(k^2)$$
$$1 \le r \le N,\ s \ge 1;\ \text{explicit} \qquad (4.7.14)$$

The associated computational molecule is

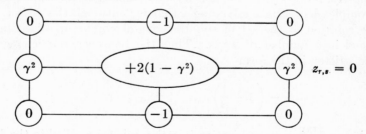

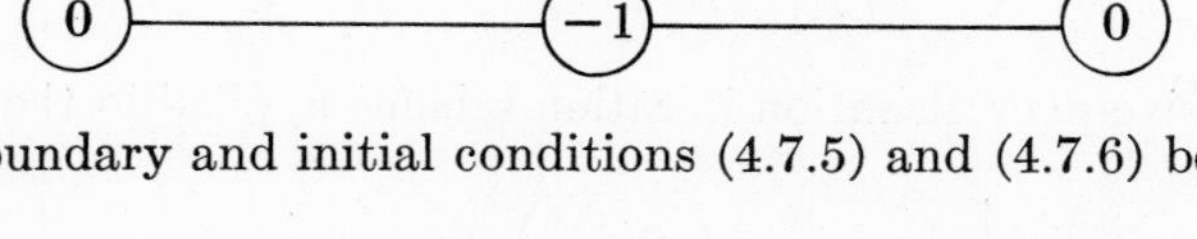

$z_{r,s} = 0$

The boundary and initial conditions (4.7.5) and (4.7.6) become

$$\begin{aligned} z_{0,s} &= f_0(sk) && s \ge 0 \\ z_{M,s} &= f_1(sk) && s \ge 0 \\ z_{r,0} &= g_0(rh) && 0 < r < M \qquad (4.7.15) \\ z_{r,1} &= z_{r,0} + kg_1(rh) \\ &= g_0(rh) + kg_1(rh) && 0 < r < M \end{aligned}$$

An implicit representation can be obtained by replacing z_{xx} with the average on the $s + 1$ and $s - 1$ rows:

$$z_{xx} - z_{tt} = 0 = \frac{1}{2h^2}[(z_{r+1,s+1} - 2z_{r,s+1} + z_{r-1,s+1}) + (z_{r+1,s-1} - 2z_{r,s-1} + z_{r-1,s-1})] - \frac{z_{r,s+1} - 2z_{r,s} + z_{r,s-1}}{k^2}$$

or

$$\frac{\gamma^2}{2} z_{r+1,s+1} - (1 + \gamma^2)z_{r,s+1} + \frac{\gamma^2}{2} z_{r-1,s+1} + 2z_{r,s} + \frac{\gamma^2}{2} z_{r+1,s-1} - (1 + \gamma^2)z_{r,s-1} + \frac{\gamma^2}{2} z_{r-1,s-1} + O(h^2) + O(k^2) = 0 \qquad \text{implicit} \quad (4.7.16)$$

The computational molecule is given by

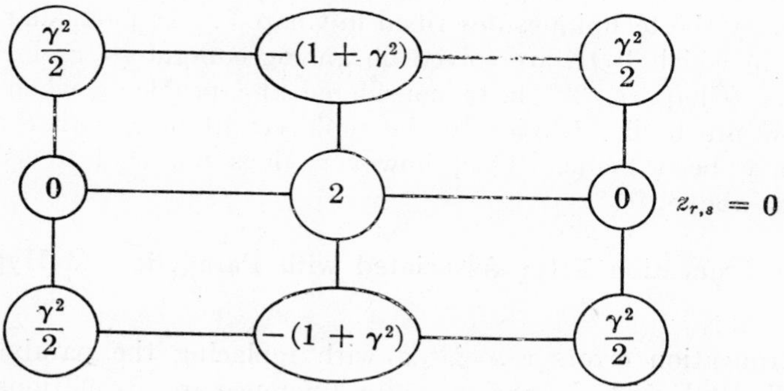

The computational details for implementing (4.7.14) or (4.7.16) are much the same as in the parabolic case. From the initial conditions of (4.7.15) the values of $z_{r,0}$ and $z_{r,1}$ (the first two rows) are known. The explicit formula (4.7.14) uses a line-by-line calculation to evaluate $z_{r,2}$ from $z_{r,0}$ and $z_{r,1}$. In sequence the $s + 1$ rows are then evaluated using both s and $s - 1$ rows. The implicit formula, as before, requires the solution of a set of N simultaneous equations using the $s + 1$ row values as unknowns.

It should also be pointed out that there is another general approach for solving PDE of the parabolic type (or others) which is different from that outlined above. Instead of replacing both the z_{xx} and z_t derivatives with finite-difference approximations, suppose that only one, say, z_{xx}, is replaced. This leads to an equation of the form

$$\alpha \frac{z_{r+1,s} - 2z_{r,s} + z_{r-1,s}}{h^2} = \frac{\partial z_{r,s}}{\partial t} = \frac{dz_{r,s}}{dt}$$

or

$$\frac{h^2}{\alpha}\frac{dz_{r,s}}{dt} = z_{r+1,s} - 2z_{r,s} + z_{r-1,s} \qquad (4.7.17)$$

Equation (4.7.17) is a linear first-order ODE. When it is applied to the points $r = 1, 2, \ldots, N-1, N$, there results, with the s subscript dropped,

$$\frac{h^2}{\alpha}\frac{dz_1}{dt} + 2z_1 - z_2 = z_0$$

$$\frac{h^2}{\alpha}\frac{dz_2}{dt} + 2z_2 - z_1 - z_3 = 0$$

$$\cdots\cdots\cdots\cdots\cdots\cdots$$

$$\frac{h^2}{\alpha}\frac{dz_{N-1}}{dt} + 2z_{N-1} - z_{N-2} - z_N = 0$$

$$\frac{h^2}{\alpha}\frac{dz_N}{dt} + 2z_N - z_{N-1} = z_{N+1}$$

This is a set of N first-order differential-difference equations, which may be solved by the techniques described in Chap. 3. In particular, this is the way in which PDE are solved on analog computers, and Fox and coworkers (Chap. 1, 32) have considered the problems when digital computers are used. Obviously the replacement of z_t rather than z_{xx} could have been made. This, however, does not lead to as nice a system as above.

4.8. The Truncation Error Associated with Parabolic and Hyperbolic PDE

The truncation errors associated with replacing the parabolic and hyperbolic PDE with the various finite-difference approximations can be ascertained from suitable Taylor series expansions, just as was done for the elliptic case. By using the two equations before (4.5.1), with y replaced by t and the point x_0, t_0, there results

$$\begin{aligned} z(x_0 + h, t_0) = z(x_0,t_0) + hz_x(x_0,t_0) + \frac{h^2}{2!} z_{xx}(x_0,t_0) + \frac{h^3}{3!} z_{xxx}(x_0,t_0) \\ + \frac{h^4}{4!} z_{xxxx}(x_0,t_0) + \frac{h^5}{5!} z_{xxxxx}(x_0,t_0) + \frac{h^6}{6!} z_{xxxxxx}(\xi_1,t_0) \end{aligned} \tag{4.8.1}$$

$$\begin{aligned} z(x_0 - h, t_0) = z(x_0,t_0) - hz_x(x_0,t_0) + \frac{h^2}{2!} z_{xx}(x_0,t_0) - \frac{h^3}{3!} z_{xxx}(x_0,t_0) \\ + \frac{h^4}{4!} z_{xxxx}(x_0,t_0) - \frac{h^5}{5!} z_{xxxxx}(x_0,t_0) + \frac{h^6}{6!} z_{xxxxxx}(\xi_2,t_0) \end{aligned} \tag{4.8.2}$$

$$z(x_0, t_0 + k) = z(x_0,t_0) + kz_t(x_0,t_0) + \frac{k^2}{2!} z_{tt}(x_0,t_0) + \frac{k^3}{3!} z_{ttt}(x_0,\xi_3) \tag{4.8.3}$$

where

$$x_0 < \xi_1 < x_0 + h$$
$$x_0 - h < \xi_2 < x_0$$
$$x_0 < \xi_3 < t_0 + k$$

Adding (4.8.1) and (4.8.2), subtracting (4.8.3) from the result, rearranging, and multiplying by α leads to

$$\alpha z_{xx}(x_0,t_0) - z_t(x_0,t_0) = \frac{\alpha}{h^2}[z(x_0 + h,\, t_0) - 2z(x_0,t_0) + z(x_0 - h,\, t_0)]$$
$$- \frac{z(x_0,\, t_0 + k) - z(x_0,t_0)}{k} - \frac{\alpha}{h^2}\left[\frac{2h^4}{4!} z_{xxxx}(x_0,t_0) + \frac{h^6}{6!} z_{xxxxxx}(\xi_1,t_0)\right.$$
$$\left. + \frac{h^6}{6!} z_{xxxxxx}(\xi_2,t_0)\right] + \frac{1}{k}\left[\frac{k^2}{2!} z_{tt}(x_0,t_0) + \frac{k^3}{3!} z_{ttt}(x_0,\xi_3)\right]$$

Upon comparing this with (4.7.8), the explicit finite-difference representation for the parabolic PDE, it can be seen that the truncation error $z_{\mathrm{TE}}(x_0,t_0)$ or $kz_{\mathrm{TE}}(x_0,t_0)$ is given by

$$kz_{\mathrm{TE}}(x_0,t_0) = \frac{\alpha k}{h^2}\left[\frac{2h^4}{4!} z_{xxxx}(x_0,t_0) + \frac{h^6}{6!} z_{xxxxxx}(\xi_1,t_0) + \frac{h^6}{6!} z_{xxxxxx}(\xi_2,t_0)\right]$$
$$- \left[\frac{k^2}{2!} z_{tt}(x_0,t_0) + \frac{k^3}{3!} z_{ttt}(x_0,\xi_3)\right]$$

But since $\alpha z_{xx} = z_t$, it follows that $\alpha^2 z_{xxxx} = z_{tt}$ and $\alpha^3 z_{xxxxxx} = z_{ttt}$, leading to

$$kz_{\mathrm{TE}}(x_0,t_0) = \left(\frac{2\alpha k}{h^2}\frac{h^4}{4!} - \frac{\alpha^2 k^2}{2!}\right) z_{xxxx}(x_0,t_0) + \left(\frac{2\alpha k}{h^2}\frac{h^6}{6!} - \frac{\alpha^3 k^3}{3!}\right) z_{xxxxxx}(\xi_4,\xi_5)$$

The major truncation error is given by the first term of this expression. This is seen to be $O(h^2)$ and $O(k)$. If the fourth derivatives are bounded, this error will become smaller and smaller as the mesh sizes h and k decrease. Further, if the special choice that

$$\beta = \frac{\alpha k}{h^2} = \frac{1}{6}$$

is made, the coefficient on $z_{xxxx}(x_0,t_0)$ becomes

$$2\beta\frac{h^4}{4!} - \frac{\alpha^2 k^2}{2!} = \frac{2}{6}\frac{h^4}{4!} - \frac{h^4}{36}\frac{1}{2} = 0$$

The truncation error now results from the second term and is seen to be $O(h^4)$ and $O(k^2)$. This particular value of $\beta = \frac{1}{6}$ may be termed an optimum one, since the difference equation approaches the analytical solution of the parabolic PDE at the fastest rate as h and k are decreased.

The same approach can be used for the implicit representation of the parabolic PDE and for either representation of the hyperbolic PDE. Without carrying out the necessary steps here, the appropriate order of the truncation error has been added to the difference equations in the text. In the general case of (4.7.13), however, the truncation error has the form

$$h^2\left(\frac{\beta}{2} - \frac{1}{12} - \beta\Theta\right) z_{tt}(x_0,t_0) + h^4\left(\frac{\beta^2}{6} - \frac{1}{360} - \frac{\beta^2\Theta}{2} - \frac{\beta\Theta}{12}\right) z_{ttt}(x_0,t_0)$$

with the first term yielding $O(h^2)$ and $O(k)$. If the special choice of

$$\Theta = \frac{1}{2}\left(1 - \frac{1}{6\beta}\right)$$

is made, the coefficient on the z_{tt} term becomes zero. For this optimum choice of β the truncation error becomes $O(h^4)$ and $O(k^2)$. Note that if $\Theta = 0$ this optimum criterion on β reduces to $\beta = \frac{1}{6}$, as given previously for the explicit equation. For further details on this optimum choice of β plus other features of the problem, the reader is referred to the work of Crandell (15). For a discussion of the round-off error problem specifically applied to the parabolic case, see Douglas (21) and Lowan (57).

4.9. On the Convergence and Stability of the Solution of Parabolic and Hyperbolic PDE

It is important to inquire whether or not the particular choice of the parameters β and γ in the previous difference formulations has any influence on the numerical solution. In particular, the influence of these parameters on the convergence of the numerical process (convergence meaning that the solution of the difference equation as h and k go toward zero with β fixed approaches the exact solution of the PDE) and on the stability of the numerical process (stability meaning that errors committed in the numerical solution of the difference equation do not grow exponentially but damp out instead) is of interest.

The importance of the magnitude of β or γ used in a calculation is simple to ascertain. If a particular value of β is chosen for the integration (with the same result holding for γ), it is possible to vary only either h or k independently, but not both together. For a fixed β any attempt to decrease the truncation error by decreasing h implies that k must also be decreased. But since $t = sk$ = real time covered through the sth step in the integration, a small value of k means that a large number of computations are required to obtain a reasonable value of t. It is not unusual to find that these small values of k result in completely excessive computer time. As a result the ideal finite-difference approximation is one in which a large β or γ can be used and which still converges and leads to stable solutions.

The necessary and sufficient conditions for convergence have been developed by Courant et al. (12) by comparing the analytical solution of the PDE with that obtained by the different finite-difference approximations. O'Brien, Hyman, and Kaplan (63) have also carried out equivalent calculations and presented the results in a very clear manner. In summary form the convergence conditions may be listed as:

Parabolic PDE:

Explicit form — Converges as h and $k \to 0$ if and only if

$$\beta = \frac{\alpha k}{h^2} \leq \frac{1}{2} \tag{4.9.1}$$

Implicit form — Converges as h and $k \to 0$ if and only if

$$2\beta \leq \frac{1}{1 - 2\Theta} \qquad \text{for } 0 \leq \Theta \leq \frac{1}{2} \tag{4.9.2}$$

but for all β's if $1 \geq \Theta \geq \frac{1}{2}$

Hyperbolic PDE:

Explicit form — Converges as h and $k \to 0$ if and only if

$$\gamma = \frac{k}{h} \leq 1.0 \tag{4.9.3}$$

Implicit form — Converges always independent of value of γ (4.9.4)

If we consider (4.9.2) and recall that the case of $\Theta = 0$ corresponds to the explicit representation, we can see that convergence is limited to $\beta \leq \frac{1}{2}$ for the explicit formula, whereas convergence occurs for all values of β with the implicit formulas ($\Theta = \frac{1}{2}$ and 1.0). From (4.9.3) and (4.9.4), it is apparent that, for the hyperbolic equation, convergence is limited to $\gamma \leq 1.0$ with the explicit formula but is unlimited when the implicit formula is employed. As a result, the explicit formulations are restrictive in the sense that only certain values of β and γ can be used, while there are no such restrictions with an implicit formulation.

A detailed analysis of stability of the difference representation for PDE was first presented by O'Brien, Hyman, and Kaplan (63) as due to von Neumann. The work of Lax and Richtmeyer (54) and Douglas (19) showed that, under certain conditions, stability is sufficient to imply convergence of the linear difference equations. However, it should be pointed out that in general the questions of stability and convergence are essentially independent. In particular, convergence does not imply stability; i.e., a system which is convergent can be unstable depending on the magnitude of the errors introduced. For perhaps the most lucid discussion of the problems of stability and convergence the reader is referred to the paper of Evans, Brousseau, and Keirstead (30).

Since stability of the various systems is of extreme importance, one case will be detailed here for illustration. Upon defining the error at the x_r, t_s mesh point by $\epsilon_{r,s}$ the explicit difference equation for the parabolic system, (4.7.8), becomes

$$\epsilon_{r,s+1} = \begin{cases} \beta\epsilon_{r+1,s} + (1 - 2\beta)\epsilon_{r,s} + \beta\epsilon_{r-1,s} & \text{inside } R \\ 0 & \text{on boundary} \end{cases} \tag{4.9.5}$$

Since (4.9.5) is a linear partial difference equation, it can be solved by separation of variables. Let

$$\epsilon_{r,s} = u_r v_s$$

which, when substituted into (4.9.5), yields

$$u_r v_{s+1} = \beta u_{r+1} v_s + (1 - 2\beta) u_r v_s + \beta u_{r-1} v_s$$

or

$$\frac{1}{\beta} \frac{v_{s+1} - v_s}{v_s} = \frac{u_{r+1} - 2u_r + u_{r-1}}{u_r}$$

Because the left side is only a function of s and the right side only of r, each side must equal a constant. Calling the constant $-\lambda$ and expanding leads to

$$v_{s+1} - (1 - \beta\lambda) v_s = 0 \tag{4.9.6}$$

$$u_{r+1} - (2 - \lambda) u_r + u_{r-1} = 0 \tag{4.9.7}$$

Equations (4.9.6) and (4.9.7) are simple linear difference equations, of order first and second, respectively. The solution of (4.9.6) is given by

$$v_s = c_1 (1 - \beta\lambda)^s \tag{4.9.8}$$

where c_1 is an arbitrary constant determined by the error on the initial condition of the system (or the error at any starting point in the integration). Equation (4.9.7) must be solved with the conditions that

$$\epsilon_0 = \epsilon_{N+1} = 0$$

implying that the boundary values are known with zero error. Since (4.9.7) holds for $1 \leq r \leq N$, it can be rewritten in the form

$$u_{r+2} - (2 - \lambda) u_{r+1} + u_r = 0$$

for $0 \leq r \leq N - 1$. This equation is of the boundary-value type, and it is desired to find solutions which are not trivial. The solution u_r may be written in the form

$$u_r = A \cos (r\Theta + B)$$

where A and B are arbitrary constants. Using $\epsilon_0 = u_0 = 0$ leads to

$$0 = A \cos B$$

But for nontrivial solutions $A \neq 0$, and thus $\cos B = 0$ or $B = \pi/2$. As a result

$$u_r = A \cos (r\Theta + \pi/2) = -A \sin r\Theta$$

Now, using $= \epsilon_{N+1} = 0$,

$$0 = -A \sin (N + 1)\Theta$$

and because $A \neq 0$, $\sin (N + 1)\Theta = 0$. But since $\sin n\pi = 0$ for every integer n, Θ may be chosen such that

$$\Theta = \frac{n\pi}{N + 1}$$

or

$$\Theta_n = \frac{n\pi}{N + 1} \qquad n = 1, 2, \ldots, N$$

Because A is arbitrary, call $A = -1$, and the result is

$$u_r = \sin \frac{n\pi r}{N + 1} \qquad n = 1, 2, \ldots, N$$

There is, however, a relationship between Θ and λ. In terms of the shift operator E, (4.9.7) may be written

$$[E^2 - (2 - \lambda)E + 1]u_r = 0$$

and there are two roots E_1 and E_2 of the characteristic equation

$$E^2 - (2 - \lambda)E + 1 = 0$$

These roots are given by

$$\tfrac{1}{2}[(2 - \lambda) \pm \sqrt{\lambda(\lambda - 4)}]$$

By some algebraic manipulation it is simple to show that the sum of the roots is $2 - \lambda$ or $2 \cos \Theta$. Thus

$$2 - \lambda = 2 \cos \Theta$$

or

$$\lambda = 2(1 - \cos \Theta)$$

and upon recalling that

$$\frac{1 - \cos \Theta}{2} = \sin^2 \frac{\Theta}{2}$$

(a trigonometric identity) there results

$$\lambda = 4 \sin^2 \frac{\Theta}{2}$$

Finally,

$$\lambda_n = 4 \sin^2 \frac{n\pi}{2(N + 1)} \qquad n = 1, 2, \ldots, N$$

These values of λ_n are the eigenvalues of the original boundary-value problem. If we use this requirement on the λ_n, we see that the solution of (4.9.5), by back substitution, is

$$\epsilon_{r,s} = c_1 \left[1 - 4\beta \sin^2 \frac{n\pi}{2(N + 1)}\right]^s \sin \frac{n\pi r}{N + 1} \qquad n = 1, 2, \ldots, N \tag{4.9.9}$$

The term in brackets raised to the powers is called the stability ratio

$$\rho = 1 - 4\beta \sin^2 \frac{n\pi}{2(N+1)} \qquad \text{explicit form of parabolic PDE}$$

It can be seen that, if $|\rho| > 1.0$, the solution for $\epsilon_{r,s}$ oscillates with greater and greater amplitude as s increases. Since s is directly related to t, the real time, this means that an error committed at any time will propagate itself as the calculation proceeds. If $|\rho| = 1.0$, the error oscillates with constant amplitude, while if $|\rho| < 1.0$, the error damps out as the calculation proceeds. Thus the criteria for stability rests in the inequality $|\rho| \leq 1.0$. However, when this criterion is met, $4\beta \sin^2 [n\pi/2(N+1)] \leq 2.0$ and $\beta \leq \frac{1}{2}$. The stability criterion for the explicit representation of the parabolic PDE is seen to be identical with the convergence criterion, namely, that $\beta \leq \frac{1}{2}$.

In the same manner the stability ratios for the implicit formulas are given by

$$\rho = \frac{1}{1 + 4\beta \sin^2 [n\pi/2(N+1)]} \qquad \text{Laasonen implicit form of parabolic PDE}$$

$$\rho = \frac{2 - 4\beta \sin^2 [n\pi/2(N+1)]}{2 + 4\beta \sin^2 [n\pi/2(N+1)]} \qquad \text{Crank-Nicholson implicit form of parabolic PDE}$$

In these two cases $|\rho| < 1.0$, and the system is nonconditionally stable for all $\beta > 0$. Thus, just as for convergence, the explicit representation is valid only for a restricted range of β (conditionally stable), whereas the implicit representations have no restrictions on β (unconditionally stable).

This type of analysis also can be used to show why the first derivative z_t in the parabolic equation is not replaced with $(z_{r,s+1} - z_{r,s-1})/2h$. When this substitution is made, the explicit finite-difference representation becomes

$$z_{r,s+1} = z_{r,s-1} + 2\beta(z_{r+1,s} - 2z_{r,s} + z_{r-1,s})$$

which is unstable for all β's.

The stability ratios for the corresponding hyperbolic PDE are, by the same process,

$$\rho = 1 - 2\gamma^2 \sin^2 \frac{n\pi}{2(N+1)} + \left[\left(1 - 2\gamma^2 \sin^2 \frac{n\pi}{2(N+1)}\right)^2 - 1\right]^{\frac{1}{2}}$$

explicit form of hyperbolic PDE

$$\rho = \frac{1}{1 + 2\gamma^2 \sin^2 \frac{n\pi}{2(N+1)}} + \left\{\left[\frac{1}{1 + 2\gamma^2 \sin^2 \frac{n\pi}{2(N+1)}}\right]^2 - 1\right\}^{\frac{1}{2}}$$

implicit form of hyperbolic PDE

In the explicit case, $|\rho| \leq 1.0$ only if $\gamma \leq 1.0$, whereas the implicit method is stable for all γ's. Thus the stability and the convergence criteria are also the same for the hyperbolic case.

These stability limits point out the computational importance of the implicit type of formulation. k is not restricted by stability (or convergence), but only by the allowable truncation error. Larger steps in time are possible with the implicit representation than with the corresponding explicit equations. This must, of course, be balanced by the fact that sets of simultaneous equations are solved per s line. The more important factor, however, is the increased time step, as can be shown with an actual computation.

The question of the effect of round-off errors is, as usual in any numerical calculation, very important. Unfortunately, there seems little that can be done with generalizing an estimate of this error, although Mitchell (62) and Douglas (21) have made notable efforts.

The finite-difference representation can be extended directly to the case of more than two independent variables. In the particular case of the parabolic equation in two or more space variables the method of Peaceman and Rachford discussed briefly in Sec. 4.4 is important. In the present context this method uses an alternating-direction implicit representation which is unconditionally stable for all time increments. To illustrate, consider

$$\alpha\left(\frac{\partial^2 z}{\partial x^2} + \frac{\partial^2 x}{\partial y^2}\right) = \frac{\partial z}{\partial t} \tag{4.9.10}$$

with the boundary of the two space variables taken as a square. For simplicity the boundary values of z may be taken as zero and the initial condition as $z(x,y,0) = 1.0$. Upon using the terminology that e is the grid spacing in the y direction as indicated by the subscript g the explicit representation for (4.9.10) is

$$\alpha(z_{xx} + z_{yy}) - z_t = 0 = \alpha\left(\frac{z_{g,r+1,s} - 2z_{g,r,s} + z_{g,r-1,s}}{h^2} + \frac{z_{g+1,r,s} - 2z_{g,r,s} + z_{g-1,r,s}}{e^2}\right) - \frac{z_{g,r,s+1} - z_{g,r,s}}{k}$$

Without showing the resultant difference equation or computation molecule, it suffices here to point out merely that the stability ratio for this explicit scheme yields the conditional stability criteria that $\beta \leq \frac{1}{4}$. Here $\beta = \alpha k/h^2 = \alpha k/e^2$.

An implicit representation can be obtained by replacing z_{xx} and z_{yy} with differences on the $s + 1$ row. While this always leads to stable solutions, the number of simultaneous equations which must be solved at each s row becomes too large, that is, N^2. Another way of looking at this is that one must solve the elliptic problem at each time step. Instead Peaceman and Rachford and also Douglas (20) suggested that one derivative, z_{xx} be evaluated at the $s + 1$ row and the other, z_{yy}, at the s row. This leads to an implicit equation in the x direction. The equations are then rewritten with z_{xx} and z_{yy} reversed to yield an equation implicit in the y direction. By applying the first equation with a fixed time increment and then the second equation with the same time increment (both equations are applied once per time step) only as many simultaneous equations need be solved as in the one space-variable problem. In addition the difference equations are unconditionally stable. The two equations may be written as

$$\alpha\left(\frac{z_{g,r+1,2s+1} - 2z_{g,r,2s+1} + z_{g,r-1,2s+1}}{h^2} + \frac{z_{g+1,r,2s} - 2z_{g,r,2s} + z_{g-1,r,2s}}{e^2}\right) = \frac{z_{g,r,2s+1} - z_{g,r,2s}}{k}$$

and

$$\alpha\left(\frac{z_{g,r+1,2s+1} - 2z_{g,r,2s+1} + z_{g,r-1,2s+1}}{h^2} + \frac{z_{g+1,r,2s+2} - z_{g,r,2s+2} + z_{g-1,r,2s+2}}{e^2}\right) = \frac{z_{g,r,2s+2} - z_{g,r,2s+1}}{k}$$

or, in rearranged form,

$$z_{g,r+1,2s+1} - \left(2 + \frac{1}{\beta}\right) z_{g,r,2s+1} + z_{g,r-1,2s+1} = -z_{g+1,r,2s} + \left(2 - \frac{1}{\beta}\right) z_{g,r,2s} - z_{g-1,r,2s} \tag{4.9.11}$$

$$z_{g+1,r,2s+2} - \left(2 + \frac{1}{\beta}\right) z_{g,r,2s+2} + z_{g-1,r,2s+2} = -z_{g,r+1,2s+1} + \left(2 - \frac{1}{\beta}\right) z_{g,r,2s+1} - z_{g,r-1,2s+1} \tag{4.9.12}$$

[Note that these equations are equivalent to (4.4.4) with the nomenclature difference that $1/\beta = \rho$, $g = r$, $r = s$, and $s = n$. Whereas the time increments were shown as superscripts in (4.4.4), they are shown as subscripts now.] The time steps used in the present case may be thought of as iteration steps in solving Laplace's equation. When the two equations (4.9.11) and (4.9.12) are used to alter a row and then a column, respectively, the stability ratio is given by

$$\rho = \frac{1 - 4\beta \sin^2 [n\pi/2(N + 1)]}{1 + 4\beta \sin^2 [n\pi/2(N + 1)]} \frac{1 - 4\beta \sin^2 [m\pi/2(N + 1)]}{1 + 4\beta \sin^2 [m\pi/2(N + 1)]} \qquad n, m = 1, \ldots, N$$

The absolute value of ρ is always less than 1, and the process is always stable.

In the limit as $t \to \infty$ (or when the number of iterations converges in the elliptic sense) the resulting solution will be equal to the solution of Laplace's equation. In particular the choice of $1/\beta$ as successive values from

$$\frac{1}{\beta_n} = 4 \sin^2 \frac{n\pi}{2(N+1)} \qquad n = 1, \ldots, N$$

leads to the most efficient time steps or convergence rate. The solution of the simultaneous equations at each row or column is once again best performed by the method of Thomas.

4.10. The Method of Characteristics for Hyperbolic PDE

It has already been pointed out that the only class of PDE having two real characteristic curves is the hyperbolic. On this basis it is possible to develop an extremely powerful numerical technique for these PDE. The procedure can be illustrated with two first-order nonlinear PDE

$$A_1 \frac{\partial z_1}{\partial x} + B_1 \frac{\partial z_1}{\partial y} = R_1(z_1,z_2) \tag{4.10.1}$$

$$A_2 \frac{\partial z_2}{\partial x} + B_2 \frac{\partial z_2}{\partial y} = R_2(z_1,z_2) \tag{4.10.2}$$

and with

$$\left.\begin{aligned} z_1 &= z_{10} \\ z_2 &= z_{20} \end{aligned}\right\} \qquad x = 0$$

$$\left.\begin{aligned} z_1 &= z_{100} \\ z_2 &= z_{200} \end{aligned}\right\} \qquad y = 0$$

as boundary conditions. Equations (4.10.1) and (4.10.2) have a form found in many chemical-engineering problems. Since $z_1 = z_1(x,y)$ and $z_2 = z_2(x,y)$, the total differentials are given by

$$dz_1 = \frac{\partial z_1}{\partial x}\, dx + \frac{\partial z_1}{\partial y}\, dy \tag{4.10.3}$$

$$dz_2 = \frac{\partial z_2}{\partial x}\, dx + \frac{\partial z_2}{\partial y}\, dy \tag{4.10.4}$$

Upon writing

$$\frac{\partial z_1}{\partial x} = z_{1x} \qquad \frac{\partial z_2}{\partial x} = z_{2x}$$

$$\frac{\partial z_1}{\partial y} = z_{1y} \qquad \frac{\partial z_2}{\partial y} = z_{2y}$$

(4.10.1) and (4.10.3) become

$$\begin{aligned} A_1 z_{1x} + B_1 z_{1y} &= R_1(z_1,z_2) \\ dx\, z_{1x} + dy\, z_{1y} &= dz_1 \end{aligned} \tag{4.10.5}$$

and (4.10.2) and (4.10.4) become

$$\begin{aligned} A_2 z_{2x} + B_2 z_{2y} &= R_2(z_1,z_2) \\ dx\, z_{2x} + dy\, z_{2y} &= dz_2 \end{aligned} \tag{4.10.6}$$

Equations (4.10.5) and (4.10.6) may be considered as simultaneous equations in the unknowns z_{1x}, z_{1y} and z_{2x}, z_{2y}, respectively. Setting the determinant of the coefficient values equal to zero leads to

$$\begin{vmatrix} A_1 & B_1 \\ dx & dy \end{vmatrix} = 0 = A_1\, dy - B_1\, dx$$

$$\begin{vmatrix} A_2 & B_2 \\ dx & dy \end{vmatrix} = 0 = A_2\, dy - B_2\, dx$$

or

$$\left.\frac{dy}{dx}\right)_{\text{I}} = \frac{B_1}{A_1} \qquad \text{for characteristic curve I} \tag{4.10.7}$$

$$\left.\frac{dy}{dx}\right)_{\text{II}} = \frac{B_2}{A_2} \qquad \text{for characteristic curve II} \tag{4.10.8}$$

Equations (4.10.7) and (4.10.8) define the two characteristic curves marked as I and II, respectively.

Using the characteristic curve I [Eq. (4.10.7)] and substituting into (4.10.3) yields

$$dz_1 = \left(\frac{\partial z_1}{\partial x} + \frac{B_1}{A_1}\frac{\partial z_1}{\partial y}\right) dx$$

and using (4.10.1)

$$\left.\frac{dz_1}{dx}\right)_{\text{I}} = \frac{R_1}{A_1} \tag{4.10.9}$$

where the symbol $dz_1/dx_1)_{\text{I}}$ indicates the derivative of z_1 with respect to x along the characteristic curve I. In the same way, but using (4.10.8), (4.10.4), and (4.10.2),

$$\left.\frac{dz_2}{dx}\right)_{\text{II}} = \frac{R_2}{A_2} \tag{4.10.10}$$

The original PDE system of (4.10.1) and (4.10.2) has now been replaced by the ODE system of (4.10.9) and (4.10.10) holding along the characteristic curves specified by (4.10.7) and (4.10.8). To use the new system, a two-dimensional plane diagram of y versus x is first constructed. On this diagram two family of curves, labeled I and II, are constructed as a result of integrating (4.10.7) and (4.10.8), with initial conditions corresponding to the boundary condition of the original PDE. The two families of curves will cross each other at a number of common mesh points. Equation (4.10.9) can be integrated along the curve I and (4.10.10) along II to calculate z_1 and z_2 at the intersection points. The actual integrations can be performed by the methods developed in Chap. 3. It is obvious that, in terms of numerical computation, a considerable degree of simplification has been achieved when compared with the original PDE.

4.11. Numerical Examples

Example 4.1. The following PDE represents the steady-state heat equation in a square (two dimensions) with an internal-heat-generation term R:

$$k\left(\frac{\partial^2 T}{\partial x^2} + \frac{\partial^2 T}{\partial y^2}\right) + R = 0 \qquad 0 < x < 1.0, 0 < y < 1.0 \tag{4.11.1}$$

R is here taken as a constant independent of x, y, and T. The more general case of $R(x,y,T)$ would not change the approach used. Computationally such a functionality would not change the problem materially. For the choice of parameters $k = 0.10$ and $R = 4.0$ and the boundary conditions

$$\begin{aligned} T &= 300^\circ & x &= 0 \\ T &= 300^\circ & x &= 1 \\ T &= 100^\circ & y &= 0 \\ T &= 100^\circ & y &= 1 \end{aligned} \tag{4.11.2}$$

it is desired to calculate T as a function of x and y. Note that this system is an extension of Laplace's equation (called "Poisson's equation"), and thus the methods discussed for the Dirichlet type of elliptic PDE are appropriate.

Replacing the derivatives in (4.11.1) with the simplest difference representation (4.2.16) and rearranging leads to

$$4T_{r,s} = T_{r+1,s} + T_{r-1,s} + T_{r,s+1} + T_{r,s-1} + \frac{h^2 R}{k}$$

where the domain has been covered with a square mesh of width h. The iteration sequence corresponding to (4.4.3) becomes

$$T_{r,s}^{(n+1)} = T_{r,s}^{(n)} + \alpha(T_{r+1,s}^{(n)} + T_{r-1,s}^{(n+1)} + T_{r,s+1}^{(n)} + T_{r,s-1}^{(n+1)} + K - 4T_{r,s}^{(n)}) \tag{4.11.3}$$

where $K = h^2R/k$ and α is the overrelaxation factor.

Two different-sized meshes were used; $h = 0.05$, and $h = 0.025$. Since the range of both x and y is bounded by 0 and 1.0, this mesh spacing means that there are 19 internal points on any row or column ($N = 19$) for the first case and 39 internal points for the second case. These correspond to having 361 and 1,521 simultaneous equations, respectively. Further, the values of K are 0.1000 and 0.0250 for each case.

The optimum value of α corresponding to Laplace's equation can be obtained for each h by solving

$$\alpha^2 t_m^2 - 4\alpha + 1 = 0$$

for the smallest root, where

$$t_m = 2\cos\frac{\pi}{N+1}$$

For $h = 0.05$, $N = 19$ and $h = 0.025$, $N = 39$ the optimum values are $\alpha = 0.4323635$ and $\alpha = 0.4636403$, respectively. Table 4.1 serves to tabulate all these preliminary results.

In the calculations the iteration cycle was checked for completion by the requirement that

$$|T_{r,s}^{(n+1)} - T_{r,s}^{(n)}| < 5 \times 10^{-4} \tag{4.11.4}$$

hold for all internal points. This essentially means that numerical values for all internal points must become constant to at least six decimal places before convergence (this follows from the numerical magnitude of the temperatures).

TABLE 4.1. OPERATING PARAMETERS FOR STEADY-STATE HEAT-FLOW PROBLEM

Case	h	N	N^2	K	$\alpha_{optimum}$
1	0.050	19	361	0.1000	0.4323635
2	0.025	39	1,521	0.0250	0.4636403

To start all the calculations, the initial temperature distribution shown in Table 4.2 was used. The exterior boundary values correspond to (4.11.2) except at the four corner points, where the average of 300° and 100° was used. All the interior points were given a value of 150°. Note in Table 4.2 that there are only 9 interior columns, rather than the 19 which exist when $h = 0.05$. For ease of tabulation each alternate column has been left out; this arrangement corresponds to including only every fourth column when $h = 0.025$. All the rows are shown, however.

The result of iterating the case $h = 0.05$ and $\alpha_{optimum} = 0.4323635$ to the accuracy given by (4.11.4) is shown in Table 4.3. The symmetry of the results is as expected (the four quadrants are images of each other), and vague temperature patterns can be ascertained. Using this optimum value of α, 56 iterations of (4.11.3) were required to achieve convergence. To indicate the saving in computation time (as given by the number of iterations) obtained by using the overrelaxation with the optimum α, the calculation was repeated with a value of $\alpha = 0.25$. This corresponds to the Liebmann method. Convergence to the same accuracy now required 170 iterations. Thus the overrelaxation has cut the machine time down by a factor of about 3. Since the optimum α was calculated on the basis of Laplace's equation and the equation of interest here is a modified version of this, it was felt advisable to investigate the behavior of the system in the neighborhood of the suggested optimum. Thus a further series of runs were made with different α's. The results are $\alpha = 0.470$, about 100 iterations, $\alpha = 0.455$, about 69 iterations, $\alpha = 0.400$, about 100 iterations, and $\alpha = 0.3745$, about 115 iterations. Thus the value of α chosen for the optimum is close enough to yield the desired result. As a final point it is interesting to note that it is better to choose an α greater rather than less than the optimum. The author's experience tends to confirm this point. With an $h = 0.05$ and $K = 1.0$ (rather than $K = 0.1$) the use of the optimum α required 52 iterations to achieve final conversion.

The calculation using $h = 0.025$ (one-half of that above), $K = 0.1$, and $\alpha_{optimum}$ required 90 iterations to the criteria of (4.11.4). Thus the $1/h$ rule mentioned in the text is a fair approximation. The temperature values obtained now were within 0.1° of those shown in Table 4.3 and thus are probably accurate enough for most use.

These calculations were performed on the IBM 704 in floating-point mode. A single complete iteration for $h = 0.05$ required about 3 to 4 sec. Thus the entire calculation using $\alpha_{optimum}$ took about 2 min of computer time.

Example 4.2. Consider a first-order chemical reaction being carried out under isothermal steady-state conditions in a tubular-flow reactor. On the assumption of

TABLE 4.2. INITIAL TEMPERATURE DISTRIBUTION FOR STEADY-STATE HEAT-FLOW PROBLEM

	$x = 1.0$	$x = 0.90$	$x = 0.80$	$x = 0.70$	$x = 0.60$	$x = 0.50$	$x = 0.40$	$x = 0.30$	$x = 0.20$	$x = 0.10$	$x = 0$
$y = 1.0$	200.0000	100.0000	100.0000	100.0000	100.0000	100.0000	100.0000	100.0000	100.0000	100.0000	200.0000
	300.0000	150.0000	150.0000	150.0000	150.0000	150.0000	150.0000	150.0000	150.0000	150.0000	300.0000
	300.0000	150.0000	150.0000	150.0000	150.0000	150.0000	150.0000	150.0000	150.0000	150.0000	300.0000
	300.0000	150.0000	150.0000	150.0000	150.0000	150.0000	150.0000	150.0000	150.0000	150.0000	300.0000
$y = 0.80$	300.0000	150.0000	150.0000	150.0000	150.0000	150.0000	150.0000	150.0000	150.0000	150.0000	300.0000
	300.0000	150.0000	150.0000	150.0000	150.0000	150.0000	150.0000	150.0000	150.0000	150.0000	300.0000
	300.0000	150.0000	150.0000	150.0000	150.0000	150.0000	150.0000	150.0000	150.0000	150.0000	300.0000
	300.0000	150.0000	150.0000	150.0000	150.0000	150.0000	150.0000	150.0000	150.0000	150.0000	300.0000
	300.0000	150.0000	150.0000	150.0000	150.0000	150.0000	150.0000	150.0000	150.0000	150.0000	300.0000
	300.0000	150.0000	150.0000	150.0000	150.0000	150.0000	150.0000	150.0000	150.0000	150.0000	300.0000
$y = 0.50$	300.0000	150.0000	150.0000	150.0000	150.0000	150.0000	150.0000	150.0000	150.0000	150.0000	300.0000
	300.0000	150.0000	150.0000	150.0000	150.0000	150.0000	150.0000	150.0000	150.0000	150.0000	300.0000
	300.0000	150.0000	150.0000	150.0000	150.0000	150.0000	150.0000	150.0000	150.0000	150.0000	300.0000
	300.0000	150.0000	150.0000	150.0000	150.0000	150.0000	150.0000	150.0000	150.0000	150.0000	300.0000
	300.0000	150.0000	150.0000	150.0000	150.0000	150.0000	150.0000	150.0000	150.0000	150.0000	300.0000
	300.0000	150.0000	150.0000	150.0000	150.0000	150.0000	150.0000	150.0000	150.0000	150.0000	300.0000
$y = 0.20$	300.0000	150.0000	150.0000	150.0000	150.0000	150.0000	150.0000	150.0000	150.0000	150.0000	300.0000
	300.0000	150.0000	150.0000	150.0000	150.0000	150.0000	150.0000	150.0000	150.0000	150.0000	300.0000
	300.0000	150.0000	150.0000	150.0000	150.0000	150.0000	150.0000	150.0000	150.0000	150.0000	300.0000
	300.0000	150.0000	150.0000	150.0000	150.0000	150.0000	150.0000	150.0000	150.0000	150.0000	300.0000
$y = 0.0$	200.0000	100.0000	100.0000	100.0000	100.0000	100.0000	100.0000	100.0000	100.0000	100.0000	200.0000

TABLE 4.3. FINAL TEMPERATURE DISTRIBUTION FOR STEADY-STATE HEAT-FLOW PROBLEM

$h = 0.05,\ \alpha = 0.4323635$

	$x = 1.0$	$x = 0.90$	$x = 0.80$	$x = 0.70$	$x = 0.60$	$x = 0.50$	$x = 0.40$	$x = 0.30$	$x = 0.20$	$x = 0.10$	$x = 0$
$y = 1.0$	200.0000	100.0000	100.0000	100.0000	100.0000	100.0000	100.0000	100.0000	100.0000	100.0000	200.0000
	300.0000	160.7871	132.3852	122.5625	118.4677	117.2968	118.4677	122.5625	132.3852	160.7871	300.0000
	300.0000	200.5200	160.6897	143.6976	136.1318	133.9236	136.1318	143.6976	160.6897	200.5200	300.0000
	300.0000	225.2386	183.5899	162.4968	152.3979	149.3719	152.3979	162.4968	183.5899	225.2386	300.0000
$y = 0.80$	300.0000	240.9754	201.3822	178.5340	166.8370	163.2361	166.8370	178.5340	201.3822	240.9754	300.0000
	300.0000	251.3479	214.8877	191.7297	179.1847	175.2262	179.1847	191.7297	214.8877	251.3479	300.0000
	300.0000	258.3479	224.9254	202.1889	189.3077	185.1577	189.3077	202.1889	224.9254	258.3479	300.0000
	300.0000	263.0693	232.1446	210.0840	197.1601	192.9279	197.1601	210.0840	232.1446	263.0693	300.0000
	300.0000	266.1210	237.0075	215.5860	202.7441	198.4899	202.7441	215.5860	237.0075	266.1210	300.0000
	300.0000	267.8398	239.8141	218.8305	206.0810	201.8283	206.0810	218.8305	239.8141	267.8398	300.0000
$y = 0.50$	300.0000	268.3954	240.7318	219.9024	207.1907	202.9409	207.1907	219.9024	240.7318	268.3954	300.0000
	300.0000	267.8398	239.8141	218.8305	206.0810	201.8283	206.0810	218.8305	239.8141	267.8398	300.0000
	300.0000	266.1210	237.0075	215.5860	202.7441	198.4899	202.7441	215.5860	237.0075	266.1210	300.0000
	300.0000	263.0693	232.1446	210.0840	197.1601	192.9279	197.1601	210.0840	232.1446	263.0693	300.0000
	300.0000	258.3479	224.9254	202.1889	189.3077	185.1577	189.3077	202.1889	224.9254	258.3479	300.0000
	300.0000	251.3479	214.8877	191.7297	179.1847	175.2262	179.1847	191.7297	214.8877	251.3479	300.0000
$y = 0.20$	300.0000	240.9754	201.3822	178.5340	166.8370	163.2361	166.8370	178.5340	201.3822	240.9754	300.0000
	300.0000	225.2386	183.5899	162.4968	152.3979	149.3719	152.3979	162.4968	183.5899	225.2386	300.0000
	300.0000	200.5200	160.6897	143.6976	136.1318	133.9236	136.1318	143.6976	160.6897	200.5200	300.0000
	300.0000	160.7871	132.3852	122.5625	118.4677	117.2968	118.4677	122.5625	132.3852	160.7871	300.0000
$y = 0$	200.0000	100.0000	100.0000	100.0000	100.0000	100.0000	100.0000	100.0000	100.0000	100.0000	200.0000

laminar flow and that negligible axial diffusion exists, the material-balance equation is (7)

$$-v_0\left[1-\left(\frac{r}{R}\right)^2\right]\frac{\partial c}{\partial z}+D\left(\frac{\partial^2 c}{\partial \rho^2}+\frac{1}{\rho}\frac{\partial c}{\partial \rho}\right)-kc=0 \tag{4.11.5}$$

where v_0 = velocity of central stream line
R = tube radius
k = reaction-velocity constant
c = concentration of reactant
D = radial diffusion constant
z = axial distance down tube
ρ = radial distance from center

Upon defining the new variables

$$\lambda=\frac{kz}{v_0} \qquad C=\frac{c}{c_0} \qquad \alpha=\frac{D}{kR^2} \qquad U=\frac{\rho}{R} \tag{4.11.6}$$

(4.11.5) becomes

$$(1-U^2)\frac{\partial C}{\partial \lambda}=\alpha\left(\frac{\partial^2 C}{\partial U^2}+\frac{1}{U}\frac{\partial C}{\partial U}\right)-C \tag{4.11.7}$$

c_0 is the entering concentration of the reactant to the reactor. Equation (4.11.7) is a PDE with two independent variables. These are λ, which involves the reactor length, and U, which involves the reactor radius. The boundary conditions associated with (4.11.7) are

$$\begin{array}{lll} C=1.0 & \lambda=0 & \text{bed entrance} \\ \dfrac{\partial C}{\partial U}=0 & \begin{cases} U=1.0 \\ U=0 \end{cases} & \begin{array}{l}\text{at tube wall} \\ \text{symmetry at centerline}\end{array} \end{array} \tag{4.11.8}$$

expressing the known feed concentration at the reactor inlet, the fact that the reactant cannot pass through the reactor wall and symmetry at the centerline. For a given value of α, $\alpha = 0.1$, it is desired to calculate C as a function of λ and U.

The first step in solving this problem is to determine the class of PDE. Consideration of (4.11.7) shows that $B^2 - 4AC = 0$ in the context of Sec. 4.1 and thus that (4.11.7) is a parabolic PDE. The next step is to replace the PDE with an appropriate difference form; in view of the stability discussion in the text on parabolic equations an implicit formulation seems the best to use. Thus the right-hand side of (4.11.7) is replaced by an average over the $s + 1$ and s row and the left side by an explicit type of difference. In the present nomenclature the radius variable U will be given the subscript designation r and the axial variable λ the subscript designation s.

The following difference representations are then used:

$$\begin{aligned} \frac{\partial^2 C}{\partial U^2} &= \frac{1}{2h^2}[(C_{r+1,s+1}-2C_{r,s+1}+C_{r-1,s+1})+(C_{r+1,s}-2C_{r,s}+C_{r-1,s})] \\ \frac{1}{U}\frac{\partial C}{\partial U} &= \frac{1}{4U_r h}[(C_{r+1,s+1}-C_{r-1,s+1})+(C_{r+1,s}-C_{r-1,s})] \\ C &= \tfrac{1}{2}(C_{r,s+1}+C_{r,s}) \\ (1-U^2)\frac{\partial C}{\partial \lambda} &= (1-U_r^2)\frac{C_{r,s+1}-C_{r,s}}{k} \end{aligned}$$

Substituting these differences into (4.11.7), collecting C_{s+1} terms on one side, and C_s terms on the other, and rearranging leads to

$$A_rC_{r+1,s+1}+B_rC_{r,s+1}+F_rC_{r-1,s+1}=D_r \qquad 1\le r\le N \tag{4.11.9}$$

where
$$A_r = \frac{\alpha}{2h^2} + \frac{\alpha}{4U_r h}$$
$$B_r = -\frac{\alpha}{h^2} - \frac{1 - U_r^2}{k} - \frac{1}{2}$$
$$F_r = \frac{\alpha}{2h^2} - \frac{\alpha}{4U_r h} \tag{4.11.10}$$
$$D_r = C_{r+1,s}\left(-\frac{\alpha}{2h^2} - \frac{\alpha}{4U_r h}\right) + C_{r,s}\left(\frac{\alpha}{h^2} - \frac{1 - U_r^2}{k} + \frac{1}{2}\right) + C_{r-1,s}\left(-\frac{\alpha}{2h^2} + \frac{\alpha}{4U_r h}\right)$$

Equation (4.11.9) involves the values of C in the $s + 1$ column in terms of the coefficients A_r, B_r, F_r, and D_r, with C in the s column entering through D_r. If there are N interior points in the U-direction mesh, (4.11.9) holds in the form given at these N points, $1 \le r \le N$. At $r = 0$, corresponding to the centerline of the reactor, (4.11.9) must be modified to account for the symmetry condition $\partial C/\partial U = 0$. This modification is straightforward and is presented below. Further, the no-flux term must be applied at the wall to complete the specification of the system of difference equations. This, however, can be accomplished in a number of different ways. From the requirement that $\partial C/\partial U = 0$ at $U = 1.0$ the derivative could be approximated by a simple backward-difference formula to yield $C_{N+1,s+1} = C_{N,s+1}$, where $C_{N+1,s+1}$ is the concentration at the tube wall. However, this involves a truncation error which is different from that at the centerline; i.e., at the centerline $C_{-1,s+1} = C_{1,s+1}$ is used with $O(h^2)$. Thus it seems appropriate to extend the U domain one radial position beyond the wall, $r = N + 2$, and apply the method illustrated below. It is important to note here that $C_{0,s+1}$ and $C_{N+1,s+1}$ must be evaluated because of the peculiar boundary conditions in the present problem.

At $r = 0$, $\dfrac{1}{U}\dfrac{\partial C}{\partial U} = \dfrac{0}{0}$, which is an indeterminate value. As shown at the end of Sec. 4.3, this indeterminacy can be removed by using Lhopital's rule to yield the explicit formula

$$\alpha\left(\frac{\partial^2 C}{\partial U^2} + \frac{1}{U}\frac{\partial C}{\partial U}\right)_{U=0} = \frac{4\alpha}{h^2}(C_{1,s} - C_{0,s})$$

A corresponding implicit formula would be

$$\alpha\left(\frac{\partial^2 C}{\partial U^2} + \frac{1}{U}\frac{\partial C}{\partial U}\right)_{U=0} = \frac{2\alpha}{h^2}([C_{1,s+1} - C_{0,s+1}) + (C_{1,s} - C_{0,s})]$$

On this basis (4.11.7) can be converted to

$$\frac{1 - 0^2}{k}(C_{0,s+1} - C_{0,s}) = \frac{2\alpha}{h^2}[(C_{1,s+1} - C_{0,s+1}) + (C_{1,s} - C_{0,s})] - \frac{C_{0,s+1} + C_{0,s}}{2}$$

or, upon rearranging,

$$A_0 C_{1,s+1} + B_0 C_{0,s+1} = D_0 \tag{4.11.11}$$

where
$$A_0 = -\frac{2\alpha}{h^2}$$
$$B_0 = \frac{1}{k} + \frac{2\alpha}{h^2} + \frac{1}{2} \tag{4.11.12}$$
$$D_0 = C_{0,s}\left(\frac{1}{k} - \frac{2\alpha}{h^2} - \frac{1}{2}\right) + C_{1,s}\frac{2\alpha}{h^2}$$

At $r = N + 1$, the tube wall, $U = 1.0$ and $\partial C/\partial U = 0$, and (4.11.7) becomes

$$\alpha \frac{\partial^2 C}{\partial U^2} = C \qquad U = 1.0 \text{ or } r = N + 1 \tag{4.11.13}$$

But since

$$\left.\frac{\partial C}{\partial U}\right|_{\substack{r=N+1\\ s=s+1}} = \frac{C_{N+2,s+1} - C_{N,s+1}}{2h} = 0$$

and

$$C_{N+2,s+1} = C_{N,s+1}$$

it follows that

$$\left.\frac{\partial^2 C}{\partial U^2}\right|_{\substack{r=N+1\\ s=s+1}} = \frac{C_{N+2,s+1} - 2C_{N+1,s+1} + C_{N,s+1}}{h^2} = \frac{2}{h^2}(C_{N,s+1} - C_{N+1,s+1})$$

Upon substituting into (4.11.13) with $C = C_{N+1,s+1}$ there finally results

$$C_{N,s+1} + B_{N+1}C_{N+1,s+1} = 0 \tag{4.11.14}$$

with

$$B_{N+1} = -\left(1 + \frac{h^2}{2\alpha}\right) \tag{4.11.15}$$

Equations (4.11.9), (4.11.11), and (4.11.14) constitute a set of $N + 2$ simultaneous algebraic equations with $N + 2$ unknowns. By using the known feed condition to the reactor, $C = 1.0$ at $\lambda = 0$, this set of equations can be solved to yield $C_{0,1}$, $C_{1,1}$, . . . , $C_{N,1}$, $C_{N+1,1}$; these values in turn are used to calculate $C_{0,2}$, $C_{1,2}$, . . . , $C_{N,2}$, $C_{N+1,2}$, etc.

In the nomenclature of Chap. 5 the system of simultaneous equations has a tri-diagonal coefficient matrix and can be solved by the method of Thomas. The parameters chosen were $h = 0.05$ and $k = 0.05$; this value of h means that $N = 19$, and thus 21 simultaneous equations must be handled at each step forward in the axial direction. Without presenting the details of the Thomas method it need be stated merely that the following equations are used,

$$C_{20} = g_{20}$$
$$C_r = g_r - b_r C_{r+1} \qquad 0 \le r \le 19 \tag{4.11.16}$$

where

$$b_0 = \frac{A_0}{B_0}$$
$$b_r = \frac{A_r}{B_r - F_r b_{r-1}} \qquad 1 \le r \le 19$$
$$g_0 = \frac{D_0}{B_0}$$
$$g_r = \frac{D_r - F_r g_{r-1}}{B_r - F_r b_{r-1}} \qquad 1 \le r \le 20$$

The b's and g's are calculated in the order of increasing r and the C's then calculated in the order of decreasing r.

Table 4.4 presents some of the results of this calculation for a selected set of values of λ. At $\lambda = 2.40$ it can be seen that the gradients have almost disappeared. Note that the slopes always approach zero at the centerline and the tube wall. Table 4.5 presents the values of A_r, B_r, and F_r for $\lambda = 0.05$.

These calculations were performed on the IBM 650 by use of the Bell I floating-point interpretive mode. Approximately 40 min was required, including output, to reach $\lambda = 2.40$.

TABLE 4.4. RADIAL CONCENTRATION PROFILES AT VARIOUS AXIAL POSITIONS

C	$\lambda = 0.05$	$\lambda = 0.50$	$\lambda = 1.0$	$\lambda = 2.40$
C_0	0.950727	0.558061	0.259874	0.025094
	0.950601	0.556710	0.258872	0.024986
	0.950219	0.552648	0.255888	0.024668
	0.949568	0.545856	0.250999	0.024147
	0.948624	0.536312	0.244326	0.023441
C_5	0.947351	0.524018	0.236037	0.022570
	0.945697	0.509019	0.226342	0.021561
	0.943584	0.491430	0.215483	0.020442
	0.940898	0.471462	0.203734	0.019244
	0.937472	0.449430	0.191386	0.017998
C_{10}	0.933052	0.425767	0.178742	0.016737
	0.927257	0.401014	0.166106	0.015491
	0.919521	0.375800	0.153776	0.014288
	0.909027	0.350814	0.142037	0.013155
	0.894676	0.326803	0.131148	0.012114
C_{15}	0.875186	0.304564	0.121381	0.011185
	0.849476	0.284782	0.112891	0.010386
	0.817613	0.267832	0.105944	0.009740
	0.782547	0.254650	0.100465	0.009239
	0.752537	0.248006	0.097622	0.008954
C_{20}	0.743246	0.244944	0.096416	0.008843

Example 4.3. A problem of practical importance is the evaluation of the transient behavior of multicomponent ion-exchange columns. With the assumptions that isothermal operation exists, the fluid is in plug flow, and negligible axial diffusion exists a material balance on a small elemental section of the ion-exchange bed leads to (26)

$$\frac{\partial x_i}{\partial z} + \frac{\epsilon}{L}\frac{\partial x_i}{\partial \theta} + \frac{\rho Q}{LC_0}\frac{\partial y_i}{\partial \theta} = 0 \qquad i = 1, 2, 3, \ldots, n \tag{4.11.17}$$

where x_i = equivalent fraction of ion i in solution = $x(z,\theta)$

y_i = equivalent fraction of ion i on ion-exchange resin = $y(z,\theta)$

θ = time of operation

z = axial distance in bed measured from top down

ϵ = void fraction of packed bed

L = solution-flow rate

ρ = packing density of ion-exchange resin

Q = total resin capacity

C_0 = total solution concentration in feed to column inlet

The three terms in (4.11.17) represent the concentration at any point or cross section in the bed caused by solution flow through that point, liquid holdup in the voids at that point, and exchange with the resin phase at the same point.

TABLE 4.5. VALUES OF A_r, B_r, AND F_r FOR THE AXIAL POSITION $\lambda = 0.05$

Subscript r	A_r	B_r	F_r
0	80.0000	−100.50	
	30.0000	−60.45	10.00
	25.0000	−60.30	15.00
	23.3333	−60.05	16.6666
	22.5000	−59.70	17.50
5	22.0000	−59.25	18.00
	21.6666	−58.70	18.3333
	21.4286	−58.05	18.5714
	21.2500	−57.30	18.75
	21.1111	−56.45	18.8888
10	21.0000	−55.50	19.0000
	20.9090	−54.45	19.0909
	20.8333	−53.30	19.1666
	20.7692	−52.05	19.2308
	20.7143	−50.70	19.2857
15	20.6666	−49.25	19.3333
	20.6250	−47.70	19.3750
	20.5882	−46.05	19.4118
	20.5555	−44.30	19.4444
	20.5263	−42.45	19.4737
20	....	−1.0125	1.0000

Since (4.11.17) has two dependent variables x_i and y_i, it is necessary further to specify another equation relating these quantities. It is convenient to write this second equation in the form

$$\frac{\partial y_i}{\partial \theta} = R_i \qquad i = 1, 2, 3, \ldots, n \tag{4.11.18}$$

where R_i is a rate expression determined by the diffusional and chemical rate steps existing between the solution and the resin. R_i involves both x_i and y_i in a nonlinear way and couples (4.11.17) and (4.11.18) together.

Because of over-all material-balance considerations (C_0 must be maintained constant), it is necessary to write equations for only $n - 1$ of the n components present; for the specific case of $n = 3$ (a ternary system) (4.11.17) and (4.11.18) may be written explicitly as

$$\frac{\partial x_A}{\partial z} + \frac{\epsilon}{L}\frac{\partial x_A}{\partial \theta} + \frac{\rho Q}{LC_0}\frac{\partial y_A}{\partial \theta} = 0 \tag{4.11.19}$$

$$\frac{\partial x_B}{\partial z} + \frac{\epsilon}{L}\frac{\partial x_B}{\partial \theta} + \frac{\rho Q}{LC_0}\frac{\partial y_B}{\partial \theta} = 0 \tag{4.11.20}$$

$$\frac{\partial y_A}{\partial \theta} = R_A \tag{4.11.21}$$

$$\frac{\partial y_B}{\partial \theta} = R_B \tag{4.11.22}$$

The subscripts A and B are used to indicate two components in the ternary mixture.

The proper boundary and initial conditions must be added to complete the description of this system. If the entering solution is maintained constant for $\theta > 0$,

$$\left.\begin{aligned} x_A &= x_{A0} \\ x_B &= x_{B0} \end{aligned}\right\} \qquad z = 0,\ \theta > 0 \tag{4.11.23}$$

Also, no change in solution or resin concentrations will occur at any point in the bed until the entering solution has had time to flow down to that point. This condition can be expressed as

$$\begin{aligned} &\left.\begin{aligned} y_A &= y_{A0} \\ y_B &= y_{B0} \end{aligned}\right\} \qquad \theta \leq \frac{\epsilon}{L} z,\ z > 0 \\ &x_A = x_B = x_C = 0 \qquad \theta \leq \frac{\epsilon}{L} z,\ z > 0 \end{aligned} \tag{4.11.24}$$

where the bed initially has been assumed to have zero liquid concentrations. The system of Eqs. (4.11.19) to (4.11.24) completely defines the transient behavior of the ternary fixed-bed exchange column. Solution of this system will yield concentrations of any ion in either phase for any z or θ. As one final point the rate expressions R_A and R_B are here taken to have the explicit form

$$R_A = C_0(-k_f^{(1)} x_B y_A + k_b^{(1)} x_A y_B - k_f^{(2)} y_A x_C + k_b^{(2)} x_A y_C) \tag{4.11.25}$$
$$R_B = C_0(k_f^{(1)} x_B y_A - k_b^{(1)} x_A y_B - k_f^{(3)} x_C y_B + k_b^{(3)} x_B y_C) \tag{4.11.26}$$

where $k_f^{(1)}$, $k_b^{(1)}$, . . . are appropriate constants.

The system can be simplified by defining the new variables

$$s = \frac{\epsilon}{L} z \qquad t = \theta - \frac{\epsilon}{L} z \tag{4.11.27}$$

These transform (4.11.19) to (4.11.24) to

$$\frac{\partial x_A}{\partial s} + \frac{\rho Q}{\epsilon C_0} \frac{\partial y_A}{\partial t} = 0 \tag{4.11.28}$$
$$\frac{\partial x_B}{\partial s} + \frac{\rho Q}{\epsilon C_0} \frac{\partial y_B}{\partial t} = 0 \tag{4.11.29}$$
$$\frac{\partial y_A}{\partial t} = R_A \tag{4.11.30}$$
$$\frac{\partial y_B}{\partial t} = R_B \tag{4.11.31}$$
$$\left.\begin{aligned} x_A &= x_{A0} \\ x_B &= x_{B0} \end{aligned}\right\} \qquad s = 0 \tag{4.11.32}$$
$$\left.\begin{aligned} y_A &= y_{A0} \\ y_B &= y_{B0} \end{aligned}\right\} \qquad t = 0,\ s > 0 \tag{4.11.33}$$
$$a_A = x_B = x_C = 0 \qquad t = 0,\ s > 0 \tag{4.11.34}$$

The system of interest, (4.11.28) to (4.11.34), having been suitably defined, the question immediately arises as to the means of solving this set of coupled nonlinear

PDE. It will be left for the reader to show that the PDE equations are hyperbolic; with this result as a basis, it is possible to postulate a way of replacing derivatives with finite differences and also to use the method of characteristics. Figure 4.7 is used to aid in detailing the two approaches. The upper part of this diagram shows the mesh layout for the finite-difference approach and the lower part the analogous arrangement for the method of characteristics. The subscript r is used for the distance variable and w for the t variable. A spacing of h and k is used for the s and t directions, respec-

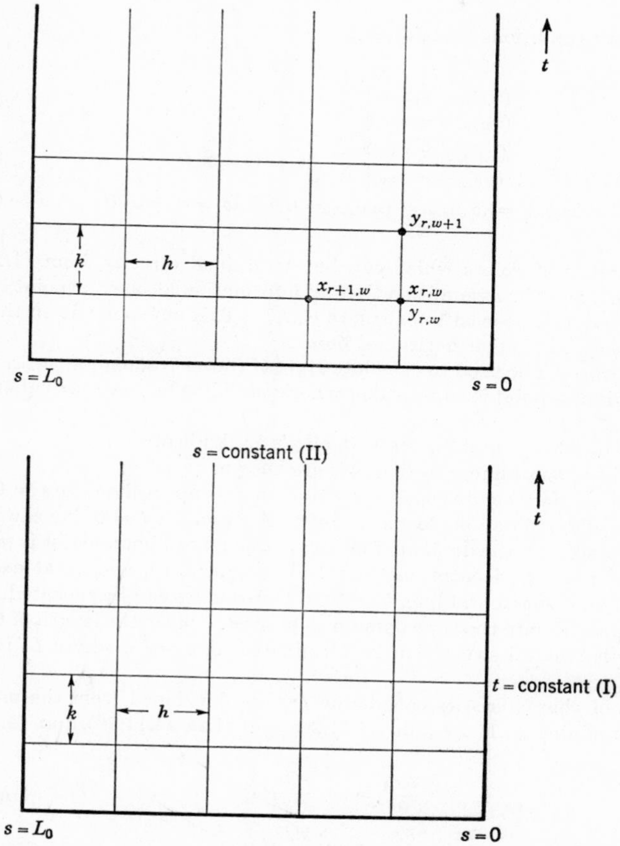

FIG. 4.7. Mesh diagrams for two methods of solving the system (4.11.28) to (4.11.34).

tively. The finite-difference representation can be obtained by replacing the first derivatives in the normal way,

$$\frac{\partial x_{r,w}}{\partial s} = \frac{x_{r+1,w} - x_{r,w}}{h}$$

$$\frac{\partial y_{r,w}}{\partial t} = \frac{y_{r,w+1} - y_{r,w}}{k}$$

Substituting into (4.11.28) to (4.11.31) yields

$$(x_A)_{r+1,w} = (x_A)_{r,w} + \frac{\rho Q}{\epsilon C_0}\frac{h}{k}[(y_A)_{r,w} - (y_A)_{r,w+1}] \tag{4.11.35}$$

$$(y_A)_{r,w+1} = (y_A)_{r,w} + k(R_A)_{r,w} \tag{4.11.36}$$

$$(x_B)_{r+1,w} = (x_B)_{r,w} + \frac{\rho Q}{\epsilon C_0}\frac{h}{k}[(y_B)_{r,w} - (y_B)_{r,w+1}] \tag{4.11.37}$$

$$(y_B)_{r,w+1} = (y_B)_{r,w} + k(R_B)_{r,w} \tag{4.11.38}$$

with the boundary conditions transformed to

$$\left.\begin{aligned}(x_A)_{0,w} &= x_{A0}\\ (x_B)_{0,w} &= x_{B0}\end{aligned}\right\} \qquad r = 0 \tag{4.11.39}$$

$$\left.\begin{aligned}(y_A)_{r,0} &= y_{A0}\\ (y_B)_{r,0} &= y_{B0}\end{aligned}\right\} \qquad w = 0,\ r > 0 \tag{4.11.40}$$

$$(x_A)_{r,0} = (x_B)_{r,0} = (x_C)_{r,0} = 0 \qquad w = 0,\ r > 0 \tag{4.11.41}$$

There are a number of points which can be ascertained directly from (4.11.35) to (4.11.41), Fig. 4.7, and the assumption that all information at one r, w point is known:

1. Any point $y_{r,w}$ can be used to calculate $y_{r,w+1}$. This new point is on the same r vertical line but on one higher horizontal line.
2. Any point $x_{r,w}$ can be used to calculate $x_{r+1,w}$ if the corresponding $y_{r,w+1}$ has been calculated. This new point is on the same w horizontal line but on one further vertical line.
3. On the bottom horizontal line, $w = 0$, all y's are known.
4. On the right vertical line, $r = 0$, all x's are known.

By using the boundary conditions it is possible to pass upward on the $s = 0$ vertical line to calculate all y's; in an analogous fashion all x's on the $t = 0$ line can be calculated. The two sides of the domain of interest having been bounded, it is possible to sweep along the $t = k$ horizontal line to calculate x_A, x_B, y_A, and y_B at each point. Upon moving up one horizontal line, $t = 2k$, the procedure can be repeated. This in turn is repeated as far into the time domain as desired. Since the length of the bed is finite, any one horizontal sweep can be terminated at $s = L_0$, where L_0 is the bed length.

The method of characteristics calculation can be developed from the material in Sec. 4.10. Combining (4.11.28) and (4.11.29) and then (4.11.30) and (4.11.31) to form

$$\frac{\partial x_A}{\partial s} = -\frac{\rho Q}{\epsilon C_0} R_A \tag{4.11.42}$$

$$\frac{\partial x_B}{\partial s} = -\frac{\rho Q}{\epsilon C_0} R_B \tag{4.11.43}$$

shows that these are equivalent to (4.10.1) and (4.10.2) with

$$B_1 = B_2 = 0$$

$$-\frac{\rho Q}{\epsilon C_0} R_A = \frac{R_1}{A_1}$$

$$-\frac{\rho Q}{\epsilon C_0} R_B = \frac{R_2}{A_2}$$

Thus from (4.10.7) and (4.10.8) the characteristic curves are given by

$$\left.\frac{dt}{ds}\right|_{\mathrm{I}} = \frac{B_1}{A_1} = 0 \qquad \text{or} \qquad t = \text{constant} \tag{4.11.44}$$

$$\left.\frac{dt}{ds}\right|_{\mathrm{II}} = \frac{B_2}{A_2} = 0 \qquad \text{or} \qquad s = \text{constant} \tag{4.11.45}$$

and in a way analogous to that in which (4.10.9) and (4.10.10) are obtained there results

$$\left.\frac{dx_A}{ds}\right|_{\mathrm{I}} = -\frac{\rho Q}{\epsilon C_0} R_A \tag{4.11.46}$$

$$\left.\frac{dx_B}{ds}\right|_{\mathrm{I}} = -\frac{\rho Q}{\epsilon C_0} R_B \tag{4.11.47}$$

$$\left.\frac{dy_A}{dt}\right|_{\mathrm{II}} = R_A \tag{4.11.48}$$

$$\left.\frac{dy_B}{dt}\right|_{\mathrm{II}} = R_B \tag{4.11.49}$$

The boundary and initial conditions are still as given in (4.11.32) to (4.11.34).

Figure 4.7 illustrates the domain used for solution. Horizontal lines (t = constant) represent the characteristics I and vertical lines (s = constant) represent the characteristics II. However, the actual mechanics of computation do not require discussion since a comparison between (4.11.35) to (4.11.38) and (4.11.46) to (4.11.49) indicates that the systems are quite similar. The method of characteristics integrates a set of ODE, while the finite-difference approach uses difference equations. Actually (4.11.35) to (4.11.38) are merely a particular form of (4.11.46) to (4.11.49) in which the derivatives are replaced with the lowest-order difference form. On this basis it would be expected that, if the Runge-Kutta-Gill method (or an analogous one) is used in the method of characteristics, it will be more accurate than the finite-difference approach, which, in effect, uses Euler's method. The computation time is, of course, in the reverse order.

The physical system chosen for analysis was the ternary system of H^+-Ag^+-Na^+ with Dowex-50 resin. The constants used (26) are listed below:

$$\begin{aligned}
L_0 &= 0.50 \text{ unit in } s \\
Q &= 5.1 \text{ meq/g dry resin} \\
C_0 &= 0.10 \text{ meq/ml} \\
L &= 1.0 \text{ ml/(sec)(cm}^2) \\
\rho &= 0.35 \text{ g/ml} \\
\epsilon &= 0.42 \\
k_f^{(1)} &= 1.8 \qquad & k_b^{(1)} &= 0.20 \\
k_f^{(2)} &= 1.124 \qquad & k_b^{(2)} &= 0.40 \\
k_f^{(3)} &= 3.20 \qquad & k_b^{(3)} &= 1.0
\end{aligned}$$

The resin is assumed to have initially a concentration of $y_{H^+} = 1.0$ and the feed taken to consist of $x_{Ag^+} = x_{Na^+} = 0.50$.

The method of finite differences and the method of characteristics were both run with $h = 0.01$ and $k = 0.5$ and with $h = 0.10$ and $k = 1.0$. The calculations were stopped on any horizontal row at $s = 0.5$ and $t = 20$. Table 4.6 shows a selected portion of the data for $h = 0.01$ and $k = 0.5$, both methods being used; the effluent concentration of H^+ ions, $\left.x_{H^+}\right|_{s=0.50}$, is tabulated versus t. For this size of increments both computational techniques yield values which are in close agreement. When the increments are increased to $h = 0.10$ and $k = 1.0$, however, the method of characteristics still agrees with the results obtained by using the fine mesh; the finite-difference method does not. This disparity was expected, as indicated above.

TABLE 4.6. EFFLUENT H^+ CONCENTRATION FROM ION-EXCHANGE COLUMN
$h = 0.01$ and $k = 0.5$

t	x_{H^+} at $s = 0.50$	
	Method of characteristics	Finite differences
1.0	0.9397	0.9407
2.0	0.9319	0.9331
3.0	0.9232	0.9242
5.0	0.9020	0.9032
7.0	0.8757	0.8765
10.0	0.8243	0.8237
12.0	0.7810	0.7788
15.0	0.7020	0.6958
17.0	0.6405	0.6310
20.0	0.5391	0.5241

These calculations were performed on the IBM 650 in the Bell I interpretive floating-point mode. The data given below indicate the computation times for each method:

	Computing time, hr $h = 0.01$, $k = 0.50$	Computing time, min $h = 0.10$, $k = 1.0$
Finite differences	1.9	6
Method of characteristics	11.9	50

Even though the finite difference approach is six to eight times faster than the method of characteristics for an equivalent h and k spacing, the latter method is actually the best because of its higher accuracy. This allows the use of much larger grid increments, which cut the computing time below that required by the finite differencing.

BIBLIOGRAPHY

1. Arms, L. J., L. D. Gates, and B. Zondek: *J. SIAM*, **4**: 220 (1956).
2. Bauer, W. F.: *J. SIAM*, **6**: 438 (1958).
3. Birkhoff, G., and R. S. Varga: *Trans. Am. Math. Soc.*, **92**: 13 (1959).
4. Blair, A., N. Metropolis, J. Von Neumann, A. H. Taub, and M. Tsingou: *Math. Tables Aids Comput.*, **13**: 145 (1959).
5. Blanch, G.: *J. Research Natl. Bur. Standards*, **50**: 343 (1953).

6. Bruce, G. H., D. W. Peaceman, H. H. Rachford, and J. D. Rice: *Trans. AIME*, **198**: 79 (1953).
7. Cleland, F. A., and R. H. Wilhelm: *J. AIChE*, **2**: 489 (1956).
8. Coats, K. H., M. R. Tek, and D. L. Katz: Unsteady State Liquid Flow through Porous Media Having Elliptic Boundaries, presented at AIChE meeting, Kansas City, 1959.
9. Conte, S. D.: *J. Assoc. Comput. Mach.*, **4**: 18 (1957).
10. Conte, S. D., and R. T. Dames: *Math. Tables Aids Comput.*, **12**: 198 (1958).
11. Cornock, A. F.: *Proc. Cambridge Phil. Soc.*, **50**: 524 (1954).
12. Courant, R., K. Friedrichs, and H. Lewy: *Math. Ann.*, **100**: 32 (1928).
13. Crandell, S. H.: *J. Assoc. Comput. Mach.*, **1**: 111 (1954).
14. Crandell, S. H.: *J. Assoc. Comput. Mach.*, **2**: 42 (1955).
15. Crandell, S. H.: *Quart. Appl. Math.*, **13**: 318 (1955).
16. Crandell, S. H.: *J. Assoc. Comput. Mach.*, **4**: 467 (1957).
17. Crank, J., and P. Nicholson: *Proc. Cambridge Phil. Soc.*, **43**: 50 (1947).
18. Douglas, J., Jr.: *J. SIAM*, **3**: 42 (1955).
19. Douglas, J., Jr.: *J. SIAM*, **4**: 20 (1956).
20. Douglas, J., Jr.: *Pacific J. Math.*, **6**: 35 (1956).
21. Douglas, J., Jr.: *J. Assoc. Comput. Mach.*, **6**: 48 (1959).
22. Douglas, J., Jr.: *J. Math. Phys.*, **38**: 150 (1959).
23. Douglas, J., Jr., and T. M. Gallie, Jr.: *Proc. Am. Math. Soc.*, **6**: 787 (1955).
24. Douglas, J., Jr., and D. W. Peaceman: *J. AIChE*, **1**: 505 (1955).
25. Douglas, J., Jr., and H. H. Rachford, Jr.: *Trans. Am. Math. Soc.*, **82**: 421 (1956)
26. Dranoff, J. S., and L. Lapidus: *Ind. Eng. Chem.*, **50**: 1648 (1958).
27. Du Fort, E. C., and S. P. Frankel: *Math. Tables Aids Comput.*, **7**: 135 (1953).
28. Ehrlich, L. W.: *J. Assoc. Comput. Mach.*, **6**: 204 (1959).
29. Esch, R. E.: *J. Assoc. Comput. Mach.*, **7**: 163 (1960).
30. Evans, G. W., R. Brousseau, and R. Keirstead: *J. Math. Phys.*, **34**: 267 (1956).
31. Forsythe, G. E.: *Communs. Pure Appl. Math.*, **9**: 425 (1956).
32. Frank, W. L.: *Thompson Ramo-Wooldridge Tech. Note* 2, 1959.
33. Frankel, S.: *Math. Tables Aids Comput.*, **4**: 65 (1950).
34. Franklin, J. N.: *J. Math. Phys.*, **37**: 305 (1959).
35. Friedmann, N. E.: *J. Math. Phys.*, **35**: 299 (1955).
36. Friedmann, N. E.: *Trans. ASME*, **80**: 635 (1958).
37. Garabedian, P. R.: *Math. Tables Aids Comput.*, **10**: 183 (1956).
38. Gee, R. E., and J. B. Lyon: *Ind. Eng. Chem.*, **49**: 956 (1957).
39. Greenspan, D.: *J. Franklin Inst.*, **263**: 425 (1957).
40. Greenspan, D.: *J. Franklin Inst.*, **264**: 453 (1957).
41. Greenspan, D.: *Math. Tables Aids Comput.*, **11**: 150 (1957).
42. Greenspan, D.: *J. Franklin Inst.*, **266**: 39 (1958).
43. Greenspan, D.: *J. Franklin Inst.*, **268**: 46 (1959).
44. Greenspan, D.: *Quart. J. Mech. Appl. Math.*, **12**: 111 (1959).
45. Greenstadt, J.: *IBM J.*, **3**: 355 (1959).
46. Heller, J.: *J. SIAM*, **8**: 150 (1960).
47. Hildebrand, F. B.: *J. Math. Phys.*, **31**: 35 (1952).
48. John, F.: *Communs. Pure Appl. Math.*, **5**: 155 (1952).
49. Juncosa, M. L., and T. W. Mullikin: *J. Assoc. Comput. Mach.*, **7**: 29 (1960).
50. Juncosa, M. L., and D. Young: *Proc. Am. Math. Soc.*, **5**: 168 (1954).
51. Keller, H. B.: *Quart. Appl. Math.*, **16**: 209 (1958).
52. King, G. W.: *Ind. Eng. Chem.*, **43**: 2475 (1951).
53. Laasonen, P.: *J. Assoc. Comput. Mach.*, **5**: 32 (1958).
54. Lax, P. D., and R. D. Richtmeyer: *Communs. Pure Appl. Math.*, **9**: 267 (1956).

55. Levine, C. A., and A. Opler: *Chem. Eng.*, January, 1956.
56. Lotkin, M.: *J. Math. Phys.*, **37**: 178 (1958).
57. Lowan, A. N.: *Math. Comput.*, **14**: 139, 223, 266 (1960).
58. Milnes, H. W., and T. Chow: *J. Assoc. Comput. Mach.*, **7**: 37 (1960).
59. Milnes, H. W., and R. B. Potts: *J. Assoc. Comput. Mach.*, **6**: 226 (1959).
60. Mitchell, A. R.: *Appl. Sci. Research A*, **4**: 109 (1953).
61. Mitchell, A. R.: *Appl. Sci. Research B*, **3**: 456 (1954).
62. Mitchell, A. R.: *Quart. J. Mech. Appl. Math.*, **9**: 111 (1956).
63. O'Brien, G. G., M. A. Hyman, and S. Kaplan: *J. Math. Phys.*, **29**: 223 (1951).
64. Opler, A.: *Ind. Eng. Chem.*, **45**: 2621 (1953).
65. Opler, A., and N. K. Hiester: "Tables for Predicting the Performance of Fixed Bed Processes," Stanford Research Institute, 1954.
66. Ostrowski, A.: *Math. Tables Aids Comput.*, **7**: 152 (1953).
67. Peaceman, D. W., and H. H. Rachford: *J. SIAM*, **3**: 28 (1955).
68. Philip, J. R.: *Trans. Faraday Soc.*, **51**: 885 (1955).
69. Pollock, A. W., M. F. Brown, and C. W. Dempsey: *Ind. Eng. Chem.*, **50**: 725 (1958).
70. Radd, M. E., and M. R. Tek: *J. AIChE*, **5**: 111 (1959).
71. Rose, A., R. J. Lombardo, and T. J. Williams: *Ind. Eng. Chem.*, **43**: 2454 (1951).
72. Rose, A., R. F. Sweeny, and V. N. Schrodt: *Ind. Eng. Chem.*, **50**: 737 (1958).
73. Rose, M.: *Math. Comput.*, **14**: 240 (1960).
74. Rose, M. E.: *Quart. Appl. Math.*, **14**: 237 (1956).
75. Rosen, J. B.: *Ind. Eng. Chem.*, **46**: 387 (1952).
76. Rosen, J. B.: *J. Chem. Phys.*, **22**: 733, 743 (1954).
77. Schechter, R. S., and T. L. Kang: *Ind. Eng. Chem.*, **51**: 1373 (1959).
78. Schneider, P. J.: *J. Appl. Phys.*, **24**: 27 (1953).
79. Sheldon, J. W.: *Math. Tables Aids Comput.*, **9**: 101 (1955).
80. Stark, R. H.: *J. Assoc. Comput. Mach.*, **3**: 29 (1956).
81. Strang, W. G.: *J. Math. Phys.*, **38**: 141 (1959).
82. Sugai, I.: *IBM J.*, **3**: 187 (1959).
83. Thomsen, J. S.: *J. AIChE*, **5**: 268 (1959).
84. Tien, C., and G. Thodos: *J. AIChE*, **5**: 373 (1959).
85. Todd, J.: *Communs. Pure Appl. Math.*, **9**: 597 (1956).
86. Trench, W. F.: *J. SIAM*, **7**: 184 (1959).
87. Varga, R. S.: *J. SIAM*, **5**: 39 (1957).
88. Varga, R. S.: *Pacific J. Math.*, **9**: 617 (1959).
89. Varga, R. S.: Remarks on Peaceman-Rachford Iteration, *Rept.* WAPD-TM-139, 1958, Overrelaxation Applied to Implicit Alternating Direction Methods, *Rept.* WAPT-T-1014, 1959, from Bettis Plant, Westinghouse Electric Corp., Pittsburgh, Pa.
90. Walsh, J. L., and D. Young: *J. Math. Phys.*, **33**: 80 (1954).
91. Wasow, W.: *J. Research Natl. Bur. Standards*, **48**: 345 (1952).
92. Young, D.: *Trans. Am. Math. Soc.*, **76**: 92 (1954).

CHAPTER 5

SYSTEMS OF LINEAR ALGEBRAIC EQUATIONS

Various methods for solving systems of linear algebraic equations are discussed in the present chapter. Implicit in much of the discussion is the assumption that five or more simultaneous equations are involved. For systems in this size, machine computation becomes mandatory.

There are a number of important chemical-engineering areas which involve, in one form or another, linear algebraic equations. Some of these may be listed as follows:

1. Material balances around N stages of any general staged operation lead to N linear or nonlinear equations. If steady state is assumed, the equations are algebraic; if transient conditions are involved, the equations are differential in form.
2. In the same sense as (1) multicomponent systems even for one stage lead to similar types of equations.
3. The solution of complex boundary value or two-point ordinary differential equations usually is carried out by solving sets of simultaneous finite-difference equations (see Chap. 3). Fixed-bed problems are often of this type.
4. The solution of partial differential equations by finite-difference techniques usually leads to systems of linear or nonlinear equations (see Chap. 4).
5. Optimization of complex chemical assemblies such as refinery units involves the handling of large sets of simultaneous equations when a technique like linear programming is used (see Chap. 8).
6. Linear-regression techniques in statistical analysis often require the solution of sets of linear algebraic equations.

In discussing the methods and means of solving these problems (and others) it is preferable to use the shorthand nomenclature of matrices. Thus the development of this nomenclature is the first item of the present chapter.

5.1. Matrix Notation and Operations

A matrix is a rectangular array of numbers. The matrix **A** is written as

$$\mathbf{A} = \begin{bmatrix} a_{11} & a_{12} & \cdots & a_{1n} \\ a_{21} & a_{22} & \cdots & a_{2n} \\ \cdots & \cdots & \cdots & \cdots \\ a_{m1} & a_{m2} & \cdots & a_{mn} \end{bmatrix} \tag{5.1.1}$$

As shown, the matrix has m rows and n columns and is called an $m \times n$ matrix. Each element of the matrix **A** is located at the "intersection" of a row and a column. The elements of **A** are denoted by a_{ij}, with the first subscript referring to the row and the second to the column in which the element is located. The matrix elements are shown enclosed in brackets, **A** given in boldface to distinguish it from the scalar A. Two matrices are equal if and only if all the corresponding elements of the two matrices are identical.

A matrix which contains only a single column and m rows is called a column vector and is shown as

$$\mathbf{x} = \begin{bmatrix} x_1 \\ x_2 \\ \cdot \\ \cdot \\ \cdot \\ x_m \end{bmatrix} \tag{5.1.2}$$

In the same way a matrix which contains only a single row and n columns is called a row vector and shown as

$$\mathbf{y} = [y_1 \quad y_2 \quad \cdots \quad y_n] \tag{5.1.3}$$

The transpose of a matrix **A** is indicated by $\mathbf{A}^T$ and results from a complete interchange of the rows and columns of **A**. The ith row of **A** is equal to the ith column of $\mathbf{A}^T$, and if **A** is an $m \times n$ matrix, $\mathbf{A}^T$ is an $n \times m$ matrix. Thus

$$\mathbf{A}^T = \begin{bmatrix} a_{11} & a_{21} & \cdots & a_{m1} \\ a_{12} & a_{22} & \cdots & a_{m2} \\ \cdots & \cdots & \cdots & \cdots \\ a_{1n} & a_{2n} & \cdots & a_{mn} \end{bmatrix}$$

Note that the transpose of a column vector is a row vector; i.e., using (5.1.2),

$$\mathbf{x}^T = [x_1 \quad x_2 \quad \cdots \quad x_m]$$

To help prevent any confusion in subsequent discussion the convention will be used that any vector shown is assumed to be a column vector. Row vectors are then shown as the transpose of column vectors.

The operation of addition or subtraction of two matrices may be defined in the following way: If **A** and **B** are matrices of the same order (or the same number of rows and columns) with elements a_{ij} and b_{ij} respectively, then writing

$$\mathbf{A} \pm \mathbf{B} = \mathbf{C}$$

means $a_{ij} \pm b_{ij} = c_{ij}$. The c_{ij}'s are the elements of the resulting matrix **C**. From this definition the statement follows that matrices are commutative and associative in addition or subtraction. That is,

$$\mathbf{A} \pm \mathbf{B} = \mathbf{B} \pm \mathbf{A}$$

and

$$\mathbf{A} + (\mathbf{B} + \mathbf{C}) = (\mathbf{A} + \mathbf{B}) + \mathbf{C}$$

In the same manner it is possible to define linear combinations of vectors on the assumption that these are all the same type of vector and have the same number of elements. Thus, if

$$\mathbf{x} = \begin{bmatrix} 1 \\ 2 \\ 3 \end{bmatrix} \qquad \mathbf{v} = \begin{bmatrix} 2 \\ 3 \\ 4 \end{bmatrix} \qquad \mathbf{x} + \mathbf{v} = \begin{bmatrix} 3 \\ 5 \\ 7 \end{bmatrix}$$

The operation in which a matrix is multiplied by a scalar or by another matrix can also be defined by a simple set of rules. When a matrix **A** is multiplied by a scalar α, all the elements of the matrix are multiplied by that number. Thus

$$\alpha\mathbf{A} = \mathbf{B}$$

where $b_{ij} = \alpha a_{ij}$. The product of an $m \times n$ matrix **A** and an $n \times p$ matrix **B** is an $m \times p$ matrix **C** whose elements are given by

$$c_{ij} = \sum_{k=1}^{n} a_{ik}b_{kj} \qquad i = 1, 2, \ldots, m; j = 1, 2, \ldots, p \tag{5.1.4}$$

This result may be simply illustrated by taking

$$\mathbf{A} = \begin{bmatrix} 1 & 2 & 3 \\ 1 & 0 & 1 \end{bmatrix} \qquad 2 \times 3 \text{ matrix}$$

$$\mathbf{B} = \begin{bmatrix} 1 & 0 \\ 2 & 1 \\ 0 & 2 \end{bmatrix} \qquad 3 \times 2 \text{ matrix}$$

such that

$$\mathbf{AB} = \mathbf{C} = \begin{bmatrix} 1 \times 1 + 2 \times 2 + 3 \times 0 & 1 \times 0 + 2 \times 1 + 3 \times 2 \\ 1 \times 1 + 0 \times 2 + 1 \times 0 & 1 \times 0 + 0 \times 1 + 1 \times 2 \end{bmatrix} \qquad 2 \times 2 \text{ matrix}$$

This product of two matrices is defined only if the number of columns of

A = number of rows of **B**. In such a case the two matrices are said to be conformable.

It is necessary to differentiate between premultiplication of **B** by **A** to yield **AB** and postmultiplication of **B** by **A** to yield **BA**. In general,

$$\mathbf{AB} \neq \mathbf{BA}$$

i.e., the commutative law of multiplication does not hold for matrices. This can be seen easily if **A** is an $m \times n$ matrix and **B** an $n \times m$ matrix. In this case **AB** is an $m \times m$ matrix, whereas **BA** is an $n \times n$ matrix.

Multiplication of vectors follows in exactly the same way. When a row vector premultiplies a column vector, the result is a scalar. This may be seen by letting

$$\mathbf{x} = \begin{bmatrix} x_1 \\ x_2 \\ \cdot \\ \cdot \\ \cdot \\ x_m \end{bmatrix} \qquad \mathbf{v} = \begin{bmatrix} v_1 \\ v_2 \\ \cdot \\ \cdot \\ \cdot \\ v_m \end{bmatrix}$$

and then

$$\mathbf{x}^T\mathbf{v} = x_1v_1 + x_2v_2 + \cdots + x_mv_m = \sum_{k=1}^{m} x_iv_i = \mathbf{v}^T\mathbf{x} \tag{5.1.5}$$

In the same way premultiplication of a row vector by its own transpose leads to the sum of squares of the elements of the vector.

$$\mathbf{x}^T\mathbf{x} = x_1^2 + x_2^2 + \cdots + x_m^2 = \sum_{k=1}^{m} x_i^2 \tag{5.1.6}$$

The scalar result in (5.1.5) (a 1×1 matrix) is called the scalar, dot, or inner, product of the two vectors. If the scalar product vanishes, i.e.,

$$\mathbf{x}^T\mathbf{v} = 0 \tag{5.1.7}$$

the two vectors are said to be orthogonal to each other.

Because of the noncommutative nature of matrix multiplication the reverse procedure, in which a column vector premultiplies a row vector, does not lead to a scalar. Instead a matrix is formed whose elements are the squares and products of the elements of the individual vectors.

$$\mathbf{x}\mathbf{v}^T = \begin{bmatrix} x_1v_1 & x_1v_2 & \cdots & x_1v_m \\ x_2v_1 & x_2v_2 & \cdots & \cdots \\ \cdots & \cdots & \cdots & \cdots \\ x_mv_1 & x_mv_2 & \cdots & x_mv_m \end{bmatrix}$$

In the particular case where a vector premultiplies its own transpose

$$\mathbf{x}\mathbf{x}^T = \begin{bmatrix} x_1^2 & x_1x_2 & \cdots & x_1x_m \\ x_2x_1 & x_2^2 & \cdots & \cdots \\ \cdots & \cdots & \cdots & \cdots \\ x_mx_1 & \cdots & \cdots & x_m^2 \end{bmatrix}$$

One of the important advantages of using matrices is that they afford a convenient shorthand notation for dealing with systems of linear algebraic equations. Thus the system

$$\begin{aligned} a_{11}x_1 + a_{12}x_2 + \cdots + a_{1n}x_n &= c_1 \\ a_{21}x_1 + a_{22}x_2 + \cdots + a_{2n}x_n &= c_2 \\ \cdots\cdots\cdots\cdots\cdots\cdots & \\ a_{m1}x_1 + a_{m2}x_2 + \cdots + a_{mn}x_n &= c_m \end{aligned} \tag{5.1.8}$$

can be written concisely as

$$\mathbf{A}\mathbf{x} = \mathbf{c} \tag{5.1.9}$$

where $\mathbf{A}$ is an $m \times n$ matrix with the form of (5.1.1) and

$$\mathbf{x} = \begin{bmatrix} x_1 \\ x_2 \\ \cdot \\ \cdot \\ \cdot \\ x_n \end{bmatrix} \quad n \times 1 \text{ vector}$$

$$\mathbf{c} = \begin{bmatrix} c_1 \\ c_2 \\ \cdot \\ \cdot \\ \cdot \\ c_m \end{bmatrix} \quad m \times 1 \text{ vector}$$

From (5.1.9) it can be seen that the matrix $\mathbf{A}$ is a linear operator which premultiplies $\mathbf{x}$ to yield $\mathbf{c}$. Equations (5.1.8) can also be written in another way. Let

$$\mathbf{a}_1 = \begin{bmatrix} a_{11} \\ a_{21} \\ \cdot \\ \cdot \\ \cdot \\ a_{m1} \end{bmatrix} \quad \mathbf{a}_2 = \begin{bmatrix} a_{12} \\ a_{22} \\ \cdot \\ \cdot \\ \cdot \\ a_{m2} \end{bmatrix} \quad \cdots \quad a_n = \begin{bmatrix} a_{1n} \\ a_{2n} \\ \cdot \\ \cdot \\ \cdot \\ a_{mn} \end{bmatrix}$$

and (5.1.8) is identified with

$$\mathbf{a}_1 x_1 + \mathbf{a}_2 x_2 + \cdots + \mathbf{a}_n x_n = \mathbf{c} \tag{5.1.10}$$

In this case a linear weighted sum of the vectors formed from the **A** matrix yields **c**.

There are a number of special types of matrices and vectors which are important. Some of these are listed below:

1. A square matrix is one in which the number of rows equals the number of columns, i.e., an $n \times n$ matrix.

2. A diagonal matrix is a square matrix with all elements equal to zero except the a_{ii}'s. This matrix is given the special symbol **D** and has the form

$$\mathbf{D} = \begin{bmatrix} a_{11} & 0 & \cdots & 0 \\ 0 & a_{22} & \cdots & \cdots \\ \cdots & \cdots & a_{33} & \cdots \\ \cdots & \cdots & \cdots & \cdots \\ 0 & \cdots & \cdots & a_{nn} \end{bmatrix} \tag{5.1.11}$$

The diagonal running from top left to bottom right is called the main diagonal of the matrix.

3. A scalar matrix is a diagonal matrix whose elements a_{ii} are all equal but not necessarily 1.0.

4. The unit, or identity, matrix is a diagonal matrix in which the elements of the main diagonal are each equal to 1.0. Denoting this matrix by **I**,

$$\mathbf{I} = \begin{bmatrix} 1 & 0 & \cdots & 0 \\ 0 & 1 & \cdots & \cdots \\ \cdots & \cdots & 1 & \cdots \\ \cdots & \cdots & \cdots & \cdots \\ 0 & \cdots & \cdots & 1 \end{bmatrix} \tag{5.1.12}$$

The unit matrix plays the same role in matrix algebra as the scalar 1.0 does in normal algebra.

5. The null, or zero, matrix, denoted by **0**, is one in which all the elements are zero.

6. A symmetric matrix is one in which $a_{ij} = a_{ji}$ for all i's and j's. Thus a symmetric matrix **A** equals its transpose $\mathbf{A}^T$ and is always square.

7. A skew-symmetric matrix is one for which

$$\mathbf{A} = -\mathbf{A}^T$$

This implies that all $a_{ij} = 0$ for $i = j$.

8. A triangular matrix is a square matrix in which all $a_{ij} = 0$ for $i > j$

or all $a_{ij} = 0$ for $i < j$. Thus

$$\begin{bmatrix} a_{11} & a_{12} & \cdots & a_{1n} \\ 0 & a_{22} & \cdots & \cdots \\ \cdots & \cdots & \cdots & \cdots \\ 0 & \cdots & 0 & a_{nn} \end{bmatrix}$$

is a triangular matrix.

Certain of these special matrices have an equivalent form as vectors. The unit vectors are the set formed from the unit matrix with the designation

$$\mathbf{e}_1 = \begin{bmatrix} 1 \\ 0 \\ \cdot \\ \cdot \\ \cdot \\ 0 \end{bmatrix} \qquad \mathbf{e}_2 = \begin{bmatrix} 0 \\ 1 \\ \cdot \\ \cdot \\ \cdot \\ 0 \end{bmatrix} \qquad \cdots \; \mathbf{e}_n = \begin{bmatrix} 0 \\ 0 \\ \cdot \\ \cdot \\ \cdot \\ 1 \end{bmatrix}$$

and the null vector is one with all zero elements.

Some elementary rules for manipulating these special matrices in conjunction with any other matrix **A** can be developed from the previous definitions for addition, subtraction, and multiplication. Thus

$$\mathbf{AI} = \mathbf{IA} = \mathbf{A}$$

and pre- or postmultiplication of **A** by a suitably sized identity matrix leaves the **A** matrix unchanged. In addition

$$\mathbf{A0} = \mathbf{0A} = \mathbf{0} \qquad \mathbf{A} + \mathbf{0} = \mathbf{A}$$

and

$$\mathbf{DA} = \mathbf{AD}$$

A further set of relations in terms of the transpose of **A** are given by

$$(\mathbf{A} + \mathbf{B})^T = \mathbf{A}^T + \mathbf{B}^T \qquad (\mathbf{AB})^T = \mathbf{B}^T\mathbf{A}^T$$

These identities can be easily proved by the reader.

It is important to note that matrix division has not been defined. The reason for this is that matrix division in the normal algebraic sense does not exist. Instead, an inverse operator is defined which uses multiplication to achieve the same result. If a matrix **A** and another matrix **B** (both square and of the same size) lead to the identity matrix **I** when multiplied together,

$$\mathbf{AB} = \mathbf{I}$$

then **B** is written as $\mathbf{A}^{-1}$ and called the inverse of **A**. It follows that

$$\mathbf{AA}^{-1} = \mathbf{A}^{-1}\mathbf{A} = \mathbf{I}$$

The question immediately arises as to when the **A** matrix has an inverse.

As will be shown shortly, the necessary requirement is that **A** be nonsingular or that the determinant of **A** is not equal to zero. It can be easily determined also that

$$(\mathbf{AB})^{-1} = \mathbf{B}^{-1}\mathbf{A}^{-1}$$

Of further interest is the fact that, if **D** is a diagonal matrix with elements d_{ii}, the elements of $\mathbf{D}^{-1}$ are $1/d_{ii}$. This follows directly from the relationship $\mathbf{DD}^{-1} = \mathbf{I}$. Finally, the inverse of a triangular matrix is a matrix of the same shape (see Sec. 5.15).

5.2. Determinants and Their Properties

For every square matrix **A** there exists a determinant, det **A**, such that

$$\det \mathbf{A} = \begin{vmatrix} a_{11} & a_{12} & \cdots & a_{1n} \\ a_{21} & a_{22} & \cdots & \cdots \\ \cdots & \cdots & \cdots & \cdots \\ a_{n1} & \cdots & \cdots & a_{nn} \end{vmatrix} \tag{5.2.1}$$

To differentiate from a matrix, vertical bars instead of brackets are used to enclose the a_{ij}'s. Actually (5.2.1) as shown above is deceptive in appearance. The determinant det **A** is a number or scalar obtained by operating on the elements within the vertical bars in some predetermined arithmetic manner. In particular, det **A** is obtained as the sum of all possible products in each of which there appears one and only one element from each row and each column of **A**, each product of this sum being assigned a plus or minus sign according to the following rule: Let the elements in a given product be joined in pairs by line segments. If the total number of such segments sloping upward to the right is even, prefix a plus sign to the product; otherwise prefix a negative sign.

With this definition of a determinant the following specific properties may be verified:

1. If all the elements of any row or column of a matrix are zero, its determinant is equal to zero.
2. If the corresponding rows and columns of a matrix are interchanged, its determinant is unchanged.
3. If two rows or columns of a matrix are interchanged, this changes the sign of the determinant.
4. If the elements of two rows or columns of a matrix are equal, its determinant is zero.
5. If the elements of any row or column of a matrix are multiplied by a scalar, this is equivalent to multiplying the determinant by the scalar.
6. Adding the product of a scalar and any row or column to any other row or column of a matrix leaves the determinant unchanged.

The determinant of the matrix resulting from deleting the *i*th row and jth column is called the minor of a_{ij} and denoted by M_{ij}. The cofactor of this same element a_{ij} is defined by the relation

$$A_{ij} = (-1)^{i+j} M_{ij}$$

Since M_{ij} is a scalar, A_{ij} is also a scalar. Based upon these definitions, Laplace's expansion theorem can be used to evaluate a determinant numerically. This theorem states that a determinant is equal to the sum of the products of the elements of any single row or column and their corresponding cofactors, i.e.,

$$\det \mathbf{A} = \sum_{k=1}^{n} a_{ik} A_{ik} = \sum_{k=1}^{n} a_{kj} A_{kj} \tag{5.2.2}$$

where $\mathbf{A}$ is an $n \times n$ matrix. Computationally this definition of det $\mathbf{A}$ is of little use, since the number of multiplications required is excessive.

There are, however, a number of practical means of evaluating a determinant. The techniques of Chio and the elimination method will be illustrated here. The simple fourth-order (4×4) determinant

$$\det \mathbf{A} = \begin{vmatrix} a_{11} & a_{12} & a_{13} & a_{14} \\ a_{21} & a_{22} & a_{23} & a_{24} \\ a_{31} & a_{32} & a_{33} & a_{34} \\ a_{41} & a_{42} & a_{43} & a_{44} \end{vmatrix}$$

will be used for both methods. In Chio's method the first step is to convert the element a_{11} into the numerical value of 1.0. This is accomplished by dividing the entire first row by a_{11} and bringing a_{11} out in front of the determinant. For ease in presentation assume that $a_{11} = 1.0$ to start. The second step is to convert a_{12}, a_{13}, and a_{14} (or the equivalent a_{12}/a_{11}, a_{13}/a_{11}, and a_{14}/a_{11}) to zero. This is accomplished by multiplying the elements of column 1 by a_{12}, a_{13}, and a_{14}, respectively, and subtracting the results from columns 2, 3, and 4. This does not change the value of the determinant and yields

$$\det \mathbf{A} = \begin{vmatrix} 1 & 0 & 0 & 0 \\ a_{21} & a_{22} - a_{12}a_{21} & a_{23} - a_{13}a_{21} & a_{24} - a_{14}a_{21} \\ a_{31} & a_{32} - a_{12}a_{31} & a_{33} - a_{13}a_{31} & a_{34} - a_{14}a_{31} \\ a_{41} & a_{42} - a_{12}a_{41} & a_{43} - a_{13}a_{41} & a_{44} - a_{14}a_{41} \end{vmatrix}$$

Expanding by minors with respect to the a_{11} element yields

$$\det \mathbf{A} = (-1)^{1+1} \begin{vmatrix} 3 \times 3 \\ \text{determinant} \\ \text{shown} \\ \text{in dashed} \\ \text{lines} \end{vmatrix}$$

The original fourth-order determinant has thus been reduced to a third-order one. One further application of this procedure will reduce the determinant to second-order which can be used to evaluate det **A**. The following rule is seen to represent the series of steps corresponding to reduction of the order by 1.0:

After the pivotal element (a_{11} *in above case*) *is chosen, strike out the corresponding row and column. Every other element in the original determinant is reduced by the product of the intersection on the eliminated row and column from the present element in question. The resulting determinant is then multiplied by* $(-1)^{i+j}$ *corresponding to the* a_{ij} *originally chosen.*

On the assumption that none of the elements is zero to start, the application of Chio's method requires about $n^3/3$ multiplications to evaluate det **A** (n being the order of the determinant).

The basic feature of the elimination method is to convert the original square determinant to triangular form. The elements of the first row are multiplied by a_{21}/a_{11}, a_{31}/a_{11}, and a_{41}/a_{11}, respectively, and then subtracted from the second, third, and fourth rows. This produces

$$\det \mathbf{A} = \begin{vmatrix} a_{11} & a_{12} & a_{13} & a_{14} \\ 0 & a'_{22} & a'_{23} & a'_{24} \\ 0 & a'_{32} & a'_{33} & a'_{34} \\ 0 & a'_{42} & a'_{43} & a'_{44} \end{vmatrix}$$

where

$$a'_{22} = a_{22} - \frac{a_{21}}{a_{11}} a_{12}$$

$$a'_{32} = a_{32} - \frac{a_{31}}{a_{11}} a_{12}$$

$$\cdots\cdots\cdots$$

The elements of the second row are next multiplied by a'_{32}/a'_{22} and a'_{42}/a'_{22}, respectively, and then subtracted from the third and fourth rows. This yields

$$\det \mathbf{A} = \begin{vmatrix} a_{11} & a_{12} & a_{13} & a_{14} \\ 0 & a'_{22} & a'_{23} & a'_{24} \\ 0 & 0 & a''_{33} & a''_{34} \\ 0 & 0 & a''_{43} & a''_{44} \end{vmatrix}$$

where

$$a''_{33} = a'_{33} - \frac{a'_{32}}{a'_{22}} a'_{23}$$

$$\cdots\cdots\cdots$$

One more step in this process yields

$$\det \mathbf{A} = \begin{vmatrix} a_{11} & a_{12} & a_{13} & a_{14} \\ 0 & a'_{22} & a'_{23} & a'_{24} \\ 0 & 0 & a''_{33} & a''_{34} \\ 0 & 0 & 0 & a'''_{44} \end{vmatrix}$$

Expanding by minors with respect to each first element of the final determinant shows that

$$\det \mathbf{A} = a_{11}a'_{22}a''_{33}a'''_{44}$$

The elimination method requires approximately $n^3/3$ multiplication, just as with Chio's scheme. For $n = 100$ it can easily be seen that a considerable number of multiplications or, since computing time is usually determined by the multiplications, a considerable amount of computing time may be required to evaluate the determinant, even with the fastest machines available.

Just as there are a number of special types of matrices there are also a number of special determinants. In particular,

$$\det \mathbf{O} = 0 \qquad \det \mathbf{I} = 1.0$$

Further, from the relationship $\mathbf{AA}^{-1} = \mathbf{I}$ and $\det |\mathbf{AB}| = \det \mathbf{A} \cdot \det \mathbf{B}$, it follows that, if $\det \mathbf{A} = \alpha$, then $\det \mathbf{A}^{-1} = 1/\alpha$.

The cofactor having been defined, it is possible to define the adjoint of a square matrix **A** for use in subsequent discussion. The adjoint of a square matrix **A**, indicated as adj **A**, is the matrix formed from **A** by replacing each element by its cofactor and then interchanging row and columns. Thus

$$\text{adj } \mathbf{A} = \begin{bmatrix} A_{11} & A_{21} & \cdots & A_{n1} \\ A_{12} & A_{22} & \cdots & \cdots \\ \cdots & \cdots & \cdots & \cdots \\ A_{1n} & \cdots & \cdots & A_{nn} \end{bmatrix} \tag{5.2.3}$$

5.3. Use of Determinants

To illustrate some further features of determinants, consider the simple simultaneous set of two algebraic equations

$$\begin{aligned} a_{11}x_1 + a_{12}x_2 &= c_1 \\ a_{21}x_1 + a_{22}x_2 &= c_2 \end{aligned} \tag{5.3.1}$$

From (5.1.8) with $m = n = 2$, (5.3.1) can be written in matrix form as

$$\mathbf{Ax} = \mathbf{c}$$

where $$\mathbf{A} = \begin{bmatrix} a_{11} & a_{12} \\ a_{21} & a_{22} \end{bmatrix} \qquad \mathbf{x} = \begin{bmatrix} x_1 \\ x_2 \end{bmatrix} \qquad \mathbf{c} = \begin{bmatrix} c_1 \\ c_2 \end{bmatrix}$$

x_2 can be eliminated directly from (5.3.1) to yield

$$(a_{11}a_{22} - a_{12}a_{21})x_1 = a_{22}c_1 - a_{12}c_2$$

or, in determinant form,

$$(\det \mathbf{A})x_1 = \det \mathbf{A}(1) \tag{5.3.2}$$

In (5.3.2),

$$\det \mathbf{A} = \begin{vmatrix} a_{11} & a_{12} \\ a_{21} & a_{22} \end{vmatrix} = a_{11}a_{22} - a_{12}a_{21}$$

$$\det \mathbf{A}(1) = \begin{vmatrix} c_1 & a_{12} \\ c_2 & a_{22} \end{vmatrix} = a_{22}c_1 - a_{12}c_2 \tag{5.3.3}$$

In the same way, but eliminating x_1 in (5.3.1), there results

$$(\det \mathbf{A})x_2 = \det \mathbf{A}(2) \tag{5.3.4}$$

where

$$\det \mathbf{A}(2) = \begin{vmatrix} a_{11} & c_1 \\ a_{21} & c_2 \end{vmatrix} = a_{11}c_2 - a_{21}c_1 \tag{5.3.5}$$

There are a number of interesting points which follow from this simple example. The unknowns x_1 and x_2 can be evaluated from (5.3.2) and (5.3.4) if $\det \mathbf{A} \neq 0$. In such a case

$$x_1 = \frac{\det \mathbf{A}(1)}{\det \mathbf{A}}$$

$$x_2 = \frac{\det \mathbf{A}(2)}{\det \mathbf{A}}$$

since division by $\det \mathbf{A}$ is possible. Further it is noted that $\det \mathbf{A}(1)$ and $\det \mathbf{A}(2)$ can be formed from $\det \mathbf{A}$ by replacing the elements of column 1 and column 2, respectively, by c_1, c_2.

Cramer's rule for solving a set of n nonhomogeneous linear algebraic equations follows directly from this example. For the system

$$\begin{aligned} a_{11}x_1 + a_{12}x_2 + \cdots + a_{1n}x_n &= c_1 \\ a_{21}x_1 + a_{22}x_2 + \cdots + a_{2n}x_n &= c_2 \\ \cdots\cdots\cdots\cdots\cdots\cdots\cdots \\ a_{n1}x_1 + a_{n2}x_2 + \cdots + a_{nn}x_n &= c_n \end{aligned} \tag{5.3.6}$$

$$\begin{aligned} x_1 &= \frac{\det \mathbf{A}(1)}{\det \mathbf{A}} \\ x_2 &= \frac{\det \mathbf{A}(2)}{\det \mathbf{A}} \\ &\cdots\cdots\cdots \\ x_k &= \frac{\det \mathbf{A}(k)}{\det \mathbf{A}} \\ &\cdots\cdots\cdots \\ x_n &= \frac{\det \mathbf{A}(n)}{\det \mathbf{A}} \end{aligned} \tag{5.3.7}$$

where

$$\det \mathbf{A} = \begin{vmatrix} a_{11} & a_{12} & \cdots & a_{1n} \\ a_{21} & a_{22} & \cdots & \cdots \\ \cdots & \cdots & \cdots & \cdots \\ a_{n1} & \cdots & \cdots & a_{nn} \end{vmatrix} \neq 0$$

and det $\mathbf{A}(k)$ is equal to det $\mathbf{A}$ except for the kth column, which contains $c_1, c_2, \ldots, c_n$. It can thus be deduced that the system of (5.3.6) has a nontrivial or unique solution as given by Cramer's rule (5.3.7) if det $\mathbf{A} \neq 0$. A square matrix $\mathbf{A}$ whose determinant is equal to zero, det $\mathbf{A} = 0$, is called a singular matrix; if det $\mathbf{A} \neq 0$, then the matrix $\mathbf{A}$ is called nonsingular.

By using Laplace's expansion for a determinant [(5.2.2)], det $\mathbf{A}(k)$ can be written as

$$\det \mathbf{A}(k) = c_1 A_{1k} + c_2 A_{2k} + \cdots + c_n A_{nk} \tag{5.3.8}$$

while $k = 1, 2, \ldots, n$. The expansion of (5.3.8) has been made around the column containing the $c_1, c_2, \ldots, c_n$. By using (5.3.8) in (5.3.7) there results

$$\begin{aligned} x_1 &= \frac{1}{\det \mathbf{A}} (c_1 A_{11} + c_2 A_{21} + \cdots + c_n A_{n1}) \\ x_2 &= \frac{1}{\det \mathbf{A}} (c_1 A_{12} + c_2 A_{22} + \cdots + c_n A_{n2}) \\ &\cdots\cdots\cdots\cdots\cdots\cdots \\ x_n &= \frac{1}{\det \mathbf{A}} (c_1 A_{1n} + c_2 A_{2n} + \cdots + c_n A_{nn}) \end{aligned} \tag{5.3.9}$$

Equation (5.3.9) can be written in matrix form as

$$\mathbf{x} = \mathbf{Bc} \tag{5.3.10}$$

where

$$\mathbf{B} = \frac{1}{\det \mathbf{A}} \begin{bmatrix} A_{11} & A_{21} & \cdots & A_{n1} \\ A_{12} & A_{22} & \cdots & \cdots \\ \cdots & \cdots & \cdots & \cdots \\ A_{1n} & \cdots & \cdots & A_{nn} \end{bmatrix}$$

But from the definition of the adjoint matrix of $\mathbf{A}$ [(5.2.3)] $\mathbf{B}$ can also be given as

$$\mathbf{B} = \frac{\operatorname{adj} \mathbf{A}}{\det \mathbf{A}} \tag{5.3.11}$$

on the assumption that det $\mathbf{A} \neq 0$. $\mathbf{B}$ is seen to be a linear operator in (5.3.10) such that when it premultiplies $\mathbf{c}$ the result is $\mathbf{x}$. In a qualitative sense $\mathbf{B}$ accomplishes the inverse result of $\mathbf{A}$ in $\mathbf{Ax} = \mathbf{c}$. Premultiplying the relation $\mathbf{Ax} = \mathbf{c}$ by $\mathbf{A}^{-1}$ yields

$$\mathbf{A}^{-1}\mathbf{Ax} = \mathbf{A}^{-1}\mathbf{c}$$

and since

$$\mathbf{A}^{-1}\mathbf{A} = \mathbf{I}$$

there results

$$\mathbf{x} = \mathbf{A}^{-1}\mathbf{c} \tag{5.3.12}$$

Comparing this equation with (5.3.10) shows that

$$\mathbf{B} = \mathbf{A}^{-1}$$

That is, **B** is equal to the inverse of **A**. It is now possible to say that the square matrix **A** has a unique inverse $\mathbf{A}^{-1}$ if and only if **A** is nonsingular or det $\mathbf{A} \neq 0$.

Equation (5.3.12) points out one of the important uses of the inverse matrix. Premultiplication of the known **c** vector by the inverse matrix yields the vector of unknowns, $x_1, x_2, \ldots, x_n$, in the original system of simultaneous equations (5.3.6). In a later section of this chapter a number of efficient methods will be developed for determining $\mathbf{A}^{-1}$. As a preliminary point note that if

$$\mathbf{Ax} = \mathbf{I}$$

then

$$\mathbf{x} = \mathbf{A}^{-1}$$

Thus a number of the techniques for evaluating $\mathbf{A}^{-1}$ involve solving the simultaneous system with the nonhomogeneous part taken as the identity matrix.

It is now possible to define an orthogonal matrix **A** such that

$$\mathbf{A}^{-1} = \mathbf{A}^T$$

This matrix has the property that

$$\mathbf{AA}^{-1} = \mathbf{AA}^T = \mathbf{I}$$

It has already been pointed out that the nonhomogeneous set of linear equations (5.3.6) has a unique nontrivial solution **x** if the **A** matrix is nonsingular or det $\mathbf{A} \neq 0$. The solution may be obtained by Cramer's rule [(5.3.7)] or other methods to be developed shortly. If **A** is singular, det $\mathbf{A} = 0$, the question of whether or not a solution exists resides in the minors of det **A** or the rank of **A**. The rank of a matrix is defined as the order of the largest square array in that matrix formed by deleting various rows and columns whose determinant does not vanish. In other words, if r is the largest integer for which some minor of **A** of order r is not zero, then the matrix is of rank r. To state that a matrix of order 10 is of rank 4 means that every minor of this matrix of order 5 or more has a determinant equal to zero. For the $n \times n$ simultaneous set of (5.3.6) it is possible to state the following possibilities:

1. If the rank of the matrix **A** is equal to n, $r = n$, then det $\mathbf{A} \neq 0$ and the system has a unique solution.

2. If the rank of the matrix **A** is less than n, $r < n$, and any of the determinants det $\mathbf{A}(1)$, det $\mathbf{A}(2)$, . . . , det $\mathbf{A}(n)$ have rank greater than r, there is no solution to the simultaneous set.

3. If the rank of the matrix **A** is less than n, $r < n$, and the rank of none of det $\mathbf{A}(1)$, det $\mathbf{A}(2)$, . . . , det $\mathbf{A}(n)$ exceeds r, there are an infinite number of possible solutions.

Of futher importance is the requirement for obtaining a unique solution of the homogeneous form of (5.3.6), i.e.,

$$
\begin{aligned}
a_{11}x_1 = a_{12}x_2 + \cdots + a_{1n}x_n &= 0 \\
a_{21}x_1 + a_{22}x_2 + \cdots + a_{2n}x_n &= 0 \\
\cdots\cdots\cdots\cdots\cdots\cdots\cdots\cdots \\
a_{n1}x_1 + a_{n2}x_2 + \cdots + a_{nn}x_n &= 0
\end{aligned}
$$

or

$$\mathbf{Ax} = 0 \tag{5.3.13}$$

An obvious solution is the trivial one $\mathbf{x} = 0$ for det $\mathbf{A} \neq 0$. However, for (5.3.13) to have a solution other than the trivial one, one may show that it is necessary that det $\mathbf{A} = 0$.

To summarize, the nonhomogeneous set of algebraic equations has a unique nontrivial solution if det $\mathbf{A} \neq 0$; the homogeneous set has a unique nontrivial solution if det $\mathbf{A} = 0$.

The case of a nonsingular $\mathbf{A}$ matrix can also lead to an important relation in terms of the $\mathbf{a}_1, \mathbf{a}_2, \ldots, \mathbf{a}_n$ vectors of (5.1.10). To develop this point, it is first necessary to discuss linearly independent and dependent sets of vectors. A set of n vectors $\mathbf{v}_1, \mathbf{v}_2, \ldots, \mathbf{v}_n$ is said to be linearly independent if no set of scalar constants $\alpha_1, \alpha_2, \ldots, \alpha_n$ exists such that

$$\alpha_1\mathbf{v}_1 + \alpha_2\mathbf{v}_2 + \cdots + \alpha_n\mathbf{v}_n = 0$$

except $\alpha_1 = \alpha_2 = \cdots = \alpha_n = 0$. Otherwise the vectors are said to be linearly dependent. The unit vectors $\mathbf{e}_1, \mathbf{e}_2, \ldots, \mathbf{e}_n$ form a set of linearly independent vectors, i.e., for $n = 2$,

$$\alpha_1\mathbf{e}_1 + \alpha_2\mathbf{e}_2 = \mathbf{0}$$

$$\alpha_1\begin{bmatrix}1\\0\end{bmatrix} + \alpha_2\begin{bmatrix}0\\1\end{bmatrix} = \begin{bmatrix}0\\0\end{bmatrix}$$

$$\begin{bmatrix}\alpha_1\\0\end{bmatrix} + \begin{bmatrix}0\\\alpha_2\end{bmatrix} = \begin{bmatrix}\alpha_1\\\alpha_2\end{bmatrix} = \begin{bmatrix}0\\0\end{bmatrix}$$

As a result $\alpha_1 = \alpha_2 = 0$ and $\mathbf{e}_1$ and $\mathbf{e}_2$ are linearly independent. If, however, the set of $\mathbf{e}_1$, $\mathbf{e}_2$, $\mathbf{e}_3$, and $\mathbf{v}_3 = \begin{bmatrix}1\\1\end{bmatrix}$ is considered, there results

$$\alpha_1\mathbf{e}_1 + \alpha_2\mathbf{e}_2 + \alpha_3\mathbf{v}_3 = \mathbf{0}$$

$$\alpha_1\begin{bmatrix}1\\0\end{bmatrix} + \alpha_2\begin{bmatrix}0\\1\end{bmatrix} + \alpha_3\begin{bmatrix}1\\1\end{bmatrix} = \begin{bmatrix}0\\0\end{bmatrix}$$

$$\begin{bmatrix}\alpha_1\\0\end{bmatrix} + \begin{bmatrix}0\\\alpha_2\end{bmatrix} + \begin{bmatrix}\alpha_3\\\alpha_3\end{bmatrix} = \begin{bmatrix}\alpha_1+\alpha_3\\\alpha_2+\alpha_3\end{bmatrix} = \begin{bmatrix}0\\0\end{bmatrix}$$

Thus,

$$\alpha_1 = -\alpha_3 \qquad \alpha_2 = -\alpha_3$$

and

$$\alpha_1 = \alpha_2 \neq 0$$

This set is linearly dependent.

Consider now that **A** is a nonsingular matrix whose columns are given by the vectors $\mathbf{a}_1, \mathbf{a}_2, \ldots, \mathbf{a}_n$. If these vectors are assumed to be linearly dependent, then one of the α_i's in an expression of the form

$$\alpha_1\mathbf{a}_1 + \alpha_2\mathbf{a}_2 + \cdots + \alpha_n\mathbf{a}_n = \mathbf{0}$$

must be nonzero. Let i be 1, and thus $\alpha_1 \neq 0$. As a result

$$\mathbf{a}_1 = -\left(\frac{\alpha_2}{\alpha_1}\mathbf{a}_2 + \frac{\alpha_3}{\alpha_1}\mathbf{a}_3 + \cdots + \frac{\alpha_n}{\alpha_1}\mathbf{a}_n\right)$$

If now the second column in the **A** matrix is multiplied by α_2/α_1 and added to the first column, the third column multiplied by α_3/α_1 and added to the first column, etc., the result is a zero vector for the first column. Since these arithmetic operations have not changed the value of det **A** (see previous rules), it follows that det $\mathbf{A} = 0$ and the **A** matrix is singular. However, this contradicts the original assumption on **A**. As a result the vectors $\mathbf{a}_1, \mathbf{a}_2, \ldots, \mathbf{a}_n$ must be linearly independent if the matrix **A** is nonsingular, det $\mathbf{A} \neq 0$.

5.4. Matrix Partitioning

A matrix **A** may be sectioned or partitioned into smaller components in any manner desired. To illustrate, the 4×4 matrix below

$$\mathbf{A} = \begin{bmatrix} a_{11} & a_{12} & a_{13} & a_{14} \\ a_{21} & a_{22} & a_{23} & a_{24} \\ a_{31} & a_{32} & a_{33} & a_{34} \\ a_{41} & a_{42} & a_{43} & a_{44} \end{bmatrix}$$

may be written in the form

$$\mathbf{A} = \begin{bmatrix} \mathbf{L} & \mathbf{N} \\ \mathbf{M} & \mathbf{P} \end{bmatrix}$$

where

$$\mathbf{L} = \begin{bmatrix} a_{11} & a_{12} \\ a_{21} & a_{22} \end{bmatrix} \qquad \mathbf{N} = \begin{bmatrix} a_{13} & a_{14} \\ a_{23} & a_{24} \end{bmatrix}$$

$$\mathbf{M} = \begin{bmatrix} a_{31} & a_{32} \\ a_{41} & a_{42} \end{bmatrix} \qquad \mathbf{P} = \begin{bmatrix} a_{33} & a_{34} \\ a_{43} & a_{44} \end{bmatrix}$$

L, **M**, **N**, and **P** are called the submatrices of **A**. The partitioning was accomplished by symbolically drawing a dashed vertical and horizontal line between two columns and two rows, i.e.,

$$\mathbf{A} = \left[\begin{array}{cc:cc} a_{11} & a_{12} & a_{13} & a_{14} \\ a_{21} & a_{22} & a_{23} & a_{24} \\ \hdashline a_{31} & a_{32} & a_{33} & a_{34} \\ a_{41} & a_{42} & a_{43} & a_{44} \end{array}\right]$$

If another square matrix **B**, of the same size as **A**, is partitioned in the same way, the submatrices may be treated as elements of **A** and **B** and all arithmetic manipulations performed by using the submatrices. In this way the $n \times n$ matrices may be manipulated on a macroscopic scale as if they were 2×2 matrices or any size smaller than $n \times n$. The application of this partitioning will be illustrated shortly.

5.5. Matrix Polynomials and Power Series

The result of multiplying a square matrix of order n by itself j times is

$$\underbrace{\mathbf{A}\mathbf{A}\cdots}_{j\text{ times}} = \mathbf{A}^j$$

$\mathbf{A}^j$ is a new square matrix of order n. In the same context $\mathbf{A}^0 = I$ by definition. As a result the finite sum

$$\alpha_0\mathbf{A}^j + \alpha_1\mathbf{A}^{j-1} + \cdots + \alpha_{j-1}\mathbf{A} + \alpha_j I$$

with the α's as scalars is also a matrix of order n. This may be written as

$$\mathbf{P}(\mathbf{A}) = \sum_{k=0}^{j} \alpha_k \mathbf{A}^{j-k} \tag{5.5.1}$$

where $\mathbf{P}(\mathbf{A})$ is said to be a polynomial function of **A** of the jth degree. This is equivalent to the scalar definition of a polynomial.

An obvious extension of this representation is to describe an infinite series of matrices. For a sequence $\mathbf{A}_0, \mathbf{A}_1, \mathbf{A}_2, \ldots$ of square matrices of the same size the sum can be represented by

$$\mathbf{S}_m = \sum_{k=0}^{m} \mathbf{A}_k$$

The infinite series $\sum_{k=0}^{\infty} \mathbf{A}_k$ is said to be convergent if every partial sum $\mathbf{S}_m$ converges to a bounded limit as $m \to \infty$. Of particular interest are the infinite power series, i.e., matrices of the form $\sum_{k=0}^{\infty} \alpha_k \mathbf{A}^k$. Without discussing here the question of convergence, it is possible to define a number of such series which have the form used in scalar notation. In particular, the exponential function $e^{\mathbf{A}}$ is defined by

$$e^{\mathbf{A}} = \mathbf{I} + \mathbf{A} + \frac{\mathbf{A}^2}{2!} + \frac{\mathbf{A}^3}{3!} + \cdots = \sum_{k=0}^{\infty} \frac{\mathbf{A}^k}{k!} \tag{5.5.2}$$

and
$$\sin \mathbf{A} = \mathbf{A} - \frac{\mathbf{A}^3}{3!} + \frac{\mathbf{A}^5}{5!} - \cdots$$
$$\cos \mathbf{A} = \mathbf{I} - \frac{\mathbf{A}^2}{2!} + \frac{\mathbf{A}^4}{4!} - \cdots$$
$$\sinh \mathbf{A} = \mathbf{A} + \frac{\mathbf{A}^3}{3!} + \frac{\mathbf{A}^5}{5!} + \cdots$$
$$\cosh \mathbf{A} = \mathbf{I} + \frac{\mathbf{A}^2}{2!} + \frac{\mathbf{A}^4}{4!} + \cdots$$

It is a relatively easy matter to show that if **A** and **B** commute

$$e^{\mathbf{A}}e^{\mathbf{B}} = e^{\mathbf{A}+\mathbf{B}}$$

and, as a consequence,

$$e^{\mathbf{A}}e^{-\mathbf{A}} = \mathbf{I}$$

Thus the inverse of $e^{\mathbf{A}}$ is $e^{-\mathbf{A}}$.

5.6. Differentiation and Integration

If the elements of the matrix **A** are functions of a scalar such as t, the matrix is called a function of t and denoted as $\mathbf{A}(t)$. The derivative of $\mathbf{A}(t)$ with respect to t is defined as the matrix obtained by differentiating each element of $\mathbf{A}(t)$. Thus

$$\frac{d\mathbf{A}(t)}{dt} = \left[\frac{da_{ij}(t)}{dt}\right]$$

On this basis it follows that

$$\frac{d}{dt}\left[\mathbf{A}(t) + \frac{d\mathbf{A}(t)}{dt}\right] = \mathbf{B}(t) + \frac{d\mathbf{B}(t)}{dt}$$
$$\frac{d}{dt}[\mathbf{A}(t)\cdot\mathbf{B}(t)] = \mathbf{A}(t)\frac{d\mathbf{B}(t)}{dt} + \mathbf{B}(t)\frac{d\mathbf{A}(t)}{dt}$$

As an illustration, the exponential matrix can be written as

$$e^{\mathbf{A}t} = \mathbf{I} + t\mathbf{A} + \frac{t^2}{2!}\mathbf{A}^2 + \cdots = \sum_{k=0}^{\infty}\frac{t^k\mathbf{A}^k}{k!}$$

and thus

$$\frac{d}{dt}e^{\mathbf{A}t} = \mathbf{A} + t\mathbf{A}^2 + \frac{t^2}{2!}\mathbf{A}^3 + \cdots = \mathbf{A}\left(\mathbf{I} + t\mathbf{A} + \frac{t^2}{2!}\mathbf{A}^2 + \cdots\right) = \mathbf{A}e^{\mathbf{A}t}$$

The integral of $\mathbf{A}(t)$ is defined in an analogous way, namely, as the matrix obtained by integrating each element of $\mathbf{A}(t)$. This is indicated by

$$\int\mathbf{A}(t)\,dt = \left[\int a_{ij}(t)\,dt\right]$$

with the obvious implications.

5.7. The Characteristic Equation of a Matrix

In the present section linear algebraic equations of the form

$$\begin{aligned} a_{11}x_1 + a_{12}x_2 + \cdots + a_{1n}x_n &= \lambda x_1 \\ a_{21}x_1 + a_{22}x_2 + \cdots + a_{2n}x_n &= \lambda x_2 \\ \cdots\cdots\cdots\cdots\cdots\cdots \\ a_{n1}x_1 + a_{n2}x_2 + \cdots + a_{nn}x_n &= \lambda x_n \end{aligned} \tag{5.7.1}$$

are considered, where λ is a scalar. In matrix form this system may be written as either

$$\mathbf{Ax} = \lambda\mathbf{x} \tag{5.7.2}$$

or

$$[\mathbf{A} - \lambda\mathbf{I}]\mathbf{x} = \mathbf{0} \tag{5.7.3}$$

For (5.7.3) to have solutions $\mathbf{x}$ other than the trivial $\mathbf{x} = 0$, it is necessary that

$$\det(\mathbf{A} - \lambda\mathbf{I}) = 0 \tag{5.7.4}$$

The matrix $[\mathbf{A} - \lambda\mathbf{I}]$ is called the characteristic matrix of $\mathbf{A}$ and $\det(\mathbf{A} - \lambda\mathbf{I})$ the characteristic function or equation of $\mathbf{A}$. The latter equation is merely an nth-degree polynomial in λ. This polynomial has n roots designated as $\lambda_1, \lambda_2, \ldots, \lambda_n$ and called the characteristic values, roots, or eigenvalues of $\mathbf{A}$. Corresponding to each λ_i is a vector $\mathbf{x}_i$ called the characteristic vector, or the eigenvector resulting from satisfying (5.7.2).

The determinant equation (5.7.4) can be expanded to the polynomial forms

$$\det(\mathbf{A} - \lambda\mathbf{I}) = [\lambda^n - \alpha_1\lambda^{n-1} + \alpha_2\lambda^{n-2} - \cdots + (-1)^n\alpha_n] = 0$$

or

$$\det(\mathbf{A} - \lambda\mathbf{I}) = (-1)^n[\lambda^n - \alpha_1\lambda^{n-1} + \alpha_2\lambda^{n-2} - \cdots + (-1)^n\alpha_n] = 0 \tag{5.7.5}$$

with $\alpha_1, \alpha_2, \ldots, \alpha_n$ as scalars. Since there are n characteristic values of λ (or roots of this polynomial), it is also possible to write

$$\det(\mathbf{A} - \lambda\mathbf{I}) = (\lambda - \lambda_1)(\lambda - \lambda_2) \cdots (\lambda - \lambda_n) = 0$$

or

$$\det(\mathbf{A} - \lambda\mathbf{I}) = (-1)^n[(\lambda - \lambda_1)(\lambda - \lambda_2) \cdots (\lambda - \lambda_n)] = 0 \tag{5.7.6}$$

Multiplying out the right-hand side of (5.7.6) and equating the coefficients of λ in (5.7.5) and (5.7.6) yields

$$\begin{aligned} \alpha_1 &= \lambda_1 + \lambda_2 + \cdots + \lambda_n \\ \alpha_2 &= \lambda_1\lambda_2 + \lambda_1\lambda_3 + \cdots + \lambda_{n-1}\lambda_n \\ \cdots&\cdots\cdots\cdots\cdots \\ \alpha_n &= \lambda_1\lambda_2\lambda_3 \cdots \lambda_n \end{aligned} \tag{5.7.7}$$

The scalar α_2 contains all the products of two λ's, etc. Both α_1 and α_n may be related directly to the matrix **A**. Letting $\lambda = 0$ in (5.7.5) shows that

$$\det \mathbf{A} = (-1)^n(-1)^n\alpha_n = \alpha_n$$

Further, some elementary expansions yield

$$\alpha_1 = a_{11} + a_{22} + \cdots + a_{nn} = \sum_{k=1}^{n} a_{kk}$$

This sum of the elements on the main diagonal of a square matrix is called the trace, or "spur," of **A** and is denoted by tr **A**. It can be seen that

$$\text{tr } \mathbf{A} = \sum_{k=1}^{n} a_{kk}$$

and from (5.7.7)

$$\text{tr } \mathbf{A} = \sum_{k=1}^{n} \lambda_k \tag{5.7.8}$$

Thus the trace of a square matrix is equal to the sum of the characteristic roots and to the sum of the main diagonal elements. If **A** is an $n \times m$ matrix and **B** an $m \times n$ matrix,

$$\text{tr } (\mathbf{AB}) = \text{tr } (\mathbf{BA})$$

Of importance is the Cayley-Hamilton theorem, which states that the matrix polynomial **P**(**A**),

$$\mathbf{P}(\mathbf{A}) = \mathbf{A}^n - \alpha_1\mathbf{A}^{n-1} + \alpha_2\mathbf{A}^{n-2} - \cdots + (-1)^n\alpha_n\mathbf{I} = \mathbf{0} \tag{5.7.9}$$

is the null matrix. Another statement for this theorem is merely that a matrix satisfies its characteristic equation. If **A** is nonsingular, (5.7.9) may be solved for **I** to yield

$$\mathbf{I} = -\frac{1}{(-1)^n\alpha_n}[\mathbf{A}^n - \alpha_1\mathbf{A}^{n-1} + \cdots + (-1)^{n-1}\alpha_{n-1}\mathbf{A}]$$

Multiplying by $\mathbf{A}^{-1}$ converts this equation to

$$\mathbf{A}^{-1} = -\frac{1}{(-1)^n\alpha_n}[\mathbf{A}^{n-1} - \alpha_1\mathbf{A}^{n-2} + \cdots + (-1)^{n-1}\alpha_{n-1}\mathbf{I}]$$

In this form the Cayley-Hamilton theorem yields an equation for evaluating the inverse matrix $\mathbf{A}^{-1}$ in terms of successive powers of **A**. In practice, however, this technique usually involves too much computational effort to be of importance.

5.8. Similarity or Equivalence

For **P** and **Q** as two nonsingular square matrices the matrices **A** and **B** are said to be similar or equivalent if

$$\mathbf{B} = \mathbf{PAQ} \tag{5.8.1}$$

This may be thought of as a transformation on **A** in which **A** is premultiplied by **P** and postmultiplied by **Q** to yield **B**. In many cases the computational characteristics of **B** are more favorable in some way than those of the original **A**. In a sense this transformation is similar to the change of variables frequently used in scalar notation.

Depending on the particular form of **P** and **Q** the linear transformation of (5.8.1) may be classified in a number of ways. In particular:

1. If $\mathbf{PQ} = \mathbf{I}$ or $\mathbf{P} = \mathbf{Q}^{-1}$, then

$$\mathbf{B} = \mathbf{Q}^{-1}\mathbf{AQ}$$

and the process is termed a similarity transformation.

2. If $\mathbf{P} = \mathbf{Q}^T$, then

$$\mathbf{B} = \mathbf{Q}^T\mathbf{AQ}$$

and the process is termed a congruence transformation.

3. If $\mathbf{P} = \mathbf{Q}^T = \mathbf{Q}^{-1}$, then

$$\mathbf{B} = \mathbf{Q}^T\mathbf{AQ} = \mathbf{Q}^{-1}\mathbf{AQ}$$

and the process is termed an orthogonal transformation. Here **Q** is an orthogonal matrix.

Since

$$\mathbf{B} = \mathbf{Q}^{-1}\mathbf{AQ}$$

then

$$\mathbf{B} - \lambda\mathbf{I} = \mathbf{Q}^{-1}\mathbf{AQ} - \lambda\mathbf{I}$$

But

$$\mathbf{Q}^{-1}\mathbf{Q} = \mathbf{I} = \mathbf{I}^2$$

and thus

$$\mathbf{B} - \lambda\mathbf{I} = \mathbf{Q}^{-1}(\mathbf{A} - \lambda\mathbf{I})\mathbf{Q}$$

Taking the determinant of both sides and using

$$\det(\mathbf{ABC}) = \det\mathbf{A}\det\mathbf{B}\det\mathbf{C}$$
$$\det(\mathbf{B} - \lambda\mathbf{I}) = \det\mathbf{Q}^{-1}\det(\mathbf{A} - \lambda\mathbf{I})\det\mathbf{Q}$$

Recalling that $\det\mathbf{Q}^{-1}$ and $\det\mathbf{Q}$ are inverses of each other,

$$\det(\mathbf{B} - \lambda\mathbf{I}) = \det(\mathbf{A} - \lambda\mathbf{I})$$

As a result the characteristic roots of **A** and **B** are the same under any similarity transformation. It also follows directly that

$$\operatorname{tr}\mathbf{A} = \operatorname{tr}\mathbf{B} \qquad \text{and} \qquad \det\mathbf{A} = \det\mathbf{B}$$

under the same transformation.

5.9. Symmetric and Hermitian Matrices

The square symmetric matrix has already been defined as one whose elements are related by

$$a_{ij} = a_{ji}$$

and for which $\mathbf{A} = \mathbf{A}^T$. If the elements are complex and if the symmetrically situated elements are complex conjugates, i.e.,

$$a_{ij} = \bar{a}_{ji}$$

the matrix **A** is called "Hermitian." Note that a real symmetric matrix is a special case of a Hermitian matrix and that the elements of the main diagonal must be real in either case.

An extremely important property of both types of matrices can be developed by considering **A** as symmetric and assuming that one of the characteristic roots is complex. Upon calling this root

$$\lambda_1 = \alpha + i\beta \qquad \alpha, \beta = \text{scalars}$$

and the corresponding characteristic vector

$$\mathbf{x}_1 = \mathbf{y} + i\mathbf{z}$$

Eq. (5.7.2) becomes

$$\mathbf{A}(\mathbf{y} + i\mathbf{z}) = \lambda(\mathbf{y} + i\mathbf{z})$$

Premultiplying both sides by $(\mathbf{y} - i\mathbf{z})^T$ yields

$$(\mathbf{y} - i\mathbf{z})^T\mathbf{A}(\mathbf{y} + i\mathbf{z}) = \lambda(\mathbf{y} - i\mathbf{z})^T(\mathbf{y} + i\mathbf{z})$$

Expanding both sides,

$$\mathbf{y}^T\mathbf{A}\mathbf{y} + \mathbf{z}^T\mathbf{A}\mathbf{z} + i(\mathbf{y}^T\mathbf{A}\mathbf{z} - \mathbf{z}^T\mathbf{A}\mathbf{y}) = \lambda[\mathbf{y}^T\mathbf{y} + \mathbf{z}^T\mathbf{z} + i(\mathbf{y}^T\mathbf{z} - \mathbf{z}^T\mathbf{y})] \quad (5.9.1)$$

But for **A** symmetric

$$\mathbf{y}^T\mathbf{A}\mathbf{z} = \mathbf{z}^T\mathbf{A}\mathbf{y}$$

and also

$$\mathbf{y}^T\mathbf{z} = \mathbf{z}^T\mathbf{y}$$

Thus the term multiplying i on each side of (5.9.1) is zero, and λ must be real. It then follows that the characteristic roots of a real symmetric matrix are all real. The same result can also be proved for Hermitian matrices.

Consider next the case of **A** symmetric, and assume that all the characteristic roots are distinct, that is, $\lambda_1 \neq \lambda_2 \neq \cdots \neq \lambda_n$. Using λ_1 and λ_2 in (5.7.2) results in

$$\mathbf{A}\mathbf{x}_1 = \lambda_1\mathbf{x}_1 \quad (5.9.2)$$

$$\mathbf{A}\mathbf{x}_2 = \lambda_2\mathbf{x}_2 \quad (5.9.3)$$

where $\mathbf{x}_1$ and $\mathbf{x}_2$ are the respective characteristic vectors. The transpose of (5.9.2) is

$$\mathbf{x}_1^T\mathbf{A}^T = \lambda_1\mathbf{x}_1^T$$

and postmultiplying by $\mathbf{x}_2$ yields

$$\mathbf{x}_1^T\mathbf{A}^T\mathbf{x}_2 = \lambda_1\mathbf{x}_1^T\mathbf{x}_2 \tag{5.9.4}$$

Premultiplying (5.9.3) by $\mathbf{x}_1^T$ leads to

$$\mathbf{x}_1^T\mathbf{A}\mathbf{x}_2 = \lambda_2\mathbf{x}_1^T\mathbf{x}_2 \tag{5.9.5}$$

and subtracting (5.9.4) from (5.9.5),

$$\mathbf{x}_1^T\mathbf{A}\mathbf{x}_2 - \mathbf{x}_1^T\mathbf{A}^T\mathbf{x}_2 = (\lambda_2 - \lambda_1)\mathbf{x}_1^T\mathbf{x}_2$$

But since $\mathbf{A} = \mathbf{A}^T$ from the symmetrical property of $\mathbf{A}$, the left side of this equation is zero. Thus

$$(\lambda_2 - \lambda_1)\mathbf{x}_1^T\mathbf{x}_2 = 0$$

and since $\lambda_1 \neq \lambda_2$,

$$\mathbf{x}_1^T\mathbf{x}_2 = 0$$

This result leads to the conclusion that two different characteristic vectors of a real symmetric matrix are orthogonal to each other, i.e.,

$$\mathbf{x}_i^T\mathbf{x}_j = 0 \qquad i \neq j$$

In much the same way it can be shown that two different characteristic vectors of a Hermitian matrix are orthogonal to each other in the sense

$$\bar{\mathbf{x}}_i^T\mathbf{x}_j = 0 \qquad i \neq j$$

One further point of interest results from the assumption of n distinct characteristic roots. Without presenting the necessary proof it merely need be stated that the characteristic vectors are linearly independent if the characteristic roots are distinct.

5.10. Transformation to Diagonal Form

In the present section a number of procedures are developed for transforming the square $\mathbf{A}$ matrix to a diagonal matrix. To start the discussion, consider $\mathbf{A}$ as symmetric, with n distinct characteristic roots and n characteristic vectors. Now form a matrix $\mathbf{Q}$ whose columns are made up of the successive characteristic vectors $\mathbf{x}_1, \mathbf{x}_2, \ldots, \mathbf{x}_n$ of $\mathbf{A}$. Thus

$$\mathbf{Q} = [\mathbf{x}_1 \quad \mathbf{x}_2 \quad \cdots \quad \mathbf{x}_i \quad \cdots \quad \mathbf{x}_n]$$

Since these vectors are linearly independent $\mathbf{Q}$ is nonsingular and possesses an inverse $\mathbf{Q}^{-1}$. Use of the fact that

$$\mathbf{A}[\mathbf{x}_1 \quad \mathbf{x}_2 \quad \cdots \quad \mathbf{x}_i \quad \cdots \quad \mathbf{x}_n] = [\mathbf{A}\mathbf{x}_1 \quad \mathbf{A}\mathbf{x}_2 \quad \cdots \quad \mathbf{A}\mathbf{x}_n]$$

and $\mathbf{Ax}_i = \lambda_i\mathbf{x}_i$ results in

$$\mathbf{AQ} = [\lambda_1\mathbf{x}_1 \quad \lambda_2\mathbf{x}_2 \quad \cdots \quad \lambda_n\mathbf{x}_n]$$

Finally,

$$\mathbf{AQ} = \mathbf{Q}\begin{bmatrix} \lambda_1 & & & \\ & \lambda_2 & & \\ & & \cdots & \\ & & & \lambda_n \end{bmatrix} \tag{5.10.1}$$

The matrix on the right-hand side has elements on the main diagonal which are the successive characteristic roots and which may be written as

$$\mathbf{\Lambda} = \begin{bmatrix} \lambda_1 & & & \\ & \lambda_2 & & \\ & & \cdots & \\ & & & \lambda_n \end{bmatrix}$$

Multiplying both sides of (5.10.1) by $\mathbf{Q}^{-1}$,

$$\mathbf{\Lambda} = \mathbf{Q}^{-1}\mathbf{AQ} \tag{5.10.2}$$

and a similarity transformation on **A** yields the diagonal matrix Λ.

If normalized characteristic vectors are considered, an interesting result may be obtained. A normalized vector is obtained by dividing each element in the vector by the square root of the sum of squares of the elements of that vector. For the vector

$$\mathbf{x} = \begin{bmatrix} 1 \\ 2 \\ 3 \end{bmatrix}$$

the normalized vector $\mathbf{x}^1$ is obtained by dividing each element by

$$(1^2 + 2^2 + 3^2)^{\frac{1}{2}} = \sqrt{14}$$

and thus

$$\mathbf{x}^1 = \begin{bmatrix} \dfrac{1}{\sqrt{14}} \\ \dfrac{2}{\sqrt{14}} \\ \dfrac{3}{\sqrt{14}} \end{bmatrix}$$

Using the normalized characteristic vectors (5.1.6) leads to

$$\mathbf{x}^{1T}\mathbf{x}^1 = 1.0 \tag{5.10.3}$$

When **Q** is made up of normalized characteristic vectors, it is readily confirmed that $\mathbf{Q}^T\mathbf{Q} = \mathbf{I}$ or that $\mathbf{Q}^T = \mathbf{Q}^{-1}$. On this basis **Q** is an orthogonal matrix and the transformation to diagonal form is an orthogonal one.

This discussion has shown that when the characteristic roots of the **A** matrix are distinct an orthogonal transformation will yield a true diagonal matrix. If the characteristic values are not distinct, i.e., repeated roots occur, then it may not be possible to transform to a true diagonal matrix. Instead a similarity transformation (not necessarily orthogonal) can be shown to convert any square matrix to the so-called "Jordan canonical matrix." This matrix has the form

$$\begin{bmatrix} \lambda^1 & \beta^1 & & & \\ & \lambda_2 & \beta_2 & & \\ & & \lambda_3 & \beta_3 & \\ & & & \cdots & \beta_{n-1} \\ & & & & \lambda_n \end{bmatrix}$$

where the $\beta_1, \beta_1, \ldots, \beta_{n-1}$ are either 1 or 0. Therefore every square matrix is similar to the Jordan canonical matrix. In the special case that the characteristic values are all distinct the canonical matrix reduces to the true diagonal matrix. Further, if the **A** matrix is symmetrical or Hermitian, it is similar to the diagonal matrix even if the characteristic values are not distinct. The proof of some of these statements will not be presented here.

5.11. Quadratic Forms

By a quadratic form associated with an $n \times n$ symmetric matrix **A** is meant a scalar function of the vector **x** given by

$$Q(\mathbf{x},\mathbf{A}) = \mathbf{x}^T\mathbf{A}\mathbf{x} = \sum_{i=1}^{n} \sum_{j=1}^{n} x_i a_{ij} x_j \tag{5.11.1}$$

When the summation of (5.11.1) is expanded, i.e.,

$$Q(\mathbf{x},\mathbf{A}) = a_{11}x_1^2 + a_{12}x_1x_2 + \cdots + a_{nn}x_n^2$$

it is seen that $Q(\mathbf{x},\mathbf{A})$ is the weighted sum of all possible cross products of the components of the vector **x**. If **A** is the identity matrix **I**, the quadratic form $Q(\mathbf{x},\mathbf{A})$ becomes simply the sum of squares of the elements of **x**, that is,

$$Q(\mathbf{x},\mathbf{I}) = x_1^2 + x_2^2 + \cdots + x_n^2 \tag{5.11.2}$$

The quadratic form is positive semidefinite if $Q(\mathbf{x},\mathbf{A}) \geq 0$ for all **x**'s. If, in addition, $Q(\mathbf{x},\mathbf{A}) = 0$ implies $\mathbf{x} = 0$, then the quadratic form is positive definite. For example, (5.11.2) is positive definite since it is always positive and zero only when each component of **x** is zero. One says, with a slight abuse of language, that the matrix **A** is positive (semi-) definite if $Q(\mathbf{x},\mathbf{A})$ is positive (semi-) definite. Of particular importance is the fact that if **A** is positive definite the characteristic roots are all positive. A suitable test is that if all the principal minors of **A** are positive the matrix **A** is positive definite.

For all the characteristic roots of **A** distinct and **Q** orthogonal, set

$$\mathbf{x} = \mathbf{Q}\mathbf{y}$$

so that

$$\mathbf{y} = \mathbf{Q}^{-1}\mathbf{x} = \mathbf{Q}^T\mathbf{x}$$

As a result

$$\mathbf{x}^T\mathbf{A}\mathbf{x} = \mathbf{y}^T\mathbf{Q}^T\mathbf{A}\mathbf{Q}\mathbf{y}$$

and from (5.10.2)

$$\mathbf{x}^T\mathbf{A}\mathbf{x} = \mathbf{y}^T\Lambda\mathbf{y} = \sum_{i=1}^{n} \lambda_i y_i^2 \qquad (5.11.3)$$

The right-hand side of this equation is merely a sum of squares of the y_i with weighting factors λ_i. Thus the quadratic form in **x** is transformed to a quadratic form in **y**. Such a transformation is possible, in general, even if the characteristic roots are not all distinct.

5.12. Characteristic Roots of Special Matrices

It is now possible to make some general comments about the characteristic roots of certain special matrices. These are given in Table 5.1.

TABLE 5.1

Matrix	*Characteristic roots*
Singular	At least one root zero
Nonsingular	No roots zero
$\mathbf{A} = \mathbf{0}$	All zero
$\mathbf{A} = \mathbf{I}$	All unity
$\mathbf{A} = \mathbf{D}$	Equal to diagonal terms of **A**
$\mathbf{A} = \mathbf{A}^T$ (symmetric)	All real
Hermitian	All real
$\mathbf{B} = \mathbf{PAQ}$	Roots of $\mathbf{B}$ = roots of $\mathbf{A}$
Positive definite	All roots real and positive
$\mathbf{A}^{-1}$	Inverse roots of **A**
Idempotent ($\mathbf{A} = \mathbf{A}^k$)	All roots are 1 or 0

All have been discussed except the last two. In the case of the inverse $\mathbf{A}^{-1}$ (on the assumption that **A** is nonsingular) the result given can be obtained by noting that

$$(\mathbf{A} - \lambda\mathbf{I}) = K\left(\mathbf{I} - \frac{\mathbf{A}}{\lambda}\right) = K\mathbf{A}\left(\mathbf{A}^{-1} - \frac{\mathbf{I}}{\lambda}\right)$$

where K is a constant containing λ. To find the characteristic roots of **A**,

$$\det |\mathbf{A} - \lambda\mathbf{I}| = 0$$

or since det $\mathbf{A} \neq 0$,

$$\det\left(\mathbf{A}^{-1} - \frac{\mathbf{I}}{\lambda}\right) = 0$$

Thus the characteristic roots of $\mathbf{A}^{-1}$ are the inverse of those for $\mathbf{A}$.

An idempotent matrix is one which has the property that any power of the matrix is the same as the original matrix, that is, $\mathbf{A} = \mathbf{A}^2 = \mathbf{A}^3, \ldots$. A simple example of such a matrix is one with diagonal elements $1 - 1/n$ and off-diagonal elements $-1/n$. Thus

$$\mathbf{A}\text{ (idempotent)} = \begin{bmatrix} 1 - \frac{1}{n} & -\frac{1}{n} & \cdots & -\frac{1}{n} \\ -\frac{1}{n} & 1 - \frac{1}{n} & \cdots & \cdots \\ \cdots & \cdots & \cdots & \cdots \\ -\frac{1}{n} & \cdots & \cdots & 1 - \frac{1}{n} \end{bmatrix}$$

It can easily be verified that $\mathbf{A} = \mathbf{A}^k$, $k = 1, 2, 3, \ldots$. If $\mathbf{x}_1$ is a characteristic vector of $\mathbf{A}$ corresponding to λ_1,

$$\mathbf{A}\mathbf{x}_1 = \lambda_1\mathbf{x}_1$$

premultiplying by $\mathbf{A}$,

$$\mathbf{A}\mathbf{A}\mathbf{x}_1 = \lambda_1\mathbf{A}\mathbf{x}_1$$

which equals $$\mathbf{A}^2\mathbf{x}_1 = \lambda_1(\lambda_1\mathbf{x}_1) = \lambda_1^2\mathbf{x}_1$$

But $\mathbf{A} = \mathbf{A}^2$, and consequently

$$\mathbf{A}\mathbf{x}_1 = \lambda_1\mathbf{x}_1 = \lambda_1^2\mathbf{x}_1$$

The only numbers for λ_1 which will satisfy this identity are $\lambda_1 = 0$ or 1.0.

5.13. Methods for Evaluating the Characteristic Roots

In many problems of practical importance, i.e., the stability and dynamic response of chemical-engineering systems, the evaluation of the characteristic roots and vectors of a square matrix is of primary concern. The more important methods may be subdivided into two general categories:

1. Those which form either the characteristic polynomial or which change the **A** matrix into a particular form of matrix (tridiagonal). These are noniterative or direct methods.
2. Those which iterate on the **A** matrix.

In discussing these different techniques an effort will be made to compare the number of multiplications (or roughly the machine time) required and also the type of matrix for which the technique is suitable.

Noniterative Methods or Direct Methods. 1. There are a large number of techniques which work through developing the characteristic polynomial. One of the oldest is due to Leverrier. Since

$$\mathbf{A}\mathbf{x} = \lambda\mathbf{x}$$

then

$$\mathbf{A}^2\mathbf{x} = \lambda^2\mathbf{x}$$

and

$$\mathbf{A}^r\mathbf{x} = \lambda^r\mathbf{x} \tag{5.13.1}$$

In much the same way as (5.7.8) was derived, i.e.,

$$\text{tr } \mathbf{A} = \lambda_1 + \lambda_2 + \cdots + \lambda_n$$

(5.13.1) can be used to show that

$$\text{tr } \mathbf{A}^2 = \lambda_1^2 + \lambda_2^2 + \cdots + \lambda_n^2$$

and

$$\text{tr } \mathbf{A}^r = \lambda_1^r + \lambda_2^r + \cdots + \lambda_n^r$$

If we call $s_1 = \text{tr } \mathbf{A}$, $s_2 = \text{tr } \mathbf{A}^2$, . . . , $s_r = \text{tr } \mathbf{A}^r$, we can now calculate the coefficients in (5.7.5),

$$\det (\mathbf{A} - \lambda\mathbf{I}) = [\lambda^n - \alpha_1\lambda^{n-1} + \alpha_2\lambda^{n-2} + \cdots + (-1)^n\alpha_n] = 0$$

From (5.7.7),

$$\alpha_1 = \lambda_1 + \lambda_2 + \cdots + \lambda_n = \text{tr } \mathbf{A} = s_1 \tag{5.13.2}$$

and

$$\alpha_2 = \lambda_1\lambda_2 + \lambda_1\lambda_3 + \cdots + \lambda_{n-1}\lambda_n$$

But the right side of this last equation can be written as

$$\alpha_2 = \tfrac{1}{2}(\alpha_1 s_1 - s_2) \tag{5.13.3}$$

This can be shown quite easily by choosing $n = 2$ so that

$$\begin{aligned} \alpha_1 &= \lambda_1 + \lambda_2 = s_1 \\ s_2 &= \text{tr } \mathbf{A}^2 = \lambda_1^2 + \lambda_2^2 \\ \alpha_2 &= \tfrac{1}{2}[(\lambda_1 + \lambda_2)^2 - (\lambda_1^2 + \lambda_2^2)] = \lambda_1\lambda_2 \end{aligned}$$

Proceeding in the same way,

$$\alpha_3 = \tfrac{1}{3}(\alpha_2 s_1 - \alpha_1 s_2 + s_3) \tag{5.13.4}$$

$$\cdots\cdots\cdots\cdots$$

$$\alpha_n = \frac{1}{n}[\alpha_{n-1}s_1 - \alpha_{n-2}s_2 + \cdots + (-1)^{n-1}s_n] \tag{5.13.5}$$

Thus Leverrier's method requires the successive squaring of the **A** matrix, the corresponding computation of $s_1, s_2, \ldots, s_n$, and the use of (5.13.3) to (5.13.5) to calculate $\alpha_1, \alpha_2, \ldots, \alpha_n$. The successive traces are, of course, calculated from the sum of the main diagonal elements of **A**, $\mathbf{A}^2, \ldots, \mathbf{A}^n$.

Unfortunately, this procedure, while it will work for an arbitrary matrix **A**, requires approximately n^4 multiplications to evaluate $\alpha_1, \alpha_2, \ldots, \alpha_n$ in the characteristic polynomial and this must be followed by a root-locating technique (see Chap. 6). Thus the method can be recommended only for small matrices.

2. A variation on the method of Leverrier is due to Souriau-Frame.

Upon writing

$$\text{adj}\,(\mathbf{I}\lambda - \mathbf{A}) = \mathbf{A}_0\lambda^{n-1} - \mathbf{A}_1\lambda^{n-2} + \mathbf{A}_2\lambda^{n-3} - \cdots (-1)^n\mathbf{A}_{n-1}$$

where $\mathbf{A}_0, \mathbf{A}_1, \ldots$ are square matrices, it follows that

$$(\lambda\mathbf{I} - \mathbf{A})\,\text{adj}\,(\lambda\mathbf{I} - \mathbf{A}) = \det\,(\lambda\mathbf{I} - \mathbf{A})\mathbf{I}$$

The right-hand side of this equation can be written as

$$\det\,(\lambda\mathbf{I} - \mathbf{A})\mathbf{I} = [\lambda^n - \alpha_1\lambda^{n-1} + \alpha_2\lambda^{n-2} - \cdots (-1)^n\alpha_n]\mathbf{I}$$

Now equating coefficients of $\lambda^n, \lambda^{n-1}, \ldots$ leads to the sequence

$$\begin{aligned} \mathbf{A}_0 &= \mathbf{I} \\ \mathbf{A}_1 &= \alpha_1\mathbf{I} - \mathbf{A}\mathbf{A}_0 \\ \mathbf{A}_2 &= \alpha_2\mathbf{I} - \mathbf{A}\mathbf{A}_1 \\ &\cdots\cdots\cdots\cdots \\ \mathbf{A}_{n-1} &= \alpha_{n-1}\mathbf{I} - \mathbf{A}\mathbf{A}_{n-2} \\ \mathbf{0} &= \alpha_n\mathbf{I} - \mathbf{A}\mathbf{A}_{n-1} \end{aligned} \tag{5.13.6}$$

But from the first term in (5.13.6)

$$\begin{aligned} \mathbf{A}_0 &= \mathbf{I} \\ \mathbf{A}\mathbf{A}_0 &= \mathbf{A} \\ \text{tr}\,(\mathbf{A}\mathbf{A}_0) &= \text{tr}\,\mathbf{A} = s_1 = \alpha_1 \end{aligned} \tag{5.13.7}$$

and using the second term,

$$\begin{aligned} \mathbf{A}\mathbf{A}_1 &= \alpha_1\mathbf{A} - \mathbf{A}^2\mathbf{A}_0 = \alpha_1\mathbf{A} - \mathbf{A}^2 \\ \text{tr}\,(\mathbf{A}\mathbf{A}_1) &= \alpha_1\,\text{tr}\,\mathbf{A} - \text{tr}\,\mathbf{A}^2 = \alpha_1 s_1 - s_2 \end{aligned}$$

But since

$$2\alpha_2 = \alpha_1 s_1 - s_2$$

$$\tfrac{1}{2}\,\text{tr}\,(\mathbf{A}\mathbf{A}_1) = \alpha_2 \tag{5.13.8}$$

In the same way

$$\begin{aligned} \tfrac{1}{3}\,\text{tr}\,(\mathbf{A}\mathbf{A}_2) &= \alpha_3 \\ \tfrac{1}{4}\,\text{tr}\,(\mathbf{A}\mathbf{A}_3) &= \alpha_4 \end{aligned}$$

$$\frac{1}{r}\,\text{tr}\,(\mathbf{A}\mathbf{A}_{r-1}) = \alpha_r \tag{5.13.9}$$

The Souriau-Frame algorithm can be described as using (5.13.6) to calculate $\mathbf{A}_0 = \mathbf{I}$ and form $\mathbf{A}\mathbf{A}_0$ and its trace α_1. By using (5.13.8), $\mathbf{A}_1$ is calculated and $\mathbf{A}\mathbf{A}_1$ formed and its trace $2\alpha_2$. This is continued for $3\alpha_3$, $4\alpha_4$, . . . , with the check on the computation being that $\mathbf{A}_n = \mathbf{0}$ or $\alpha_{n+1} = 0$.

At the end of this calculation further information is available. If λ is a characteristic root,

$$(\lambda\mathbf{I} - \mathbf{A})\,\text{adj}\,(\lambda\mathbf{I} - \mathbf{A}) = \mathbf{0}$$

and any column of adj $(\lambda\mathbf{I} - \mathbf{A})$ yields a characteristic vector corresponding to the λ used. It is further possible to evaluate $\mathbf{A}^{-1}$ from the calculated matrices. Unfortunately, this algorithm also requires about n^4

multiplications to calculate the $\alpha_1, \alpha_2, \ldots, \alpha_n$ and thus is suitable only for small matrices. In addition Forsythe and Straus (27) have shown that it is very susceptible to excessive round-off errors.

3. There are a number of other methods which can be used to determine the characteristic equation. Each of these requires a root-locating technique to determine the characteristic roots; rather than discuss all the methods, only that of Hessenberg, which is computationally efficient, will be described here. The basis of this method is a similarity transformation

$$\mathbf{Q}^{-1}\mathbf{A}\mathbf{Q} = -\mathbf{P} \tag{5.13.10}$$

or

$$\mathbf{A}\mathbf{Q} + \mathbf{Q}\mathbf{P} = \mathbf{0} \tag{5.13.11}$$

The $\mathbf{Q}$ matrix is given by

$$\mathbf{Q} = [\mathbf{q}_1 \quad \mathbf{q}_2 \quad \mathbf{q}_3 \quad \cdots \quad \mathbf{q}_n]$$

with

$$\begin{aligned}
\mathbf{q}_1 &= [1 \quad 0 \quad 0 \quad \cdots \quad 0]^T \\
\mathbf{q}_2 &= [0 \quad q_{22} \quad q_{32} \quad \cdots \quad q_{n2}]^T \\
\mathbf{q}_3 &= [0 \quad 0 \quad q_{33} \quad q_{43} \quad \cdots \quad q_{n3}]^T \\
&\cdots\cdots\cdots\cdots\cdots\cdots \\
\mathbf{q}_n &= [0 \quad 0 \quad \cdots \quad 0 \quad q_{nn}]^T
\end{aligned}$$

$\mathbf{q}_1$ has a 1 as its first element and all others zero. $\mathbf{q}_r$ has the first $r - 1$ elements as zero and the remaining nonzero. In the same sequence

$$\mathbf{q}_{n+1} = [0 \quad 0 \quad \cdots \quad 0 \quad 0]^T$$

A scalar p_{11} is chosen such that

$$\mathbf{q}_2 = \mathbf{A}\mathbf{q}_1 + p_{11}\mathbf{q}_1$$

and a p_{12} and p_{22} such that

$$\mathbf{q}_3 = \mathbf{A}\mathbf{q}_2 + p_{12}\mathbf{q}_1 + p_{22}\mathbf{q}_2$$

In turn,

$$\begin{aligned}
\mathbf{q}_4 &= \mathbf{A}\mathbf{q}_3 + p_{13}\mathbf{q}_1 + p_{23}\mathbf{q}_2 + p_{33}\mathbf{q}_3 \\
&\cdots\cdots\cdots\cdots\cdots\cdots \\
\mathbf{q}_{n+1} &= \mathbf{A}\mathbf{q}_n + p_{1n}\mathbf{q}_1 + p_{2n}\mathbf{q}_2 + \cdots + p_{nn}\mathbf{q}_n
\end{aligned} \tag{5.13.12}$$

Upon defining the $\mathbf{P}$ matrix,

$$\mathbf{P} = \begin{bmatrix} p_{11} & p_{12} & \cdots & p_{1n} \\ -1 & p_{22} & \cdots & p_{2n} \\ & -1 & \cdots & \cdot \\ & & \cdots & \cdots \\ & & -1 & p_{nn} \end{bmatrix}$$

multiplication shows that

$$\mathbf{A}\mathbf{Q} + \mathbf{Q}\mathbf{P} = \mathbf{0}$$

To determine the various scalar quantities, the matrices $[\mathbf{A} \mid \mathbf{Q}]$ and $\begin{bmatrix} \mathbf{Q} \\ \hline \mathbf{P} \end{bmatrix}$

are first formed. But the similarity transformation shows that if $[\mathbf{A} \mid \mathbf{Q}]$ is postmultiplied by $\begin{bmatrix} \mathbf{Q} \\ \hdashline \mathbf{P} \end{bmatrix}$ the result is the null matrix; thus a row by column multiplication must lead to a scalar product of zero. To illustrate,

$$[a_{11} \quad a_{12} \quad \cdots \quad a_{1n} \mid 1 \quad 0 \quad \cdots \quad 0] \begin{bmatrix} 1 \\ 0 \\ \cdot \\ \cdot \\ \cdot \\ 0 \\ \hdashline p_{11} \\ -1 \\ \cdot \\ \cdot \\ \cdot \\ 0 \end{bmatrix} = a_{11} + p_{11} = 0$$

Thus p_{11} is determined. In the same way, but using the second row of $[\mathbf{A} \mid \mathbf{Q}]$,

$$[a_{21} \quad a_{22} \quad \cdots \quad a_{2n} \mid 0 \quad q_{22} \quad 0 \quad \cdots \quad 0] \begin{bmatrix} 1 \\ 0 \\ \cdot \\ \cdot \\ \cdot \\ 0 \\ \hdashline p_{11} \\ -1 \\ \cdot \\ \cdot \\ \cdot \\ 0 \end{bmatrix} = a_{21} - q_{22} = 0$$

and q_{22} is known. By continuing this process all the scalar q's and p's can be determined.

Because of similarity the characteristic roots of $-\mathbf{P}$ are the same as for $\mathbf{A}$. Thus the use of the characteristic equation for $-\mathbf{P}$ is equivalent to that for $\mathbf{A}$.

$$\det(\mathbf{P} + \lambda\mathbf{I}) = \begin{vmatrix} \lambda + p_{11} & p_{12} & \cdots & p_{1n} \\ -1 & \lambda + p_{22} & \cdots & p_{2n} \\ & -1 & \cdots & \cdot \\ & & \cdots & \cdot \\ & & -1 & \lambda + p_{nn} \end{vmatrix} = 0$$

Expansion of the determinant leads to

$$p_{1n} + p_{2n}D_1 + p_{3n}D_2 + \cdots + (\lambda + p_{nn})D_{n-1} = 0 \quad (5.13.13)$$

where

$$\begin{aligned} D_1 &= \lambda + p_{11} \\ D_2 &= (\lambda + p_{22})D_1 + p_{12} \\ D_3 &= (\lambda + p_{33})D_2 + p_{23}D_1 + p_{13} \\ &\cdots\cdots\cdots\cdots\cdots \end{aligned}$$

Substituting D_1, D_2, D_3, . . . into (5.13.13) yields the characteristic equation.

The number of multiplications required to calculate the characteristic polynomial (with **A** a general matrix) by Hessenberg's algorithm is approximately n^3. This is much more efficient than the previous methods. A defect of the method is that the three matrices **A**, **Q**, and **P** must be stored in memory; this is not considered a serious disadvantage.

4. The two methods which currently are receiving the most attention are those of Givens and Lanczos. In both cases the **A** matrix is transformed into a tridiagonal matrix which has properties which are superior in the present context to the original matrix. Before discussing the specific transformations consideration can be given to the general form of the tridiagonal matrix

$$\mathbf{B} = \begin{bmatrix} a_1 & b_1 & & & \\ c_1 & a_2 & b_2 & & \\ & c_2 & a_3 & b_3 & \\ & & \cdots & \cdots & b_{n-1} \\ & & & c_{n-1} & a_n \end{bmatrix} \quad (5.13.14)$$

A simpler form of (5.13.14) has $c_1 = b_1$, $c_2 = b_2$, . . . , $c_{n-1} = b_{n-1}$ so that **B** is symmetric. Consider now the sequence

$$\begin{aligned} P_{-1}(\lambda) &= 0 \\ P_0(\lambda) &= 1 \\ P_1(\lambda) &= (a_1 - \lambda)P_0(\lambda) \\ P_2(\lambda) &= \begin{vmatrix} a_1 - \lambda & b_1 \\ c_1 & a_2 - \lambda \end{vmatrix} \\ &= (a_2 - \lambda)P_1(\lambda) - b_1c_1P_0(\lambda) \\ P_3(\lambda) &= \begin{vmatrix} a_1 - \lambda & b_1 & 0 \\ c_1 & a_2 - \lambda & b_2 \\ 0 & c_2 & a_3 - \lambda \end{vmatrix} \\ &\cdots\cdots\cdots\cdots\cdots \\ P_r(\lambda) &= (a_r - \lambda)P_{r-1}(\lambda) - b_{r-1}c_{r-1}P_{r-2}(\lambda) \\ &\qquad r = 1, 2, \ldots, n \end{aligned} \quad (5.13.15)$$

The recurrence polynomial functions $P_r(\lambda)$ are the expansions of successively larger determinants of the matrix $\mathbf{B} - \lambda\mathbf{I}$. In the case $r = n$,

$P_n(\lambda)$ is equal to det $(\mathbf{B} - \lambda\mathbf{I})$, and the characteristic polynomial has been obtained. Equation (5.13.15) is quite simple to use and is ideally suited for digital computation. To find the characteristic roots, either a root-finding routine is applied to the characteristic polynomial, or, and this is usually a much better way, various values of λ are assumed and (5.13.15) used till $P_n(\lambda) = 0$ is satisfied. Further, the sequence $P_0(\lambda)$, $P_1(\lambda)$, . . . , $P_n(\lambda)$ forms a so-called "Sturm chain"; by noting the signs of these terms it is possible approximately to locate the roots of the characteristic polynomial. Once a characteristic root has been found, the associated characteristic vector may be evaluated by solving the linear homogeneous set $(\mathbf{B} - \lambda\mathbf{I})\mathbf{x} = 0$. This may be written as

$$\begin{aligned}
(a_1 - \lambda)x_1 + b_1x_2 &= 0 \\
c_1x_1 + (a_2 - \lambda)x_2 + b_2x_3 &= 0 \\
\cdots\cdots\cdots\cdots\cdots\cdots & \\
c_{r-2}x_{r-2} + (a_{r-1} - \lambda)x_{r-1} + b_{r-1}x_r &= 0 \\
\cdots\cdots\cdots\cdots\cdots\cdots & \\
c_{n-1}x_{n-1} + (a_n - \lambda)x_n &= 0
\end{aligned}$$

or

$$\begin{aligned}
x_2 &= \frac{1}{b_1}[(a_1 - \lambda)x_1] \\
x_3 &= \frac{1}{b_2}[c_1x_1 + (a_2 - \lambda)x_2] \\
&\cdots\cdots\cdots\cdots\cdots\cdots \\
x_r &= \frac{1}{b_{r-1}}[c_{r-2}x_{r-2} + (a_{r-1} - \lambda)x_{r-1}] \\
&\cdots\cdots\cdots\cdots\cdots\cdots \\
0 &= [c_{n-1}x_{n-1} + (a_{n-1} - \lambda)x_n]
\end{aligned} \tag{5.13.16}$$

By assuming an $x_1 \neq 0$, (5.13.16) can be used to calculate the corresponding $x_2, x_3, \ldots, x_n$. The check on the correct x_1 corresponding to the root λ is the last equation in the sequence. In this way

$$\mathbf{x} = [x_1 \quad x_2 \quad \cdots \quad x_n]^T$$

can be calculated for the root λ. For a detailed analysis of this procedure and some of the problems encountered the paper of Wilkinson (92) is recommended. In particular, the case when some of the b_r's are equal to zero or very small may lead to meaningless answers, since the method involves division by these numbers. From the brief discussion presented here, it is apparent that the transformation of the **A** matrix to tridiagonal form will considerably simplify the calculation of the characteristic roots.

The method of Givens as described in this section applies to the case of **A** a real symmetric matrix. By performing a finite set of orthogonal transformations, the **A** matrix is converted to a symmetric tridiagonal matrix. In the case that **A** is not symmetric the technique yields a supertriangular matrix, i.e.,

$$\mathbf{B} = \begin{bmatrix} b_{11} & b_{12} & \cdots & b_{1n} \\ b_{21} & b_{22} & \cdots & b_{2n} \\ & b_{32} & \cdots & \cdots \\ & & b_{n,n-1} & b_{nn} \end{bmatrix}$$

which has properties still superior to those of the original matrix. For **A** symmetric each orthogonal transformation annihilates (makes zero) an element in the **A** matrix. The sequence of annihilations is $a_{13}, a_{14}, \ldots, a_{1n}, a_{24}, a_{25}, \ldots, a_{2n}, a_{35}, \ldots, a_{3n}, \ldots$, with a maximum of $\frac{1}{2}(n-1)(n-2)$ annihilations required. If there are initial zeros in the off-tridiagonal elements of **A**, fewer annihilations or transformations are required. To illustrate the procedure, consider the simple third-order matrix

$$\mathbf{A} = \begin{bmatrix} a_{11} & a_{12} & a_{13} \\ a_{21} & a_{22} & a_{23} \\ a_{31} & a_{32} & a_{33} \end{bmatrix}$$

Postmultiplying **A** by

$$\mathbf{Q}_1 = \begin{bmatrix} 1 & 0 & 0 \\ 0 & c & -s \\ 0 & s & c \end{bmatrix}$$

and premultiplying by $\mathbf{Q}_1^{-1} = \mathbf{Q}_1^T$ results in

$$\mathbf{Q}_1^{-1}\mathbf{A}\mathbf{Q}_1 = \mathbf{B}_1 = \begin{bmatrix} a_1 & b_1 & 0 \\ b_1 & a_2 & b_2 \\ 0 & b_2 & a_3 \end{bmatrix} \tag{5.13.17}$$

The scalars c and s are chosen to satisfy

$$-sa_{12} + ca_{13} = 0 \qquad c^2 + s^2 = 1.0$$

Thus the orthogonal transformation has annihilated the elements a_{13} (and a_{31}), yielding a tridiagonal matrix. The same result can be obtained by letting

$$\mathbf{A} = [\mathbf{a}_1 \quad \mathbf{a}_2 \quad \mathbf{a}_3]$$

and replacing the column vectors $\mathbf{a}_2$ and $\mathbf{a}_3$ with $c\mathbf{a}_2 + s\mathbf{a}_3$ and $-s\mathbf{a}_2 + c\mathbf{a}_3$, respectively. The resulting matrix can be written as

$$\mathbf{A}_1 = \begin{bmatrix} \mathbf{b}_1 \\ \mathbf{b}_2 \\ \mathbf{b}_3 \end{bmatrix}$$

Replacing the row vectors $\mathbf{b}_2$ and $\mathbf{b}_3$ with $c\mathbf{b}_2 + s\mathbf{b}_3$ and $-s\mathbf{b}_2 + c\mathbf{b}_3$, respectively, yields the tridiagonal matrix of (5.13.17). This column and row interchange can be used in the form

$$\begin{aligned} &c\mathbf{a}_2 + s\mathbf{a}_r \\ -&s\mathbf{a}_2 + c\mathbf{a}_r \\ &c\mathbf{b}_2 + s\mathbf{b}_r \\ -&s\mathbf{b}_2 + c\mathbf{b}_r \end{aligned}$$

to remove $a_{13}, a_{14}, \ldots, a_{1n}$ on the first row, $a_{24}, a_{25}, \ldots, a_{2n}$ on the second row, etc., till the tridiagonal matrix is obtained.

In similarity-transform nomenclature the sequence of operations can be written as

$$\begin{aligned} \mathbf{Q}_1^{-1}\mathbf{A}\mathbf{Q}_1 &= \mathbf{B}_1 \\ \mathbf{Q}_2^{-1}\mathbf{B}_1\mathbf{Q}_2 &= \mathbf{B}_2 \\ \cdots\cdots&\cdots \\ \mathbf{Q}_r^{-1}\mathbf{B}_{r-1}\mathbf{Q}_r &= \mathbf{B}_r \end{aligned}$$

where r is the necessary number of annihilations. $\mathbf{Q}_1, \mathbf{Q}_2, \ldots, \mathbf{Q}_r$ are orthogonal matrices. The entire sequence may be written as

$$\mathbf{Q}_r^{-1} \cdots \mathbf{Q}_2^{-1}\mathbf{Q}_1^{-1}\mathbf{A}\mathbf{Q}_1\mathbf{Q}_2 \cdots \mathbf{Q}_r = \mathbf{B}_r$$

or as

$$\mathbf{Q}^{-1}\mathbf{A}\mathbf{Q} = \mathbf{B}$$

and the symmetric matrix $\mathbf{A}$ has been transformed to a symmetric tridiagonal matrix $\mathbf{B}$. The characteristic roots and vectors of $\mathbf{B}$ can now be determined from (5.13.15) and (5.13.16). Noting that

$$\mathbf{B}\mathbf{x} = (\mathbf{Q}^{-1}\mathbf{A}\mathbf{Q})\mathbf{x} = \lambda\mathbf{x}$$

where λ and $\mathbf{x}$ are for the $\mathbf{B}$ matrix, it follows that

$$\mathbf{A}\mathbf{Q}\mathbf{x} = \lambda\mathbf{Q}\mathbf{x} \qquad \mathbf{A}(\mathbf{Q}\mathbf{x}) = \lambda(\mathbf{Q}\mathbf{x})$$

Thus $\mathbf{Q}\mathbf{x}$ is the characteristic vector of $\mathbf{A}$ corresponding to the root λ.

The formation of the tridiagonal matrix $\mathbf{B}$ from $\mathbf{A}$ requires about $\frac{4}{3}n^3$ multiplications, and the calculation of the characteristic vectors of $\mathbf{B}$ and of $\mathbf{A}$ requires $3n^2$ and $2n^3$ more. The process is ideal for digital computation.

5. The n-step finite-iteration algorithm of Lanczos can be applied when $\mathbf{A}$ is an arbitrary matrix. Actually the process is not an iterative one, since only a finite number of steps are required. Symmetric and Hermitian matrices with widely separated or closely spaced characteristic roots can all be handled in the same way. For ease of presentation the analysis for $\mathbf{A}$ symmetric will be given, followed by the extension to $\mathbf{A}$ arbitrary. In the symmetric case the method involves the development of a sequence of orthogonal vectors; the result of the sequence is a similarity transformation which yields the tridiagonal matrix of (5.13.14) with the special feature that $c_1 = c_2 = \cdots = c_{n-1} = 1.0$.

For $\mathbf{A}$ symmetric and of order n choose an initial arbitrary vector $\mathbf{q}_1$, and form the new vector

$$\mathbf{q}_2 = \mathbf{A}\mathbf{q}_1 - a_1\mathbf{q}_1 \tag{5.13.18}$$

with a_1 a scalar. Imposing the condition that $\mathbf{q}_2$ be orthogonal to $\mathbf{q}_1$ leads to

$$\mathbf{q}_1{}^T\mathbf{q}_2 = 0 = \mathbf{q}_1{}^T\mathbf{A}\mathbf{q}_1 - a_1\mathbf{q}_1{}^T\mathbf{q}_1$$

or

$$a_1 = \frac{\mathbf{q}_1{}^T\mathbf{A}\mathbf{q}_1}{\mathbf{q}_1{}^T\mathbf{q}_1}$$

Now form the new vector $\mathbf{q}_3$ by

$$\mathbf{q}_3 = \mathbf{A}\mathbf{q}_2 - a_2\mathbf{q}_2 - b_1\mathbf{q}_1 \tag{5.13.19}$$

with a_2 and b_1 as scalars. Imposing the condition that $\mathbf{q}_3$ is orthogonal to both $\mathbf{q}_2$ and $\mathbf{q}_1$ leads to

$$a_2 = \frac{\mathbf{q}_2{}^T\mathbf{A}\mathbf{q}_2}{\mathbf{q}_2{}^T\mathbf{q}_2} \qquad b_1 = \frac{\mathbf{q}_1{}^T\mathbf{A}\mathbf{q}_2}{\mathbf{q}_1{}^T\mathbf{q}_1}$$

Continuing in the same manner, the vector $\mathbf{q}_4$ is formed,

$$\mathbf{q}_4 = \mathbf{A}\mathbf{q}_3 - a_3\mathbf{q}_3 - b_2\mathbf{q}_2 - d_1\mathbf{q}_1 \tag{5.13.20}$$

with a_3, b_2, and d_1 as scalars. Imposing the condition that $\mathbf{q}_4$ be orthogonal to $\mathbf{q}_3$, $\mathbf{q}_2$, and $\mathbf{q}_1$ leads to

$$a_3 = \frac{\mathbf{q}_3{}^T\mathbf{A}\mathbf{q}_3}{\mathbf{q}_3{}^T\mathbf{q}_3} \qquad b_2 = \frac{\mathbf{q}_2{}^T\mathbf{A}\mathbf{q}_3}{\mathbf{q}_2{}^T\mathbf{q}_2} \qquad d_1 = \frac{\mathbf{q}_1{}^T\mathbf{A}\mathbf{q}_3}{\mathbf{q}_1{}^T\mathbf{q}_1}$$

But using (5.13.18),

$$\mathbf{q}_2{}^T = (\mathbf{A}\mathbf{q}_1)^T - a_1\mathbf{q}_1{}^T = \mathbf{q}_1{}^T\mathbf{A}^T - a_1\mathbf{q}_1{}^T$$

and thus

$$\mathbf{q}_1{}^T\mathbf{A}^T = \mathbf{q}_2{}^T + a_1\mathbf{q}_1{}^T \tag{5.13.21}$$

But since $\mathbf{A} = \mathbf{A}^T$,

$$d_1 = \frac{\mathbf{q}_1{}^T\mathbf{A}\mathbf{q}_3}{\mathbf{q}_1{}^T\mathbf{q}_1} = \frac{\mathbf{q}_1{}^T\mathbf{A}^T\mathbf{q}_3}{\mathbf{q}_1{}^T\mathbf{q}_1}$$

and the use of (5.13.21) yields

$$d_1 = \frac{(\mathbf{q}_2{}^T + \mathbf{a}_1\mathbf{q}_1{}^T)\mathbf{q}_3}{\mathbf{q}_1{}^T\mathbf{q}_1} = 0$$

The formation of new vectors $\mathbf{q}_5$, $\mathbf{q}_6$, . . . can be continued as before, but in each case only two scalars are needed. These may be defined as

$$\mathbf{q}_{r+1} = \mathbf{A}\mathbf{q}_r - a_r\mathbf{q}_r - b_{r-1}\mathbf{q}_{r-1} \tag{5.13.22}$$

with $\mathbf{q}_{r+1}$ orthogonal to $\mathbf{q}_r, \mathbf{q}_{r-1}, \ldots, \mathbf{q}_2, \mathbf{q}_1$ and

$$a_r = \frac{\mathbf{q}_r{}^T\mathbf{A}\mathbf{q}_r}{\mathbf{q}_r{}^T\mathbf{q}_r} \qquad b_r = \frac{\mathbf{q}_{r-1}^T\mathbf{A}\mathbf{q}_r}{\mathbf{q}_{r-1}^T\mathbf{q}_{r-1}} \tag{5.13.23}$$

Since $\mathbf{A}$ can have only n independent vectors, this process must terminate with $\mathbf{q}_{n+1} = \mathbf{0}$; that is, the index on r in (5.13.22) is $r = 1, 2, \ldots, n$ with $b_0 = 0$. This can be used as a check feature to see whether or not the succeeding vectors are correct.

The system vector equations (5.13.22) can be written as

$$\mathbf{A}[\mathbf{q}_1 \quad \mathbf{q}_2 \quad \cdots \quad \mathbf{q}_n] = [\mathbf{q}_1 \quad \mathbf{q}_2 \quad \cdots \quad \mathbf{q}_n]\begin{bmatrix} a_1 & b_1 & & & \\ 1 & a_2 & b_2 & & \\ & 1 & a_3 & b_3 & \\ & & \cdots & \cdots & b_{n-1} \\ & & & 1 & a_n \end{bmatrix}$$

or, calling $\mathbf{Q}$ the matrix with columns $\mathbf{q}_1, \mathbf{q}_2, \ldots, \mathbf{q}_n$,

$$\begin{aligned} \mathbf{AQ} &= \mathbf{QB} \\ \mathbf{Q}^{-1}\mathbf{AQ} &= \mathbf{B} \end{aligned} \tag{5.13.24}$$

where $\mathbf{B}$ is the tridiagonal matrix

$$\mathbf{B} = \begin{bmatrix} a_1 & b_1 & & & \\ 1 & a_2 & b_2 & & \\ & 1 & a_3 & b_3 & \\ & & \cdots & \cdots & b_{n-1} \\ & & & 1 & a_n \end{bmatrix}$$

The characteristic roots and vectors of $\mathbf{A}$ now follow directly from $\mathbf{B}$.

The extension to $\mathbf{A}$ unsymmetric follows in much the same way. Now, however, it is necessary to use two sequences of vectors to remove elements above and below the tridiagonals. Starting with an arbitrary column vector $\mathbf{q}_1$ and an arbitrary row vector $\mathbf{p}_1$, a sequence is built up with the recurrence relations

$$\begin{aligned} \mathbf{q}_{r+1} &= \mathbf{A}\mathbf{q}_r - a_r\mathbf{q}_r - b_{r-1}\mathbf{q}_{r-1} \\ \mathbf{p}_{r+1} &= \mathbf{p}_r\mathbf{A}^* - a_r^*\mathbf{p}_r - b_{r-1}^*\mathbf{p}_{r-1} \end{aligned}$$

such that $\mathbf{q}_{r+1}$ and $\mathbf{p}_{r+1}$ are biorthogonal. This means that $\mathbf{p}_r^*\mathbf{q}_s = 0$ for $r \neq s$; the asterisk denotes the complex conjugate vector. On this basis the scalars a_r and b_{r-1} are determined by

$$a_r = \frac{\mathbf{p}_r^*\mathbf{A}\mathbf{q}_r}{\mathbf{p}_r^*\mathbf{q}_r} \qquad b_{r-1} = \frac{\mathbf{p}_{r-1}^*\mathbf{A}\mathbf{q}_r}{\mathbf{p}_{r-1}^*\mathbf{q}_{r-1}} \qquad b_0 = 0$$

As before $\mathbf{q}_{n+1} = \mathbf{p}_{n+1} = \mathbf{0}$ can be used as a check condition. The matrix $\mathbf{Q}$ formed from $\mathbf{q}_1, \mathbf{q}_2, \ldots, \mathbf{q}_n$ leads to (5.13.24).

There are two possible problems associated with the use of the Lanczos method. One of the $\mathbf{q}_r$'s, $r \leq n$, may become zero, and small rounding errors tend to destroy the orthogonalization of the vectors. The first problem may usually be overcome by restarting the process with new vectors, as pointed out by Wilkinson (93). Gregory (41) has indicated the means for maintaining the orthogonalization, but this requires some additional computation and leads to a supertriangular instead of a tridiagonal matrix. These defects are not very serious and the corrections do much to improve the over-all process. For a symmetric matrix the number of computations in the Lanczos method is roughly equivalent to Givens's method; an unsymmetric matrix requires approximately twice as many computations as in the symmetric case.

Iterative Methods. 1. One of the earliest and still useful iterative methods for determining the characteristic roots is due to Jacobi. It applies to real symmetric and Hermitian matrices and yields all the roots at one time. The basic procedure involves an annihilation of the off-diagonal elements using a series of orthogonal matrices; the result is a diagonal matrix with the characteristic roots on the diagonal. In certain ways this approach resembles that of Givens as already described.

To illustrate the procedure, consider the matrix $\mathbf{A}$ as symmetric, of order 2, and using

$$\mathbf{Q}_1 = \begin{bmatrix} \cos\alpha & -\sin\alpha \\ \sin\alpha & \cos\alpha \end{bmatrix}$$

form

$$\mathbf{Q}_1{}^T\mathbf{A}\mathbf{Q}_1 = \mathbf{B}$$

Upon performing the indicated multiplications the elements of the $\mathbf{B}$ matrix become

$$\begin{aligned} b_{11} &= a_{11}\cos^2\alpha + a_{12}\sin\alpha\cos\alpha + a_{21}\cos\alpha\sin\alpha + a_{22}\sin^2\alpha \\ &= a_{11}\cos^2\alpha + a_{12}\sin 2\alpha + a_{22}\sin^2\alpha \qquad a_{12} = a_{21} \\ b_{22} &= a_{11}\sin^2\alpha - a_{12}\sin 2\alpha + a_{22}\cos^2\alpha \\ b_{12} &= b_{21} = (a_{11} - a_{22})\sin\alpha\cos\alpha - a_{12}(\cos^2\alpha - \sin^2\alpha) \end{aligned}$$

Now if the off-diagonal elements of $\mathbf{B}$ are to be zero,

$$b_{12} = b_{21} = 0$$

and

$$\frac{a_{12}}{a_{11} - a_{22}} = \frac{\sin\alpha\cos\alpha}{\cos^2\alpha - \sin^2\alpha}$$

But by using some trigonometric identities there follows

$$\frac{2a_{12}}{a_{11} - a_{22}} = \tan 2\alpha \tag{5.13.25}$$

and the choice of α as given in (5.13.25) annihilates the off-diagonal elements. The main diagonal elements in $\mathbf{B}$ are merely λ_1 and λ_2.

In the case $\mathbf{A}$ of order n the $\mathbf{Q}_1$ matrix above is replaced with an nth-order matrix,

$$\mathbf{Q}_1 = \begin{bmatrix} 1 & & & & & & & \\ & 1 & & & & & & \\ & & 1 & & & & & \\ & & & (\cos\alpha)_{ii} & \cdots & (-\sin\alpha)_{ij} & & \\ & & & \cdots & 1 & \cdots & & \\ & & & (\sin\alpha)_{ji} & \cdots & (\cos\alpha)_{jj} & & \\ & & & & & & 1 & \\ & & & & & & & \cdots \\ & & & & & & & & 1 \end{bmatrix}$$

This is a revised identity matrix with $\cos\alpha$ as the ith and jth diagonal elements, $\sin\alpha$ as the jth row and ith column element, and $-\sin\alpha$ as the ith row and jth column. This will annihilate the elements a_{ij} and a_{ji}. α is determined by using (5.13.25) and involves only a single off-diagonal element $a_{ij} = a_{ji}$ and elements on the major diagonal. In the method of Jacobi the largest off-diagonal element is first annihilated, then the remaining largest, etc. Unfortunately, when one element is forced to be zero during the iteration, some of the elements which were previously made zero may be altered and may thus assume a nonzero value. Hence the process must be repeated over and over and the off-diagonal elements continuously annihilated. Eventually the entire process will converge so that all the off-diagonal elements are smaller than a chosen upper limit. At this point the main diagonal contains the characteristic roots. This procedure corresponds to [see (5.10.2)]

$$\mathbf{Q}_r^{-1} \cdots \mathbf{Q}_3^{-1}\mathbf{Q}_2^{-1}\mathbf{Q}_1^{-1}\mathbf{A}\mathbf{Q}_1\mathbf{Q}_2\mathbf{Q}_3 \cdots \mathbf{Q}_r = \mathbf{\Lambda}$$

or

$$\mathbf{Q}^{-1}\mathbf{A}\mathbf{Q} = \mathbf{\Lambda} = \mathbf{Q}^T\mathbf{A}\mathbf{Q}$$

Note that this method is iterative, whereas Givens's method requires only a fixed number of annihilations. However, one now gets the $\mathbf{\Lambda}$ matrix instead of the tridiagonal matrix, and all the characteristic roots are available at once.

In actual practice the annihilation of the a_{ij} element can be performed by calling $\mathbf{a}_i$ and $\mathbf{a}_j$ the ith and jth column vector and then replacing these two vectors with $\cos\alpha\mathbf{a}_i + \sin\alpha\mathbf{a}_j$ and $\cos\alpha\mathbf{a}_j - \sin\alpha\mathbf{a}_i$, respectively. The new ith and jth row vectors $\mathbf{b}_i$ and $\mathbf{b}_j$ are then replaced with $\cos\alpha\mathbf{b}_i + \sin\alpha\mathbf{b}_j$ and $\cos\alpha\mathbf{b}_j - \sin\alpha\mathbf{b}_i$. A further feature of the Jacobi iteration is that $\sum_{i,j}^{n} a_{ij}^2$ in the original and subsequent transformed matrices remains constant during the computation. In fact, $\sum_{i,j}^{n} a_{ij}^2$ equals

$\sum_1^n \lambda_i^2$, and this fact can be used as a test to determine when the iteration process is completed.

If the characteristic vectors are desired, the over-all transformation is changed to

$$\mathbf{AQ} = \mathbf{Q\Lambda}$$

Since $\mathbf{\Lambda}$ is the diagonal matrix containing the characteristic roots, the columns of the $\mathbf{Q}$ matrix must be the corresponding vectors.

2. One of the defects of the Jacobi process is that the off-diagonal elements must be scanned repeatedly to determine the largest value. Since this is very time-consuming, the cyclic, or serial, Jacobi method has become popular. In this case the off-diagonal elements are annihilated in some preset pattern, such as row by row. This procedure has been shown always to converge if $-\pi/4 \leq \alpha \leq \pi/4$. More annihilations are required than in the standard Jacobi method, but the total machine time is decreased by a significant amount, since the scanning is not required. In this form the Jacobi method has found wide application.

3. The Jacobi iteration process above is very inviting and works for real symmetric or Hermitian matrices because all the characteristic roots are real. Greenstadt (39) has attempted to generalize the method to the general type of matrices. While this method works for many cases, there are a number of matrices for which convergence will not occur. In effect what seems to happen is that these particular matrices keep returning to the original form and thus never converge. However, even in the present form without any measure of convergence, the method probably will prove very useful.

4. An extremely important iterative procedure used to find one characteristic root at a time is the power method. To illustrate the procedure, let the roots of the $\mathbf{A}$ matrix be real and distinct, and adopt the convention

$$|\lambda_1| \geq |\lambda_2| \geq |\lambda_2| \geq \cdots \geq |\lambda_n|$$

λ_1 is the largest root, sometimes called the dominant root. Starting with an almost arbitrary vector $\mathbf{y}^{(0)}$, i.e., say,

$$\mathbf{y}^{(0)} = \begin{bmatrix} 1 \\ 0 \\ \cdot \\ \cdot \\ \cdot \\ 0 \end{bmatrix} \quad \text{or} \quad \mathbf{y}^{(0)} \begin{bmatrix} 1 \\ 1 \\ \cdot \\ \cdot \\ \cdot \\ 1 \end{bmatrix}$$

generate the sequence

$$\mathbf{y}^{(r+1)} = k^{(r+1)}\mathbf{A}\mathbf{y}^{(r)} \qquad r = 0, 1, 2, \ldots \tag{5.13.26}$$

where $k^{(r+1)}$ is chosen to make the component in $\mathbf{y}^{(r+1)}$ of largest absolute value equal to 1. In other words, $\frac{1}{k^{(r+1)}}$ is merely the largest element in $\mathbf{y}^{(r+1)}$. As shown by von Mises, this sequence will converge to the vector $\mathbf{x}_1$, $\mathbf{y}^{(r+1)} \to \mathbf{x}_1$, corresponding to the dominant characteristic root λ_1. When convergence has occurred,

$$\mathbf{y}^{(r+1)} = \mathbf{A}\mathbf{y}^{(r)}$$

can be used to calculate the root λ_1, since $\mathbf{y}^{(r+1)}$ and $\mathbf{y}^{(r)}$ must be a scalar multiple λ_1 of each other. The test on the convergence is usually

$$|\lambda_1^{(r+1)} - \lambda_1^{(r)}| < 10^{-p}$$

or

$$\left|\frac{\lambda_1^{(r+1)} - \lambda_1^{(r)}}{\lambda_1^{(r+1)}}\right| < 10^{-p}$$

where p is an integer.

Since the roots are all real and distinct, any arbitrary vector can be uniquely expressed as a linear combination of the characteristic vectors of the $\mathbf{A}$ matrix. Upon using α_i as a scalar this means that

$$\mathbf{y}^{(0)} = \sum_{i=1}^{n} \alpha_i \mathbf{x}_i \tag{5.13.27}$$

or

$$\mathbf{A}^r\mathbf{y}^{(0)} = \sum_{1}^{n} \alpha_i \mathbf{A}^r \mathbf{x}_i$$

But upon recalling that

$$\mathbf{A}^r\mathbf{x} = \lambda^r\mathbf{x}$$

there follows

$$\mathbf{A}^r\mathbf{y}^{(0)} = \sum_{1}^{n} \alpha_i \lambda_i^r \mathbf{x}_i$$

and by noting that

$$d\mathbf{y}^{(r)} = \mathbf{A}^r\mathbf{y}^{(0)}$$

where d is the inverse of normalizing components in (5.13.26),

$$d\mathbf{y}^{(r)} = \sum_{1}^{n} \alpha_i \lambda_i^r \mathbf{x}_i$$

This may be rewritten as

$$\begin{aligned} d\mathbf{y}^{(r)} &= \lambda_1^r \sum_{1}^{n} \alpha_i \left(\frac{\lambda_i}{\lambda_1}\right)^r \mathbf{x}_i \\ &= \lambda_1^r \left[\alpha_1\mathbf{x}_1 + \alpha_2\left(\frac{\lambda_2}{\lambda_1}\right)^r \mathbf{x}_2 + \alpha_3\left(\frac{\lambda_3}{\lambda_1}\right)^r \mathbf{x}_3 + \cdots + \alpha_n\left(\frac{\lambda_n}{\lambda_1}\right)^r \mathbf{x}_n\right] \end{aligned}$$

But since λ_1 is the largest root, $\lambda_i/\lambda_1 < 1.0$ for $i \neq 1.0$, and as r increases, $(\lambda_i/\lambda_1)^r \rightarrow 0$. Thus, for r large,

$$d\mathbf{y}^{(r)} = \lambda_1{}^r\alpha_1\mathbf{x}_1$$

The rate of convergence of $\mathbf{y}^{(r)}$ to $\mathbf{x}_1$ is dictated largely by the ratio of λ_2/λ_1; if this ratio is approximately equal to 1.0, convergence is slow, whereas a wide separation of λ_1 and λ_2 leads to rapid convergence. Since the roots have been assumed distinct, the only possible case of $|\lambda_1| = |\lambda_2|$ is $\lambda_1 = -\lambda_2$. Actually Wilkinson has shown that a ratio as low as 1/1.1 is capable of convenient handling by the power method (see Example 5.1).

The power method has all the advantages and disadvantages of any iterative process. Because (5.13.26) yields $\mathbf{y}^{(r+1)}$ as a function of only $\mathbf{y}^{(r)}$ and not $\mathbf{y}^{(r-1)}, \mathbf{y}^{(r-2)}, \ldots$, this is termed a linear iterative procedure (see Sec. 5.15). An error made in one step of the calculation is self-correcting by the continued application of the iteration. A serious defect in some cases, however, may be the rate of convergence. Since each iteration requires n^2 multiplications, rapid convergence is desired to minimize machine time. In the case of a bad initial choice of $\mathbf{y}^{(0)}$ or when equal or nearly equal roots exist, the process may not converge or, if it does converge, it may be too slow for practical use. To illustrate the problem of a bad guess of $\mathbf{y}^{(0)}$, consider that $\mathbf{A}$ is symmetric and $|\lambda_1| \neq |\lambda_2|$. Starting with (5.13.27),

$$\mathbf{y}^{(0)} = \sum_1^n \alpha_i\mathbf{x}_i$$

and let $\mathbf{y}^{(0)}$ be orthogonal to $\mathbf{x}_1$. As a result

$$\mathbf{x}_1{}^T\mathbf{y}^{(0)} = 0 = \alpha_1\mathbf{x}_1{}^T\mathbf{x}_1 + \alpha_2\mathbf{x}_1{}^T\mathbf{x}_2 + \cdots + \alpha_n\mathbf{x}_1{}^T\mathbf{x}_n$$

But since $\mathbf{A}$ is symmetric, the scalar product of any two characteristic roots is zero and thus

$$\alpha_1\mathbf{x}_1{}^T\mathbf{x}_1 = 0$$

For this equality to hold, $\alpha_1 = 0$ and (5.13.27) becomes

$$\mathbf{y}^{(0)} = \alpha_2\mathbf{x}_2 + \alpha_3\mathbf{x}_3 + \cdots + \alpha_n\mathbf{x}_n$$

The iteration now converges to λ_2 and $\mathbf{x}_2$, and not the dominant root and vector. In actual practice the effect of rounding the numbers will gradually destroy the orthogonality, but the iteration to the dominant root will be very slow. A classic example of such a situation was presented by Bodewig (10) for the matrix

$$\mathbf{A} = \begin{bmatrix} 2 & 1 & 3 & 4 \\ 1 & -3 & 1 & 5 \\ 3 & 1 & 6 & 2 \\ 4 & 5 & -2 & -1 \end{bmatrix}$$

e roots of this matrix are

$$\lambda_1 = -8.0285 \qquad \lambda_2 = 7.9329 \qquad \lambda_3 = 5.6688 \qquad \lambda_4 = -1.5732$$

d

$$\mathbf{x}_1 = [1 \quad 2.5011 \quad -0.75773 \quad -2.5642]^T$$

the starting vector $\mathbf{y}^{(0)} = [1 \quad 1 \quad 1 \quad 1]^T$ is chosen, the iteration yields

$\lambda_1 = 7.5$	3d iteration
$\lambda_1 = 7.85$	4th iteration
$\lambda_1 = 7.56$	5th iteration
$\lambda_1 = 8.00$	6th iteration
. . . . . .	
$\lambda_1 = 7.285$	100th iteration
$\lambda_1 = 8.647$	101st iteration
. . . .	
$\lambda_1 = -1.751$	400th iteration
$\lambda_1 = -36.469$	401st iteration
. . . .	
$\lambda_1 = -7.943$	800th iteration
$\lambda_1 = -8.113$	801st iteration
. . . .	
$\lambda_1 = -8.0278$	1,200th iteration
$\lambda_1 = -8.0292$	1,201st iteration

us, 1,201 iterations lead to a result with less than four-place accuracy. e slowness of convergence is due to two reasons: $\mathbf{y}^{(0)}$ was chosen nost orthogonal to $\mathbf{x}_1$, and the absolute values of λ_1 and λ_2 are almost ual. When the iteration starts, $\alpha_1 \simeq 0$ and convergence tends toward However, the contribution of λ_1 gradually becomes important, and e iteration finally approaches this value.

5. In an effort to speed up the rate of convergence of the power method number of simple variations have been proposed. The first variation be described uses $\mathbf{A} - \beta\mathbf{I}$ in (5.13.26), instead of $\mathbf{A}$. This has been tailed by Wilkinson (90). β is a scalar, and for the particular case of $= 0$ the method reduces to the standard power iteration. To illustrate e utility of this approach, note that

$$\mathbf{Ax} = \lambda\mathbf{x}$$

d thus

$$(\mathbf{A} - \beta\mathbf{I})\mathbf{x} = (\lambda - \beta)\mathbf{x}$$

is equation has the roots $\lambda_1 - \beta, \lambda_2 - \beta, \ldots, \lambda_n - \beta$ but the me characteristic vectors as the first equation. For $n = 3$, $\lambda_1 = 20$, $= 10$, and $\lambda_3 = 5$, the power iteration with $\mathbf{A}$ will converge in the ratio $/\lambda_1 = \frac{10}{20} = \frac{1}{2}$ to λ_1. If we use an iteration with $\mathbf{A} - 5\mathbf{I}$, the converg-ce will occur in the ratio $(\lambda_2 - 5)/(\lambda_1 - 5) = \frac{5}{15} = \frac{1}{3}$ to λ_1. Thus the convergence is speeded up with the criteria for convergence residing in t values $|\lambda_1 - \beta|, |\lambda_2 - \beta|, \ldots, |\lambda_n - \beta|$. On the assumption that t normal power method converges too slowly it is easily possible to adj the β so that convergence is rapid. In this form the modified pow method is a very powerful computational tool for evaluating the do inant root.

At the same time it is also possible to find the least dominant ro λ_n. If β is chosen large enough, the absolute values of all the ro are reversed, i.e., in the case above with $\beta = 25$, $\lambda_1 - 25 = -5$,

$$\lambda_2 - 25 = -15$$

and $\lambda_3 - 25 = -20$, and the iteration will proceed to the root λ_3. by chance β is chosen equal to λ_1, the net effect is to annihilate the infl ence of λ_1 and iterate to λ_2. The reader can see how versatile the ite tion with $\mathbf{A} - \beta\mathbf{I}$ makes the normal power method.

6. Wilkinson has also pointed out the advantages of performing t iteration with various powers of the **A** matrix, i.e., with $\mathbf{A}^2, \mathbf{A}^4, \mathbf{A}^6, \ldots$ $\mathbf{A}^{2^p}$. In this case convergence occurs at the rate $(\lambda_2/\lambda_1)^{2^p}$ and is fast than in the normal power method. However, each iteration requi about n^3 multiplications per step, or n more than previously. This m prove serious when the **A** matrix is large. A further disadvantage the squaring iteration is that the **A** matrix itself, which is usually kno to the highest accuracy, is not used, but rather powers of the **A** matr This may introduce rounding errors which leave the final result in err In such a case the answer from the squared iteration should be subject to one or two steps of the normal power iteration to "tighten up" t final answers.

7. The normal power method can also frequently be speeded up by t application of the extrapolation technique discussed previously for OD In summary form this method uses $\mathbf{y}^{(r)}$, $\mathbf{y}^{(r+1)}$, and $\mathbf{y}^{(r+2)}$ to yield improved vector component y_i by means of

$$y_i = \frac{y_i^{(r)} y_i^{(r+2)} - (y_i^{(r+1)})^2}{y_i^{(r)} - 2y_i^{(r+1)} + y_i^{(r+2)}}$$

The subscript i is taken to mean the ith component of the vectors. the same sense the value of λ_1 can be extrapolated. As a word of ca tion, it is necessary that the three vectors be representative of the co vergence vectors to λ_1. Otherwise, valid answers will not be obtain This means that some criteria in the computer program must be used determine when to switch from the power method to the extrapolati

8. Once the dominant root and vector λ_1 and $\mathbf{x}_1$ are evaluated, t next step is to remove their influence in the **A** matrix and calculate

ıd $\mathbf{x}_2$. This process is termed deflation of the matrix; it is repeated me after time to yield successively $\lambda_2, \lambda_3, \ldots, \lambda_n$.

For $\mathbf{A}$ symmetric the deflation can be performed by using the orthog-ıal feature of the characteristic vectors. If the arbitrary vector is :pressed as

$$\mathbf{y}^{(0)} = \alpha_1\mathbf{x}_1 + \alpha_2\mathbf{x}_2 + \cdots + \alpha_n\mathbf{x}_n$$

new vector is defined,

$$\mathbf{z}^{(0)} = \mathbf{y}^{(0)} - \alpha_1\mathbf{x}_1$$

ıch that $\mathbf{z}^{(0)}$ and $\mathbf{x}_1$ are orthogonal. This can be achieved by letting

$$\mathbf{x}_1{}^T\mathbf{z}^{(0)} = \mathbf{x}_1{}^T\mathbf{y}^{(0)} - \alpha_1\mathbf{x}_1{}^T\mathbf{x}_1 = 0$$

ıd thus

$$\alpha_1 = \frac{\mathbf{x}_1{}^T\mathbf{y}^{(0)}}{\mathbf{x}_1{}^T\mathbf{x}_1}$$

n this basis $\mathbf{z}^{(0)}$ can be calculated and used in the form

$$\mathbf{z}^{(0)} = \alpha_2\mathbf{x}_2 + \alpha_3\mathbf{x}_3 + \cdots + \alpha_n\mathbf{x}_n$$

he power method will now converge to λ_2 and $\mathbf{x}_2$. As the calculation oceeds, round-off errors will probably lead to a gradual loss in the thogonality and a build-up of the influence of $\mathbf{x}_1$ and λ_1. This can be evented by reorthogonalizing the vectors from time to time.

Once λ_1, λ_2, and $\mathbf{x}_1$, $\mathbf{x}_2$ are known, the same procedure can be used to aluate λ_3 and $\mathbf{x}_3$. This leads to equations of the form

$$\mathbf{x}_1{}^T(\mathbf{z}^{(0)} - \alpha_1\mathbf{x}_1 - \alpha_2\mathbf{x}_2) = 0$$
$$\mathbf{x}_2{}^T(\mathbf{z}^{(0)} - \alpha_1\mathbf{x}_1 - \alpha_2\mathbf{x}_2) = 0$$

hich must be solved for α_1 and α_2 to achieve orthogonality. It seems ›vious that this approach will be fruitful only for the first few vectors, nce it is necessary to solve sets of simultaneous equations of higher der as $\lambda_3, \lambda_4, \ldots$ are calculated.

It is also possible to use the matrix $\mathbf{A} - \beta\mathbf{I}$ to evaluate $\lambda_2, \lambda_3, \ldots, \lambda_n$. oting that

$$(\mathbf{A} - \beta\mathbf{I})\mathbf{y}^{(0)} = (\mathbf{A}\mathbf{x}_1 - \beta\mathbf{x}_1) + (\mathbf{A}\mathbf{x}_2 - \beta\mathbf{x}_2) + \cdots$$
$$= (\lambda_1\mathbf{x}_1 - \beta\mathbf{x}_1) + (\lambda_2\mathbf{x}_2 - \beta\mathbf{x}_2) + \cdots$$

e choice of $\beta = \lambda_1$ will lead to

$$(\mathbf{A} - \lambda_1\mathbf{I})\mathbf{y}^{(0)} = 0 + (\lambda_2\mathbf{x}_2 - \lambda_1\mathbf{x}_2) + \cdots = (\lambda_2 - \lambda_1)\mathbf{x}_2 + \cdots$$

ɔrming the vector $(\mathbf{A} - \lambda_1\mathbf{I})\mathbf{y}^{(0)}$ and power iterating with $\mathbf{A}$ will thus nd toward λ_2 and $\mathbf{x}_2$. As before, round-off will gradually destroy the nvergence to λ_2; operating with $\mathbf{A} - \lambda_1\mathbf{I}$ on the vectors occasionally thus necessary. This can then be extended to calculate λ_3 and $\mathbf{x}_3$ by ing $(\mathbf{A} - \lambda_1\mathbf{I})(\mathbf{A} - \lambda_2\mathbf{I})$ and can be continued further. Since this approach works for **A** symmetric or not and the power method is us with the **A** matrix itself, this proves to be a powerful tool for eval ating the successive roots and vectors.

A completely different approach to the calculation of $\lambda_2, \lambda_3, \ldots,$ $\mathbf{x}_3, \ldots$ is possible when λ_1 and $\mathbf{x}_1$ are known. The technique is illu trated for **A** symmetric. As a first step the vector $\mathbf{x}_1$ is normalized that the scalar product is 1.0, i.e.,

$$\mathbf{x}_1{}^T\mathbf{x}_1 = 1.0$$

A new matrix is then defined by

$$\mathbf{A}_1 = \mathbf{A} - \lambda_1\mathbf{x}_1\mathbf{x}_1{}^T$$

This new matrix has some nice properties. To illustrate,

$$\mathbf{A}_1\mathbf{x}_1 = (\mathbf{A} - \lambda_1\mathbf{x}_1\mathbf{x}_1{}^T)\mathbf{x}_1 = \mathbf{A}\mathbf{x}_1 - \lambda_1\mathbf{x}_1\mathbf{x}_1{}^T\mathbf{x}_1 = \mathbf{A}\mathbf{x}_1 - \lambda_1\mathbf{x}_1 = 0$$

and thus one characteristic root is zero. This root is λ_1 corresponding $\mathbf{x}_1$. At the same time

$$\mathbf{A}_1\mathbf{x}_i = (\mathbf{A} - \lambda_1\mathbf{x}_1\mathbf{x}_1{}^T)\mathbf{x}_i = \mathbf{A}\mathbf{x}_i - \lambda_1\mathbf{x}_1\mathbf{x}_1{}^T\mathbf{x}_i = \mathbf{A}\mathbf{x}_i = \lambda_i\mathbf{A}$$

by using the orthogonality of the vectors of a symmetric matrix. As result $\mathbf{A}_1$ has the roots $0, \lambda_2, \lambda_3, \ldots, \lambda_n$. If we iterate with $\mathbf{A}_1$ in t power method, the sequence will converge to λ_2 and $\mathbf{x}_2$. Further roo and vectors can be obtained in an analogous way.

5.14. Sylvester's Theorem

Equation (5.7.9) can be written in the form

$$\mathbf{A}^n = \alpha_1\mathbf{A}^{n-1} + \alpha_2\mathbf{A}^{n-2} + \cdots + (-1)^{n-1}\alpha_n\mathbf{I}$$

in which the nth power of **A** is a linear combination of **I** and $\mathbf{A}^{n-1}$, $\mathbf{A}^{n-}$ . . . . An alternative arrangement is given by

$$\begin{aligned}\mathbf{P}(\mathbf{A}) = \mathbf{A}^n = a_1[(\mathbf{A} - \lambda_2\mathbf{I})(\mathbf{A} - \lambda_3\mathbf{I}) \cdots (\mathbf{A} - \lambda_n\mathbf{I})]& \\ + a_2[(\mathbf{A} - \lambda_1\mathbf{I})(\mathbf{A} - \lambda_3\mathbf{I}) \cdots (\mathbf{A} - \lambda_n\mathbf{I})]& \\ \cdots\cdots\cdots\cdots\cdots\cdots\cdots\cdots& \\ + a_n[(\mathbf{A} - \lambda_1\mathbf{I})(\mathbf{A} - \lambda_2\mathbf{I}) \cdots (\mathbf{A} - \lambda_{n-1}\mathbf{I})]& \quad (5.14.\end{aligned}$$

This is in the form of the Lagrangian interpolation formula. Po multiplying both sides of (5.14.1) with $\mathbf{x}_1$ and using $\mathbf{A}\mathbf{x}_1 = \lambda_1\mathbf{x}_1$ results

$$\mathbf{P}(\mathbf{A})\mathbf{x}_1 = a_1[(\mathbf{A} - \lambda_2\mathbf{I})(\mathbf{A} - \lambda_3\mathbf{I}) \cdots (\mathbf{A} - \lambda_n\mathbf{I})]\mathbf{x}_1$$

In the same way, but using $\mathbf{x}_i$,

$$\begin{aligned}\mathbf{P}(\mathbf{A})\mathbf{x}_i &= a_i[(\mathbf{A} - \lambda_1\mathbf{I}) \cdots (\mathbf{A} - \lambda_{i-1}\mathbf{I})(\mathbf{A} - \lambda_{i+1}\mathbf{I}) \cdots (\mathbf{A} - \lambda_n\mathbf{I})]\mathbf{x} \\ &= a_i[(\lambda_i - \lambda_1) \cdots (\lambda_i - \lambda_{i-1})(\lambda_i - \lambda_{i+1}) \cdots (\lambda_i - \lambda_n)]\mathbf{x}_i\end{aligned}$$

But since

$$\mathbf{A}^r\mathbf{x}_i = \lambda_i{}^r\mathbf{x}_i$$

it follows that

$$\mathbf{P}(\mathbf{A})\mathbf{x}_i = P(\lambda_i)\mathbf{x}_i$$

and

$$P(\lambda_i) = a_i[(\lambda_i - \lambda_1) \cdot \cdot \cdot (\lambda_i - \lambda_{i-1})(\lambda_i - \lambda_{i+1}) \cdot \cdot \cdot (\lambda_i - \lambda_n)]$$

Finally,

$$a_i = \frac{P(\lambda_i)}{\prod\limits_{j \neq i}^{n} (\lambda_i - \lambda_j)}$$

and from (5.14.1)

$$\mathbf{P}(\mathbf{A}) = \sum_{i=1}^{n} \frac{P(\lambda_i)}{\prod\limits_{j \neq i}^{n} (\lambda_i - \lambda_j)} \prod_{j \neq i}^{n} (\mathbf{A} - \lambda_j\mathbf{I}) \tag{5.14.2}$$

Equation (5.14.2) is Sylvester's theorem for the case where all the characteristic roots of **A** are distinct.

Fractional powers of a matrix and transcendental matrices can now be defined and evaluated. To illustrate the use of this theorem, consider **A** of third order with distinct roots λ_1, λ_2, and λ_3. Equation (5.14.2) yields for $e^{\mathbf{A}}$

$$\mathbf{P}(\mathbf{A}) = e^{\mathbf{A}} = e^{\lambda_1} \frac{(\mathbf{A} - \lambda_2\mathbf{I})(\mathbf{A} - \lambda_3\mathbf{I})}{(\lambda_1 - \lambda_2)(\lambda_1 - \lambda_3)} + e^{\lambda_2} \frac{(\mathbf{A} - \lambda_1\mathbf{I})(\mathbf{A} - \lambda_3\mathbf{I})}{(\lambda_2 - \lambda_1)(\lambda_2 - \lambda_3)} + e^{\lambda_3} \frac{(\mathbf{A} - \lambda_1\mathbf{I})(\mathbf{A} - \lambda_2\mathbf{I})}{(\lambda_3 - \lambda_1)(\lambda_3 - \lambda_2)}$$

As a second illustration consider $\mathbf{A}^N$, where N is a scalar integer and **A** has distinct roots $\lambda_1, \lambda_2, \ldots, \lambda_n$. From (5.14.2)

$$\mathbf{A}^N = \sum_{i=1}^{n} \lambda_i{}^N \frac{\prod\limits_{j \neq i}^{n} (\mathbf{A} - \lambda_j\mathbf{I})}{\prod\limits_{j \neq i}^{n} (\lambda_i - \lambda_j)}$$

If N is large, the major root λ_1 will occur as $\lambda_1{}^N$ and dominate over $\lambda_2{}^N, \lambda_3{}^N, \ldots, \lambda_n{}^N$. Thus

$$\mathbf{A}^N \simeq \lambda_1{}^N \frac{\prod\limits_{j=2}^{n} (\mathbf{A} - \lambda_j\mathbf{I})}{\prod\limits_{j=2}^{n} (\lambda_1 - \lambda_j)} \qquad N = \text{large integer}$$

and $\mathbf{A}^N$ can be quickly evaluated.

Sylvester's theorem can be extended to handle repeated roots, etc., but the formulas now become cumbersome. In any event the usefulness of the theorem resides in the ease of determining the characteristic roots; on this basis the case outlined above is the most useful.

5.15. Matrix Inversion and the Solution of Linear Equations

On the assumption that the **A** matrix is nonsingular, (5.1.9) can be converted to

$$\mathbf{x} = \mathbf{A}^{-1}\mathbf{c} \tag{5.15.1}$$

The present section will be concerned with techniques for evaluating the unknown **x** vector. This can be accomplished either by solving (5.1.9) directly or by evaluating the inverse of the **A** matrix and postmultiplying by the known vector **c**[(5.15.1)]. If **x** must be evaluated for a large number of different **c**'s, the prior calculation of $\mathbf{A}^{-1}$ followed by the matrix-vector multiplication is more efficient than solving (5.1.9) directly. This is especially true if the order of the matrix **A** is large, only n^2 multiplications being necessary once the inverse is known, rather than the approximately n^3 multiplications required for solving (5.1.9) directly.

It is possible to categorize the **A** matrix into two general types. The matrix may be of low order with no zero elements; in this form it is called a dense matrix. At the other extreme the matrix may be very large (of high order) with many zero elements; in this form it is called a sparse matrix. The dense matrix usually results from a statistical analysis, and the corresponding system is solved by a variation of the elimination method to be described. The sparse matrix usually arises from the difference approximation to PDE, and the corresponding system is solved by the iteration techniques to be described.

It should be pointed out that even though a matrix is nonsingular there is no guarantee that the inverse can be obtained with as much accuracy as desired. It is quite possible that small changes in the elements of **A** may make large changes in the inverse elements. In such a case the **A** matrix is termed ill-conditioned. To illustrate this point, consider the following simultaneous equations:

$$x_1 + x_2 = c_1 \qquad x_1 + (1 + \epsilon)x_2 = c_2$$

Solving for the unknowns leads to

$$x_1 = c_1 - \frac{c_2 - c_1}{\epsilon} \qquad x_2 = \frac{c_2 - c_1}{\epsilon}$$

and if ϵ is small, a slight change in its numerical value causes disproportionately large changes in x_1 and x_2. In the same way the **A** matrix for this system is

$$\mathbf{A} = \begin{bmatrix} 1 & 1 \\ 1 & 1+\epsilon \end{bmatrix}$$

and

$$\det \mathbf{A} = \epsilon$$

In this case the ill conditioning occurs from det **A** being almost zero. The question arises as to a quantitative measure of the condition of a matrix. Listed below are a number of such criteria proposed by various authors:

1. The numerical value of det **A** can be used as a measure of the condition of a matrix. When det **A** is very small, the matrix is ill-conditioned.

2. The P-condition number defined as

$$P = \frac{|\lambda_1|}{|\lambda_n|}$$

is a simple measure. λ_1 is the largest and λ_n the smallest root of **A**. When P is very large, the matrix is ill-conditioned; when $P \simeq 1.0$, there is little spread in the roots and the matrix is well conditioned.

3. The N-condition number defined as

$$N = \frac{N(\mathbf{A})N(\mathbf{A}^{-1})}{n}$$

has also been suggested. In this criterion

$$N(\mathbf{A}) = [\text{tr}\,(\mathbf{A}^T\mathbf{A})]^{\frac{1}{2}}$$

with a similar arrangement for $N(\mathbf{A}^{-1})$. For the well-conditioned matrix **I**,

$$\text{tr}\,(\mathbf{A}^T\mathbf{A}) = n$$

and thus

$$N = 1.0$$

A well-conditioned matrix has an N-condition number close to 1.0.

Unfortunately it is extremely difficult to implement any of these condition measures unless the matrix is well conditioned. Involved in the measures are such items as det **A**, $\mathbf{A}^{-1}$, and λ_i; when **A** is ill-conditioned, these items are difficult to calculate.

Just as in the case of the characteristic roots and vectors of the **A** matrix the methods for either evaluating $\mathbf{A}^{-1}$ or solving for $\mathbf{x}$ directly can be conveniently classified into direct, or finite-step, methods and iterative methods.

Direct Methods of Solution. Before proceeding to discuss the various direct methods a few simple items concerning triangular matrices should be mentioned. A lower triangular matrix **L** has the form

$$\mathbf{L} = \begin{bmatrix} l_{11} & & & \\ l_{21} & l_{22} & & \\ l_{31} & l_{32} & l_{33} & \\ \cdots & \cdots & \cdots & \cdots \\ l_{n1} & \cdots & \cdots & l_{nn} \end{bmatrix}$$

and an upper triangular matrix **U**,

$$\mathbf{U} = \begin{bmatrix} u_{11} & u_{12} & \cdots & u_{1n} \\ & u_{22} & \cdots & \cdots \\ & & \cdots & \cdots \\ & & & u_{nn} \end{bmatrix} \tag{5.15.2}$$

When the main diagonal elements of either **L** or **U** are all unity, the designation is made of unit lower or upper triangular matrices.

The square matrix **A** can be represented by many arrangements of triangular matrices. Thus

$$\mathbf{A} = \mathbf{LU} \tag{5.15.3a}$$

where **L** or **U** is unit triangular,

$$\mathbf{A} = \mathbf{LDU} \tag{5.15.3b}$$

where **L** and **U** are unit triangular and **D** is a diagonal matrix, and

$$\mathbf{A} = (\mathbf{D} + \mathbf{L})(\mathbf{I} + \mathbf{U}) \tag{5.15.4}$$

where **L** and **U** have zero as main diagonal elements. The inverse of **A** can be obtained by simple manipulation of the right-hand side of any of the equations. Upon using (5.15.3*a*) as an example it follows that

$$\mathbf{A}^{-1} = \mathbf{U}^{-1}\mathbf{L}^{-1} \tag{5.15.5}$$

Thus the inverse of **A** is determined by inverting the triangular matrices. Fortunately, the inversion of a triangular matrix can be accomplished in a simple manner. Calling

$$\mathbf{P} = \mathbf{U}^{-1} = \begin{bmatrix} p_{11} & p_{12} & \cdots & p_{1n} \\ & p_{22} & \cdots & \cdots \\ & & \cdots & \cdots \\ & & & p_{nn} \end{bmatrix}$$

it follows that

$$\mathbf{UP} = \mathbf{I}$$

Multiplying the **U** and **P** matrices together and equating the results to the corresponding coefficients of **I** leads to

$$\begin{aligned} u_{11}p_{11} &= 1 \\ u_{22}p_{22} &= 1 \\ \cdot\ \cdot\ \cdot\ &\cdot\ \cdot\ \cdot \\ u_{nn}p_{nn} &= 1 \\ u_{11}p_{12} + u_{12}p_{22} &= 0 \\ \cdot\ \cdot\ \cdot\ \cdot\ \cdot\ \cdot\ &\cdot\ \cdot\ \cdot\ \cdot \end{aligned}$$

Solving this system for the p_{ij}'s leads to the simple set of rules for obtaining the elements of the inverse,

$$\begin{aligned} p_{ij} &= 0 && j = 1, 2, \ldots, n; i > j \\ p_{ii} &= \frac{1}{u_{ii}} && i = 1, 2, \ldots, n \\ p_{ij} &= -\frac{1}{u_{ii}} \sum_{r=i+1}^{j} u_{ir}p_{rj} && j = 2, 3, \ldots, n; j > i \end{aligned} \tag{5.15.6}$$

1. The best-known direct method is the algorithm of Gauss, often called the elimination method. The methods of Jordan, Doolittle, and Crout are variations on this Gaussian elimination. To outline the important features of this method suitably, a detailed step-by-step description is first presented. In condensed form (5.1.8) can be written as

$$\begin{aligned} a_{11}x_1 + \sum_{j=2}^{n} a_{1j}x_j &= c_1 \\ a_{i1}x_1 + \sum_{j=2}^{n} a_{ij}x_j &= c_i \qquad i = 2, 3, \ldots, n \end{aligned}$$

On the assumption that $a_{11} \neq 0$ the first equation is multiplied by $1/a_{11}$, solved for x_1, and this value substituted into all the other equations. This results in

$$x_1 + \sum_{j=2}^{n} \frac{a_{1j}}{a_{11}} x_j = \frac{c_1}{a_{11}}$$

$$\sum_{j=2}^{n} \left(a_{ij} - \frac{a_{i1}a_{1j}}{a_{11}} \right) x_j = c_i - \frac{a_{i1}c_1}{a_{11}} \qquad i = 2, 3, \ldots, n$$

In more compact form this last system becomes

$$\begin{aligned} x_1 + \sum_{j=2}^{n} a_{1j}^{(1)}x_j &= c_1{}^{(1)} \\ \sum_{j=2}^{n} a_{ij}^{(1)}x_j &= c_i^{(1)} \qquad i = 2, 3, \ldots, n \end{aligned} \tag{5.15.7}$$

The superscripts in (5.15.7) indicate that the element is the result of the first set of calculations. Note that the second part of (5.15.7) contains $n - 1$ unknowns, $x_2, x_3, \ldots, x_n$, and can be expanded to

$$a_{22}^{(1)}x_2 + \sum_{j=3}^{n} a_{2j}^{(1)}x_j = c_2^{(1)}$$

$$a_{i2}^{(1)}x_2 + \sum_{j=3}^{n} a_{ij}^{(1)}x_j = c_i^{(1)} \qquad i = 3, 4, \ldots, n$$

On the assumption that $a_{22}^{(1)} \neq 0$ the first equation is multiplied by $1/a_{22}^{(1)}$, solved for x_2, and this value substituted into all the other equations. This results in

$$x_2 + \sum_{j=3}^{n} \frac{a_{2j}^{(1)}}{a_{22}^{(1)}} x_j = \frac{c_2^{(1)}}{a_{22}^{(1)}}$$

$$\sum_{j=3}^{n} \left(a_{ij}^{(1)} - \frac{a_{i2}^{(1)}a_{2j}^{(1)}}{a_{22}^{(1)}} \right) x_j = c_i^{(1)} - \frac{a_{i2}^{(1)}c_2^{(1)}}{a_{22}^{(1)}} \qquad i = 3, 4, \ldots, n$$

or in compact form

$$x_2 + \sum_{j=3}^{n} a_{2j}^{(2)}x_j = c_2^{(2)}$$

$$\sum_{j=3}^{n} a_{ij}^{(2)}x_j = c_i^{(2)} \qquad i = 3, 4, \ldots, n \tag{5.15.8}$$

The second equation of (5.15.8) now contains only $n - 2$ unknowns $x_3, x_4, \ldots, x_n$. At this point the system available is

$$x_1 + \sum_{j=2}^{n} a_{1j}^{(1)}x_j = c_1^{(1)}$$

$$x_2 + \sum_{j=3}^{n} a_{2j}^{(2)}x_j = c_i^{(2)}$$

$$\sum_{j=3}^{n} a_{ij}^{(2)}x_j = c_i^{(2)} \qquad i = 3, 4, \ldots, n$$

The pattern of operations is now clear, since the first equation has n unknowns, the second has $n - 1$ unknowns, and the remaining have $n - 2$ unknowns. If the elimination process is continued, the nth equation in the original system eventually becomes

$$a_{nn}^{(n-1)}x_n = c_n^{(n-1)} \tag{5.15.9}$$

with only one unknown x_n. The equation before (5.15.9) will have two unknowns, x_{n-1} and x_n, etc. By using (5.15.9) x_n can be calculated directly; by using the equation preceding, x_{n-1} can then be calculated with the known value of x_n. This process of back substitution yields $x_{n-2}, x_{n-3}, \ldots, x_2, x_1$ in sequence. The vector $\mathbf{x}$ is now defined. At any stage in the forward elimination

$$a_{ij}^{(r)} = a_{ij}^{(r-1)} - \frac{a_{ir}^{(r-1)} a_{rj}^{(r-1)}}{a_{rr}^{(r-1)}}$$

$$c_i^{(r)} = c_i^{(r-1)} - \frac{a_{ir}^{(r-1)} c_r^{(r-1)}}{a_{rr}^{(r-1)}}$$

The method described yields the $\mathbf{x}$ vector directly without recourse to the evaluation of $\mathbf{A}^{-1}$. Approximately $n^3/3$ and $n^3/6$ multiplications are required for $\mathbf{A}$ unsymmetrical and symmetrical, respectively. In the same sense $2n^3 + n$ and $n^2 + 3n$ storage locations are required, respectively.

As shown by Von Neumann and Goldstine (98) the Gaussian elimination is very susceptible to round-off error when n is large, and a special scaling procedure may be necessary. Interchanging two rows (or columns) of a matrix interchanges the corresponding two rows (or columns) of the inverse matrix. Von Neumann and Goldstine use this fact to suggest that the largest element in the $(n - r) \times (n - r)$ system at the rth step be moved so that it is in the upper left-hand position. This element becomes the divisor in the next elimination and because of its size assures a maximum accuracy. Scaling the original matrix and compensating the inverse matrix, however, requires an excess amount of data manipulation and machine time. In the same sense, if any leading coefficient turns out to be zero, it is necessary always to rearrange rows (or columns) irrespective of whether the above scaling is performing. For these reasons the Gaussian elimination finds its greatest use for small dense matrices.

The Gaussian elimination can be easily described in matrix notation. The $\mathbf{A}$ matrix is first multiplied by $\mathbf{L}_1$ to yield $\mathbf{U}_1$, that is,

$$\mathbf{L}_1\mathbf{A} = \mathbf{U}_1$$

or

$$\begin{bmatrix} \frac{1}{a_{11}} & & & & \\ -\frac{a_{21}}{a_{11}} & 1 & & & \\ -\frac{a_{31}}{a_{11}} & 0 & & & \\ \cdot & & & & \\ \cdot & & & & \\ \cdot & & & & \\ -\frac{a_{n1}}{a_{11}} & 0 & 0 & \cdots & 1 \end{bmatrix} \mathbf{A} = \begin{bmatrix} 1 & a_{12}^{(1)} & \cdots & a_{1n}^{(1)} \\ 0 & a_{22}^{(1)} & & \\ 0 & \cdots & & \\ \cdots & \cdots & \cdots & \cdots \\ 0 & a_{n2}^{(1)} & \cdots & a_{nn}^{(1)} \end{bmatrix}$$

In the next step $\mathbf{U}_1$ is multiplied by $\mathbf{L}_2$ to yield $\mathbf{U}_2$, that is,

$$\mathbf{L}_2\mathbf{U}_1 = \mathbf{U}_2$$

or

$$\begin{bmatrix} 1 & 0 & & \\ 0 & \dfrac{1}{a_{22}^{(1)}} & & \\ 0 & -\dfrac{a_{32}^{(1)}}{a_{22}^{(1)}} & 1 & \\ \cdots & \cdots & \cdots & \cdots \\ 0 & -\dfrac{a_{n2}^{(1)}}{a_{22}^{(1)}} & \cdots & 1 \end{bmatrix} \mathbf{U}_1 = \begin{bmatrix} 1 & a_{12}^{(1)} & \cdots & \cdots & a_{1n}^{(1)} \\ 0 & 1 & a_{23}^{(2)} & \cdots & \cdots \\ \cdots & 0 & a_{33}^{(2)} & \cdots & \cdots \\ \cdots & \cdots & \cdots & \cdots & \cdots \\ 0 & 0 & a_{n3}^{(2)} & \cdots & a_{nn}^{(2)} \end{bmatrix}$$

The process is continued in the form

$$\begin{aligned} \mathbf{L}_3\mathbf{U}_2 &= \mathbf{U}_3 \\ \mathbf{L}_4\mathbf{U}_3 &= \mathbf{U}_4 \\ &\cdots\cdots \\ \mathbf{L}_{n-1}\mathbf{U}_{n-2} &= \mathbf{U}_{n-1} \end{aligned}$$

where each successive $\mathbf{L}$ has nonzero values only in the next right colum and along the main diagonal. The over-all sequence becomes

$$\mathbf{L}_{n-1}\mathbf{L}_{n-2} \cdots \mathbf{L}_2\mathbf{L}_1\mathbf{A} = \mathbf{U}_{n-1}$$

or

$$\mathbf{LA} = \mathbf{U}$$

where $\mathbf{L}$ is a lower triangular matrix and $\mathbf{U}$ is an upper triangular matri given by

$$\mathbf{U} = \begin{bmatrix} 1 & a_{12}^{(1)} & \cdots & \cdots & a_{1n}^{(1)} \\ & 1 & a_{23}^{(2)} & \cdots & a_{2n}^{(2)} \\ & & 1 & \cdots & \cdots \\ & & & \cdots & \cdots \\ & & & & a_{nn}^{(n-1)} \end{bmatrix}$$

Note that the final matrix equation follows from (5.15.2) when one recall that the inverse of a triangular matrix has the same shape. If desired $\mathbf{A}^{-1}$ can be calculated from

$$\mathbf{A}^{-1} = \mathbf{U}^{-1}\mathbf{L}$$

by using (5.15.6). Further, postmultiplication by $\mathbf{x}$ yields

$$\mathbf{LAx} = \mathbf{Ux}$$

or, with $\mathbf{Ax} = \mathbf{c}$,

$$\mathbf{U}^{-1}\mathbf{Lc} = \mathbf{x}$$

2. A variation on the Gaussian elimination is due to Jordan. In th second stage of the Gauss calculation the x_2 is eliminated from th third, fourth, . . . , nth equations. In the Jordan modification x_2 i eliminated from the first equation as well. Thus at each stage in th

calculation not only is x_i eliminated from all the following equations, but from the preceding ones as well. The net result is a series of equations with only one unknown variable per equation; i.e., the first equation has x_1, the second x_2, ... Back substitution is no longer required.

In matrix notation

$$\mathbf{L}_1\mathbf{A} = \mathbf{U}_1$$

or

$$\begin{bmatrix} \frac{1}{a_{11}} & & & \\ -\frac{a_{21}}{a_{11}} & 1 & & \\ \cdots & \cdots & \cdots & \cdots \\ -\frac{a_{n1}}{a_{11}} & \cdots & & 1 \end{bmatrix} \mathbf{A} = \begin{bmatrix} 1 & a_{12}^{(1)} & \cdots & a_{1n}^{(1)} \\ 0 & a_{22}^{(1)} & \cdots & \cdots \\ \cdots & \cdots & \cdots & \cdots \\ 0 & a_{n2}^{(1)} & & a_{nn}^{(1)} \end{bmatrix}$$

This is followed by

$$\mathbf{L}_2\mathbf{U}_1 = \mathbf{U}_2$$

or

$$\begin{bmatrix} 1 & \frac{a_{12}^{(1)}}{a_{22}^{(1)}} & & & \\ 0 & \frac{1}{a_{22}^{(1)}} & & & \\ 0 & \cdots & \cdots & & \\ \cdots & \cdots & \cdots & 1 & \\ \cdots & \cdots & \cdots & \cdots & \cdots \\ 0 & \frac{a_{n2}^{(1)}}{a_{22}^{(1)}} & \cdots & \cdots & 1 \end{bmatrix} \mathbf{U}_1 = \begin{bmatrix} 1 & 0 & a_{13}^{(2)} & \cdots & a_{1n}^{(2)} \\ 0 & 1 & a_{23}^{(2)} & \cdots & \cdots \\ \cdots & 0 & 0 & \cdots & \cdots \\ \cdots & \cdots & \cdots & \cdots & \cdots \\ 0 & 0 & a_{n3}^{(2)} & \cdots & a_{nn}^{(2)} \end{bmatrix}$$

This is continued, to yield

$$\mathbf{L}_n\mathbf{L}_{n-1} \cdots \mathbf{L}_2\mathbf{L}_1\mathbf{A} = \mathbf{U}_n$$

or

$$\mathbf{LA} = \mathbf{D} = \mathbf{I}$$

The final matrix is merely the identity matrix, and the inverse is given by

$$\mathbf{A}^{-1} = \mathbf{L}$$

3. It is also possible to modify the Gaussian elimination so as to minimize the storage requirements and data handling. Two such processes are due to Doolittle and Crout and are referred to as compact elimination schemes. In Crout's method, for example, only two triangular matrices are held in storage, with all intermediate results used immediately and discarded. Only Crout's method will be described here. Crout starts with the so-called "augmented" matrix for the system. This is comprised of the **A** matrix with the **c** vector added as an additional

column. Upon calling **B** the augmented matrix,

$$\mathbf{B} = \left[\begin{array}{cccc:c} a_{11} & a_{12} & \cdots & a_{1n} & c_1 \\ \cdots & \cdots & \cdots & \cdots & \cdots \\ a_{n1} & a_{n2} & \cdots & a_{nn} & c_n \end{array}\right] = \mathbf{A} \,\vdots\, \mathbf{c}$$

the elimination scheme is used to calculate the elements of an auxiliary matrix **B′**.

$$\mathbf{B}' = \left[\begin{array}{cccc:c} a'_{11} & a'_{12} & \cdots & a'_{1n} & c'_1 \\ \cdots & \cdots & \cdots & \cdots & \cdots \\ a'_{n1} & a'_{n2} & \cdots & a'_{nn} & c'_n \end{array}\right] = \mathbf{A}' \,\vdots\, \mathbf{c}'$$

The elements of this auxiliary matrix are obtained directly from the elements of **B** by the following set of rules:

a. The elements are determined in the following order: elements of first column, then elements of first row to right of first column; elements of second column below first row, then elements of second row to right of second column; elements of third column below second row, then elements of third row to right of third column; and so on, until all elements are determined.

b. The first column is identical with the first column of the given matrix. Each element of the first row except the first is obtained by dividing the corresponding element of the given matrix by that first element.

c. Each element on or below the principal diagonal is equal to the corresponding element of the given matrix minus the sum of those products of elements in its row and corresponding elements in its column (in the auxiliary matrix) which involve only previously computed elements.

d. Each element to the right of the principal diagonal is given by a calculation which differs from rule 3 only in that there is a final division by its diagonal element in the auxiliary matrix.

In equation form these rules may be stated as follows, where the elements of **B** are a_{ij} and of **B′** are a'_{ij}:

$$a'_{ij} = a_{ij} - \sum_{r=1}^{j-1} a'_{ir}a'_{rj} \qquad i \geq j$$

$$a'_{ij} = \frac{1}{a'_{ii}}\left(a_{ij} - \sum_{r=1}^{i-1} a'_{ir}a'_{rj}\right) \qquad i < j$$

$$c'_i = \frac{1}{a'_{ii}}\left(c_i - \sum_{r=1}^{i-1} a'_{ir}c'_r\right)$$

Actually the auxiliary matrix contains a number of elements which are the result of intermediate calculations and are not significant for the next step. The significant elements are

$$\mathbf{B}' = \left[\begin{array}{cccccc:c} 1 & a'_{12} & \cdots & \cdots & & a'_{1n} & c'_1 \\ & 1 & a'_{23} & \cdots & & a'_{2n} & c'_2 \\ & & 1 & \cdots & & \cdots & \cdots \\ & & & \cdots & & \cdots & \cdots \\ & & & & & 1 & c'_n \end{array}\right]$$

which relate to the general system of equations

$$x_i = c'_i - \sum_{r=i+1}^{n} a'_{ir}x_r \qquad i = 1, 2, \ldots, n$$

(The reader should compare this equation with the sequential steps of the Gauss algorithm.)

From the $\mathbf{B}'$ matrix the $\mathbf{x}$ vector can be obtained by back substitution. Thus,

$$\begin{array}{ll} i = n & x_n = c'_n \\ i = n - 1 & x_{n-1} = c'_{n-1} - a'_{n-1,n}x_n \\ \cdots & \cdots \end{array}$$

Just as with Gauss' algorithm the Crout algorithm requires $n^3/3$ multiplication to evaluate one $\mathbf{x}$ if $\mathbf{A}$ is unsymmetrical. However, only $n^2 + n$ storage locations are required plus working storage, a saving of n^2 locations.

4. An important method when $\mathbf{A}$ is symmetric is the Cholesky, or square-root, algorithm. If the matrix $\mathbf{B}$ is defined by

$$\mathbf{B}^2 = \mathbf{A}$$

then $\mathbf{B}$ may be termed the square root of $\mathbf{A}$. Writing $\mathbf{A}$ in the form

$$\mathbf{A} = \mathbf{LDU}$$

where $\mathbf{L}$ and $\mathbf{U}$ are unit lower and upper triangular matrices, it follows that

$$\mathbf{A} = (\mathbf{LD}^{\frac{1}{2}})(\mathbf{D}^{\frac{1}{2}}\mathbf{U})$$

But since $\mathbf{A}$ is symmetric, $\mathbf{LD}^{\frac{1}{2}}$ is the transpose of $\mathbf{D}^{\frac{1}{2}}\mathbf{U}$, and calling $\mathbf{B} = \mathbf{D}^{\frac{1}{2}}\mathbf{U}$,

$$\mathbf{A} = \mathbf{B}^T\mathbf{B} \tag{5.15.10}$$

Thus the symmetrical matrix $\mathbf{A}$ can be represented as the product $\mathbf{B}^T\mathbf{B}$ of two triangular matrices symmetrical to each other. Further,

$$\mathbf{A}^{-1} = (\mathbf{B}^{-1})(\mathbf{B}^T)^{-1}$$

and once the elements of **B** are obtained, the inverse of **A** results from inversion of a triangular matrix and one matrix multiplication.

The Cholesky algorithm is concerned with determining the b_{ij}'s which satisfy (5.15.10). If we let

$$\mathbf{B} = \begin{bmatrix} b_{11} & b_{12} & \cdots & b_{1n} \\ & b_{22} & \cdots & \cdots \\ & & \cdots & \cdots \\ & & & b_{nn} \end{bmatrix}$$

(5.15.10) can be written as

$$\begin{bmatrix} a_{11} & a_{12} & \cdots & a_{1n} \\ a_{21} & a_{22} & \cdots & \cdots \\ \cdots & \cdots & \cdots & \cdots \\ a_{n1} & \cdots & \cdots & a_{nn} \end{bmatrix} = \begin{bmatrix} b_{11} & & & \\ b_{12} & b_{22} & & \\ \cdots & \cdots & \cdots & \\ b_{1n} & \cdots & \cdots & b_{nn} \end{bmatrix} \begin{bmatrix} b_{11} & b_{12} & \cdots & b_{1n} \\ & b_{22} & \cdots & \cdots \\ & & \cdots & \cdots \\ & & & b_{nn} \end{bmatrix}$$

But for this arrangement to be an identity

$$\begin{aligned} b_{11}^2 &= a_{11} \\ b_{11}b_{12} &= a_{12} \\ b_{12}^2 + b_{22}^2 &= a_{22} \\ \cdots&\cdots \end{aligned}$$

or

$$\begin{aligned} b_{11} &= \sqrt{a_{11}} \\ b_{12} &= \frac{a_{12}}{b_{11}} \\ b_{22} &= \sqrt{a_{22} - b_{12}^2} \\ \cdots&\cdots \end{aligned}$$

These relations may be written in general form as

$$b_{11} = \sqrt{a_{11}}$$

$$b_{1j} = \frac{a_{1j}}{b_{11}} \qquad j = 2, 3, \ldots, n$$

$$b_{ii} = \sqrt{a_{ii} - \sum_{r=1}^{i-1} b_{ri}^2} \qquad i = 2, 3, \ldots, n$$

$$b_{ij} = \frac{1}{b_{ii}}\left(a_{ij} - \sum_{r=1}^{i-1} b_{ri}b_{rj}\right) \qquad i = 2, 3, \ldots, n; j = i+1, i+2, \ldots, n$$

n this way all the elements of **B** can be calculated from the a_{ij} of **A**. $\mathbf{A}^{-1}$ can be evaluated as previously indicated.

If the **x** vector is desired, a new column vector **z** is defined such that

$$\mathbf{B}^T\mathbf{z} = \mathbf{c}$$

nd then

$$\mathbf{B}\mathbf{x} = \mathbf{z}$$

n both steps only triangular matrices are involved.

The direct evaluation of $\mathbf{A}^{-1}$ by Cholesky's method requires about $n^3/2$ multiplications and of **x** about $n^3/6$. Thus there is no saving in multiplications over the previous elimination methods. However, as many as $n^2/2 - n/2$ storage locations can be saved as compared with Crout's method, with the disadvantage that n square roots must be calculated. A real advantage of the Cholesky algorithm is the smaller round-off error when compared with the previous methods. Because f the use of the square-root operation all the elements in the matrices re brought closer together. Subsequent arithmetic operations are then subject to smaller rounding errors.

When the **A** matrix is positive definite, all the square-root terms are real and the process can be carried out with no complications. If, owever, **A** is not positive definite, imaginary terms may result. This problem can be eliminated but extra computation is required.

5. A method which has achieved a certain degree of popularity is he partitioning, or submatrices, algorithm. For the square matrix **A** f order n, partitioning is performed to yield

$$\mathbf{A} = \left[\begin{array}{c|c} \mathbf{A}_1 & \mathbf{A}_2 \\ \hline \mathbf{A}_3 & \mathbf{A}_4 \end{array}\right] \tag{5.15.11}$$

here $\mathbf{A}_1$ and $\mathbf{A}_4$ are square matrices of order n_1 and n_2, respectively, nd $\mathbf{A}_2$ and $\mathbf{A}_3$ are $n_1 \times n_2$ and $n_2 \times n_1$ nonsquare matrices, respectively. Of course $n_1 + n_2 = n$. Let the inverse of A be written as

$$\mathbf{A}^{-1} = \left[\begin{array}{c|c} \mathbf{B}_1 & \mathbf{B}_2 \\ \hline \mathbf{B}_3 & \mathbf{B}_4 \end{array}\right] \tag{5.15.12}$$

ith $\mathbf{B}_1$, $\mathbf{B}_2$, $\mathbf{B}_3$, and $\mathbf{B}_4$ of the same order as the corresponding $\mathbf{A}_r$. As a esult

$$\mathbf{A}\mathbf{A}^{-1} = \mathbf{I}$$

r

$$\begin{bmatrix} \mathbf{A}_1\mathbf{B}_1 + \mathbf{A}_2\mathbf{B}_3 & \mathbf{A}_1\mathbf{B}_2 + \mathbf{A}_2\mathbf{B}_4 \\ \mathbf{A}_3\mathbf{B}_1 + \mathbf{A}_4\mathbf{B}_3 & \mathbf{A}_3\mathbf{B}_2 + \mathbf{A}_4\mathbf{B}_4 \end{bmatrix} = \begin{bmatrix} \mathbf{I} & \mathbf{0} \\ \mathbf{0} & \mathbf{I} \end{bmatrix}$$

But this means that

$$\begin{aligned} \mathbf{A}_1\mathbf{B}_1 + \mathbf{A}_2\mathbf{B}_3 &= \mathbf{I} && \text{of order } n_1 \\ \mathbf{A}_3\mathbf{B}_1 + \mathbf{A}_4\mathbf{B}_3 &= \mathbf{0} && \text{of order } n_2 \times n_1 \\ \mathbf{A}_1\mathbf{B}_2 + \mathbf{A}_2\mathbf{B}_4 &= \mathbf{0} && \text{of order } n_1 \times n_2 \\ \mathbf{A}_3\mathbf{B}_2 + \mathbf{A}_4\mathbf{B}_4 &= \mathbf{I} && \text{of order } n_2 \end{aligned}$$

Solving the four equations simultaneously leads to

$$\begin{aligned} \mathbf{B}_4 &= (\mathbf{A}_4 - \mathbf{A}_3\mathbf{A}_1^{-1}\mathbf{A}_2)^{-1} \\ \mathbf{B}_3 &= -\mathbf{B}_4\mathbf{A}_3\mathbf{A}_1^{-1} \\ \mathbf{B}_2 &= -\mathbf{A}_1^{-1}\mathbf{A}_2\mathbf{B}_4 \\ \mathbf{B}_1 &= \mathbf{A}_1^{-1} - \mathbf{A}_1^{-1}\mathbf{A}_2\mathbf{B}_3 \end{aligned} \tag{5.15.13}$$

for the partitioned matrices of $\mathbf{A}^{-1}$. Thus the calculation leads to $\mathbf{B}_4$, $\mathbf{B}_3$, $\mathbf{B}_2$, and $\mathbf{B}_1$ and finally $\mathbf{A}^{-1}$. The inverse $\mathbf{A}^{-1}$ is determined by inverting an $n_1 \times n_1$ matrix instead of an $n \times n$ matrix.

The solution of the simultaneous equations can be obtained in the same way. The system $\mathbf{Ax} = \mathbf{c}$ can be partitioned into

$$\mathbf{A}\begin{bmatrix} \mathbf{y} \\ - \\ \mathbf{z} \end{bmatrix} = \begin{bmatrix} \mathbf{b} \\ - \\ \mathbf{d} \end{bmatrix}$$

where $\mathbf{y}$ and $\mathbf{b}$ are $n_1 \times 1$ vectors and $\mathbf{z}$ and $\mathbf{d}$ are $n_2 \times 1$ vectors. It follows that

$$\begin{aligned} \mathbf{A}_1\mathbf{y} + \mathbf{A}_2\mathbf{z} &= \mathbf{b} \\ \mathbf{A}_3\mathbf{y} + \mathbf{A}_4\mathbf{z} &= \mathbf{d} \end{aligned}$$

From the first equation

$$\mathbf{y} = \mathbf{A}_1^{-1}\mathbf{b} - \mathbf{A}_1^{-1}\mathbf{A}_2\mathbf{z}$$

and from the second equation

$$\mathbf{z} = (\mathbf{A}_4 - \mathbf{A}_3\mathbf{A}_1^{-1}\mathbf{A}_2)^{-1}(-\mathbf{A}_3\mathbf{A}_1^{-1}\mathbf{b} + \mathbf{d}) = \mathbf{B}_3\mathbf{b} + \mathbf{B}_4\mathbf{d}$$

In the same way

$$\begin{aligned} \mathbf{y} = \mathbf{A}_1^{-1}\mathbf{b} - \mathbf{A}_1^{-1}\mathbf{A}_2(\mathbf{B}_3\mathbf{b} + \mathbf{B}_4\mathbf{d}) &= (\mathbf{A}_1^{-1} - \mathbf{A}_1^{-1}\mathbf{A}_2\mathbf{B}_3)\mathbf{b} - \mathbf{A}_1^{-1}\mathbf{A}_2\mathbf{B}_4\mathbf{d} \\ &= \mathbf{B}_1\mathbf{b} + \mathbf{B}_2\mathbf{d} \end{aligned}$$

and the vector $\mathbf{x}$ can be obtained from $\mathbf{y}$ and $\mathbf{z}$. Once again the partitioning has allowed the nth-order equation to be solved by merely using an n_1 set of equations. Obviously this technique has considerable virtue if

$\mathbf{A}_1$ happens to be a matrix whose inverse is known ahead of time or if the $\mathbf{A}$ matrix is too large for manipulation in the storage space of the computer.

An efficient variation on this approach can be made by defining the following matrices:

$$\mathbf{E}_1 = [a_{11}]$$

$$\mathbf{E}_2 = \begin{bmatrix} a_{11} & a_{12} \\ a_{21} & a_{22} \end{bmatrix} = \left[\begin{array}{c:c} \mathbf{E}_1 & a_{12} \\ \hdashline a_{21} & a_{22} \end{array}\right]$$

$$\mathbf{E}_3 = \left[\begin{array}{cc:c} \multicolumn{2}{c:}{\mathbf{E}_2} & \begin{matrix} a_{13} \\ a_{23} \end{matrix} \\ \hdashline a_{31} & a_{32} & a_{33} \end{array}\right]$$

$$\cdots\cdots\cdots\cdots$$

$$\mathbf{E}_n = \left[\begin{array}{ccc:c} & & & a_{1n} \\ & \mathbf{E}_{n-1} & & a_{2n} \\ & & & \vdots \\ \hdashline a_{n1} & a_{n2} & \cdots & a_{nn} \end{array}\right]$$

This sequence has the intermediate formulation of (5.15.11),

$$\mathbf{E}_r = \left[\begin{array}{c:c} \mathbf{A}_1 & \mathbf{A}_2 \\ \hdashline \mathbf{A}_3 & \mathbf{A}_4 \end{array}\right]$$

with $\mathbf{A}_1 = \mathbf{E}_{r-1}$ a square matrix of order $(r - 1) \times (r - 1)$, $\mathbf{A}_4$ is a scalar $= a_{rr}$, $\mathbf{A}_2$ is an $(r - 1) \times 1$ column vector, and $\mathbf{A}_3$ is a $1 \times (r - 1)$ row vector. The inverse of $\mathbf{E}_r$ may be partitioned as in (5.15.12) such that

$$\mathbf{E}_r^{-1} = \left[\begin{array}{c:c} \mathbf{B}_1 & \mathbf{B}_2 \\ \hdashline \mathbf{B}_3 & \mathbf{B}_4 \end{array}\right]$$

From the identity $\mathbf{E}_r\mathbf{E}_r^{-1} = \mathbf{I}$ the sequence (5.15.13) immediately follows. The computational procedure follows by picking $r = 1$; the inverse of $\mathbf{E}_1$ is merely $\mathbf{E}_1^{-1} = 1/a_{11}$. Upon picking $r = 2$ all the elements of $\mathbf{A}_1^{-1}$, $\mathbf{A}_2$, $\mathbf{A}_3$, and $\mathbf{A}_4$ are known, and the recursive set of Eqs. (5.15.13) yield

$\mathbf{B}_4$, $\mathbf{B}_3$, $\mathbf{B}_2$, and $\mathbf{B}_1$; thus $\mathbf{E}_2^{-1}$ is known. We proceed in the same manner for $r = 3, 4, \ldots, n$ and calculate the elements of $\mathbf{E}_3^{-1}$, $\mathbf{E}_4^{-1}$, . . . , $\mathbf{E}_n^{-1}$ in order. Since $\mathbf{E}_n^{-1} = \mathbf{A}^{-1}$, the inverse of the $\mathbf{A}$ matrix results.

A serious problem associated with the use of this partitioning, or submatrix, method is that rounding errors generated in the small matrices propagate seriously to the higher-order matrices. This is actually the same problem encountered in the elimination methods. However, in the present case the errors may be removed by using an iteration technique (to be described shortly) at certain points in the inversion scheme to increase the accuracy of the answers at that point. This is an important point in favor of the present method, since such a tightening up cannot be accomplished by the standard elimination method.

It is also possible that while $\mathbf{A}$ itself is not singular one of the $\mathbf{E}_r^{-1}$ may be singular. If $\mathbf{A}$ is positive definite, this will not occur and thus the partitioning method finds its greatest use for this type of matrix. For $\mathbf{A}$ nonsymmetric this method requires approximately n^3 multiplications, which is more than in the elimination method; when $\mathbf{A}$ is symmetric, instead of nonsymmetric, about half the number of multiplications are required.

6. It has previously been pointed out that a tridiagonal matrix can be obtained from the $\mathbf{A}$ matrix by the transformations of Givens or Lanczos. Further, this same type of matrix occurs when certain PDE or ODE of the boundary-value kind are differenced in a particular manner. The frequent occurrence of such matrices has led to a simple algorithm for evaluating the inverse or solving the simultaneous equations. The method to be described was outlined by Bruce et al. (13) as due to Thomas.

Consider a system of n simultaneous equations with the form

$$\begin{aligned} a_1x_1 + b_1x_2 &= d_1 \\ c_rx_{r-1} + a_rx_r + b_rx_{r+1} &= d_r \qquad r = 2, 3, \ldots, n-1 \\ c_nx_{n-1} + a_nx_n &= d_n \end{aligned} \tag{5.15.14}$$

The a, b, c, and d values are known scalars. In matrix notation (5.15.14) can be written as

$$\mathbf{Bx} = \mathbf{d}$$

or

$$\begin{bmatrix} a_1 & b_1 & & & \\ c_2 & a_2 & b_2 & & \\ & c_3 & a_3 & b_3 & \\ & & \cdots & \cdots & b_{n-1} \\ & & & c_n & a_n \end{bmatrix} \begin{bmatrix} x_1 \\ x_2 \\ \cdot \\ \cdot \\ \cdot \\ x_n \end{bmatrix} = \begin{bmatrix} d_1 \\ d_2 \\ \cdot \\ \cdot \\ \cdot \\ d_n \end{bmatrix} \tag{5.15.15}$$

To solve (5.15.14), the unknowns are eliminated from the top down by letting

$$w_1 = a_1$$
$$w_r = a_r - c_r q_{r-1} \qquad r = 2, 3, \ldots, n$$
$$q_{r-1} = \frac{b_{r-1}}{w_{r-1}}$$

and

$$g_1 = \frac{d_1}{w_1}$$
$$g_1 = \frac{d_r - c_r g_{r-1}}{w_r} \qquad r = 2, 3, \ldots, n \tag{5.15.16}$$

These transform (5.15.14) to

$$x_n = g_n$$
$$x_r = g_r - q_r x_{r+1} \qquad r = 1, 2, \ldots, n-1 \tag{5.15.17}$$

If the w, q, and g are calculated in order of increasing r, it follows that (5.15.17) can be used to calculate the x in order of decreasing r, that is, $x_n, x_{n-1}, \ldots, x_2, x_1$.

The algorithm is easily described in matrix notation. The **B** matrix is decomposed into two triangular matrices

$$\mathbf{B} = \mathbf{WQ}$$

where

$$\mathbf{W} = \begin{bmatrix} w_1 & & & & \\ c_2 & w_2 & & & \\ & c_3 & \cdots & & \\ & & \cdots & \cdots & \\ & & & c_n & w_n \end{bmatrix} \qquad \mathbf{Q} = \begin{bmatrix} 1 & q_1 & & & \\ & 1 & q_2 & & \\ & & \cdots & \cdots & \\ & & & \cdots & q_{n-1} \\ & & & & 1 \end{bmatrix}$$

Thus

$$\mathbf{WQx} = \mathbf{d}$$

and upon defining the column vector

$$\mathbf{g} = \begin{bmatrix} g_1 \\ g_2 \\ \cdot \\ \cdot \\ \cdot \\ g_n \end{bmatrix}$$

(5.15.16) can be written as

$$\mathbf{Wg} = \mathbf{d}$$

Equating the last two matrix equations results in

$$\mathbf{Qx} = \mathbf{g}$$

which is merely (5.15.17).

7. All the methods presented to this point have the feature of decomposition of the **A** matrix into some form of triangular matrix. It is also possible to calculate $\mathbf{A}^{-1}$ or **x** by transforming to an orthogonal matrix. This technique is usually called the "Gram-Schmidt orthogonalization."

The first step is to construct a set of n orthogonal vectors $\mathbf{w}_1, \mathbf{w}_2, \ldots, \mathbf{w}_n$ from the elements of **A**. Writing **A** in the form

$$\mathbf{A} = \begin{bmatrix} \mathbf{a}_1 \\ \mathbf{a}_2 \\ \cdot \\ \cdot \\ \cdot \\ \mathbf{a}_n \end{bmatrix}$$

where $\mathbf{a}_r$ represents the rth row of **A**, let

$$\mathbf{w}_1 = \mathbf{a}_1$$

Next let

$$\mathbf{w}_2 = \mathbf{a}_2 - b_{21}\mathbf{w}_1$$

and since $\mathbf{w}_1\mathbf{w}_1^T = 0$ from the required orthogonality (note that $\mathbf{w}_1$ is a row vector)

$$\mathbf{w}_2\mathbf{w}_1^T = \mathbf{a}_2\mathbf{w}_1^T - b_{21}\mathbf{w}_1\mathbf{w}_1^T \qquad b_{21} = \frac{\mathbf{a}_2\mathbf{w}_1^T}{\mathbf{w}_1\mathbf{w}_1^T} = \frac{\mathbf{a}_2\mathbf{w}_1^T}{w_1^2}$$

w_1^2 is merely a scalar. Continuing in the same manner, let

$$\mathbf{w}_3 = \mathbf{a}_3 - b_{32}\mathbf{w}_2 - b_{31}\mathbf{w}_1$$

and the orthogonality of $\mathbf{w}_3$ to $\mathbf{w}_2$ and $\mathbf{w}_1$ yields

$$b_{32} = \frac{\mathbf{a}_3\mathbf{w}_2^T}{w_2^2} \qquad b_{31} = \frac{\mathbf{a}_3\mathbf{w}_1^T}{w_1^2}$$

This is continued until finally

$$\mathbf{w}_n = \mathbf{a}_n - \sum_{r=1}^{n-1} b_{nr}\mathbf{w}_r$$

where

$$b_{nr} = \frac{\mathbf{a}_n\mathbf{w}_r^T}{w_r^2}$$

However, this sequence of equations can be summarized by

$$\mathbf{A} = \begin{bmatrix} \mathbf{a}_1 \\ \mathbf{a}_2 \\ \cdot \\ \cdot \\ \cdot \\ \mathbf{a}_n \end{bmatrix} = \begin{bmatrix} 1 & & & \\ b_{21} & 1 & & \\ b_{31} & b_{32} & & \\ \cdot\cdot\cdot & \cdot\cdot\cdot & \cdot\cdot\cdot & \cdot\cdot\cdot \\ b_{n1} & b_{n2} & \cdots & 1 \end{bmatrix} \begin{bmatrix} \mathbf{w}_1 \\ \mathbf{w}_2 \\ \cdot \\ \cdot \\ \cdot \\ \mathbf{w}_n \end{bmatrix}$$

or

$$\mathbf{A} = \mathbf{L}_1\mathbf{Q}$$

Q is the matrix whose rows are $\mathbf{w}_1, \mathbf{w}_2, \ldots, \mathbf{w}_n$. It is noted, while

$$\mathbf{Q}\mathbf{Q}^{-1} = \mathbf{I}$$

that

$$\mathbf{Q}\mathbf{Q}^T = \mathbf{D}$$

where **D** is a diagonal matrix. Thus **Q** is not a true orthogonal matrix such that $\mathbf{Q}^T = \mathbf{Q}^{-1}$. If the $\mathbf{w}_r$'s are normalized by dividing by $\sqrt{w_r^2}$, a true orthogonal matrix can be obtained. Let

$$\mathbf{L}_2 = \mathbf{L}_1\mathbf{D}^{\frac{1}{2}} \quad \text{and} \quad \mathbf{C} = \mathbf{D}^{\frac{1}{2}}\mathbf{B}$$

where

$$\mathbf{D} = \begin{bmatrix} \frac{1}{w_1^2} & & & \\ & \frac{1}{w_2^2} & & \\ & & \cdots & \\ & & & \frac{1}{w_n^2} \end{bmatrix}$$

Under this transformation

$$\mathbf{C}\mathbf{C}^T = \mathbf{I}$$

It then follows that

$$\mathbf{A} = \mathbf{L}_2\mathbf{C} \quad \text{and} \quad \mathbf{A}^{-1} = \mathbf{C}^T\mathbf{L}_2^{-1}$$

To obtain $\mathbf{A}^{-1}$, the inverse of a triangle matrix and a matrix multiplication is required. The vector **x** can be obtained by solving

$$\mathbf{z} = \mathbf{L}_2^{-1}\mathbf{C}$$

and then

$$\mathbf{x} = \mathbf{C}^T\mathbf{z}$$

This procedure requires approximately $n^3/2$ multiplications for $\mathbf{A}^{-1}$.

Iterative Methods of Solution. The reader is aware by now that one of the defects of all the direct methods for solving for $\mathbf{A}^{-1}$ or **x** is the susceptibility of the calculation to excessive round-off error. The iterative procedures to be described do not have this drawback. However, as in any iterative procedure, the questions arise as to whether convergence will occur and if so at what rate. Since slow convergence implies an excessive number of multiplications, convergence by itself is not an adequate requirement. A convenient criterion for rapid convergence is that the main diagonal elements be larger than the off-diagonal elements.

1. Any inverse which has been calculated approximately by one of the direct methods may have its accuracy increased by an iteration process. Let **B** be the approximate value of $\mathbf{A}^{-1}$ and $\mathbf{B} + \Delta\mathbf{B}$ the exact inverse. It follows that

$$\mathbf{A}(\mathbf{B} + \Delta\mathbf{B}) = \mathbf{I}$$

and premultiplication by **B** followed by a rearrangement yields

$$\mathbf{BA}\,\Delta\mathbf{B} = \mathbf{B}(\mathbf{I} - \mathbf{AB})$$

But since $\mathbf{BA} \approx \mathbf{I}$, an approximate relation is

$$\Delta\mathbf{B} = \mathbf{B}(\mathbf{I} - \mathbf{AB})$$

or

$$\mathbf{B} + \Delta\mathbf{B} = \mathbf{B}(2\mathbf{I} - \mathbf{AB}) \tag{5.15.18}$$

This suggests the iteration sequence of substituting the approximate value of $\mathbf{A}^{-1}$ into the right side of (5.15.18) to yield a better approximation on the left side. This better approximation is resubstituted to yield a further improved value, etc. Upon calling the initial approximation $\mathbf{B}^{(0)}$ (5.15.18) becomes

$$\mathbf{B}^{(1)} = \mathbf{B}^{(0)}(2\mathbf{I} - \mathbf{AB}^{(0)})$$

followed by

$$\begin{aligned} \mathbf{B}^{(2)} &= \mathbf{B}^{(1)}(2\mathbf{I} - \mathbf{AB}^{(1)}) \\ &\cdots\cdots\cdots \\ \mathbf{B}^{(r+1)} &= \mathbf{B}^{(r)}(2\mathbf{I} - \mathbf{AB}^{(r)}) \end{aligned} \tag{5.15.19}$$

If (5.15.19) converges to a limit as r becomes large, then

$$\lim_{r\to\infty} \mathbf{B}^{(r+1)} = \mathbf{A}^{-1}$$

Equation (5.15.18) has the form of Newton's iteration process for reciprocal values of a scalar and as shown in Chap. 6 is a second-order iteration process. This means that if

$$\mathbf{E}^{(r)} = \mathbf{I} - \mathbf{AB}^{(r)}$$

where $\mathbf{E}^{(r)}$ is the error at the rth step, then

$$\mathbf{E}^{(r+1)} = (E^{(r)})^2$$

When such an iteration process converges, it converges rapidly. The necessary and sufficient condition for (5.15.19) to converge is that the characteristic roots of $\mathbf{I} - \mathbf{AB}^{(0)}$ have moduli less than 1.0. In practice this condition is achieved when $\mathbf{B}^{(0)}$ is a good initial approximation to $\mathbf{A}^{-1}$. Unfortunately, each iteration requires $2n^3$ multiplications and both **A** and $\mathbf{B}^{(r)}$ must be kept in storage.

An important application of the iteration pattern of (5.15.19) is to tighten up the successive inverses generated by the direct partitioning scheme of pages 251 to 254. If $\mathbf{E}_3^{-1}$, for example, has been calculated and it is felt that the round-off errors are beginning to color the results, the application of (5.15.19) one or two times will remove this defect. Suitable repetition can be used at desired intervals to assure that $\mathbf{E}_n^{-1} = \mathbf{A}^{-1}$ has the necessary accuracy. Since the inverses used in the iteration are close to the correct values and matrices whose size is less than n are involved, most of the defects of the algorithm of (5.15.18) are not involved.

A variation on this method has been suggested by Hotelling (47). Let $\mathbf{C}^{(0)} = \mathbf{I} - \mathbf{AB}^{(0)}$, and thus

$$\mathbf{AB}^{(0)} = \mathbf{I} - \mathbf{C}^{(0)}$$

or

$$\begin{aligned} \mathbf{A}^{-1} &= \mathbf{B}^{(0)}(\mathbf{I} - \mathbf{C}^{(0)})^{-1} \\ &= \mathbf{B}^{(0)}(\mathbf{I} + \mathbf{C}^{(0)} + \mathbf{C}^{(0)^2} + \mathbf{C}^{(0)^3} + \mathbf{C}^{(0)^4} + \cdots) \\ &= \mathbf{B}^{(0)}\left(\mathbf{I} + \sum_{r=1}^{\infty} \mathbf{C}^{(0)^r}\right) \end{aligned}$$

Further, since

$$\begin{aligned} (\mathbf{I} + \mathbf{C}^{(0)})(\mathbf{I} + \mathbf{C}^{(0)^2}) &= \mathbf{I} + \mathbf{C}^{(0)} + \mathbf{C}^{(0)^2} + \mathbf{C}^{(0)^3} \\ (\mathbf{I} + \mathbf{C}^{(0)})(\mathbf{I} + \mathbf{C}^{(0)^2})(\mathbf{I} + \mathbf{C}^{(0)^4}) &= \mathbf{I} + \mathbf{C}^{(0)} + \mathbf{C}^{(0)^2} + \cdots + \mathbf{C}^{(0)^7} \end{aligned}$$

it follows that

$$\mathbf{A}^{-1} = \mathbf{B}^{(0)}(\mathbf{I} + \mathbf{C}^{(0)})(\mathbf{I} + \mathbf{C}^{(0)^2})(\mathbf{I} + \mathbf{C}^{(0)^4}) \cdots = \mathbf{B}^{(0)} \prod_{r=1}^{\infty} (\mathbf{I} + \mathbf{C}^{(0)^{2^{r-1}}}) \tag{5.15.20}$$

It is usually necessary to use only a few terms of (5.15.20) to achieve convergence on the assumption that $\mathbf{B}^{(0)}$ is a good starting approximation to $\mathbf{A}^{-1}$. For implementation, the required power of $\mathbf{C}^{(0)}$ is generated, $\mathbf{I}$ is added, and the result multiplied by the previous approximate inverse. This follows from

$$\begin{aligned} \mathbf{G}^{(0)} &= \mathbf{B}^{(0)}(\mathbf{I} + \mathbf{C}^{(0)}) \\ \mathbf{G}^{(1)} &= \mathbf{G}^{(0)}(\mathbf{I} + \mathbf{C}^{(0)^2}) \\ \mathbf{G}^{(2)} &= \mathbf{G}^{(1)}(\mathbf{I} + \mathbf{C}^{(0)^4}) \\ &\cdots\cdots\cdots \end{aligned}$$

As before, the excessive number of multiplications precludes the use of this method unless convergence occurs in one or two steps.

2. The iteration technique most often used is the Gauss-Seidel algorithm. A simpler version, however, will be described first. Starting with the normal set of linear equations, solve for x_1 in the first equation, x_2 in the second equation, . . . , x_n in the nth equation. This yields

$$\begin{aligned} x_1 &= \frac{1}{a_{11}}(c_1 - a_{12}x_2 - a_{13}x_3 \cdots\cdots a_{1n}x_n) \\ x_2 &= \frac{1}{a_{22}}(c_2 - a_{21}x_1 - a_{23}x_3 \cdots\cdots a_{2n}x_n) \\ &\cdots\cdots\cdots\cdots\cdots\cdots \\ x_n &= \frac{1}{a_{nn}}(c_n - a_{n1}x_1 - a_{n2}x_2 \cdots a_{n,n-1}x_{n-1}) \end{aligned} \tag{5.15.21}$$

A possible iteration scheme would be to make an initial estimate at $\mathbf{x}$. Upon substituting this first guess into the right-hand side of (5.15.21) the left-hand side yields a new value $\mathbf{x}^{(1)}$. This vector is substituted and a new value $\mathbf{x}^{(2)}$ calculated, etc. If the process converges, $\lim_{r\to\infty} \mathbf{x}^{(r)} \to \mathbf{x}$ and the desired result is obtained. Because of the substitution of the entire vector into the right-hand side of (5.15.21) this procedure is called iteration by total steps.

Another way of writing (5.15.21) is

$$\begin{aligned} a_{11}x_1^{(r+1)} + a_{12}x_2^{(r)} + \cdots + a_{1n}x_n^{(r)} &= c_1 \\ a_{21}x_1^{(r)} + a_{22}x_2^{(r+1)} + \cdots + a_{2n}x_n^{(r)} &= c_2 \\ \cdots\cdots\cdots\cdots\cdots\cdots\cdots\cdots \\ a_{n1}x_1^{(r)} + a_{n2}x_2^{(r)} + \cdots + a_{nn}x_n^{(r+1)} &= c_n \end{aligned} \tag{5.15.22}$$

with the main diagonal terms containing the $r + 1$ values. If the $\mathbf{A}$ matrix is written as

$$\mathbf{A} = \mathbf{L} + \mathbf{D} + \mathbf{U}$$

where

$$\mathbf{L} = \begin{bmatrix} 0 & & & & \\ a_{21} & 0 & & & \\ a_{31} & a_{32} & \cdots & & \\ \cdots & \cdots & \cdots & \cdots & \\ a_{n1} & \cdots & \cdots & a_{n,n-1} & 0 \end{bmatrix}$$

$$\mathbf{D} = \begin{bmatrix} a_{11} & & & \\ & a_{22} & & \\ & & \cdots & \\ & & & a_{nn} \end{bmatrix} \qquad \mathbf{U} = \begin{bmatrix} 0 & a_{12} & \cdots & a_{1n} \\ & 0 & \cdots & \cdots \\ & & \cdots & a_{n-1,n} \\ & & & 0 \end{bmatrix}$$

then (5.15.22) and the iteration are represented by

$$\mathbf{L}\mathbf{x}^{(r)} + \mathbf{D}\mathbf{x}^{(r+1)} + \mathbf{U}\mathbf{x}^{(r)} = \mathbf{c} \qquad r = 0, 1, 2, \ldots \tag{5.15.23}$$

Equation (5.15.23) becomes

$$\mathbf{L}\mathbf{x}^{(\infty)} + \mathbf{D}\mathbf{x}^{(\infty)} + \mathbf{U}\mathbf{x}^{(\infty)} = \mathbf{c}$$

when $r \to \infty$. $\mathbf{x}^{(\infty)}$ is the exact value of $\mathbf{x}$. Subtracting the two equations leads to

$$\mathbf{D}\boldsymbol{\varepsilon}^{(r+1)} + (\mathbf{L} + \mathbf{U})\boldsymbol{\varepsilon}^{(r)} = \mathbf{0}$$

when $\boldsymbol{\varepsilon}^{(r)} = \mathbf{x} - \mathbf{x}^{(r)}$ = error vector at rth stage in calculation. This equation can be transformed to

$$\boldsymbol{\varepsilon}^{(r+1)} = -\mathbf{D}^{-1}(\mathbf{L} + \mathbf{U})\boldsymbol{\varepsilon}^{(r)} = \mathbf{H}\boldsymbol{\varepsilon}^{(r)} \qquad r = 0, 1, 2, \ldots \tag{5.15.24}$$

where $\mathbf{H} = -\mathbf{D}^{-1}(\mathbf{L} + \mathbf{U})$. Starting with $r = 0$ (5.15.24) yields

$$\boldsymbol{\varepsilon}^{(1)} = \mathbf{H}\boldsymbol{\varepsilon}^{(0)}$$

With $r = 1$,

$$\boldsymbol{\varepsilon}^{(2)} = \mathbf{H}\boldsymbol{\varepsilon}^{(1)} = \mathbf{H}^2\boldsymbol{\varepsilon}^{(0)}$$

and if this is continued,

$$\boldsymbol{\varepsilon}^{(r)} = \mathbf{H}^r\boldsymbol{\varepsilon}^{(0)} \tag{5.15.25}$$

From (5.15.25) it can be seen that convergence of the total step iteration will occur if and only if

$$\lim_{r\to\infty} \mathbf{H}^r\boldsymbol{\varepsilon}^{(0)} \to \mathbf{0} \tag{5.15.26}$$

For the moment all that will be said is that this criterion is satisfied if the $|\lambda_i| < 1.0$ for $\mathbf{H}$. Details will be given shortly.

If the total step iteration is modified by always replacing the most recently calculated value of x_i into (5.15.21) before the next calculation is performed, an improved version of the iteration is achieved. Storage is minimized, and convergence occurs faster. Under such conditions the method becomes the Gauss-Seidel iteration and is a cyclic single-step process. Note the similarity of the two methods described here to those of Richardson and Liebmann for solving elliptic PDE. Equations (5.15.22) and (5.15.23) now take the form

$$\begin{aligned}
a_{11}x_1^{(r+1)} + a_{12}x_2^{(r)} + \cdots + a_{1n}x_n^{(r)} &= c_1 \\
a_{21}x_1^{(r+1)} + a_{22}x_2^{(r+1)} + \cdots + a_{2n}x_n^{(r)} &= c_2 \\
a_{31}x_1^{(r+1)} + a_{32}x_2^{(r+1)} + a_{33}x_3^{(r+1)} + \cdots + a_{3n}x_n^{(r)} &= c_3 \\
\cdots\cdots\cdots\cdots\cdots\cdots\cdots\cdots\cdots\cdots \\
a_{n1}x_1^{(r+1)} + a_{n2}x_2^{(r+1)} + \cdots + a_{nn}x_n^{(r+1)} &= c_n
\end{aligned} \tag{5.15.27}$$

and

$$\mathbf{Lx}^{(r+1)} + \mathbf{Dx}^{(r+1)} + \mathbf{Ux}^{(r)} = \mathbf{c} \tag{5.15.28}$$

In the same way as (5.15.24) and (5.15.25) were obtained, (5.15.28) leads now to

$$\left.\begin{aligned}
\boldsymbol{\varepsilon}^{(r+1)} &= \mathbf{P}\boldsymbol{\varepsilon}^{(r)} \\
\boldsymbol{\varepsilon}^{(r)} &= \mathbf{P}^r\boldsymbol{\varepsilon}^{(0)}
\end{aligned}\right\} \quad r = 0, 1, 2, \ldots \qquad \begin{aligned}(5.15.29)\\(5.15.30)\end{aligned}$$

where $\mathbf{P} = -(\mathbf{L} + \mathbf{D})^{-1}\mathbf{U}$. The criterion for convergence now rests in

$$\lim_{r\to\infty} \mathbf{P}^r\boldsymbol{\varepsilon}^{(0)} \to \mathbf{0}$$

If the matrix $\mathbf{P}$ (or $\mathbf{H}$) has n distinct characteristic roots, then there exists a similarity transformation such that

$$\mathbf{P} = \mathbf{Q}^{-1}\boldsymbol{\Lambda}\mathbf{Q}$$

where

$$\boldsymbol{\Lambda} = \begin{bmatrix} \lambda_1 & & & \\ & \lambda_2 & & \\ & & \cdots & \\ & & & \lambda_n \end{bmatrix}$$

and the $\lambda_1, \lambda_2, \ldots, \lambda_n$ are the roots of $\mathbf{P}$ (or $\mathbf{H}$). Thus,

$$\mathbf{P}^r = \mathbf{Q}^{-1}\boldsymbol{\Lambda}^r\mathbf{Q}$$

and convergence occurs if, and only if, $\lambda_1^r, \lambda_2^r, \ldots, \lambda_n^r$ tend to zero as $r \to \infty$. As a result it can now be stated that the total step or cyclic single-step iterations will converge to the true solution if, and only if, the characteristic roots of **H** or **P** have their moduli less than 1.

There are also several sufficient conditions for convergence of the Gauss-Seidel iteration scheme. Without proof, one of these may be stated as follows:

$$1 = a_{ii} > \sum_{\substack{j \neq i \\ j=1}}^{n} |a_{ij}| \qquad i = 1, 2, \ldots, n$$

For **A** symmetric a necessary and sufficient condition for convergence is that **A** be positive definite. Under these conditions convergence will always occur to the correct **x** no matter how bad an initial estimate $\mathbf{x}^{(0)}$. The rate of convergence is, however, determined by $\mathbf{x}^{(0)}$.

As one further point (5.15.23) and (5.15.28) clearly show that the iteration processes are linear, i.e., are of the form

$$\mathbf{x}^{(r+1)} = \mathbf{K}\mathbf{x}^{(r)} + \mathbf{N}$$

Since all the matrices under consideration are constant and not functions of r, these are further referred to as stationary linear iterations.

There are a number of other methods for solving a system of simultaneous linear equations. In particular the steepest-descent method (5), the conjugate-gradient method (5), and the Monte Carlo technique (8, 68) are of interest. However, these will not be discussed beyond the brief comments which follow. Actually the steepest-descent and conjugate-gradient approaches are the same up to a point. Consider a quadratic form

$$Q(\mathbf{x}) = \tfrac{1}{2}(\mathbf{x}^T\mathbf{A}\mathbf{x}) - \mathbf{x}^T\mathbf{c}$$

For $Q(\mathbf{x})$ to be a maximum or minimum

$$\frac{\partial Q(\mathbf{x})}{\partial x_i} = \sum_{j=1}^{n} a_{ij}x_j - c_i = 0 \qquad i = 1, 2, \ldots, n$$

Further, the solution of this system of equations is a minimum if the matrix

$$\frac{\partial^2 Q(\mathbf{x})}{\partial x_i \, \partial x_j} = \mathbf{A}$$

is positive definite. Thus, if a minimum of $Q(\mathbf{x})$ can be found, this will be equivalent to solving the set of linear simultaneous equations. Given a starting initial vector $\mathbf{x}^{(0)}$ and an arbitrary vector $\mathbf{z}$, a scalar α is chosen which will minimize $Q(\mathbf{x}^{(0)} + \alpha\mathbf{z})$. This scalar is given by

$$\alpha^{(0)} = \frac{-(\mathbf{z}^T\boldsymbol{\varepsilon}^{(0)})}{\mathbf{z}^T\mathbf{A}\mathbf{z}}$$

where $\boldsymbol{\varepsilon}^{(0)}$ is the error vector defined by $\boldsymbol{\varepsilon}^{(0)} = \mathbf{A}\mathbf{x}^{(0)} - \mathbf{c}$. In the steepest-descent method the arbitrary vector $\mathbf{z}^{(0)}$ is chosen as $\mathbf{z}^{(0)} = -\boldsymbol{\varepsilon}^{(0)}$. In the conjugate-gradient method a set of $\mathbf{z}$'s are chosen such that

$$\mathbf{z}^{(0)} = \boldsymbol{\varepsilon}^{(0)} \qquad \mathbf{z}^{(r)} = -\boldsymbol{\varepsilon}^{(r)} + \gamma^{(r-1)}\mathbf{z}^{(r-1)}$$

where

$$\gamma^{(r+1)} = \frac{\boldsymbol{\varepsilon}^{(r)T}\boldsymbol{\varepsilon}^{(r)}}{\boldsymbol{\varepsilon}^{(r-1)T}\boldsymbol{\varepsilon}^{(r-1)}}$$

Both methods will converge to the desired minimum. However, the conjugate-gradient scheme, which is much like the Lanczos procedure for characteristic roots, takes no more than n steps. The Monte Carlo involves a set of rules based upon random numbers, which generates approximate values of the inverse matrix elements. The accuracy of the result is low, but the number of multiplications is proportioned to n^2 rather than n^3. A Monte Carlo calculation plus an iteration step or two may prove very useful in evaluating an inverse matrix.

5.16. Numerical Examples

Example 5.1. The properties of three different matrices will be here examined. These matrices, called I, II, and III, have the following form:

(*a*) Matrix I is symmetric, of order 5 × 5, and results from a least-square analysis of heat-transfer data. The details for the elements obtained are given in Example 7.1 with the explicit numbers listed below (because of symmetry only a triangular matrix is given).

$$\text{Matrix I} = \begin{bmatrix} 18.000000 & -11.0469009 & 116.9184217 & 124.9330502 & 110.7005453 \\ & 9.2544317 & -69.7708397 & -75.1989851 & -67.7681227 \\ & & 765.1817856 & 813.8419876 & 719.3762970 \\ & & & 869.0698929 & 768.7408600 \\ & & & & 684.0605316 \end{bmatrix}$$

(*b*) Matrix II is the Hilbert matrix of various sizes up to 10 × 10. This is a matrix which is notorious for its ill condition and which has elements

$$a_{ij} = \frac{1}{i + j - 1} \qquad i, j = 1, 2, 3, \ldots, n$$

It is symmetrical, and all elements on any positive diagonal are equal. It is of importance that this type of matrix occurs frequently in physical systems.

(*c*) Matrix III results from an analysis of the transient behavior of a 10-plate absorption tower. If Lapidus and Amundson (58) are followed and specific values for the gas- and liquid-flow rates, the plate holdups, and the equilibrium relationship used, the matrix becomes

$$\text{Matrix III} = \begin{bmatrix} 1.173 & -0.634 & & & & \\ -0.539 & 1.173 & -0.634 & & & \\ & -0.539 & 1.173 & -0.634 & & \\ & & -0.539 & 1.173 & \cdots & \\ & & & \cdots & \cdots & -0.634 \\ & & & & -0.539 & 1.173 \end{bmatrix}$$

Note that Matrix III is tridiagonal, of order 10×10, with constant elements along any diagonal.

Of particular interest in connection with these three matrices will be various means of calculating the inverses and the characteristic roots λ_i and vectors $\mathbf{x}_i$. As an illustration of the usefulness of these items consider matrix III, which is denoted as **A**. The dynamic response of the absorption tower is obtained by solving

$$\frac{d\mathbf{x}}{dt} = -\mathbf{A}\mathbf{x} + \mathbf{z} \tag{5.16.1}$$

where **x** is a vector made up of the liquid compositions on each plate and **z** is a vector containing the input feed compositions to the tower. The solution of (5.16.1) is given (see Chap. 8) by

$$\mathbf{x}(t) = (\mathbf{I} - e^{-(\mathbf{A}t)})\mathbf{A}^{-1}\mathbf{z} \tag{5.16.2}$$

Thus the dynamic response of the plate-absorption tower can be calculated when the inverse $\mathbf{A}^{-1}$ is known. As an alternative procedure (5.16.2) may be converted to a different form by using Sylvester's theorem as given by (5.14.2). This results in

$$\mathbf{x}(t) = \sum_{i=1}^{10} \frac{1}{\lambda_i}(1 - e^{-(\lambda_i t)}) \frac{\prod\limits_{j \neq i}^{10} (\mathbf{A} - \lambda_j \mathbf{I})}{\prod\limits_{j \neq 1}^{10} (\lambda_i - \lambda_j)} \mathbf{z}$$

In this form the dynamic response can be calculated from a knowledge of the characteristic roots $\lambda_1, \lambda_2, \ldots, \lambda_{10}$.

In order to have some quantitative measure of the behavior of the various matrices, the P-condition number of Sec. 5.15 will be used. This is given as

$$P = \frac{|\lambda_1|}{|\lambda_n|} \tag{5.16.3}$$

where λ_1 and λ_n are the largest and smallest characteristic roots, respectively. As a broad estimate, a value of $P < 100$ can be taken as indicating a very well-conditioned matrix. A convenient measure of the error involved in the inverse $\mathbf{A}^{-1}$ of the matrix **A** can be obtained from the criterion

$$b = \max |b_{ii}| \tag{5.16.4}$$

The elements b_{ii} are obtained from the main diagonal of

$$\mathbf{A}\mathbf{A}^{-1} - \mathbf{I} = \mathbf{B}$$

and should have a maximum value of approximately 10^{-5} to 10^{-6}. In the same sense

$$c = \max |c_{ij}| \qquad i \neq j \tag{5.16.5}$$

can be used for the off-diagonal elements of

$$\mathbf{AA}^{-1} = \mathbf{C}$$

Before discussing the actual calculations it should be noted that the matrices under consideration are small ones, $n \leq 10$, and a priori it would not be expected that any problems would exist in calculating the inverses or the characteristic roots and vectors. As will shortly be seen, this premise is far from correct.

As a start the inverse of matrix I and of successively sized matrix II (4×4 to 10×10) are calculated. Since both types of matrices are dense (all nonzero elements), the method of inversion is Gaussian elimination. The inversion of a matrix of the type of matrix III will be considered in a later example. Table 5.2 shows matrix I, its inverse, and the product of the matrix and the inverse. From the latter it can be seen that

$$\left.\begin{array}{l} b = 1.14 \times 10^{-5} \\ c = 1.144 \times 10^{-4} \end{array}\right\} \text{matrix I}$$

and thus the inverse has been obtained with the minimum acceptable accuracy stated above. Of the eight significant figures in matrix I the inverse has lost four, leaving a result accurate to at most four figures. On this basis it is obvious that matrix I is not what might be termed a well-conditioned one and yet it is not really completely ill-conditioned.

TABLE 5.2. SYMMETRIC MATRIX I, THE INVERSE, AND THE PRODUCT OF MATRIX I AND ITS INVERSE

Matrix I				
18.0000000	−11.0469009	116.9184217	124.9330502	110.7005453
−11.0469009	9.2544317	−69.7708397	−75.1989851	−67.7681227
116.9184217	−69.7708397	765.1817856	813.8419876	719.3762970
124.9330502	−75.1989851	813.8419876	869.0698929	768.7408600
110.7005453	−67.7681227	719.3762970	768.7408600	684.0605316
(Matrix I)$^{-1}$				
56.0077229	4.1650779	0.2768109	−6.7956548	−1.3052348
4.1650800	0.7478976	−0.0514011	−0.5112005	0.0286004
0.2768260	−0.0514001	0.3472523	−0.3826930	0.0149967
−6.7956818	−0.5112020	−0.3826916	1.3850333	−0.1049467
−1.3052202	0.0286014	0.0149974	−0.1049495	0.3176868
(Matrix I)(Matrix I)$^{-1}$				
1.0000076	0.0000002	0.0000001	−0.0000012	0.0000019
0.0000019	1.0000003	−0.0000000	0.0000008	−0.0000010
−0.0000687	−0.0000045	1.0000013	−0.0000200	0.0000095
−0.0001144	−0.0000112	−0.0000001	0.9999971	0.0000153
−0.0000687	−0.0000072	−0.0000030	−0.0000086	1.0000114

Table 5.3 shows an analogous set of results for matrix II; the sizes illustrated are 5×5, 7×7, and 8×8. Note in this table that the designation $-3\ 2567$ is to be interpreted as $+0.2567 \times 10^{-3}$. From these data and others not shown the following results may be listed:

n	b	c	Maximum element in A^{-1}	Minimum element in A^{-1}
4	7.629×10^{-6}	1.526×10^{-5}	6.480×10^{3}	16.00
5	1.221×10^{-4}	7.324×10^{-4}	1.795×10^{5}	25.02
6	9.177×10^{-3}	3.906×10^{-2}	4.601×10^{6}	36.70
7	1.250×10^{-1}	6.250×10^{-1}	2.980×10^{8}	77.08
8	2.750	6.250	3.683×10^{8}	80.75
10	Complete breakdown in inverse			

It is apparent that as the order of the matrix is increased the inverse becomes successively less accurate. In fact, it follows that the 6×6 and higher-order inverses have errors that are so large as to render the inverse meaningless.

It is possible to go a step further in showing that the inverse of matrix II of order 6 is highly inaccurate. The exact analytical inverse of matrix II (a Hilbert matrix) is known and tabulated in the literature (75). Table 5.4 shows a comparison between the known and the calculated 5×5 inverse plus the maximum and minimum elements in the higher-order inverses. It is apparent that even in the 5×5 case, and of course for the others, the calculated inverse leaves much to be desired in terms of significant figures. In the same sense, the elimination method outlined in Sec. 5.2 was used to evaluate det (matrix II) for the 5×5 case. The value obtained was approximately 4×10^{-12}, and thus the determinant is already approaching zero or singularity. This is merely another way of specifying that it is extremely difficult, if not almost impossible, to invert, with any accuracy, matrix II of order 6×6 or higher.

The present calculations were performed on the IBM 704 in floating-point mode. Each inverse was calculated in less than 2 sec.

The next step in this example is the calculation of the characteristic roots λ_i, $i = 1, 2, \ldots, n$, and corresponding vectors $\mathbf{x}_i$. The first method employed was the power iteration of (5.13.26),

$$\mathbf{y}^{(r+1)} = k^{(r+1)}\mathbf{A}\mathbf{y}^{(r)} \qquad r = 0, 1, 2, \ldots$$

The normalization term $k^{(r+1)}$ was always applied to the last element in $\mathbf{y}^{(r+1)}$, with the test on the over-all iteration given by

$$|\mathbf{y}^{(r+1)} - \mathbf{y}^{(r)}| < 1 \times 10^{-5}$$

Starting with the known matrix $\mathbf{A}$ (any of the three of interest) (5.13.26) is used until the convergence criterion above is met. At this point the dominant root λ_1 and the corresponding $\mathbf{x}_1$ are known. After the one root is found, a new reduced matrix $\mathbf{A}_1$ is formed by using the method outlined at the end of Sec. 5.13. Iterating on $\mathbf{A}_1$ by using (5.13.26) yields λ_2 and $\mathbf{x}_2$, at which point $\mathbf{A}_1$ is reduced to $\mathbf{A}_2$. This procedure is continued until all the roots are calculated.

To start the iteration cycle, the vector $\mathbf{y}^{(0)} = [1 \quad 1 \quad \cdots \quad 1]^T$ was used for λ_1; in succeeding iterations the last convergent vector obtained in finding root λ_r was used to start the calculation for λ_{r+1}. As a check on the final results the products $\mathbf{A}\mathbf{x}_i$ and $\lambda_i\mathbf{x}_i$ were formed for comparison.

TABLE 5.3. SYMMETRIC MATRIX II, THE INVERSE, AND THE PRODUCT OF MATRIX II AND ITS INVERSE
Various orders

Matrix II (5 × 5)				
1 10000000	0 50000000	0 33333333	0 25000000	0 20000000
0 50000000	0 33333333	0 25000000	0 20000000	0 16666667
0 33333333	0 25000000	0 20000000	0 16666667	0 14285714
0 25000000	0 20000000	0 16666667	0 14285714	0 12500000
0 20000000	0 16666667	0 14285714	0 12500000	0 11111111
(Matrix II)$^{-1}$				
2 25021923	3 − 30040884	4 10517614	4 − 14026588	3 63130028
3 − 30040904	4 48076253	5 − 18932842	5 26929564	5 − 12624236
4 10517624	5 − 18932846	5 79521441	6 − 11781343	5 56804350
4 − 14026601	5 26929565	6 − 11781341	6 17952198	5 − 88357415
3 63130075	5 − 12624233	5 56804326	5 − 88357393	5 44176943
(Matrix II)(Matrix II)$^{-1}$				
1 10000048	−4 − 61035156	−3 12207031	−3 − 73242187	−3 36621094
−5 28610229	0 99996947	−3 12207031	−3 − 24414062	−3 24414062
−5 − 19073486	−4 − 15258789	1 10000610	−3 − 24414062	−3 12207031
−6 95367432	−4 − 30517578	−4 61035156	0 99987793	−4 61035156
−6 − 95367432	0 00000000	−3 − 18310547	−3 − 12207031	0 99993896

Table 5.3. Symmetric Matrix II, the Inverse, and the Product of Matrix II and Its Inverse (*Continued*)

Matrix II (7 × 7)

1 10000000	0 50000000	0 33333333	0 25000000	0 20000000	0 16666667	0 14285714
0 50000000	0 33333333	0 25000000	0 20000000	0 16666667	0 14285714	0 12500000
0 33333333	0 25000000	0 20000000	0 16666667	0 14285714	0 12500000	0 11111111
0 25000000	0 20000000	0 16666667	0 14285714	0 12500000	0 11111111	−1 99999999
0 20000000	0 16666667	0 14285714	0 12500000	0 11111111	−1 99999999	−1 90909090
0 16666667	0 14285714	0 12500000	0 11111111	−1 99999999	−1 90909090	−1 83333329
0 14285714	0 12500000	0 11111111	−1 99999999	−1 90909090	−1 83333329	−1 76923079

(Matrix II)$^{-1}$

2 77077755	4 − 22474948	5 18839248	5 − 67516042	6 11723758	5 − 97418724	5 31051090
4 − 22423050	5 78279646	6 − 69730477	7 25728911	7 − 45427106	7 38150352	7 − 12248771
5 18755301	6 − 69595222	7 63914503	8 − 24013287	8 42905144	8 − 36335703	8 11738866
5 − 67094260	7 25638332	8 − 23976697	8 91198175	9 − 16440135	9 14016823	8 − 45522648
6 11633196	7 − 45208352	8 42787320	9 − 16420410	9 29805590	9 − 25552083	8 83358071
5 − 96546624	7 37925673	8 − 36199559	9 13986432	9 − 25527616	9 21984605	8 − 71995521
5 30741098	7 − 12165585	8 11685099	8 − 45387621	8 83213127	8 − 71939691	8 23637136

(Matrix II)(Matrix II)$^{-1}$

0 99957275	−1 27343750	−1 − 93750000	0 43750000	1 − 11250000	1 10000000	0 − 25000000
−3 − 27465820	1 10097656	−1 − 78125000	0 31250000	0 − 62500000	0 62500000	−1 − 93750000
−3 − 30517578	−2 97656250	1 10156250	0 18750000	0 − 12500000	0 − 12500000	0 00000000
−4 − 91552734	−2 48828125	−1 − 31250000	1 10000000	0 − 31250000	0 18750000	0 00000000
−4 − 61035156	−2 78125000	−1 − 46875000	0 12500000	0 87500000	0 18750000	−1 62500000
−4 30517578	−3 97656250	−1 23437500	−1 − 93750000	0 18750000	0 93749999	−1 31250000
−4 − 61035156	−2 19531250	0 00000000	0 00000000	0 00000000	−1 − 62500000	1 10625000

TABLE 5.3. SYMMETRIC MATRIX II, THE INVERSE, AND THE PRODUCT OF MATRIX II AND ITS INVERSE (*Continued*)

Matrix II (8 × 8)—Not Shown

$(\text{Matrix II})^{-1}$

2 80754759	4 − 23948163	5 20316304	5 − 73729104	6 13027128	6 − 11170083	5 38799014	4 − 16187031
4 − 23877451	5 84140781	6 − 75673617	7 28271555	7 − 50888796	7 44332764	7 − 15757227	5 78189148
5 20184187	6 − 75423141	7 69959763	8 − 26685615	8 48898175	8 − 43501369	8 16094406	7 − 10581171
5 − 72930057	7 28064369	8 − 26581535	9 10325968	9 − 19300615	9 17662017	8 − 69292439	7 62300575
6 12806795	7 − 50228637	8 48445069	9 − 19200127	9 36832280	9 − 35100648	9 14961983	8 − 18419331
6 − 10863563	7 43325320	8 − 42704462	9 17421428	9 − 34822648	9 35400976	9 − 17005135	8 28482714
5 36701105	7 − 15017669	8 15455348	8 − 67078950	9 14615330	9 − 16787532	8 96774894	8 − 21954300
4 − 10567765	5 57183310	6 − 86454027	7 55014930	8 − 17116388	8 27378722	8 − 21597543	7 66463394

$(\text{Matrix II})\,(\text{Matrix II})^{-1}$

0 99821091	−1 83618164	0 − 75195312	1 33750000	1 − 62500000	1 77812500	1 − 42812500	1 12343750
−2 − 11539459	1 10661621	0 − 66796875	1 21796875	1 − 51093750	1 56875000	1 − 31250000	0 96874999
−3 − 86307527	−1 53588867	0 50488281	1 22343750	1 − 35468750	1 44687500	1 − 24375000	0 73437500
−3 − 82874297	−1 43151855	0 − 34960937	1 25976562	1 − 31250000	1 39687500	1 − 20000000	0 63281250
−3 − 61893463	−1 41198730	0 − 37792969	1 14140625	1 − 14687500	1 33125000	1 − 19375000	0 53906250
−3 − 58746337	−1 30761718	0 − 25585937	1 11601562	1 − 20312500	1 37500000	1 − 14218750	0 47265625
−3 − 36239624	−1 24963379	0 − 23437500	0 96484374	1 − 17500000	1 23593750	0 − 31250000	0 42187500
−3 − 44631957	−1 20599365	0 − 22314453	0 96484374	1 − 17031250	1 24687500	1 − 12031250	1 14179687

TABLE 5.4. COMPARISON OF CALCULATED AND ANALYTICAL ELEMENTS OF 5×5 (MATRIX II)$^{-1}$ AND LARGEST AND SMALLEST ELEMENTS FOR OTHER SIZES†

25.021923 (25)	−300.40884 (−300)	1,051.7614 (1,050)	−1,402.6588 (−1,400)	631.30028 (630)
−300.40904 (−300)	4,807.6253 (4,800)	−18,932.842 (−18,900)	26,929.564 (26,880)	−12,624.236 (−12,600)
1,051.7624 (1,050)	−18,932.846 (−18,900)	79,521.441 (79,380)	−117,813.43 (−117,600)	56,804.350 (56,700)
−1,402.6601 (−1,400)	26,929.565 (26,880)	−117,813.41 (−117,600)	179,521.98 (179,200)	−88,357.415 (−88,200)
631.30075 (630)	−12,624.233 (−12,600)	56,804.326 (56,700)	−88,357.393 (−88,200)	44,176.943 (44,100)

Size	Largest calculated	Largest analytical	Smallest calculated	Smallest analytical
6×6	4.601×10^6	3.969×10^6	36.70	36.00
7×7	2.980×10^8	1.334×10^8	77.08	49.00
8×8	3.683×10^8	4.250×10^9	80.75	64.00

† Number in parentheses is exact analytical value.

Table 5.5 presents all the data for the power method applied to matrix I. As can be seen, the number of iterations is small at the start, since $\lambda_1/\lambda_2 = 47.2$, but increases as λ_2 and λ_3 are calculated. This follows from $\lambda_2/\lambda_3 = 2.59$ and $\lambda_3/\lambda_4 = 1.71$. Finally the number of iterations decreases because $\lambda_4/\lambda_5 = 63.8$. The total computation time on the IBM 704 was only of the order of seconds. Table 5.5 shows that the check using $\mathbf{Ax}$ and $\lambda\mathbf{x}$ agrees quite well for all the roots. Thus the roots and the vectors are probably accurate to at least six decimals (because of the convergence criterion above).

The P-condition number for matrix I is seen to be $P = |\lambda_1/\lambda_n| = |233.76/0.01749| =$ 13,367. This number is quite large and would seem to indicate that matrix I is not well conditioned. This is in agreement, in a qualitative sense, with the moderately low accuracy obtained for the inverse but is seemingly at odds with the λ_i calculation. Perhaps this is an indication that care must be used in interpreting the numerical meaning of the P-condition number.

Tables 5.6 and 5.7 present the results of the power method on a 10×10 form of matrix II and on matrix III. A priori one would guess, since the inverse was so bad, that only the first few roots of matrix II will be obtained with any accuracy, while matrix III, with its main diagonal elements larger than its off-diagonal elements, probably will yield all the roots with excellent results. Considering the matrix II results to start, it can be seen that the range of the calculated roots is tremendous.

TABLE 5.5. EFFECTS OF POWER METHOD ON MATRIX I

Root No.	λ	**x**	**Ax**	λ**x**	Number of iterations
		0 16232080	3 37943690	3 37943689	
		−1 − 98039726	3 − 22917512	3 − 22917511	
1	3 23375739	1 10581359	4 24734709	4 24734708	3
		1 11287323	4 26384952	4 26384951	
		1 10000000	4 23375740	4 23375739	
		−1 71647393	0 35465159	0 35465175	
		0 − 81011821	1 − 40100509	1 − 40100530	
2	1 49499604	0 − 88571878	1 − 43842722	1 − 43842729	14
		0 − 13630561	0 − 67470718	0 − 67470737	
		1 10000000	1 49499595	1 49499604	
		0 − 12367335	0 − 23615968	0 − 23615968	
		1 20537068	1 39216432	1 39216431	
3	1 19095439	0 − 76336257	1 − 14576743	1 − 14576743	35
		−1 25813070	−1 49291160	−1 49291189	
		1 10000000	1 19095439	1 19095439	
		0 − 25278778	0 − 28202111	0 − 28202110	
		−1 45103643	−1 50319598	−1 50319597	
4	1 11156437	1 13993442	1 15611696	1 15611696	7
		1 − 21574797	1 − 24069788	1 − 24069787	
		1 10000000	1 11156438	1 11156437	
		2 − 44197152	0 − 77291610	0 − 77291608	
		1 − 33098793	−1 − 57882894	−1 − 57882893	
5	−1 17487916	0 − 25132545	−2 − 43951584	−2 − 43951584	5
		1 54098114	−1 94606330	−1 94606330	
		1 10000000	−1 17487916	−1 17487916	

In fact, the *P*-condition number calculated from $\lambda_1 = 1.752$ and $\lambda_{10} = 0.877 \times 10^{-8}$ is $P = 1.997 \times 10^8$. This is a clear indication of the ill condition of this matrix. The comparison of **Ax** and λ**x** in Table 5.6 shows that λ_5 is already yielding large deviations and that this gets worse for $\lambda_6, \ldots, \lambda_{10}$. It must be thus concluded that only $\lambda_1 \ldots, \lambda_4$ are calculated with even four-place accuracy. As a further indication of this breakdown in the calculation of $\mathbf{x}_5, \mathbf{x}_6, \ldots,$ the number of iterations required does not correspond to the ratio of adjacent roots; $\lambda_1/\lambda_2 = 5.11, \ldots,$ $\lambda_4/\lambda_5 = 19.7$, $\lambda_5/\lambda_6 = 27.2$, $\lambda_6/\lambda_7 = 14.2, \ldots, \lambda_9/\lambda_{10} = 3.52$. While the number of iterations decreases (or remains almost constant) until λ_5 is calculated, from this point on the iterations rise continuously.

Just as in the case of the Hilbert matrix inverse, the first dominant characteristic root can be calculated by analytical means (82, 85). The value obtained is $\lambda_1 = 1.7519197$, which agrees with that given in Table 5.6 to seven significant figures. In the same sense it is known that all the λ_i's must be positive. However, in the present calculation λ_7 is negative, indicating that the last few roots are definitely in error.

TABLE 5.6. EFFECTS OF POWER METHOD ON MATRIX II

Root No.	λ		x		Ax		λx		Number of iterations
			1	56863407	1	99620122	1	99620137	
			1	34629354	1	60667847	1	60667858	
			1	25766987	1	45141691	1	45141698	
			1	20771407	1	36389836	1	36389842	
1	1	17519200	1	17499886	1	30658395	1	30658399	11
			1	15166902	1	26571194	1	26571198	
			1	13408465	1	23490554	1	23490557	
			1	12030247	1	21076027	1	21076030	
			1	10918065	1	19127574	1	19127576	
			1	10000000	1	17519198	1	17519200	
			1	− 25609254	0	− 87821663	0	− 87821702	
			0	28289323	−1	97012647	−1	97012454	
			0	93802207	0	32167564	0	32167550	
			1	11330199	0	38854614	0	38854603	
2	0	34292957	1	11794009	0	40445152	0	40445144	6
			1	11686560	0	40076678	0	40076671	
			1	11345829	0	38908208	0	38908202	
			1	10913931	0	37427100	0	37427096	
			1	10455256	0	35854170	0	35854165	
			1	10000000	0	34292960	0	34292957	
			0	86597539	−1	30952170	−1	30951535	
			1	− 17112617	−1	− 61163202	−1	− 61163606	
			1	− 10805.75	−1	− 38619348	−1	− 38619659	
			0	− 41189945	−1	− 14721783	−1	− 14722035	
3	−1	35741818	−1	78481680	−2	28052954	−2	28050780	6
			0	41932900	−1	14987773	−1	14987581	
			0	65400721	−1	23375580	−1	23375407	
			0	81524875	−1	29138624	−1	29138473	
			0	92551324	−1	33079670	−1	33079526	
			1	10000000	−1	35741945	−1	35741818	
			0	− 25151513	−3	− 63098315	−3	− 63655687	
			1	13736683	−2	34796623	−2	34766017	
			0	− 48135131	−2	− 12161033	−2	− 12182467	
			0	− 98219309	−2	− 24841595	−2	− 24858216	
4	−2	25308889	0	− 83744956	−2	− 21181321	−2	− 21194918	7
			0	− 46585676	−2	− 11778828	−2	− 11790317	
			−1	− 46241112	−3	− 11603162	−3	− 11703112	
			0	35091116	−3	88899861	−3	88811715	
			0	70131082	−2	17757308	−2	17749398	
			1	10000000	−2	25316057	−2	25308889	

TABLE 5.6. EFFECTS OF POWER METHOD ON MATRIX II (*Continued*)

Root No.	λ	x	Ax	λx	Number of iterations
		−1 65377233	−4 − 37049875	−5 84172090	
		0 − 72040261	−3 − 12135599	−4 − 92750627	
		1 13009862	−3 14582183	−3 16749979	
		0 37831845	−4 31022355	−4 48707866	
5	−3 12874832	0 − 51209147	−4 − 80966391	−4 − 65930918	7
		0 − 83629118	−3 − 12078881	−3 − 10767109	
		0 − 69024765	−3 − 10052603	−4 − 88868227	
		0 − 25021160	−4 − 42719301	−4 − 32214324	
		0 34405892	−4 34729484	−4 44297008	
		1 10000000	−3 11995807	−3 12874832	
		−1 − 16879174	−2 − 20923717	−7 − 79874059	
		0 29572630	−2 − 12226114	−5 13994086	
		1 − 11565014	−3 − 89670437	−5 − 54726883	
		0 95428859	−3 − 70391316	−5 45157959	
6	−5 47321072	0 84497560	−3 − 58692134	−5 39985151	9
		0 − 11324803	−3 − 50883554	−6 − 53590182	
		0 − 79783644	−3 − 45049469	−5 − 37754476	
		0 − 82175697	−3 − 40277885	−5 − 38886420	
		0 − 17615021	−3 − 36141975	−6 − 83356167	
		1 10000000	−3 − 32443600	−5 47321072	
		1 58151954	2 10177427	−5 − 19406614	
		1 35413305	1 61962363	−5 − 11818216	
		1 25827198	1 46098368	−6 − 86191166	
		1 22474669	1 37157749	−6 − 75003023	
7	−6 − 33372248	1 16214256	1 31303442	−6 − 54110617	11
		1 16415492	1 27129018	−6 − 54782185	
		1 13201524	1 23982865	−6 − 44056453	
		1 12543982	1 21517134	−6 − 41862086	
		1 11297143	1 19527454	−6 − 37701104	
		1 10000000	1 17885113	−6 − 33372248	
		−1 23468180	−1 29859978	−8 27544734	
		−1 − 92780216	−1 16884412	−7 − 10889666	
		0 72120407	−1 11963506	−7 84648124	
		1 − 15735379	−2 93040727	−6 − 18468702	
8	−6 11737056	0 59929612	−2 76239332	−7 70339719	
		1 12555653	−2 64615826	−6 14736640	13
		−1 39663656	−2 56079267	−8 46553454	
		1 − 10703569	−2 49539031	−6 − 12562839	
		0 − 85704030	−2 44367006	−6 − 10059130	
		1 10000000	−2 40174610	−6 11737056	

TABLE 5.6. EFFECTS OF POWER METHOD ON MATRIX II (*Continued*)

Root No.	λ	x	Ax	λx	Number of iterations
		1 − 23781306	0 − 80184852	−7 73500008	
		0 27114634	0 10048447	−8 − 83802202	
		0 89251540	0 30719356	−7 − 27584645	
		1 10129759	0 36800830	−7 − 31307673	
9	−7 − 30906632	1 12079789	0 38185064	−7 − 37334560	16
		0 93185325	0 37772246	−7 − 28800446	
		1 11607341	0 36631386	−7 − 35874382	
		1 10953615	0 35210709	−7 − 33853934	
		0 81284246	0 33712491	−7 − 25122223	
		1 10000000	0 32231028	−7 − 30906632	
		0 − 17853966	0 − 14982384	−8 − 15661597	
		−1 56446974	−1 − 70078618	−9 49515595	
		0 − 20097468	−1 − 45309624	−8 − 17629610	
		1 11631842	−1 − 33488598	−7 10203515	
10	−8 87720551	1 − 29812509	−1 − 26613698	−7 − 26151696	67
		1 49976394	−1 − 22125666	−7 43839567	
		1 − 62516793	−1 − 18965099	−7 − 54840075	
		1 59945110	−1 − 16616721	−7 52584180	
		1 − 37459687	−1 − 14801459	−7 − 32859843	
		1 10000000	−1 − 13354590	−8 87720551	

The results in Table 5.7 for matrix III reveal that the P-condition number, with $\lambda_1 = 2.245$ and $\lambda_{10} = 0.05121$, is $P = 43.8$. Thus matrix III is very well conditioned. The roots and vectors are calculated quite accurately, as revealed by the check **Ax** and $\lambda\mathbf{x}$. As an interesting feature of these results it is noted that $\lambda_1/\lambda_2 = 1.041$, $\lambda_2/\lambda_3 = 1.112, \ldots, \lambda_8/\lambda_9 = 2.15$, and $\lambda_9/\lambda_{10} = 3.699$. The number of iterations required follows this pattern by decreasing continuously. Further, the first root can be calculated even though the ratio of λ_1/λ_2 is 1.041.

These power-method calculations were all run on the IBM 704 and required about 3 min to calculate all the roots and vectors for the three matrices.

Further calculations were also carried out using the Jacobi rotation method (page 230) for the symmetric matrices I and II and Givens's method for matrix I. In the Jacobi method the off-diagonal elements were systematically searched for the largest value and this one annihilated. The criterion used for the end of the entire process was

$$|a_{ij}| < |a_{ii}|_{\min} \times 2^{-27}$$

The characteristic roots obtained by using both the Jacobi and Givens methods are given in Table 5.8. As can be seen, the most dominant roots of matrix I, by either method, agree quite well with those obtained by the power method. Only λ shows any significant deviation, yielding three identical significant figures. While the data are not shown, the characteristic vectors display about the same behavior. In using the Jacobi method 28 rotations were required for matrix I to annihilate the off-diagonal elements.

TABLE 5.7. EFFECTS OF POWER METHOD ON MATRIX III

Root No.	λ	x	Ax	λx	Number of iterations
		1 − 20760840	1 − 47641751	1 − 47641701	
		1 36733890	1 84296528	1 84296442	
		1 − 47346345	2 − 10864986	2 − 10864977	
		1 52544219	2 12057787	2 12057778	
1	1 22947868	1 − 52718962	2 − 12097885	2 − 12097878	
		1 48609112	2 11154760	2 11154755	173
		1 − 41188630	1 − 94519156	1 − 94519123	
		1 31552967	1 72407346	1 72407330	
		1 − 20812372	1 − 47759961	1 − 47759955	
		1 10000000	1 22947868	1 22947868	
		1 20760947	1 44772006	1 44771977	
		1 − 32207279	1 − 69456577	1 − 69456539	
		1 32314335	1 69687435	1 69687409	
		1 − 22749207	1 − 49059574	1 − 49059753	
2	1 21565479	0 78194139	1 16862917	1 16862940	
		0 72099021	1 15548533	1 15548499	117
		1 − 17832780	1 − 38457276	1 − 38457243	
		1 21535155	1 46441614	1 46441591	
		1 − 18247649	1 − 39351941	1 − 39351929	
		1 10000000	1 21565483	1 21565479	
		1 − 20761025	1 − 40247914	1 − 40247893	
		1 25071344	1 48604015	1 48603997	
		1 − 12626397	1 − 24477874	1 − 24477880	
		0 − 60667885	1 − 11761267	1 − 11761243	
3	1 19386275	1 18060807	1 35013200	1 35013178	
		1 − 16652798	1 − 32283578	1 − 32283573	69
		0 47556315	0 92193861	0 92193980	
		0 84145550	1 16312705	1 16312688	
		1 − 14204601	1 − 27537442	1 − 27537430	
		1 10000000	1 19386280	1 19386275	
		1 20761062	1 34435985	1 34435965	
		1 − 15904195	1 − 26379982	1 − 26379975	
		0 − 54666423	0 − 90674299	0 − 90674120	
		1 17708864	1 29373361	1 29373344	
4	1 16586803	0 − 89185225	1 − 14792972	1 − 14792978	
		0 − 82232375	1 − 13639740	1 − 13639722	61
		1 13881651	1 23025229	1 23025221	
		0 − 36431042	0 − 60427389	0 − 60427453	
		0 − 90107762	1 − 14946007	1 − 14945997	
		1 10000000	1 16586808	1 16586803	

TABLE 5.7. EFFECTS OF POWER METHOD ON MATRIX III (*Continued*)

Root No.	λ	x	Ax	λx	Number of iterations
5	1 13393862	1 − 20761074	1 − 27807112	1 − 27807096	44
		0 54485372	0 72976897	0 72976957	
		1 16220289	1 21725249	1 21725231	
		0 − 88889778	1 − 11905769	1 − 11905774	
		1 − 11456999	1 − 15345364	1 − 15345347	
		1 10563822	1 14149037	1 14149037	
		0 69679004	0 93327236	0 93327098	
		1 − 10809584	1 − 14478212	1 − 14478208	
		0 − 30869539	0 − 41346309	0 − 41346236	
		1 10000000	1 13393868	1 13393862	
6	1 10066128	1 20761102	1 20898390	1 20898391	37
		0 54485536	0 54845912	0 54845837	
		1 − 16220303	1 − 16327561	1 − 16327564	
		0 − 88889969	0 − 89477885	0 − 89477779	
		1 11457001	1 11532759	1 11532763	
		1 10563835	1 10633701	1 10633692	
		0 − 69678961	0 − 70139692	0 − 70139733	
		1 − 10809590	1 − 10881080	1 − 10881072	
		0 30869506	0 31073621	0 31073639	
		1 10000000	1 10066134	1 10066128	
7	0 68731875	1 − 20761124	1 − 14269507	1 − 14269510	21
		1 − 15904246	1 − 10931289	1 − 10931286	
		0 54666478	0 37573232	0 37573295	
		1 17708901	1 12171659	1 12171659	
		0 89185462	0 61298919	0 61298840	
		0 − 82232410	0 − 56519834	0 − 56519877	
		1 − 13881664	0 − 95411322	0 − 95411276	
		0 − 36431108	0 − 25039841	0 − 25039783	
		0 90107757	0 61932765	0 61932749	
		1 10000000	0 68731918	0 68731875	
8	0 40737166	1 20761128	0 84574908	0 84574954	13
		1 25071471	1 10213402	1 10213407	
		1 12626476	0 51436738	0 51436686	
		0 − 60667827	0 − 24714284	0 − 24714354	
		1 − 18060849	0 − 73574769	0 − 73574783	
		1 − 16652845	0 − 67839002	0 − 67838971	
		0 − 47556607	0 − 19373285	0 − 19373214	
		0 84145455	0 34278458	0 34278474	
		1 14204601	0 57865572	0 57865520	
		1 10000000	0 40737198	0 40737166	

TABLE 5.7. EFFECTS OF POWER METHOD ON MATRIX III (*Continued*)

Root No.	λ	x	Ax	λx	Number of iterations
		1 − 20761154	0 − 39332229	0 − 39332255	
		1 − 32207587	0 − 61017578	0 − 61017660	
		1 − 32314637	0 − 61220483	0 − 61220467	
		1 − 22749418	0 − 43099010	0 − 43099045	
9	0 18945120	0 − 78195220	0 − 14814267	0 − 14814178	5
		0 72098794	0 13659184	0 13659203	
		1 17832796	0 33784462	0 33784446	
		1 21535171	0 40798612	0 40798640	
		1 18247662	0 34570499	0 34570414	
		1 10000000	0 18945103	0 18945120	
		1 20761205	0 10632572	0 10632219	
		1 36734442	0 18812138	0 18812426	
		1 47346998	0 24247342	0 24247324	
		1 52544844	0 26909378	0 26909243	
10	−1 51211957	1 52719452	0 26998419	0 26998662	4
		1 48609470	0 24894088	0 24893860	
		1 41188825	0 21093532	0 21093603	
		1 31553051	0 16158950	0 16158935	
		1 20812394	0 10658432	0 10658434	
		1 10000000	−1 51211983	−1 51211957	

TABLE 5.8. THE CHARACTERISTIC ROOTS OF MATRIX I AND MATRIX II AS CALCULATED BY THE JACOBI AND GIVENS METHODS

Root No.	Jacobi method		Givens method
	Matrix I	Matrix II	Matrix I
1	233.75738	1.7519189	233.75739
2	4.9499651	0.34292935	4.9489550
3	1.9095460	$0.35741800 \times 10^{-1}$	1.9095341
4	1.11156504	$0.25309974 \times 10^{-2}$	1.11156390
5	0.017488360	$0.12874592 \times 10^{-3}$	0.017468579
6	....	$0.47324726 \times 10^{-5}$	
7	....	$0.11692118 \times 10^{-6}$	
8	....	$0.23534666 \times 10^{-8}$	
9	....	$0.73266560 \times 10^{-8}$	
10	....	$-0.82038396 \times 10^{-8}$	

The effects of the Jacobi method on matrix II show agreement with the power method up to about λ_6. λ_6 begins to show significant deviations, and λ_7 is completely different. The first negative root now occurs at λ_{10}, instead of λ_7 as in the power method; on this basis one may conclude that the Jacobi method is probably yielding more accurate roots in the range $\lambda_5, \ldots, \lambda_8$. The characteristic vectors also show about the same behavior. One hundred and eighty-one rotations were required to obtain the final diagonal matrix containing the characteristic roots. Less than 30 sec was required for all the calculations on the IBM 704.

Example 5.2. In Chap. 3 an example was worked out (Example 3.3) for the steady state concentration distribution of a single reactant in laminar flow through a tubular reactor. The equations of interest are the material balance [(3.10.11)] and the boundary conditions [(3.10.12)]. In the present example the same problem is solved, but in a completely different manner. From (3.10.11), with $n = 1$, the replacement of the derivatives with the finite differences yields

$$\frac{1}{\text{Pe}}\frac{f_{n+1} - 2f_n + f_{n-1}}{h^2} - \frac{f_{n+1} - f_{n-1}}{2h} - Rf_n = 0$$

or

$$\left(1 + \frac{\text{Pe}\,h}{2}\right)f_{n-1} - (2 + R\,\text{Pe}\,h^2)f_n + \left(1 - \frac{\text{Pe}\,h}{2}\right)f_{n+1} = 0 \qquad n = 1, 2, \ldots, N \tag{5.16.6}$$

It is assumed in (5.16.6) that the subscript of n, dealing with the independent variable z, applies to N internal mesh points $z_1, z_2, \ldots, z_N$. The boundary points z_0 and z_{N+1} then correspond to $z = 0$ and $z = 1.0$. On this basis $h = 1.0/N + 1$. The boundary conditions [(3.10.12)] can also be replaced with finite differences to yield

$$\begin{aligned} 1 &= f_0 - \frac{1}{\text{Pe}\,h}(f_1 - f_0) && z = 0 \text{ (or at } z_0) \\ f_N &= f_{N+1} && z = 1 \text{ (or at } z_{N+1}) \end{aligned} \tag{5.16.7}$$

Equations (5.16.6) and (5.16.7) form a set of N simultaneous algebraic equations in the N unknowns $f_1, f_2, \ldots, f_N$. These have the form

$$\begin{aligned} -\left[2 + R\,\text{Pe}\,h^2 - \frac{1 + (\text{Pe}\,h/2)}{1 + \text{Pe}\,h}\right]f_1 + \left(1 - \frac{\text{Pe}\,h}{2}\right)f_2 &= -\frac{1 + (\text{Pe}\,h/2)}{1 + 1/\text{Pe}\,h} \\ \left(1 + \frac{\text{Pe}\,h}{2}\right)f_1 - (2 + R\,\text{Pe}\,h^2)f_2 + \left(1 - \frac{\text{Pe}\,h}{2}\right)f_3 &= 0 \\ \left(1 + \frac{\text{Pe}\,h}{2}\right)f_2 - (2 + R\,\text{Pe}\,h^2)f_3 + \left(1 - \frac{\text{Pe}\,h}{2}\right)f_4 &= 0 \\ \cdots\cdots\cdots\cdots\cdots\cdots\cdots\cdots & \\ \left(1 + \frac{\text{Pe}\,h}{2}\right)f_{N-1} - \left(1 + R\,\text{Pe}\,h^2 + \frac{\text{Pe}\,h}{2}\right)f_N &= 0 \end{aligned} \tag{5.16.8}$$

The first equation in this set has used the condition at z_0 from (5.16.7), and the last equation has used the condition at z_{N+1}. Note that this set of simultaneous equations has a coefficient matrix which is tridiagonal; the method of Thomas can thus be used to evaluate $f_1, f_2, \ldots, f_N$. f_0 and f_{N+1} can then be calculated by using (5.16.7). Further, the elements along each diagonal are equal, just as in matrix III of Example 5.1 and are readily calculable once h is specified.

Table 5.9 shows the results of solving (5.16.8) with Pe = 1.0, R = 2.0, and various different h's. Also shown are the results obtained by integrating the original ordinary differential equations in Example 3.3. As can be seen, the case h = 0.1, N = 9 leads to results which are of the correct magnitude; as h is decreased to h = 0.025, N = 39 and h = 0.01, N = 99, the values of $f_1, f_2, \ldots, f_N$ approach quite close to those

TABLE 5.9. FIRST-ORDER REACTION IN LAMINAR-FLOW REACTOR
Solution by finite differencing technique

z	h = 0.1	h = 0.025	h = 0.01	Integration of ODE
0	. . . .	0.509850	0.515271	0.518987
0.1	0.482081	0.476018	0.474522	0.473606
0.2	0.440524	0.435444	0.434180	0.433431
0.3	0.403868	0.399778	0.398742	0.398163
0.4	0.371855	0.368782	0.367977	0.367574
0.5	0.344301	0.342297	0.341732	0.341513
0.6	0.321095	0.320238	0.319925	0.319907
0.7	0.302206	0.302605	0.302565	0.302768
0.8	0.287692	0.289493	0.289753	0.290206
0.9	0.277705	0.281102	0.281698	0.282438
1.0	0.272515	0.277750	0.278732	0.279803
Slope at z = 1.0. .	-5.190×10^{-2}	-1.371×10^{-2}	-0.5546×10^{-2}	-0.0800×10^{-2}

calculated in Example 3.3. The values could probably be refined by further decreasing h, but the points of interest have already been delineated. Because the previous integration method uses equations with a very small truncation error and the present simultaneous-equation method involves a much larger error, the value of h required to achieve about seven-place equivalence would probably have to be quite small and the number of simultaneous equations quite large.

BIBLIOGRAPHY

1. Acrivos, A., and N. R. Amundson: *Ind. Eng. Chem.*, **47**: 1533 (1955).
2. Aegerter, M. J.: *Communs. ACM*, **2**(8): 10 (1959).
3. Amundson, N. R.: *Trans. AIChE*, **42**: 939 (1946).
4. Amundson, N. R., and A. J. Pontinen: *Ind. Eng. Chem.*, **50**: 730 (1950).
5. Amundson, N. R., A. J. Pontinen, and J. W. Tierney: *J. AIChE*, **5**: 295 (1959).
6. Arms, R. J., L. D. Gates, and B. Zondek: *J. SIAM*, **4**: 220 (1956).
7. Baker, G. A., Jr.: *J. SIAM*, **7**: 143 (1959).
8. Bauer, W. F.: *J. SIAM*, **6**: 438 (1958).
9. Birkhoff, G., and R. S. Varga: *J. SIAM*, **6**: 354 (1958).
10. Bodewig, E.: *Math. Tables Aids Comput.*, **8**: 237 (1954).
11. Brenner, J. L., and G. W. Reitwiesner: *Math. Tables Aids Comput.*, **9**: 117 (1955).
12. Brooker, R. A., and F. H. Summer: *Proc. Inst. Elec. Engrs. (London) B*, suppl. 1, **103**: 114 (1956).
13. Bruce, G. H., D. W. Peaceman, H. H. Rachford, and J. D. Rice: *Trans. AIME*, **198**: 79 (1953).

14. Causey, R. L.: *J. Assoc. Comput. Mach.*, **5**: 127 (1958).
15. Causey, R. L.: *J. SIAM*, **6**: 172 (1958).
16. Clement, P. A.: *SIAM Notes*, **5**(8): 3 (1957).
17. Conte, S. D., and R. T. Dames: *J. Assoc. Comput. Mach.*, **7**: 264 (1960).
18. Craig, E. J.: *J. Math. Phys.*, **34**: 65 (1955).
19. Cuthill, E. H., and R. S. Varga: *J. Assoc. Comput. Mach.*, **6**: 236 (1959).
20. Dimsdale, B.: *J. SIAM*, **6**: 23 (1958).
21. Doyle, T. C.: *Math. Tables Aids Comput.*, **11**: 55 (1957).
22. Edmister, W. C.: *J. AIChE*, **3**: 165 (1957).
23. Fike, C. T.: *J. Assoc. Comput. Mach.*, **6**: 360 (1959).
24. Fisher, M. E., and A. T. Fuller: *Proc. Cambridge Phil. Soc.*, **54**: 417 (1958).
25. Forsythe, G. E.: *Bull. Am. Math. Soc.*, **59**: 299 (1953).
26. Forsythe, G. E.: *Am. Math. Monthly*, **65**: 229 (1958).
27. Forsythe, G. E., and L. W. Straus: *J. Math. Phys.*, **34**: 152 (1955).
28. Fox, L.: *Quart. J. Mech.*, **5**: 178 (1947).
29. Fox, L.: *Appl. Math. Ser. U.S. Bur. Standards*, **39**: 1 (1954).
30. Frank, W. L.: *J. SIAM*, **6**: 378 (1958).
31. Frank, W. L.: *Thompson Ramo-Wooldridge Tech. Note* 2, 1959.
32. Frank, W. L.: *J. Assoc. Comput. Mach.*, **7**: 274 (1960).
33. Franklin, J. N.: *J. Assoc. Comput. Mach.*, **5**: 45 (1958).
34. Gauss, E. J.: *J. Assoc. Comput. Mach.*, **6**: 476 (1959).
35. Givens, W.: *J. Assoc. Comput. Mach.*, **4**: 298 (1957).
36. Givens, W.: *J. SIAM*, **6**: 26 (1958).
37. Goldstine, H. H., and L. P. Horwitz: *J. Assoc. Comput. Mach.*, **6**: 176 (1959).
38. Goldstine, H. H., F. J. Murray, and J. Von Neumann: *J. Assoc. Comput. Mach.*, **6**: 59 (1959).
39. Greenstadt, J.: *Math. Tables Aids Comput.*, **9**: 47 (1955).
40. Gregory, R. T.: *Math. Tables Aids Comput.*, **7**: 215 (1953).
41. Gregory, R. T.: *J. SIAM*, **6**: 182 (1958).
42. Grenville, T. N. E.: *SIAM Rev.*, **1**: 38 (1959).
43. Heller, J.: *J. SIAM*, **5**: 238 (1957).
44. Hestenes, M. R.: *J. SIAM*, **6**: 51 (1958).
45. Hestenes, M. R., and E. Stiefel: *J. Research Natl. Bur. Standards*, **49**: 409 (1952).
46. Hopp, H. F., and R. Wertzler: *Anal. Chem.*, **30**: 877 (1958).
47. Hotelling, H.: *Ann. Math. Statistics*, **14**: 1 (1943).
48. Householder, A. S.: *J. SIAM*, **3**: 67 (1955).
49. Householder, A. S.: *J. Assoc. Comput. Mach.*, **3**: 314 (1956).
50. Householder, A. S.: *J. SIAM*, **5**: 155 (1957).
51. Householder, A. S.: *J. Assoc. Comput. Mach.*, **5**: 127 (1958).
52. Householder, A. S.: *J. Assoc. Comput. Mach.*, **5**: 205 (1958).
53. Householder, A. S.: *J. Assoc. Comput. Mach.*, **5**: 335 (1958).
54. Householder, A. S.: *J. Assoc. Comput. Mach.*, **5**: 339 (1958).
55. Householder, A. S.: *J. SIAM*, **6**: 189 (1958).
56. Householder, A. S., and F. L. Bauer: *Numerische Math.*, **1**: 29 (1959).
57. Kogbetliantz, E. G.: *Quart. Appl. Math.*, **13**: 123 (1955).
58. Lapidus, L., and N. R. Amundson: *Ind. Eng. Chem.*, **42**: 1071 (1950).
59. Lanczos, C.: *J. Research Natl. Bur. Standards*, **45**: 255 (1950).
60. Lanczos, C.: *J. Research Natl. Bur. Standards*, **49**: 33 (1952).
61. Lanczos, C.: *J. SIAM*, **6**: 91 (1958).
62. Lehmer, D. H.: *Pacific J. Math.*, **6**: 491 (1956).
63. Lomont, J. S., and R. A. Willoughby: *SIAM Rev.*, **1**: 64 (1959).
64. Lotkin, M.: *Math. Tables Aids Comput.*, **9**: 153 (1955).

65. Lotkin, M.: *Quart. Appl. Math.*, **14**: 267 (1956).
66. Meyer, H. I., and B. J. Hollingsworth: *Math. Tables Aids Comput.*, **11**: 94 (1957).
67. Newman, M., and J. Todd: *J. SIAM*, **6**: 466 (1958).
68. Opler, A.: *Math. Tables Aids Comput.*, **5**: 115 (1951).
69. Ortega, J. M.: *J. Assoc. Comput. Mach.*, **7**: 260 (1960).
70. Osborne, E. E.: *J. SIAM*, **6**: 279 (1958).
71. Pipes, L. A.: *J. Franklin Inst.*, **263**: 195 (1957).
72. Pope, D. A., and C. Tompkins: *J. Assoc. Comput. Mach.*, **4**: 459 (1957).
73. Rutinhauser, H.: *Natl. Bur. Standards Appl. Math. Ser.* 49, 1958.
74. Saibel, E., and W. J. Berger: *Math. Tables Aids Comput.*, **7**: 228 (1953).
75. Savage, I. R., and E. Lukacs: *Natl. Bur. Standards Ser.*, **39**: 105 (1954).
76. Schechter, S.: *Math. Tables Aids Comput.*, **13**: 73 (1959).
77. Schechter, S.: *N.Y. Univ. Inst. Math. Sci. Rept.* TID-4500, 1959.
78. Semarne, H. M.: *SIAM Rev.*, **1**: 53 (1959).
79. Sheldon, J. W.: *J. Assoc. Comput. Mach.*, **6**: 494 (1959).
80. Snyder, J. N.: *Math. Tables Aids Comput.*, **9**: 177 (1955).
81. Stroud, A. H.: *Math. Tables Aids Comput.*, **14**: 21 (1960).
82. Taussky, O.: *Quart. J. Math. (Oxford)*, **20**: 80 (1949).
83. Taussky, O.: *Math. Tables Aids Comput.*, **4**: 111 (1950).
84. Todd, J.: *Proc. Cambridge Phil. Soc.*, **46**: 116 (1949).
85. Todd, J.: *Natl. Bur. Standards* Ser., **39**: 109 (1954).
86. Turing, A. M.: *Quart. J. Mech.*, **1**: 287 (1948).
87. Turing, A. M.: *Quart. J. Mech. Appl. Math.*, **1**: 287 (1948).
88. White, P. A.: *J. SIAM*, **6**: 393 (1958).
89. Wilf, H. S.: *J. SIAM*, **7**: 149 (1959).
90. Wilkinson, J. H.: *Proc. Cambridge Phil. Soc.*, **50**: 536 (1954).
91. Wilkinson, J. H.: *Math. Tables Aids Comput.*, **9**: 184 (1955).
92. Wilkinson, J. H.: *Comput. J.*, **1**: 90 (1958).
93. Wilkinson, J. H.: *Comput. J.*, **1**: 148 (1958).
94. Wilkinson, J. H.: *Natl. Phys. Lab. Rept.* MA/43, 1958.
95. Wilkinson, J. H.: *J. Assoc. Comput. Mach.*, **6**: 336 (1959).
96. Varga, R. S.: *J. SIAM*, **5**: 39 (1957).
97. Varga, R. S.: *Pacific J. Math.*, **9**: 925 (1959).
98. Von Neumann, J., and H. H. Goldstine: *Bull. Am. Math. Soc.*, **53**: 1021 (1947).

CHAPTER 6

ROOTS OF ALGEBRAIC AND TRANSCENDENTAL EQUATIONS

Many areas of chemical-engineering analysis require the use of efficient techniques for determining the roots of algebraic and/or transcendental equations. As shown in Chap. 5, a frequently employed procedure for finding the characteristic roots of a square matrix is first to form the characteristic polynomial and then to evaluate the roots of this polynomial. The analytical solution of PDE often leads to infinite series with the summation taken over the roots of a transcendental equation. Further, the inversion of the Laplace transform of high-order systems and the location of the unstable or stable points of a dynamic system usually require the evaluation of the roots of a polynomial equation. Thus the problem of devising efficient root-locating algorithms is of considerable practical importance. It should, however, be emphasized here that frequently all that is required is a limited number rather than the total number of possible roots (see examples at end of this chapter).

The question of the accuracy required by a root-finding technique is an important one and is often determined by whether or not further computations follow which use the roots explicitly. If the calculation of the roots is only an intermediate step and subsequent calculations are to be performed using these roots, high accuracy may be required. This often will entail the need for multiple-precision arithmetic. If the degree of the polynomial increases to 50 or greater, multiple precision becomes almost mandatory. To illustrate how a problem can arise in evaluating the roots of a seemingly trivial system, consider the quadratic equation

$$x^2 + bx + c = 0$$

The roots are

$$x_{\text{roots}} = \frac{-b \pm \sqrt{b^2 - 4c}}{2}$$

If $b \gg c$, one root will be given approximately by $(-b + b)/2$; the computed value will thus involve a considerable loss of significant figures. As a consequence the resulting number may be worthless for subsequent calculation unless some precaution is taken. Multiple-precision arithmetic or the identity

$$x_{\text{root1}} \cdot x_{\text{root2}} = c$$

must be used to try to assure a significant answer (see Example 6.3).

6.1. Iteration Techniques

The problem of interest in this chapter can be stated simply as finding that value of x, denoted by $\bar{x}$, which satisfies

$$f(\bar{x}) = 0 \tag{6.1.1}$$

$f(x)$ may be a transcendental equation or a polynomial and x may be real or complex. The only restriction on $f(x)$ is that it does not contain derivative or integral terms; in this way all differential and integral equations are excluded. Note that only a single variable is considered here. The more general formulation involves $f(\mathbf{x})$, as given in Sec. 6.10.

The most efficient means of solving (6.1.1) for $x = \bar{x}$ is to devise an iterative algorithm which starts with an initial guess for $\bar{x}$ and converges through the iteration to the desired root in a finite number of steps. To develop the various possible iterative techniques, the equation $f(x) = 0$ is rewritten in the form

$$x = F(x) \tag{6.1.2}$$

This suggests the iteration pattern

$$x^{(r+1)} = F(x^{(r)}) \qquad r = 0, 1, 2, \ldots \tag{6.1.3}$$

Convergence of (6.1.3) implies that the successive values $x^{(0)}$, $x^{(1)}$, $x^{(2)}$, $\ldots$, $x^{(r)}$, $\ldots$ approach the value $\bar{x}$ as $r \to N$, where N is an integer number. As will be seen later, the requirement for convergence of (6.1.3) usually resides in the initial estimate $x^{(0)}$. Most of the methods discussed here have the defect that a bad choice of $x^{(0)}$ may lead to nonconvergence of the iteration.

Alternative iteration formulas are

$$x^{(r+1)} = x^{(r)} - \alpha f(x^{(r)}) \tag{6.1.4}$$

with α a suitably chosen constant and

$$x^{(r+1)} = x^{(r)} - \beta^{(r)} f(x^{(r)}) \tag{6.1.5}$$

with $\beta^{(r)}$ a suitably chosen sequence $\beta^{(0)}$, $\beta^{(1)}$, $\beta^{(2)}$, $\ldots$.

Since the Taylor series expansion of a function will be used extensively in this chapter, it is worth developing some of its important properties. For a function $f(x)$ which is expressed by the power series

$$f(x) = a_0 + a_1(x - x_0) + a_2(x - x_0)^2 + a_3(x - x_0)^3 + \cdots$$

and for which the $a_0, a_1, a_2, a_3, \ldots$ are unknown but constant coefficients, the use of $f(x) = f(x_0)$ at $x = x_0$ leads to

$$\begin{aligned} a_0 &= f(x_0) \\ 1\,!\,a_1 &= f'(x_0) \\ 2\,!\,a_2 &= f''(x_0) \\ &\cdots\cdots \\ r\,!\,a_r &= f^{[r]}(x_0) \end{aligned}$$

These relations convert the power series to

$$f(x) = f(x_0) + (x - x_0)f'(x_0) + \frac{(x - x_0)^2}{2!} f''(x_0) + \frac{(x - x_0)^3}{3!} f^{[3]}(x_0) + \cdots \quad (6.1.6)$$

or, by letting $x - x_0$ be h,

$$f(x_0 + h) = f(x_0) + hf'(x_0) + \frac{h^2}{2!} f''(x_0) + \frac{h^3}{3!} f^{[3]}(x_0) + \cdots \quad (6.1.7)$$

(6.1.6) or (6.1.7) represents the Taylor series expansion of the function $f(x)$ about the point $x = x_0$. The function $f(x)$ is assumed to possess continuous derivatives within the radius of convergence of the power series, i.e., on the largest circle which can be drawn to include only points where $f(x)$ is analytic.

If the function $F(x)$ is expanded in a Taylor series about $x = \bar{x}$, (6.1.2) and (6.1.6) lead to

$$F(x) = \bar{x} + (x - \bar{x})F'(\bar{x}) + \frac{(x - \bar{x})^2}{2!} F''(\bar{x}) + \frac{(x - \bar{x})^3}{3!} F^{[3]}(\bar{x}) + \cdots$$

For $x = x^{(r)}$, (6.1.3) converts this equation to

$$x^{(r+1)} = F(x^{(r)}) = \bar{x} + (x^{(r)} - \bar{x})F'(\bar{x}) + \frac{(x^{(r)} - \bar{x})^2}{2!} F''(\bar{x}) + \frac{(x^{(r)} - \bar{x})^3}{3!} F^{[3]}(\bar{x}) + \cdots \quad (6.1.8)$$

Defining the error at the rth stage of any iteration process by $\epsilon^{(r)}$ where

$$\epsilon^{(r)} = x^{(r)} - \bar{x}$$

(6.1.8) becomes

$$\begin{aligned} \epsilon^{(r+1)} &= \epsilon^{(r)}F'(\bar{x}) + \frac{\epsilon^{(r)^2}}{2!} F''(\bar{x}) + \frac{\epsilon^{(r)^3}}{3!} F^{[3]}(\bar{x}) + \cdots \\ &= b_1\epsilon^{(r)} + b_2\epsilon^{(r)^2} + b_3\epsilon^{(r)^3} + \cdots \end{aligned} \quad (6.1.9)$$

with $b_1 = F'(\bar{x})$, $b_2 = F''(\bar{x})/2!$, $b_3 = F^{[3]}(\bar{x})/3!$, ...

If the numerical value of $\epsilon^{(r)}$ is small, this series can be truncated after the first term, leading to

$$\epsilon^{(r+1)} = b_1\epsilon^{(r)} \qquad r = 0, 1, 2, \ldots \tag{6.1.10}$$

Starting with $r = 0$, (6.1.10) becomes

$$\epsilon^{(r)} = b_1{}^r\epsilon^{(0)} \tag{6.1.11}$$

and it can be seen that for this iteration process to converge, that is, $\epsilon^{(0)} > \epsilon^{(1)} > \epsilon^{(2)} > \cdots$,

$$|b_1| = |F'(\bar{x})| < 1.0$$

Following Hartree (20), an iteration process whose error conforms to (6.1.10) or (6.1.11) is referred to as a first-order iteration process. The error at the $(r + 1)$st stage in the iteration is a linear function of the error at the rth stage. The degree of improvement of $x^{(r)}$ as the iteration proceeds is determined by b_1. If $b_1 = 10^{-3}$, every iteration might improve the answer by three decimals, and if $b_1 = 10^{-1}$, then by 1 decimal. In other words, each iteration increases the number of significant figures by the same amount as the previous iteration.

For the case $b_1 = 0$ but $b_2 \neq 0$ truncation of (6.1.9) after the second term leads to

$$\left.\begin{aligned} \epsilon^{(r+1)} &= b_2\epsilon^{(r)2} \\ \text{or} \qquad b_2\epsilon^{(r)} &= (b_2\epsilon^{(0)})^{2^r} \end{aligned}\right\} \qquad r = 0, 1, 2, \ldots \qquad \begin{aligned} &(6.1.12) \\ &(6.1.13) \end{aligned}$$

Convergence of the iteration occurs if

$$|b_2\epsilon^{(0)}| = \left|\frac{F''(\bar{x})}{2!}\,\epsilon^{(0)}\right| < 1.0$$

The iteration of (6.1.12) or (6.1.13) is referred to as a second-order process, with the error at the $(r + 1)$st iteration being proportional to the square of the error at the rth iteration. At each iteration the increase in significant figures in the value of x is double the previous case. Thus, if $b_2 = 10^{-3}$, the first iteration improves the answer by three decimals, the second iteration by six decimals, etc. This second-order iteration process converges at a faster rate than the first-order iteration.

For the case $b_1 = b_2 = 0$, $b_3 \neq 0$ truncation of (6.1.9) after the third term leads to

$$\left.\begin{aligned} \epsilon^{(r+1)} &= b_3\epsilon^{(r)3} \\ \text{or} \qquad \sqrt{b_3}\,\epsilon^{(r)} &= (\sqrt{b_3}\,\epsilon^{(0)})^{3^r} \end{aligned}\right\} \qquad r = 0, 1, 2, \ldots \qquad \begin{aligned} &(6.1.14) \\ &(6.1.15) \end{aligned}$$

Convergence of the iteration occurs if

$$|\sqrt{b_3}\,\epsilon^{(0)}| = \left|\sqrt{\frac{F^{[3]}(\bar{x})}{3!}}\,\epsilon^{(0)}\right| < 1.0$$

The iteration of (6.1.14) or (6.1.15) is referred to as a third-order process, with the obvious implications. The significant figures in the value of x are tripled from one iteration step to the next.

Higher-order iteration processes can be obtained in the same manner, but these find no usage in modern-day computing techniques. Of those described, the third-order iteration is more efficient per iteration step than the second-order process; in turn the second-order is more efficient than the first-order. However, the degree of complexity of the computation increases in the reverse order. As a happy compromise the second-order process is usually employed because of its high efficiency and only moderate complexity in computation. As a second rule of thumb an iteration should converge within 10 steps and at most a maximum of 20 steps.

6.2. The First-order Reguli-falsi Iteration

The reguli-falsi, or false-position, iteration is the classic example of a first-order iteration process. It applies only to the case of real roots. To illustrate the technique, consider Fig. 6.1, on which $f(x)$ is plotted versus x. The value of the root $\bar{x}$ which satisfies $f(\bar{x}) = 0$ is shown, plus an initial estimate $x^{(0)}$ or the point $f(x^{(0)}), x^{(0)}$. This initial estimate is combined with another point $f(x^{(1)}), x^{(1)}$ and the straight line between drawn in. The point $f(x^{(1)}), x^{(1)}$ must be such that the sign of $f(x^{(0)})$ and $f(x^{(1)})$ are different from each other. The intersection of the straight line crosses the x axis at a point $x^{(2)}$ which is closer to $\bar{x}$ than $x^{(1)}$. From $x^{(2)}$ the point $f(x^{(2)}), x^{(2)}$ is located and the straight-line connection to $f(x^{(0)}), x^{(0)}$ completed. This forms $x^{(3)}$ on the x axis, which is closer to the desired result than $x^{(2)}$. The process is repeated until either the criterion

$$|x^{(r+1)} - x^{(r)}| < p^{-k}$$

or the alternative criterion

$$\left| \frac{x^{(r+1)} - x^{(r)}}{x^{(r)}} \right| < p^{-k_1}$$

is satisfied. k and k_1 are preassigned integers, and p is the radix of the number system employed ($p = 2$ for a binary machine). When the criterion used is met, the value of $x^{(r+1)}$ is taken as equal to $\bar{x}$.

Actually the reguli-falsi method is merely one of inverse linear interpolation, with the relation between successive iterations given by (see Fig. 6.1)

$$x^{(r+1)} = \frac{x^{(0)}f(x^{(r)}) - x^{(r)}f(x^{(0)})}{f(x^{(r)}) - f(x^{(0)})} \tag{6.2.1}$$

or, in a preferred form,

$$x^{(r+1)} = x^{(r)} - \frac{f(x^{(r)})(x^{(r)} - x^{(0)})}{f(x^{(r)}) - f(x^{(0)})}$$

Assumed in this discussion is that only one real root exists in the interval $(x^{(0)},x^{(1)})$. If more than one root exists, the iteration may converge to either root.

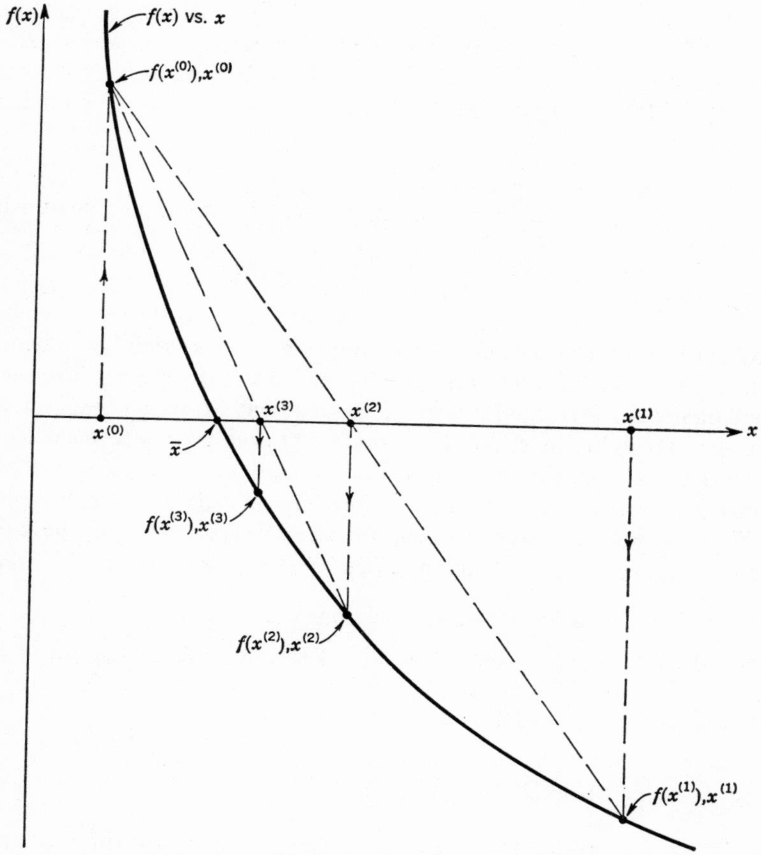

FIG. 6.1. Schematic of reguli-falsi iteration pattern.

From a Taylor series expansion of $f(x)$ around $\bar{x}$ and $f(\bar{x}) = 0$ there results

$$f(x^{(0)}) = \epsilon^{(0)}f'(\bar{x}) + \tfrac{1}{2}(\epsilon^{(0)})^2f''(\bar{x}) + \cdots$$
$$f(x^{(r)}) = \epsilon^{(r)}f'(\bar{x}) + \tfrac{1}{2}(\epsilon^{(r)})^2f''(\bar{x}) + \cdots$$

Substituting in (6.2.1),

$$x^{(r+1)} = \frac{(x^{(0)}\epsilon^{(r)} - \epsilon^{(0)}x^{(r)})f'(\bar{x})}{(\epsilon^{(r)} - \epsilon^{(0)})f'(\bar{x}) + \dfrac{(\epsilon^{(r)})^2 - (\epsilon^{(0)})^2}{2}f''(\bar{x}) + \cdots} + \cdots$$

and expanding yields

$$x^{(r+1)} = \bar{x} + \tfrac{1}{2}\epsilon^{(0)}\frac{f''(\bar{x})}{f'(\bar{x})}\,\epsilon^{(r)} + \cdots$$

or

$$\epsilon^{(r+1)} = \tfrac{1}{2}\epsilon^{(0)}\frac{f''(\bar{x})}{f'(\bar{x})}\,\epsilon^{(r)} + \cdots$$

Truncating after the first term leads to

$$\epsilon^{(r+1)} = d_1\epsilon^{(r)}$$

which defines a first-order iteration process. Convergence occurs if

$$|d_1| = \left|\frac{\epsilon^{(0)}}{2}\frac{f''(\bar{x})}{f'(\bar{x})}\right| < 1.0$$

or if $f'(x) \neq 0$ and $f''(x)$ does not change sign in the vicinity of $\bar{x}$.

The reguli-falsi method is not used too often. In a sense the method is inefficient, since the point $f(x^{(0)})$, $x^{(0)}$ is always used as one end of the successive straight lines. If the points $x^{(r)}$ and $x^{(r-1)}$ are used to form the successive lines, the process becomes of order 1.618. This represents a considerable improvement in the rate of convergence over the simple reguli-falsi scheme. However, the initial estimate $x^{(0)}$ must be close to $\bar{x}$, or the process will not converge.

6.3. The Second-order Newton Iteration

The best-known iterative process and the one most often used is the Newton algorithm (referred to as the "Newton-Raphson algorithm"). A Taylor series expansion around $x^{(0)}$ leads to

$$\begin{aligned} f(\bar{x}) = 0 &= f(x^{(0)}) + (\bar{x} - x^{(0)})f'(x^{(0)}) + \frac{(\bar{x} - x^{(0)})^2}{2!}f''(x^{(0)}) + \cdots \\ &= f(x^{(0)}) - \epsilon^{(0)}f'(x^{(0)}) + \frac{(\epsilon^{(0)})^2}{2!}f''(x^{(0)}) + \cdots \qquad (6.3.1) \end{aligned}$$

with $\epsilon^{(0)} = x^{(0)} - \bar{x}$. If the initial estimate $x^{(0)}$ is a good one, the square of the error term can be neglected. Thus

$$f(x^{(0)}) - \epsilon^{(0)}f'(x^{(0)}) = 0$$

or

$$\epsilon^{(0)} = \frac{f(x^{(0)})}{f'(x^{(0)})} \qquad (6.3.2)$$

Consider that the next improved estimate is made up as

$$x^{(1)} = x^{(0)} - \epsilon^{(0)}$$

and yields
$$x^{(1)} = x^{(0)} - \frac{f(x^{(0)})}{f'(x^{(0)})}$$

Repeating the process with $x^{(1)}$ and $\epsilon^{(1)}$ yields in the same way

$$\epsilon^{(1)} = \frac{f(x^{(1)})}{f'(x^{(1)})}$$

and with
$$x^{(2)} = x^{(1)} - \epsilon^{(1)}$$

$$x^{(2)} = x^{(1)} - \frac{f(x^{(1)})}{f'(x^{(1)})}$$

In addition,
$$x^{(2)} = x^{(0)} - \epsilon^{(0)} - \epsilon^{(1)}$$

which is a better estimate than $x^{(1)}$. Continuing the process leads to the general terms

$$x^{(r+1)} = x^{(r)} - \epsilon^{(r)}$$

$$\epsilon^{(r)} = \frac{f(x^{(r)})}{f'(x^{(r)})}$$

$$x^{(r+1)} = x^{(r)} - \frac{f(x^{(r)})}{f'(x^{(r)})} \qquad r = 0, 1, 2, \ldots \tag{6.3.3}$$

The iterative process of (6.3.3) is Newton's algorithm. It can be seen immediately that this iteration sequence differs from the reguli-falsi in that both $f(x^{(r)})$ and $f'(x^{(r)})$ must be calculated at each iteration step. This additional calculation of $f'(x^{(r)})$ may often be a serious defect of Newton's process. Equation (6.3.3) is also seen to fit (6.1.5) with $\beta^{(r)} = 1/f'(x^{(r)})$.

From (6.1.3), (6.3.3) can be written as

$$F(x^{(r)}) = x^{(r)} - \frac{f(x^{(r)})}{f'(x^{(r)})}$$

or differentiating,
$$F'(x^{(r)}) = \frac{f(x^{(r)})f''(x^{(r)})}{[f'(x^{(r)})]^2}$$

For the special case $x^{(r)} = \bar{x}$, it follows that $f(x^{(r)}) = 0$ and in turn $F'(x^{(r)}) = F'(\bar{x}) = 0$. Thus in (6.1.9) $b_1 = 0$, and the Newton iteration process is second-order.

The term $-f(x^{(r)})/f'(x^{(r)})$ in (6.3.3) may be considered as an error term in the Newton iteration process. This error term will be minimized by a large value of $f'(x)$, thus implying that, if $f(x)$ has a strong vertical trajectory at or close to $x = \bar{x}$, convergence will be quite fast. In contrast, if $f(x)$ is nearly horizontal at $x = \bar{x}$, convergence will be extremely slow.

In the limiting case where $f(x)$ is actually horizontal to the x axis at $x = \bar{x}$ (a maximum or minimum in the function), convergence will never occur.

The geometric significance of the Newton iteration (for real roots) can be seen by consideration of Fig. 6.2. With the estimate $x^{(r)}$ for $\bar{x}$ the

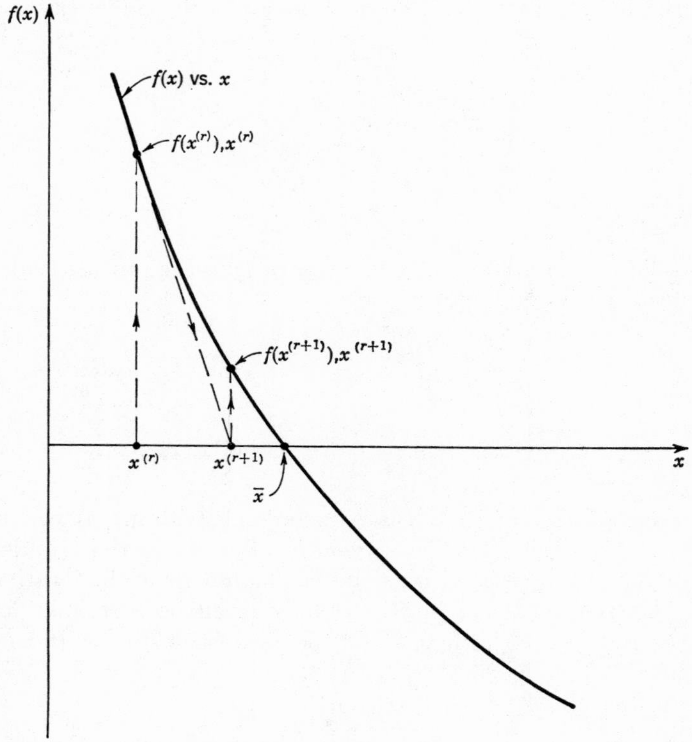

FIG. 6.2. Schematic of Newton iteration pattern.

point $f(x^{(r)})$, $x^{(r)}$ is immediately defined on the $f(x)$ versus x curve. If a straight line is drawn tangent to the $f(x)$ curve at this point, the intersection on the x axis defines a new point $x^{(i)}$. But

$$f'(x^{(r)}) = \frac{f(x^{(r)})}{x^{(r)} - x^{(i)}}$$

or

$$x^{(i)} = x^{(r)} - \frac{f(x^{(r)})}{f'(x^{(r)})}$$

Comparison with (6.3.3) shows that $x^{(i)} = x^{(r+1)}$. Thus the Newton method consists in drawing successive tangents to the $f(x)$ curve.

As with any iteration process, the present one cannot be used blindly. Depending on the initial estimate $x^{(0)}$ and the particular shape of $f(x)$ in $(x^{(0)},\bar{x})$ convergence may or may not occur to the desired root. If the function has turning points or inflections in this interval, the use of the tangent at $x^{(0)}$ may lead to an $x^{(1)}$ which is farther from $\bar{x}$ than $x^{(0)}$.

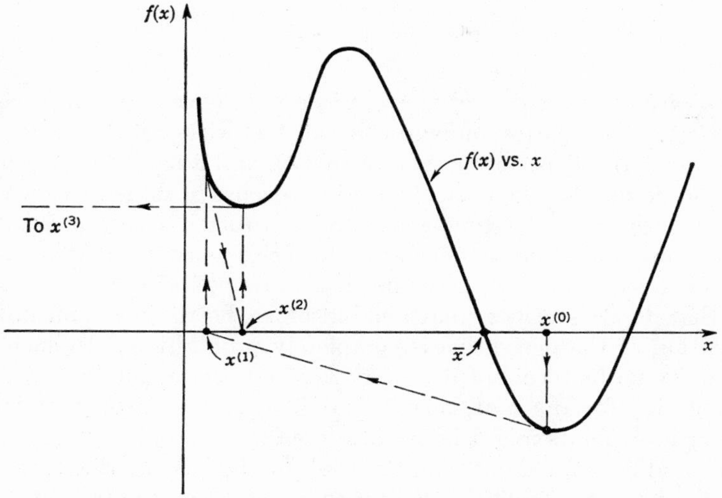

FIG. 6.3. Schematic of Newton iteration pattern when convergence does not occur.

This possibility is shown in Fig. 6.3. It is not difficult to conceive of a function such that

$$x^{(r)} = x^{(r+2)} = x^{(r+4)} \cdots \qquad \text{and} \qquad x^{(r+1)} = x^{(r+3)} = x^{(r+5)} \cdots$$

i.e., the iteration loops in a complete circle and never converges. Changing the initial value $x^{(0)}$ will usually remove this problem. The convergence requirements can be completely stated as follows:

1. If $f'(x)$ and $f''(x)$ do not change sign in the interval $(x^{(0)},\bar{x})$ and if $f(x^{(0)})$ and $f''(x^{(0)})$ have the same sign, the iteration will always converge to $\bar{x}$.

2. If the conditions in (1) are not fulfilled, convergence may or may not take place. From Fig. 6.2 it can be noted that the ideal situation is for $f(x)$ to be smoothly convex to the x axis.

The Newton iteration algorithm of (6.3.3) is probably the most widely used technique for calculating the roots of algebraic or transcendental equations. Both real and complex roots can be found, the only proviso being that if $\bar{x}$ is complex $x^{(0)}$ must also be chosen as complex. Given a proper choice of the initial estimate $x^{(0)}$, convergence normally occurs quickly because of the second-order nature of the process. If $f(x)$ is a polynomial, there are a set of recurrence relations for calculating $f(x)$ and $f'(x)$ in a particularly simple manner. These will be developed in a later section.

It is also possible to modify the Newton process of (6.3.3) by writing

$$x^{(r+1)} = x^{(r)} - \frac{f(x^{(r)})}{f'(x^{(0)})} \tag{6.3.4}$$

In this case the term $f'(x^{(0)})$ is calculated only once and is held constant thereafter. This corresponds to using (6.1.4) with $\alpha = 1/f'(x^{(0)})$. Convergence of (6.3.4) is slower than of (6.3.3), and a more careful choice of $x^{(0)}$ must be made. The principal utility occurs in those cases where the calculation of $f'(x^{(r)})$ is time-consuming. In such a case it is probably faster to use more iterative cycles with $f'(x^{(0)})$ as constant than to calculate $f'(x)$ over and over. Of course it is also possible that $f(x)$ is so complex that $f'(x)$ is either unattainable or so horribly complicated that calculation of the derivative is completely prohibitive. In such a case Newton's method cannot be used; instead the reguli-falsi or simple interpolation for the root must be used. Lagrange's polynomial using three or four points might be ideal in the latter case.

It should be pointed out that Newton's method as described is a second-order iteration process if and only if convergence occurs to a simple root. If the root is a multiple one, the equation must be revised. This has been outlined by Bodewig (3).

6.4. The Third-order Richmond Iteration

The simplest third-order iteration process is due to Richmond (29) and discussed by Hamilton (19). If $f'(\bar{x}) \neq 0$ and $f''(\bar{x})$ exist, a procedure similar to the derivation of Newton's formula yields (see Sec. 6.5 for derivation)

$$x^{(r+1)} = x^{(r)} - \frac{2f(x^{(r)})f'(x^{(r)})}{2[f'(x^{(r)})]^2 - f(x^{(r)})f''(x^{(r)})} \qquad r = 0, 1, 2, \ldots \tag{6.4.1}$$

Richmond's third-order formula (6.4.1) requires the evaluation of $f(x)$, $f'(x)$, and $f''(x)$ at each iteration step. The high rate of convergence must now be balanced against the time required to calculate $f''(x)$ as compared with Newton's method. The method assumes, of course, that both $f'x$ and $f''(x)$ can be evaluated.

An interesting variation of the Richmond iteration has been developed by Wynn (37) for transcendental equations. Consider that $f(x)$ satisfies the nonhomogeneous ordinary differential equation

$$p(x)f'' + q(x)f' + s(x)f = t(x) \tag{6.4.2}$$

with $p(x)$, $q(x)$, $s(x)$, and $t(x)$ functions of x. Solving for f'' and substituting into (6.4.1) yields

$$x^{(r+1)} = x^{(r)} - \frac{2p(x)f(x^{(r)})f'(x^{(r)})}{2p(x)[f'(x^{(r)})]^2 - t(x)f(x^{(r)}) + s(x)[f(x^{(r)})]^2 + q(x)f(x^{(r)})f'(x^{(r)})} \tag{6.4.3}$$

Equation (6.4.3), while still a third-order iteration, does not require the evaluation of $f''(x)$. While this formula holds only for functions which satisfy (6.4.2), there are many of importance which fit this category. If $p(x) = x$, $q(x) = 1.0$, $s(x) = x$, and $t(x) = 0$, (6.4.2) is Bessel's equation. Thus (6.4.3) may be used to find the roots of $J_0(x)$.

6.5. Increasing the Convergence Rate

It is possible, in many cases, to speed up the rate of convergence of the iteration process. The means of speeding up the processes are generally extrapolation procedures of the type previously described for integrating ODE. As the simplest extension consider a first-order iteration process for which

$$b_1 = \frac{\epsilon^{(1)}}{\epsilon^{(0)}} = \frac{x^{(1)} - \bar{x}}{x^{(0)} - \bar{x}}$$

Solving for $\bar{x}$,

$$\bar{x} = \frac{b_1(x^{(0)} - x^{(1)})}{b_1 - 1} + x^{(1)} \tag{6.5.1}$$

If the numerical value of b_1 were known and there were no errors involved in the assumption of a first-order process, (6.5.1) could be used after two iterations to yield the desired root by extrapolation. Unfortunately, the numerical magnitude of b_1 is usually unknown, and the iteration process is not exactly first-order. If b_1 is known, (6.5.1) can be used to estimate $\bar{x}$ even though the process is not exactly first-order; this estimate can be called $x^{(2)}$ or $\bar{x}^{(0)}$, depending on the user's preference. In any event $\bar{x}^{(0)}$ is a better estimate of $\bar{x}$ than either $x^{(0)}$ or $x^{(1)}$ and can be used as a new starting point for the iteration. After two further iterations (6.5.1) can be used again and the process continued in this manner.

To remove the unknown value of b_1, the following procedure can be used. First, it may be observed that

$$b_1 = \frac{\epsilon^{(1)}}{\epsilon^{(0)}} = \frac{\epsilon^{(2)}}{\epsilon^{(1)}}$$

and that

$$b_1 = \frac{\epsilon^{(2)} - \epsilon^{(1)}}{\epsilon^{(1)} - \epsilon^{(0)}}$$

Thus

$$b_1 = \frac{x^{(2)} - \bar{x}}{x^{(1)} - \bar{x}} = \frac{(x^{(2)} - \bar{x}) - (x^{(1)} - \bar{x})}{(x^{(1)} - \bar{x}) - (x^{(0)} - \bar{x})}$$

Solving the two right-hand terms for $\bar{x}$ yields

$$\bar{x} = \frac{x^{(0)}x^{(2)} - (x^{(1)})^2}{x^{(2)} - 2x^{(1)} + x^{(0)}}$$

or

$$\bar{x} = x^{(2)} - \frac{(x^{(2)} - x^{(1)})^2}{x^{(2)} - 2x^{(1)} + x^{(0)}} \tag{6.5.2}$$

This equation has the same connotation as (6.5.1) except that three values $x^{(0)}$, $x^{(1)}$, and $x^{(2)}$ are required and b_1 has been eliminated.

It is possible to change the rate of convergence of Newton's second-order process in a variety of ways. In particular, (6.3.1) can be truncated after the square term and this quadratic used to correct the linear term. From (6.3.1)

$$f(x^{(0)}) - \epsilon^{(0)}f'(x^{(0)}) + \frac{(\epsilon^{(0)})^2}{2!} f''(x^{(0)}) = 0$$

or

$$f(x^{(0)}) - \epsilon^{(0)}\left[f'(x^{(0)}) - \frac{\epsilon^{(0)}}{2!} f''(x^{(0)})\right] = 0 \tag{6.5.3}$$

But since the second derivative term is to be only a correction to the first derivative, the $\epsilon^{(0)}$ in the brackets can be replaced by (6.3.2), or

$$\epsilon^{(0)} = \frac{f(x^{(0)})}{f'(x^{(0)})}$$

Making this substitution and solving for $\epsilon^{(0)}$ leads to

$$\epsilon^{(0)} = \frac{2f(x^{(0)})f'(x^{(0)})}{2[f'(x^{(0)})]^2 - f(x^{(0)})f''(x^{(0)})}$$

This equation can now be used in the same way as (6.3.2) to generate the iteration pattern

$$x^{(r+1)} = x^{(r)} - \frac{2f(x^{(r)})f'(x^{(r)})}{2[f'(x^{(r)})]^2 - f(x^{(r)})f''(x^{(r)})}$$

which is seen to be Richmond's third-order iterative process.

It has already been pointed out that one of the defects of Newton's method is the need to evaluate $f'(x)$ at each step in the iteration. A possible alternative procedure is to replace the derivative with a difference quotient in terms of previously calculated values. The specific procedure discussed here has been developed by Wegstein (33) and amplified by Jeeves (21). For convergent systems this procedure tends to speed up the rate of convergence; in many cases where convergence would normally not occur because of a poor initial choice the procedure forces the system to converge.

The main feature of this technique is based upon the use of

$$\bar{x}^{(r+1)} = qx^{(r)} + (1 - q)x^{(r+1)} \tag{6.5.4}$$

with the iteration process of (6.1.3). $x^{(r)}$ and $x^{(r+1)}$ having been found from the normal iteration cycle, (6.5.4) is used with a specific value of q to calculate $\bar{x}^{(r+1)}$. This new value is a better one than $x^{(r+1)}$ and can be used to iterate $x^{(r+2)}$. The main problem is deciding on a value for q which will yield this desired result. If we let $y = x = F(x)$ from (6.1.3), we can construct Fig. 6.4. The intersection of the two curves $y = x$ and

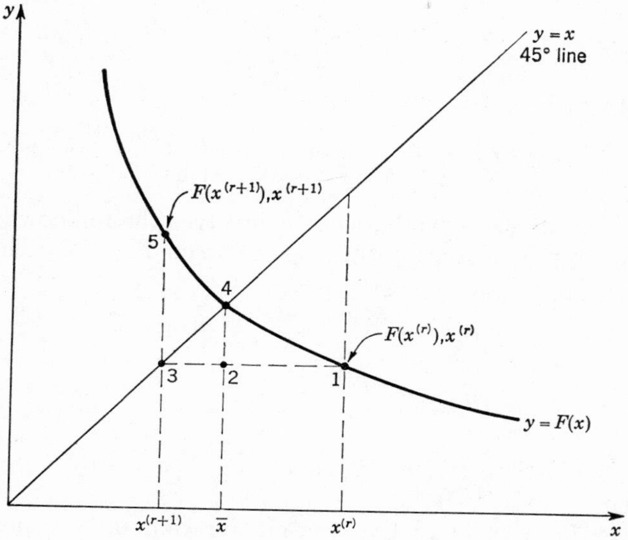

FIG. 6.4. Schematic for improved iteration process.

$y = F(x)$ yields the desired value $\bar{x}$. The normal iteration pattern can be represented by the following steps:

1. The estimate $x^{(r)}$ having been obtained or chosen, the corresponding value $F(x^{(r)})$ results by dropping a vertical line from $y = x^{(r)}$ to $y = F(x^{(r)})$.

2. From the iteration equation $x^{(r+1)} = F(x^{(r)})$ it can be seen that a horizontal line from the point $F(x^{(r)})$, $x^{(r)}$ to the 45° line yields $x^{(r+1)}$.

The value of q can then be defined from

$$\frac{q}{1-q} = \frac{\bar{x} - x^{(r+1)}}{x^{(r)} - \bar{x}} \tag{6.5.5}$$

which is seen to represent merely certain ratios in the horizontal line $x^{(r+1)}$ to $x^{(r)}$. Solving for $\bar{x}$ yields

$$\bar{x} = qx^{(r)} + (1 - q)x^{(r+1)} \tag{6.5.6}$$

so that if q were known a single application of (6.5.6) would yield the desired root. Unfortunately, q cannot be obtained exactly, since it is defined in terms of the unknown $\bar{x}$. Instead, an approximate value of q may be used, which necessarily yields an approximate value of $\bar{x}$, that is, (6.5.4). Since the triangle 3-2-4-3 is an isosceles triangle, the length $\overline{42}$ is equal to the length $\overline{32}$. The slope of the straight line between the points 4 and 1 is then given by $-a$, where

$$-a = \frac{\overline{42}}{\overline{21}} = \frac{\overline{32}}{\overline{21}}$$

and from (6.5.5)

$$-a = \frac{q}{1-q} \qquad \text{or} \qquad q = \frac{a}{1-a}$$

a cannot be determined exactly, since it involves the unknown point 2, but it can be approximated by the slope between 5 and 1. This can be written as

$$a \approx -\frac{F(x^{(r)}) - F(x^{(r-1)})}{x^{(r-1)} - x^{(r)}} \tag{6.5.7}$$

or

$$a \approx -\frac{x^{(r+1)} - x^{(r)}}{x^{(r-1)} - x^{(r)}}$$

In writing (6.5.7) the superscripts have been dropped by 1 as a matter of convenience.

With these facts in hand the over-all iteration process proceeds as follows:

1. Pick an $x^{(0)}$.
2. With (6.1.3) calculate $x^{(1)}$.
3. With (6.1.3) calculate $x^{(2)}$.
4. With (6.5.7) and $x^{(0)}$, $x^{(1)}$, and $x^{(2)}$, calculate the value of a.
5. From $a/(a - 1) = q$, calculate q.
6. Using q, $x^{(1)}$, and $x^{(2)}$, calculate $\bar{x}^{(2)}$ from (6.5.4).
7. This $\bar{x}^{(2)}$ will be a closer approximation to $\bar{x}$ than $x^{(2)}$, and thus $x^{(2)}$ is discarded and replaced with $\bar{x}^{(2)}$.
8. By using (6.1.3) and $\bar{x}^{(2)}$ a new value $x^{(3)}$ is calculated.
9. The entire process is now repeated, starting with step (4) and the values $x^{(1)}$, $\bar{x}^{(2)}$, and $x^{(3)}$. This yields $\bar{x}^{(3)}$, which replaces $x^{(3)}$.

A number of specific calculations are presented by Wegstein to show the power of this improved iteration. The order of the process is 1.618, and $f'(x)$ need never be evaluated explicitly. If $f'(x)$ is time-consuming to calculate, this procedure will converge faster than Newton's method, even though the latter is higher-order. It should also be pointed out that this procedure is similar to the modification previously mentioned for the first-order reguli-falsi method and also to replacement of the derivative term in Newton's equation with an equation of the form (6.5.7). Thus

$$f'(x^{(r)}) = \frac{f(x^{(r)}) - f(x^{(r-1)})}{x^{(r)} - x^{(r-1)}}$$

when substituted into (6.3.3) yields

$$x^{(r+1)} = \frac{f(x^{(r)})x^{(r-1)} - f(x^{(r-1)})x^{(r)}}{f(x^{(r)}) - f(x^{(r-1)})} \tag{6.5.8}$$

6.6. The Square Root of a Real Positive Number

A classical illustration of the implementation of the iteration techniques described is the calculation of the square root of a real positive number A. In terms of the previous notation the square root implies finding that value of $x = \bar{x}$ for which

$$f(x) = x^2 - A = 0$$

Since

$$f'(x) = 2x$$

the Newton iteration process leads to

$$x^{(r+1)} = x^{(r)} - \frac{[x^{(r)}]^2 - A}{2x^{(r)}} = \frac{1}{2}\left(x^{(r)} + \frac{A}{x^{(r)}}\right) \qquad r = 0, 1, 2, \ldots \tag{6.6.1}$$

Convergence of this iteration will lead to $\bar{x} = \sqrt{A}$. The usual or simplest start of the iteration is obtained with $x^{(0)} = 1.0$.

Upon defining the iteration error as

$$\epsilon^{(r)} = x^{(r)} - \sqrt{A}$$

(6.6.1) can be rearranged to

$$x^{(r+1)} - \sqrt{A} = \frac{1}{2}\left(x^{(r)} + \frac{A}{x^{(r)}}\right) - \sqrt{A} = \frac{1}{2}\left(x^{(r)} - 2\sqrt{A} + \frac{A}{x^{(r)}}\right)$$

$$= \frac{1}{2}\frac{(x^{(r)} - \sqrt{A})^2}{x^{(r)}}$$

or

$$\epsilon^{(r+1)} = \frac{(\epsilon^{(r)})^2}{2x^{(r)}} \qquad r = 0, 1, 2, \ldots$$

Convergence of this iteration thus occurs very quickly.

It is also possible to find other iteration formulas for the square root of a real positive number. Rearranging (6.6.1)

$$x^{(r+1)} = \frac{1}{2}\left(\frac{A}{x^{(r)}} - x^{(r)}\right) + x^{(r)}$$

or

$$x^{(r+1)} = x^{(r)} + \frac{1}{2}\left(\frac{A}{x^{(r)}} - x^{(r)}\right) \tag{6.6.2}$$

A third arrangement arises by considering

$$f(x) = \frac{1}{x^2} - \frac{1}{A} = 0$$

which leads to the iteration formula

$$x^{(r+1)} = x^{(r)} - \frac{1/(x^{(r)})^2 - 1/A}{-2/(x^{(r)})^3} = x^{(r)}\left[1 + \frac{A - (x^{(r)})^2}{2A}\right] \tag{6.6.3}$$

A fourth arrangement can be obtained by considering

$$f(x) = x^3 - Ax = 0$$

which leads to the iteration formula

$$x^{(r+1)} = \frac{(2x^{(r)})^3}{(3x^{(r)})^2 - A} \tag{6.6.4}$$

Finally, the case of

$$f(x) = \frac{1}{x^n} - B = 0$$

yields the iteration formula

$$x^{(r+1)} = \frac{x^{(r)}}{n}[(n + 1) - (Bx^{(r)})^n]$$

For the problem at hand $n = 2$ leads to

$$x^{(r+1)} = \frac{x^{(r)}}{2}[3 - (Bx^{(r)})^2] \tag{6.6.5}$$

Each of the iterative formulas (6.6.1) to (6.6.5) is a second-order process and may be used to obtain the square root of a real positive number. The choice of which particular equation to employ is a function of the properties of the digital computer to be used and the inclination of the programmer. Since multiplications and divisions are more time-consuming than additions and subtractions, the comparative speed of the formula used can be characterized by analyzing these arithmetic operations. The method of (6.6.1) requires only one division per iteration, an addition and a shift (on a binary machine a shift is equivalent to multiplying by $\frac{1}{2}$). The same is true for (6.6.2), which is merely (6.6.1) rearranged. Equation (6.6.3) requires two multiplications, a division, two additions, and a shift; (6.6.4) two multiplications, a division, two additions, and a shift; (6.6.5) three multiplications, an addition, and a shift. In the same context Richmond's scheme, applied to the square root, is

$$x^{(r+1)} = x^{(r)}\frac{4A - [A - (x^{(r)})^2]}{4(x^{(r)})^2 + [A - (x^{(r)})^2]}$$

which requires three multiplications, a division, three additions, and two shifts. It should be almost as fast per iteration step as (6.6.3), for example, and is third-order.

An investigation of the error propagation due to the initial estimate of $\sqrt{A}$ leads to some interesting results. Let

$$\epsilon = x^{(0)} - \sqrt{A} \tag{6.6.6}$$

where ϵ is the error in the first estimate $x^{(0)}$. From (6.6.1) and (6.6.6) there results

$$x^{(1)} = \frac{1}{2}\left(x^{(0)} + \frac{A}{x^{(0)}}\right) = \frac{1}{2}\left(\sqrt{A} + \epsilon + \frac{A}{\sqrt{A} + \epsilon}\right)$$

$$= \frac{1}{2}\left(\sqrt{A} + \epsilon + \sqrt{A}\,\frac{1}{1 + \epsilon/\sqrt{A}}\right)$$

This can be written in the form

$$x^{(1)} = \sqrt{A} + \frac{1}{2}\sum_{n=1}^{\infty} (-1)^{n+1} \frac{\epsilon^{n+1}}{\sqrt{A}^n}$$

and, expanding the infinite series,

$$x^{(1)} = \sqrt{A} + \frac{1}{2}\frac{\epsilon^2}{\sqrt{A}} - \frac{1}{2}\frac{\epsilon^3}{A} + \cdots \tag{6.6.7}$$

Note that the term containing the first power of ϵ, ϵ^1, is missing. This corresponds to the definition of a second-order iteration process. Using (6.6.1) for $x^{(2)}$ now results in

$$x^{(2)} = \sqrt{A} + \frac{\sqrt{A}}{2}\sum_{k=2}^{\infty} (-1)^k \left[\frac{1}{2}\sum_{n=1}^{\infty} (-1)^{n+1}\left(\frac{\epsilon}{\sqrt{A}}\right)^{n+1}\right]^k$$

This process can be continued as far as desired, but the complexity of the succeeding terms precludes the development here. In this way, however, the error at the end of any iteration step can be calculated as a function of the initial estimate $x^{(0)}$. From a practical point of view these equations would never actually be used, since more computation is required than to calculate the desired value of $\bar{x}$.

In the same manner, but using (6.6.3) and (6.6.6),

$$x^{(1)} = \sqrt{A} + \epsilon\left[1 + \frac{A - (\sqrt{A} + \epsilon)^2}{2A}\right] = \sqrt{A} - \frac{3}{2}\frac{\epsilon^2}{\sqrt{A}} - \frac{3}{2}\frac{\epsilon^3}{A} + \cdots \tag{6.6.8}$$

Upon comparing (6.6.7) and (6.6.8) it can be seen that the coefficient on the ϵ^2 term is larger in (6.6.8), and thus the iteration pattern of (6.6.1) converges faster than (6.6.3). Further, multiplying (6.6.7) by $\frac{3}{4}$, (6.6.8) by $\frac{1}{4}$, and adding yields an iteration equation with ϵ^2 missing. This equation is third-order and was formed by manipulating the second-order processes (this was previously done with Newton's method to yield the Richmond iteration).

An interesting technique which is sometimes used to calculate the square root of a real positive integer squared depends only on additive operations. It is based on the well-known fact that

$$1 + 3 + 5 + 7 + \cdots + (2n - 1) = n^2 \tag{6.6.9}$$

If n is not too large, the use of (6.6.9) evaluates n directly. Depending on the computer to be used, this method may actually be simpler and faster than the other methods discussed.

6.7. Real Roots of a Polynomial with Real Coefficients

The simplest case of evaluating the roots of a polynomial occurs when the polynomial has all real coefficients and the desired roots are real. Under such conditions the necessary techniques are relatively straightforward. However, as in the case of matrices, it is possible to have ill-conditioned polynomials in the sense that a small perturbation in one of the coefficients leads to completely erroneous values for some of the roots. This has been discussed by Wilkinson (35) in a monumental paper. When the polynomial is ill conditioned, it may be necessary to resort to multiple precision to obtain a valid result.

A polynomial of degree n may be written as

$$f(x) = x^n + a_1x^{n-1} + a_2x^{n-2} + \cdots + a_{n-1}x + a_n \tag{6.7.1}$$

where, in the present context, the $a_1, a_2, \ldots, a_n$ are real numbers. The roots of (6.7.1) are designated as $\bar{x}_1, \bar{x}_2, \ldots, \bar{x}_n$. The leading coefficient of the polynomial has been set equal to 1, for convenience. In the more general case where (6.7.1) has complex roots these roots must exist in pairs as complex conjugates. Thus, if n = odd, there must be at least one real root. To illustrate the above mentioned ill-conditioned feature, Wilkinson picked the case

$$\begin{aligned} n &= 20 \\ \bar{x}_1 &= -1 \\ \bar{x}_2 &= -2 \\ \bar{x}_3 &= -3 \\ &\cdot\ \cdot\ \cdot\ \cdot \\ \bar{x}_{19} &= -19 \\ \bar{x}_{20} &= -20 \end{aligned}$$

If the coefficient a_1 is perturbed slightly so that a new polynomial $g(x)$ is used, i.e.,

$$f(x) = x^{20} + 210x^{19} + \cdot \cdot \cdot$$

and

$$g(x) = f(x) + 2^{-23}x^{19}$$

Wilkinson found that some of the calculated roots were

$$\begin{gathered} -1.000000000 \\ -2.000000000 \\ -4.999999928 \\ -8.917250249 \\ -10.095266145 \pm 0.643500904i \\ -13.992358137 \pm 2.518830070i \end{gathered}$$

In other words, some of the roots were well conditioned, leading to valid answers, but others were so ill-conditioned that complex roots appeared. On this basis it should be apparent that polynomial root finding cannot be approached in a blind manner.

On the momentary assumption that an iteration process has been used to locate one real root of (6.7.1) the next step is to remove this root by synthetic division. This forms a new polynomial of degree $n - 1$ which may be called $g(x)$. Since this reduction process may occur over and over as succeeding real roots are found, a simple computational algorithm for this transformation is desirable. Calling this first root $\bar{x}_1$ and dividing (6.7.1) by $x - \bar{x}_1$ forms

$$f(x) = (x - \bar{x}_1)(x^{n-1} + b_1x^{n-2} + b_2x^{n-3} + \cdot \cdot \cdot + b_{n-2}x + b_{n-1}) \qquad (6.7.2)$$

where the $b_1, b_2, \ldots, b_{n-1}$ are the coefficients of the new reduced polynomial $g(x) = f(x)/(x - \bar{x}_1)$. Since $f(x)$ equals the right-hand side of both (6.7.1) and (6.7.2), the coefficients of $x^n, x^{n-1}, \ldots$ can be equated. These equalities can be expressed by the sequence

$$\begin{aligned} b_1 &= a_1 + \bar{x}_1 \\ b_2 &= a_2 + b_1\bar{x}_1 \\ b_3 &= a_2 + b_2\bar{x}_1 \\ &\cdots\cdots\cdots \\ b_r &= a_r + b_{r-1}\bar{x}_1 \\ &\cdots\cdots\cdots \\ b_{n-1} &= a_{n-1} + b_{n-2}\bar{x}_1 \end{aligned}$$

or by the computational algorithm

$$\left.\begin{aligned} b_0 &= 1.0 \\ b_r &= a_r + b_{r-1}\bar{x}_1 \end{aligned}\right\} \quad r = 1, 2, 3, \ldots, n - 1 \qquad (6.7.3)$$

The next step is to find a real root of $g(x) = 0$ by iteration, and by using the same form as (6.7.3), this root $\bar{x}_2$ is removed from $g(x)$ to form a new reduced polynomial $h(x)$ of degree $n - 2$. In this way all the real roots are obtained one by one by iteration on successively lower-degree polynomials. Any round-off errors introduced by this process are minimized if the roots are eliminated in order of increasing magnitude.

The following procedure has been used with considerable success to find all the real roots of a polynomial:

1. A fixed value of Δx is supplied at the start of the machine routine. The function $f(x)$ is then evaluated, starting at $x = 0$, at increasing multiples of Δx until a change in the sign of $f(x)$ is found. This is taken as an indication of the rough location of a real positive root. By backing up one Δx interval, the resultant $x = x^{(0)}$ is used in the Newton iteration to evaluate $\bar{x}_1$.
2. By using the calculated $\bar{x}_1$ the polynomial is reduced by means of (6.7.3).
3. By using a starting value of x just beyond $\bar{x}_1$ the process is repeated to find $\bar{x}_2$. This is continued until all the positive real roots have been found.
4. The entire process is repeated, with a negative Δx to evaluate all the negative real roots (actually it frequently may be wiser to locate the real positive and negative roots within an interval and proceed to larger values of x in this way).
5. When all the real roots have been obtained, each is improved by iterating on the original polynomial.

This technique can be varied, of course, depending on any a priori knowledge of the roots, behavior of the polynomial, or the need to calculate only a limited number of roots. Newton's method has been indicated as the iteration technique because of its simplicity and accuracy. If the root under investigation is ill conditioned, the iteration should be performed with multiple-precision accuracy (for simplicity in programming, multiple precision may be used on all the roots).

A simple trick which seems to work well when the roots are widely separated in magnitude is to define a new variable $z = 1/x$. This transforms the roots of the new polynomial into reciprocals of the original roots. Now the iteration procedure leads to the originally largest, etc., root. Further, it is wise to keep track of the number of iterations required as a single root is calculated. If the number becomes greater than 20 for any one root, the last value of $x^{(r)}$ should be multiplied by a constant, to get a new "start."

As a point of further interest consider dividing (6.7.1) by a factor $x - d$, where d is not a root of the polynomial, that is, $d \neq \bar{x}_1$. This will yield $g(x)$ plus a remainder term. This remainder can be found by extending (6.7.3) one more term to yield

$$\text{Remainder} = b_n = a_n + b_{n-1}d \qquad (6.7.4)$$

in conjunction with

$$\left.\begin{aligned} b_0 &= 1.0 \\ b_r &= a_r + b_{r-1}d \end{aligned}\right\} \qquad r = 1, 2, \ldots, n-1 \tag{6.7.5}$$

An important variation on the Newton iteration process, called the "Birge-Vieta iteration," can now be defined. This method uses

$$x^{(r+1)} = x^{(r)} - \frac{b_n}{c_{n-1}} \tag{6.7.6}$$

where b_n is the remainder term in (6.7.4) with $d = x^{(r)}$. c_{n-1} is the remainder term obtained by dividing out $x - d$ a second time and is calculated from

$$\left.\begin{aligned} c_0 &= 1.0 \\ c_r &= b_r + c_{r-1}d \\ c_{n-1} &= b_{n-1} + c_{n-2}d \end{aligned}\right\} \qquad r = 1, 2, \ldots, n-2$$

As the value of $x^{(r)} = d$ approaches $\bar{x}_1$, b_n will become smaller and smaller. When the root has been located with sufficient precision, $b_n = 0$ and the reduced polynomial with coefficients $b_1, b_2, \ldots, b_{n-1}$ is available for use on the next root.

In this discussion it has been assumed that equal or nearly equal real roots did not exist. In the case that such an assumption is not true the correction term would not approach zero in the iteration. In the Newton iteration both $f(x)$ and $f'(x)$ would approach zero as $x^{(r+1)} \to \bar{x}$; in the Birge-Vieta iteration b_n and c_{n-1} would behave similarly. If the root is multiple, the approach to zero is identical for the two parts of the correction term, whereas if the roots are almost equal, the approach to zero would be different. To handle this situation, Hartree (Chap. 1, 17) has proposed the following:

1. Form $f'(x)$ from $f(x)$.
2. Determine the roots of $f'(x)$ corresponding to the double or nearly double root.
3. Upon calling this root $\bar{x}_2$, $f'(\bar{x}_2) = 0$ and defining

$$\bar{x}_1 = \bar{x}_2 + \Delta$$

a Taylor series expansion yields

$$f(\bar{x}_1) = 0 = f(\bar{x}_2 + \Delta) = f(\bar{x}_2) + \Delta f'(\bar{x}_2) + \tfrac{1}{2}\Delta^2 f''(\bar{x}_2) + \cdots$$

4. Truncating after the second derivative and solving for Δ yields

$$\Delta = \pm\sqrt{\frac{-2f(\bar{x}_2)}{f''(\bar{x}_2)}}$$

with $f'(\bar{x}_2) = 0$. This value of Δ can be used with $\bar{x}_2$ to give a good approximation for $\bar{x}_1$ in the iteration process.

6.8. Complex Roots of a Polynomial with Real Coefficients

When all the real roots of a polynomial with real coefficients have been found and removed, the result is an even-degree polynomial with only complex conjugate roots (it being assumed of course that all the roots were not real). There are two good iteration methods for finding these complex roots; the first is the Newton iteration and the second a procedure called the "Lin-Bairstow iteration." Both methods are second-order iterative processes.

We denote the complex variable z by $z = a + ib$, and the problem now is to find a root of

$$f(z) = 0 \tag{6.8.1}$$

A root of (6.8.1) will be designated as $\bar{z}$, with $\bar{z} = \bar{a} + i\bar{b}$. Letting

$$\bar{a} = a^{(0)} + \epsilon \qquad \bar{b} = b^{(0)} + \Delta$$

a Taylor series expansion with $\bar{z} = \bar{z}^{(0)} + \epsilon + i\Delta$ yields

$$f(\bar{z}) = 0 = f(z^{(0)}) + (\epsilon + i\Delta)f'(z^{(0)}) + \frac{(\epsilon + i\Delta)^2}{2!} f''(z^{(0)}) + \cdots$$

Truncating between the second and the third terms,

$$\epsilon + i\Delta = \frac{f(z^{(0)})}{f'(z^{(0)})}$$

This sets up the iteration pattern

$$z^{(r+1)} = z^{(r)} - \frac{f(z^{(r)})}{f'(z^{(r)})} \qquad r = 0, 1, 2, \ldots \tag{6.8.2}$$

which is merely the Newton iteration in terms of the complex variable z. Obviously it is necessary to assume that the initial estimate $z^{(0)}$ is complex. Once $\bar{z}$ is obtained the conjugate $\bar{a} - i\bar{b}$ follows. Note, however, that complex numbers must be handled throughout. This can sometimes cause programming difficulties.

In the Lin-Bairstow iteration an attempt is made to find a quadratic factor

$$p(x) = x^2 + \alpha x + \beta \tag{6.8.3}$$

which exactly factors into the original polynomial. α and β are real numbers, and when $p(x)$ exactly factors, $\alpha = \bar{\alpha}$ and $\beta = \bar{\beta}$. When a quadratic factor [(6.8.3)] is divided into a polynomial of the form (6.7.1), the result is a reduced polynomial plus a remainder term. The remainder term is a linear function of x which becomes zero if $p(x)$ is an exact factor. This may conveniently be illustrated by

$$f(x) = p(x)g(x) + R(x) \tag{6.8.4}$$

where

$$\begin{aligned} f(x) &= (6.7.1) \\ p(x) &= (6.8.3) \\ g(x) &= x^{n-2} + b_1x^{n-3} + \cdots + b_{n-3}x + b_{n-2} \\ R(x) &= r_1x + r_2 \end{aligned}$$

$b_1, b_2, \ldots, b_{n-2}$ are the coefficients of the reduced polynomial, and r_1 and r_2 are remainder terms. If $\alpha = \bar{\alpha}$ and $\beta = \bar{\beta}$ and the quadratic factor divides exactly into (6.7.1), $r_1 = r_2 = 0$. Equating coefficients of x in (6.7.1) and (6.8.4) yields the sequence

$$\begin{aligned} a_1 &= b_1 + \alpha \\ a_2 &= b_2 + \alpha b_1 + \beta \\ a_3 &= b_3 + \alpha b_2 + \beta b_1 \\ &\cdots\cdots\cdots\cdots \\ a_{n-2} &= b_{n-2} + \alpha b_{n-3} + \beta b_{n-4} \\ a_{n-1} &= r_1 + \alpha b_{n-2} + \beta b_{n-3} \\ a_n &= r_2 + \beta b_{n-2} \end{aligned} \tag{6.8.5}$$

The first $n - 2$ terms of this sequence can be written in algorithm form as

$$b_r = a_r - \alpha b_{r-1} - \beta b_{r-2} \qquad b_{-1} = 0 \qquad b_0 = 1.0 \qquad r = 1, 2, \ldots, n-2 \tag{6.8.6}$$

If r_1 and r_2 are defined as

$$r_1 = b_{n-1} = a_{n-1} - \alpha b_{n-2} - \beta b_{n-3} \qquad r_2 = b_n + \alpha b_{n-1} = a_n - \beta b_{n-2} \tag{6.8.7}$$

the last two terms of (6.8.5) may be included in the algorithm of (6.8.6), with the index $r = 1, 2, 3, \ldots, n$. Thus the result of dividing a polynomial with a quadratic factor may be determined simply by using the sequence of (6.8.6) and (6.8.7).

If $p(x)$ were an exact factor, that is, $\alpha = \bar{\alpha}$ and $\beta = \bar{\beta}$, $b_n = b_{n-1} = 0$ from (6.8.7) and

$$a_{n-1} - \bar{\alpha} b_{n-2} - \bar{\beta} b_{n-3} = 0 \qquad a_n - \bar{\beta} b_{n-2} = 0$$

or

$$\bar{\beta} = \frac{a_n}{b_{n-2}} \qquad \bar{\alpha} = \frac{a_{n-1} - \beta b_{n-3}}{b_{n-2}} \tag{6.8.8}$$

Equation (6.8.8) suggests a possible iterative sequence to determine $\bar{\alpha}$ and $\bar{\beta}$. A first estimate is made of the values $\bar{\alpha}$ and $\bar{\beta}$, $\alpha^{(0)}$ and $\beta^{(0)}$. Based upon this estimate, the algorithm (6.8.6) can be used with (6.8.8) to generate a new, improved set $\alpha^{(1)}$ and $\beta^{(1)}$. These are

$$\beta^{(1)} = \frac{a_n}{b_{n-2}} \qquad \alpha^{(1)} = \frac{a_{n-1} - \beta^{(0)} b_{n-3}}{b_{n-2}}$$

or, for faster convergence,

$$\alpha^{(1)} = \frac{a_{n-1} - \beta^{(1)}b_{n-3}}{b_{n-2}}$$

We use the new $\beta^{(1)}$ and $\alpha^{(1)}$ and repeat the process until convergence occurs to the desired accuracy. In the general sense

$$\beta^{(r+1)} = \frac{a_n}{b_{n-2}} \qquad \alpha^{(r+1)} = \frac{a_{n-1} - \beta^{(r+1)}b_{n-3}}{b_{n-2}}$$

As outlined here, this iterative process is first-order and is called the "Lin algorithm." When convergence occurs, the factor

$$x^2 + \bar{\alpha}x + \bar{\beta} = 0$$

can be solved to yield the two complex conjugate roots. In addition, the reduced polynomial is also available, since $b_1, b_2, \ldots, b_{n-2}$ have been determined. Note that only real numbers are used in the iterative process.

In an attempt to speed up the convergence rate it would be desirable to use a second-order process instead of the first-order one. Such a variation is called the "Bairstow algorithm." Since r_1 and r_2 are functions of the two parameters α and β, the aim of the iteration process is to have $r_1(\alpha,\beta)$ and $r_2(\alpha,\beta)$ approach zero. A Taylor series expansion with $\bar{\alpha} = \alpha + \Delta\alpha$ and $\bar{\beta} = \beta + \Delta\beta$ yields

$$r_1(\bar{\alpha},\bar{\beta}) = 0 = r_1(\alpha,\beta) + \Delta\alpha \left.\frac{\partial r_1}{\partial \alpha}\right)_\beta + \Delta\beta \left.\frac{\partial r_1}{\partial \beta}\right)_\alpha + \cdots$$

$$r_2(\bar{\alpha},\bar{\beta}) = 0 = r_2(\alpha,\beta) + \Delta\alpha \left.\frac{\partial r_2}{\partial \alpha}\right)_\beta + \Delta\beta \left.\frac{\partial r_2}{\partial \beta}\right)_\alpha + \cdots$$

where $\Delta\alpha$ and $\Delta\beta$ are small changes in α and β, respectively. If the partial derivatives in the above equations can be calculated, they will provide correction factors to $r_1(\alpha,\beta)$ and $r_2(\alpha,\beta)$ as compared with $r_1(\bar{\alpha},\bar{\beta})$ and $r_2(\bar{\alpha},\bar{\beta})$. From (6.8.7) it follows that

$$r_1 = b_{n-1} \qquad r_2 = b_n + \alpha b_{n-1}$$

and thus that

$$\begin{aligned} \left.\frac{\partial r_1}{\partial \alpha}\right)_\beta &= \frac{\partial b_{n-1}}{\partial \alpha} \\ \left.\frac{\partial r_1}{\partial \beta}\right)_\alpha &= \frac{\partial b_{n-1}}{\partial \beta} \\ \left.\frac{\partial r_2}{\partial \alpha}\right)_\beta &= \frac{\partial b_n}{\partial \alpha} + \alpha\frac{\partial b_{n-1}}{\partial \alpha} + b_{n-1} \\ \left.\frac{\partial r_2}{\partial \beta}\right)_\alpha &= \frac{\partial b_n}{\partial \beta} + \alpha\frac{\partial b_{n-1}}{\partial \beta} \end{aligned} \qquad (6.8.9)$$

From (6.8.6), with a_r = constant,

$$\frac{\partial b_r}{\partial \alpha} = -\alpha \frac{\partial b_{r-1}}{\partial \alpha} - b_{r-1} - \beta \frac{\partial b_{r-2}}{\partial \alpha} \qquad \frac{\partial b_{-1}}{\partial \alpha} = \frac{\partial b_0}{\partial \alpha} = 0 \tag{6.8.10}$$

and

$$\frac{\partial b_r}{\partial \beta} = -\alpha \frac{\partial b_{n-1}}{\partial \beta} - \beta \frac{\partial b_{r-2}}{\partial \beta} - b_{r-2} \qquad \frac{\partial b_{-1}}{\partial \beta} = \frac{\partial b_0}{\partial \beta} = 0 \tag{6.8.11}$$

If we define

$$-\frac{\partial b_r}{\partial \alpha} = d_{r-1}$$

(6.8.10) can be written as

$$d_r = b_r - \alpha d_{r-1} - \beta d_{r-2} \qquad d_{-1} = 0 \qquad d_0 = 1.0 \qquad r = 1, 2, \ldots, n-2 \tag{6.8.12}$$

In the same way, if we define

$$-\frac{\partial b_{r+1}}{\partial \beta} = d_{r-1}$$

(6.8.11) can be written as

$$d_r = b_r - \alpha d_{r-1} - \beta d_{r-2} \qquad d_{-1} = 0 \qquad d_0 = 1.0 \qquad r = 1, 2, \ldots, n-2 \tag{6.8.13}$$

Upon comparing the algorithms of (6.8.6), (6.8.12), and (6.8.13) it can be seen that they are identical. Thus the d_r's or the partial derivatives of b_r can be calculated in exactly the same way from the b_r's as the b_r's themselves are calculated from the original a_r's. There results

$$\begin{aligned} \left.\frac{\partial r_1}{\partial \alpha}\right)_\beta &= -d_{n-2} & \left.\frac{\partial r_1}{\partial \beta}\right)_\alpha &= -d_{n-3} \\ \left.\frac{\partial r_2}{\partial \alpha}\right)_\beta &= -d_{n-1} - \alpha d_{n-2} + b_{n-1} & \left.\frac{\partial r_2}{\partial \beta}\right)_\alpha &= -d_{n-2} - \alpha d_{n-3} \end{aligned} \tag{6.8.14}$$

Substituting (6.8.14) into (6.8.9) yields

$$\begin{aligned} b_{n-1} - \Delta\alpha\, d_{n-2} - \Delta\beta\, d_{n-3} &= 0 \\ b_n + \alpha b_{n-1} - \Delta\alpha\,(d_{n-1} + \alpha d_{n-2} - b_{n-1}) - \Delta\beta\,(d_{n-2} + \alpha d_{n-3}) &= 0 \end{aligned}$$

or, with the first into the second,

$$\begin{aligned} b_{n-1} &= \Delta\alpha\, d_{n-2} + \Delta\beta\, d_{n-3} \\ b_n &= \Delta\alpha\,(d_{n-1} - b_{n-1}) + \Delta\beta\, d_{n-2} \end{aligned} \tag{6.8.15}$$

Since (6.8.15) has two equations with two unknowns, $\Delta\alpha$ and $\Delta\beta$, these unknowns can be solved for. Based upon the original α and β used, call them $\alpha^{(0)}$ and $\beta^{(0)}$, (6.8.15) can generate a better approximation to $\bar{\alpha}$ and $\bar{\beta}$ by

$$\begin{aligned} \alpha^{(1)} &= \alpha^{(0)} + \Delta\alpha \\ \beta^{(1)} &= \beta^{(0)} + \Delta\beta \end{aligned} \tag{6.8.16}$$

In the form outlined there is now available a good computational scheme for generating $\bar{\alpha}$ and $\bar{\beta}$. Starting with an initial estimate $\alpha^{(0)}$ and $\beta^{(0)}$, (6.8.6) can be used to generate a sequence of b_r's. From these b_r's (6.8.12) or (6.8.13) can be used to generate the necessary d_r's. From the b_r's and the d_r's (6.8.15) is solved for $\Delta\alpha$ and $\Delta\beta$. When used in (6.8.16) new improved values $\alpha^{(1)}$ and $\beta^{(1)}$ are immediately available. The entire process is then repeated to generate $\alpha^{(2)}$ and $\beta^{(2)}$ and continued until convergence to $\bar{\alpha}$ and $\bar{\beta}$ is found. Computationally the entire process is simple to use. The Bairstow iteration has all the features of the Lin iteration, such as manipulation of real numbers, finding both complex conjugate roots at one time, and generating the reduced polynomial for further computations, plus the important feature that it is a second-order iteration process.

6.9. Roots of a Polynomial with Complex Coefficients

When the polynomial under consideration has complex coefficients, the roots may be real or complex. In the latter case the complex roots do not necessarily occur as conjugate pairs. An obvious approach to this problem is to form the polynomial $f^*(x)$ in which all the i's of $f(x)$ are written as $-i$. The product of these two polynomials, $f^*(x)f(x)$, will possess only real coefficients but will be twice the degree of $f(x)$. Any of the previous techniques for polynomials with real coefficients can be applied. However, the computational effort involved in handling the $2n$-degree polynomial is considerably greater.

An extremely interesting approach has been suggested by Muller (27) for manipulating any polynomial with complex roots. In simplified form three arbitrary estimates of a desired root $\bar{x}$ are first selected; call these $x^{(0)}$, $x^{(1)}$, and $x^{(2)}$. The next estimate is based upon fitting a second-degree Lagrangian interpolation formula to the points $[f(x^{(0)}),x^{(0)}]$, $[f(x^{(1)}),x^{(1)}]$, and $[f(x^{(2)}),x^{(2)}]$ and finding $x^{(3)}$, which is a root of this formula. The iteration is continued by dropping $x^{(0)}$ and repeating the quadratic fit for the points $x^{(1)}$, $x^{(2)}$, and $x^{(3)}$ to yield $x^{(4)}$. Continued application leads to one of the roots of the original polynomial $f(x) = 0$.

In greater detail the Lagrangian interpolation formula can be written as

$$\phi_2(x) = b_0x^2 - b_1x + b_2 \tag{6.9.1}$$

where the coefficients are fitted to the points $x^{(r)}$, $x^{(r-1)}$, and $x^{(r-2)}$ to yield

$$\begin{aligned} b_0(x^{(r)})^2 + b_1(x^{(r)}) + b_2 &= f(x^{(r)}) \\ b_0(x^{(r-1)})^2 + b_1(x^{(r-1)}) + b_2 &= f(x^{(r-1)}) \\ b_0(x^{(r-2)})^2 + b_1(x^{(r-2)}) + b_2 &= f(x^{(r-2)}) \end{aligned}$$

Upon defining the new quantities

$$x^{(r)} - x^{(r-1)} = h^{(r)} \qquad \frac{h^{(r)}}{h^{(r-1)}} = \lambda^{(r)}$$

$$1 + \lambda^{(r)} = \delta^{(r)} \qquad x - x^{(r)} = h \qquad \frac{h}{h^{(r)}} = \lambda$$

(6.9.1) can be written as a quadratic in λ. A single iterative step results from letting $x^{(r+1)}$ be the value of x which makes $\phi_2(x) = 0$. This requires solving the quadratic in λ leading to a value of $\lambda^{(r+1)}$ determined as the smaller root of

$$A\lambda^2 + B\lambda + C = 0$$

where
$$A = \lambda^{(r)}[f(x^{(r-2)})\lambda^{(r)} - f(x^{(r-1)})\delta^{(r)} + f(x^{(r)})]$$
$$B = f(x^{(r-2)})(\lambda^{(r)})^2 - f(x^{(r-1)})(\delta^{(r)})^2 + f(x^{(r)})(\lambda^{(r)} + \delta^{(r)})$$
$$C = f(x^{(r)})\delta^{(r)}$$

From this $\lambda^{(r+1)}$ results $h^{(r+1)} = \lambda^{(r+1)}h^{(r)}$ and finally $x^{(r+1)} = x^{(r)} + h^{(r+1)}$. The iteration process is continued until

$$\left| \frac{x^{(r)} - x^{(r-1)}}{x^{(r)}} \right| < p^{-k}$$

where k is a predetermined integer. Once a root has been determined, it is removed from the polynomial and the process repeated for the next root.

Of importance in Muller's method is that the starting values for the iteration are not special and that $f'(x)$ need not be evaluated. This method may also be used to evaluate the roots of polynomials with real coefficients. Further, Frank (13) has shown how the method can be used to find the zeros of functions other than those expressed as polynomials. It can thus be seen that the method has wide applicability and should find increasing usage in the future.

6.10. Roots of Simultaneous Equations

The previous material in this chapter can be extended almost directly to cover the case of simultaneous sets of transcendental and algebraic equations. For the simplest case of

$$f(x,y) = 0 \qquad g(x,y) = 0 \tag{6.10.1}$$

iterative schemes corresponding to (6.1.3) and (6.1.4) would be written as

$$x^{(r+1)} = F(x^{(r)},y^{(r)}) \qquad y^{(r+1)} = G(x^{(r)},y^{(r)})$$

and
$$x^{(r+1)} = x^{(r)} - \alpha\Phi(x^{(r)},y^{(r)}) \qquad y^{(r+1)} = y^{(r)} - \beta\Psi(x^{(r)},y^{(r)})$$

respectively. The iteration equations must be solved simultaneously.

For purposes of illustration Newton's method will be developed here. Upon expanding the functions $f(x,y)$ and $g(x,y)$ in a Taylor series in terms of an arbitrary estimate to the desired roots $\bar{x}$ and $\bar{y}$ there results

$$f(\bar{x},\bar{y}) = 0 = f(x^{(0)},y^{(0)}) + (\bar{x} - x^{(0)})f_x(x^{(0)},y^{(0)}) + (\bar{y} - y^{(0)})f_y(x^{(0)},y^{(0)}) + \cdots$$
$$g(\bar{x},\bar{y}) = 0 = g(x^{(0)},y^{(0)}) + (\bar{x} - x^{(0)})g_x(x^{(0)},y^{(0)}) + (\bar{y} - y^{(0)})g_y(x^{(0)},y^{(0)}) + \cdots$$

$x^{(0)}$ and $y^{(0)}$ are the initial estimates and f_x, f_y, g_x, and g_y are partial derivatives. Calling

$$\alpha^{(0)} = \bar{x} - x^{(0)} \qquad \beta^{(0)} = \bar{y} - y^{(0)}$$

and truncating in the form shown yields

$$f(x^{(0)},y^{(0)}) + \alpha^{(0)}f_x(x^{(0)},y^{(0)}) + \beta^{(0)}f_y(x^{(0)},y^{(0)}) = 0$$
$$g(x^{(0)},y^{(0)}) + \alpha^{(0)}g_x(x^{(0)},y^{(0)}) + \beta^{(0)}g_y(x^{(0)},y^{(0)}) = 0$$

These two simultaneous equations can be solved for the $\alpha^{(0)}$ and $\beta^{(0)}$ corresponding to $x^{(0)}$ and $y^{(0)}$. Thus the iteration pattern can be set up,

$$x^{(r+1)} = x^{(r)} + \alpha^{(r)} \qquad y^{(r+1)} = y^{(r)} + \alpha^{(r)}$$

which corresponds to the Newton iteration for a single variable.

Extending the process to N variables $s_1, s_2, \ldots, s_N$, one may write

$$g_i(s_1,s_2, \ldots ,s_N) = 0 \qquad i = 1, 2, \ldots, N \tag{6.10.2}$$

where it is desired to find the values $\bar{s}_i$ such that substitution into (6.10.2) will cause g_i to vanish. The Taylor series expansion takes the form

$$g_i(\bar{s}_1,\bar{s}_1, \ldots ,\bar{s}_N) = 0 = g_i(s_1,s_2, \ldots ,s_N) + \sum_{r=1}^{N} \left(\frac{\partial g_i}{\partial \bar{s}_r}\right)(\bar{s}_r - s_r)$$

and upon calling $\bar{s}_r - s_r = \Delta s_r$ the following simultaneous equations result:

$$\sum_{r=1}^{N} \frac{\partial g_i}{\partial s_r} \Delta s_r - g_i(s_1,s_2, \ldots ,s_N) = 0$$

When the Δs_r's are calculated, a new value equal to $s_r + \Delta s_r$ is used to restart the procedure. The iteration then continues in the same way.

6.11. Numerical Examples

Example 6.1. A physical problem of importance in the textile and chemical industries is described by the following:

Two distinct finite phases are in contact with each other. For a known initial distribution of a single mass component in each phase, determine the transient change in component concentration in each phase. Transport of mass is assumed to occur by molecular diffusion, and a simple resistance to transfer exists at the interface of the two phases.

With the nomenclature

C_1 = point concentration in phase 1
C_2 = point concentration in phase 2
C_{1i} = interfacial concentration in phase 1
C_{2i} = interfacial concentration in phase 2
D_1 = diffusion coefficient in phase 1
D_2 = diffusion coefficient in phase 2
k = partition coefficient = equilibrium concentration of phase 1 divided by equilibrium concentration of phase 2
L = finite length of phase 2
M = finite length of phase 1
R = interfacial resistance
t = time
x = distance from interface
J_i = flux at interface

the system may be defined by

$$\frac{\partial C_i}{\partial t} = D_i \frac{\partial^2 C_i}{\partial x^2} \qquad i = 1, 2; \text{ diffusion in phases}$$

$$J_i = \frac{1}{R}(C_{1i} - kC_{2i}) \qquad i = 1, 2; \text{ flux at interface}$$

and

$$\left.\begin{aligned} C_1 &= 0 \\ C_2 &= C_0 \end{aligned}\right\} \quad t = 0 \qquad \begin{aligned} -M &\le x \le 0 \\ 0 &\le x \le L \end{aligned}$$

$$\left.\begin{aligned} \frac{\partial C_1}{\partial x} &= 0 \\ \frac{\partial C_2}{\partial x} &= 0 \end{aligned}\right\} \quad t > 0 \qquad \begin{aligned} x &= -M \\ x &= L \end{aligned}$$

$$D_1 \frac{\partial C_1}{\partial x} = D_2 \frac{\partial C_2}{\partial x} = \frac{1}{R}(kC_2 - C_1) \qquad x = 0,\ t \ge 0$$

This system of equations is linear and can be solved in a straightforward manner by the Laplace transform. The solutions in terms of the dimensionless parameters

$$c_2 = \frac{C_2}{C_0} \qquad p = \frac{RD_2}{Lk}$$

$$c_1 = \frac{C_1}{kC_0} \qquad T = \frac{D_2 t}{L^2}$$

$$f = \frac{L}{Mk} \qquad \beta = \frac{x}{L}$$

$$d = \frac{1}{k}\sqrt{\frac{D_2}{D_1}} \qquad \rho = -\frac{x}{M}$$

are given by

$$c_1 = \frac{f}{1+f} - 2d \sum_{r=1}^{\infty} \frac{\cos[(d/f)(1-\rho)\alpha_r] \sin \alpha_r}{A} e^{-T\alpha_r^2}$$

$$c_2 = \frac{f}{1+f} + 2d \sum_{r=1}^{\infty} \frac{\sin[(d/f)\alpha_r] \cos[(1-\beta)\alpha_r]}{A} e^{-T\alpha_r^2}$$

The denominator A is given by

$$A = \alpha_r \left[\left(p + \frac{d^2}{f} + 1 \right) \sin\left(\frac{d}{f}\alpha_r\right) \sin \alpha_r - \frac{d}{f}(f+1) \cos\left(\frac{d}{f}\alpha_r\right) \cos \alpha_r + \frac{pd}{f} \alpha_r \cos\left(\frac{d}{f}\alpha_r\right) \sin \alpha_r + p\alpha_r \cos \alpha_r \sin\left(\frac{d}{f}\alpha_r\right) \right]$$

In these equations the α_r's, $r = 1, 2, \ldots$, are the nonzero positive roots of the transcendental equation

$$d \cos\left(\frac{d}{f}\alpha\right) \sin \alpha - p\alpha \sin \alpha \sin\left(\frac{d}{f}\alpha\right) + \sin\left(\frac{d}{f}\alpha\right) \cos \alpha = 0 \qquad (6.11.1)$$

It can be seen that, in order to evaluate the analytical expressions for c_1 and c_2 at any T, it is necessary to find the roots α_r of (6.11.1). Before outlining the means of performing this calculation it is noted that if Eq. (6.11.1) is designated as $g(\alpha)$ then it follows by simple manipulation that $g' = -A/\alpha$.

The procedure to evaluate c_1 and c_2 is quite simple. By using c_1 as an illustration and with a known T an initial estimate is made for $\alpha_1^{(0)}$. From $\alpha_1^{(0)}$, $g(\alpha_1^{(0)})$ is calculated and a new $\alpha_1^{(1)}$ and $g(\alpha_1^{(1)})$ obtained by adding 0.02 to $\alpha_1^{(0)}$. $g(\alpha_1^{(0)})$ and $g(\alpha_1^{(1)})$ are then compared to see whether or not a sign change has occurred. If not, 0.02 is added to $\alpha_1^{(1)}$ to yield $\alpha_1^{(2)}$ and the comparison made again. When a change in sign is obtained, the last value of $\alpha_1^{(r)}$ is close to a root and this $\alpha_1^{(r)}$ is used in Newton's iteration formula to obtain $\alpha_1^{(\infty)}$, where $\alpha_1^{(\infty)}$ is given as $\lim_{r \to \infty} \alpha_1^{(r)} = \alpha_1^{(\infty)} = \alpha_1$. From this value the first term in the summation for c_1 can be calculated and a search then started for $\alpha_2^{(\infty)}$. The initial value $\alpha_2^{(0)}$ is obtained by adding 0.02 to $\alpha_1^{(\infty)}$ and the entire procedure repeated. Note that the change of sign as a test is based on the fact that (6.11.1) is oscillatory. Finally a value of $\alpha_m^{(\infty)}$ will be obtained whose contribution to the summation term of c_1 is negligible. At this point the infinite series has converged for the specific T used, and the c_1 is known.

Table 6.1 shows the results of such a calculation, using the parameters

$$f = 0.20$$
$$\rho = 0.20$$
$$d = 1.0$$
$$p = 1.0$$
$$T = 1.0$$
$$\frac{f}{1+f} = 0.1666667$$

The calculation is straightforward and presents no difficulties. Only six roots were required to achieve convergence. Newton's method works quite well, with convergence occurring usually in three steps.

TABLE 6.1. CALCULATION OF ROOTS OF TRANSCENDENTAL EQUATION (6.11.1) FOR TWO-PHASE DIFFUSION PROBLEM

$\alpha_1^{(r)}$	$f(\alpha_1^{(r)})$	$\alpha_2^{(r)}$	$f(\alpha_2^{(r)})$	$\alpha_3^{(r)}$	$f(\alpha_3^{(r)})$
0.02	0.6752894	0.0995101	−0.5783759	0.1654747	0.7477045
0.04	0.4692916	0.1195101	−0.6839271	0.1854747	1.1230058
0.06	0.3192631	0.1395101	−0.2166483	0.2054747	0.7818329
0.08	−0.0170021	0.1595101	0.5406054	0.2254747	−0.2061710
Iteration starts		Iteration starts		Iteration starts	
0.0795094	0.0000255	0.1448302	−0.0243500	0.2219665	−0.0014503
0.0795101	0.0000000	0.1454771	0.0000907	0.2219080	−0.0000012
		0.2454747	0.0000001	0.2219081	−0.0000001
Value of C_1					
0.2786693		0.1702559		0.1532051	

$\alpha_4^{(r)}$	$f(\alpha_4^{(r)})$	$\alpha_5^{(r)}$	$f(\alpha_5^{(r)})$	$\alpha_6^{(r)}$	$f(\alpha_6^{(r)})$
0.2419081	−1.1688526	0.3326618	1.5266212	0.4276391	−1.3025595
0.2619081	−1.9615095	0.3526618	2.4303078	0.4476391	−1.8260501
0.2819081	−1.8674066	0.3726618	2.2679129	0.4676391	−1.4436259
0.3019081	−0.9263880	0.3926618	1.1384306	0.4876391	−0.5393229
0.3219081	0.7383095	0.4126618	−0.3735202	0.5076391	0.2476484
Iteration starts		Iteration starts		Iteration starts	
0.3124998	−0.0129247	0.4074976	0.0107628	0.4983454	0.0640273
0.3126619	0.0000049	0.4076390	0.0000051	0.4999596	−0.0015249
0.3126618	0.0000001	0.4076391	0.0000001	0.4999001	−0.0000013
				0.5000000	0.0000001
Value of C_1					
0.1531987		0.1532329		0.1532329	

This problem was run on the Bendix G-15 and required approximately 5 min of computing time.

Example 6.2. In a recent presentation by Deans and Lapidus (7) it was shown that the static behavior of a catalytic fixed-bed reactor could be simulated by a two-dimensional array of properly connected, completely mixed stirred reactors. In effect, a series of axial rows, each row containing a definite number of stirred reactors, was visualized as representing the fixed-bed behavior. Each reactor in one row is fed from two adjacent reactors in the row immediately above it. For the case of a first-order reaction the system of equations describing this arrangement is given by

$$\left.\begin{aligned} \varphi_{i-1,j} - C_{i,j}(1 + ke^{-E/T_{i,j}}) &= 0 \\ \psi_{i-1,j} - T_{i,j} + \lambda C_{i,j}ke^{-E/T_{i,j}} &= 0 \end{aligned}\right\} \qquad \begin{aligned} i &= 1, 2, \ldots, N \\ j &= 1, 2, \ldots, M \end{aligned} \tag{6.11.2}$$

The number of stirred reactors in the radial direction (the subscript j) in any axial row is given by M and the number of axial rows (the subscript i) by N. Symmetry is assumed in the radial direction, and thus M corresponds to going from the tube centerline to the tube wall. The case $i = 0$ corresponds to the feed condition to the top of the fixed bed. In (6.11.2)

C = dimensionless concentration
T = dimensionless temperature
E = dimensionless energy of activation
λ = dimensionless heat release factor
k = dimensionless reaction-rate frequency factor
φ = dimensionless average feed concentration to any reactor
ψ = dimensionless average feed temperature to any reactor

The two equations in (6.11.2) must be modified at the tube wall to allow for heat flow to the cooling fluid and the no-flux of mass. The details of this change will not be given here, since they are quite straightforward. Of importance is the fact that the explicit form of the equation does not change.

In order to calculate $C_{i,j}$ and $T_{i,j}$ in the i,j reactor, the two equations of (6.11.2) (coupled nonlinear transcendental equations) must be solved simultaneously. Using the first equation to eliminate $C_{i,j}$ in the second yields

$$f(T) = \psi_{i-1,j} - T_{i,j} + \frac{\lambda\varphi_{i-1,j}}{(e^{E/T_{i,j}}/k) + 1} = 0 \tag{6.11.3}$$

and the problem is one of finding the root of a single transcendental equation. Once the value of $T_{i,j}$ which satisfies (6.11.3) is located, $C_{i,j}$ can be obtained from (6.11.2). Note that (6.11.3) has been symbolically written as $f(T)$.

The Newton iteration formula for this case can be written as

$$T^{(r+1)} = T^{(r)} - \frac{f(T^{(r)})}{f'(T^{(r)})}$$

where $T^{(r)}$ is the rth iteration value of T. The subscripts i and j have been omitted for clarity of presentation. The analytical expression for $f'(T)$, obtained by differentiating (6.11.3), is

$$f'(T) = \frac{\lambda\varphi E}{T^2}\frac{e^{E/T}/k}{(e^{E/T}/k + 1)^2} - 1 \tag{6.11.4}$$

The Richmond iteration formula for this case can be written as

$$T^{(r+1)} = T^{(r)} - \frac{f(T^{(r)})}{f'(T^{(r)}) - f(T^{(r)})f''(T^{(r)})/2f'(T^{(r)})}$$

where [differentiating (6.11.4)]

$$f''(T) = [f'(T) + 1]\left[\frac{E}{T^2}\frac{e^{E/T}/k - 1}{(e^{E/T}/k + 1)} - \frac{2}{T}\right] \tag{6.11.5}$$

Care must be exercised that no root of

$$f'(T) = 0 \tag{6.11.6}$$

lies between $T^{(0)}$, the first guess at the root of (6.11.3), and the final value of $T^{(\infty)}$ corresponding to the desired root. The requirement that $f'(T^{(r)})$ be positive for every r avoids this difficulty.

In the particular scheme used here the first guess, $T^{(1)}$, is taken to be $\psi_{i-1,j}$, the average temperature to the reactor i,j. The first stage of the process involves a search for the root of $f'(T) = 0$ by using a formula equivalent to that for $f(T)$. Each successive value of $T^{(r)}$ from this iteration is used to calculate $f'(T^{(r)})$. If the latter is positive, the desired root exists and it is located by using iteration. If $T^{(r)}$ converges to a stationary value without $f'(T^{(r)})$ becoming positive, a new guess for $T^{(0)}$ must be used. The possibility of two roots follows from the fact that a static equilibrium may exist in each reactor, corresponding to low conversion and temperature or high conversion and temperature (2).

In this example a comparison is made between using Newton's and Richmond's methods for locating the desired roots. The parameters used are

$$\lambda = 1.0 \qquad M = 6.0 \text{ (radial reactors)}$$
$$E = 10 \qquad N = 60 \text{ (axial rows)}$$
$$\frac{e^E}{k} = 250$$

The feed conditions to the bed are

$$\varphi_{o,j} = \psi_{o,j} = 1.0$$

and a cooling-water temperature $T_{wi} = 1.0$. The test used on convergence of the iterations is 5×10^{-6}.

Tables 6.2 and 6.3 present the results of using Newton's method and Richmond's method, respectively, to calculate a few of the roots for the stirred reactors located at the top of the fixed bed. $f(T), f'(T), f''(T)$, and $T^{(r+1)}$ are shown for each iteration step. Also shown is the error at each iteration step given by $T^{(r+1)} - T^{(r)} =$ error. The iteration steps shown with an asterisk in front correspond to hunting for the root of $f'(T) = 0$; as soon as $f'(T^{(r)})$ becomes positive, the next step starts the hunt for the root of $f(T) = 0$. The direction of the calculation is first to consider the inside (at the tube centerline) reactor of row $i = 1$ and then sweep across the entire row toward the wall; after the sixth reactor in row $i = 1$ has been handled, the inside reactor in row 2 is picked up, etc. In developing these results a simple exponential routine was used.

It can be seen that the Richmond method is superior to Newton's method in the sense that fewer steps are required to locate any one root. However, since both methods converge in three steps or fewer, it may be that Newton's method is faster, since (6.11.5) is never needed. Actually there is little to choose between the methods, and either one is quite satisfactory for the present case.

A feature of the data in Tables 6.2 and 6.3 is that only one step is required in the first stage of the calculation to locate a positive value of $f'(T^{(r)})$. This, however, occurs only near the top of the fixed bed. Table 6.4 presents data using the Richmond iteration for stirred reactors about halfway down the bed length. As before, the search for the positive $f'(T^{(r)})$ is indicated with an asterisk. It can be seen that for the reactors near the center of a row a considerable number of iteration steps may be required before $f'(T^{(r)})$ becomes positive. Once this has occurred, however, the location of the root of $f(T)$ follows quickly.

This problem was carried out on the IBM 704 in floating-point mode. To locate all 360 values of $T_{i,j}$ and $C_{i,j}$ required about 2 min.

TABLE 6.2. NEWTON'S ITERATION TO LOCATE ROOTS OF (6.11.3)
Steps with asterisk imply search for root of $f'(T) = 0$

j	i	$\varphi_{i-1,j}$	$\psi_{i-1,j}$	$f(T)$	$f'(T)$	$f''(T)$	$T^{(r+1)}$	Error
1	1	*1 10000000	1 10000000	3 19200007	4 − 15960006	5 16404006	1 11203007	0 12030075
		1 10000000	1 10000000	−2 − 49751225	0 95049629	0 − 39110384	1 10052342	−2 52342365
		1 10000000	1 10000000	−5 − 54189004	0 94841946	0 − 40247470	1 10052399	−5 57136115
		1 10000000	1 10000000	−8 − 58789737	0 94841716	0 − 40248715	1 10052399	−8 61987213
2	1	*1 10000000	1 10000000	3 19200007	4 − 15960006	5 16404006	1 11203007	0 12030075
		1 10000000	1 10000000	−2 − 49751225	0 95049629	0 − 39110384	1 10052342	−2 52342365
		1 10000000	1 10000000	−5 − 54189004	0 94841946	0 − 40247470	1 10052399	−5 57136115
		1 10000000	1 10000000	−8 − 58789737	0 94841716	0 − 40248715	1 10052399	−8 61987213
3	1	*1 10000000	1 10000000	3 19200007	4 − 15960006	5 16404006	1 11203007	0 12030075
		1 10000000	1 10000000	−2 − 49751225	0 95049629	0 − 39110384	1 10052342	−2 52342365
		1 10000000	1 10000000	−5 − 54189004	0 94841946	0 − 40247470	1 10052399	−5 57136115
		1 10000000	1 10000000	−8 − 58789737	0 94841716	0 − 40248715	1 10052399	−8 61987213
4	1	*1 10000000	1 10000000	3 19200007	4 − 15960006	5 16404006	1 11203007	0 12030075
		1 10000000	1 10000000	−2 − 49751225	0 95049629	0 − 39110384	1 10052342	−2 52342365
		1 10000000	1 10000000	−5 − 54189004	0 94841946	0 − 40247470	1 10052399	−5 57136115
		1 10000000	1 10000000	−8 − 58789737	0 94841716	0 − 40248715	1 10052399	−8 61987213
5	1	*1 10000000	1 10000000	3 19200007	4 − 15960006	5 16404006	1 11203007	0 12030075
		1 10000000	1 10000000	−2 − 49751225	0 95049629	0 − 39110384	1 10052342	−2 52342365
		1 10000000	1 10000000	−5 − 54189004	0 94841946	0 − 40247470	1 10052399	−5 57136115
		1 10000000	1 10000000	−8 − 58789737	0 94841716	0 − 40248715	1 10052399	−8 61987213
6	1	*0 20000000	1 10000000	3 20000008	4 − 15960006	5 16404006	1 11253133	0 12531328
		0 20000000	1 10000000	−3 − 99502450	0 99009926	−1 − 78220721	1 10010050	−2 10049745
		0 20000000	1 10000000	−7 − 49898517	0 99002043	−1 − 78655355	1 10010050	−7 50401502
1	2	*0 99476004	1 10052399	3 18391004	4 − 15127247	5 15393428	1 11268153	0 12157535
		0 99476004	1 10052399	−2 − 52124825	0 94868746	0 − 40037814	1 10107343	−2 54944149
		0 99476004	1 10052399	−5 − 61176251	0 94645467	0 − 41239043	1 10107408	−5 64637274
		0 99476004	1 10052399	−7 − 10768417	0 94645202	0 − 41240462	1 10107408	−7 11377668
2	2	*0 99476004	1 10052399	3 18391005	4 − 15127248	5 15393430	1 11268153	0 12157535
		0 99476004	1 10052399	−2 − 52124821	0 94868746	0 − 40037815	1 10107343	−2 54944144
		0 99476004	1 10052399	−5 − 61166938	0 94645468	0 − 41239039	1 10107408	−5 64627434
		0 99476004	1 10052399	−7 − 98370947	0 94645202	0 − 41240457	1 10107408	−7 10393654
3	2	*0 99476003	1 10052399	3 18391005	4 − 15127248	5 15393430	1 11268153	0 12157535
		0 99476003	1 10052399	−2 − 52124821	0 94868746	0 − 40037815	1 10107343	−2 54944144
		0 99476003	1 10052399	−5 − 61166938	0 94645468	0 − 41239039	1 10107408	−5 64627434
		0 99476003	1 10052399	−8 − 98370947	0 94645202	0 − 41240457	1 10107408	−7 10393654
4	2	*0 99476003	1 10052399	3 18391005	4 − 15127248	5 15393430	1 11268153	0 12157535
		0 99476003	1 10052399	−2 − 52124821	0 94868746	0 − 40037815	1 10107343	−2 54944144
		0 99476003	1 10052399	−5 − 61166938	0 94645468	0 − 41239039	1 10107408	−5 64627434
		0 99476003	1 10052399	−8 − 98370947	0 94645202	0 − 41240457	1 10107408	−7 10393654
5	2	*0 99476003	1 10052399	3 18391005	4 − 15127248	5 15393430	1 11268153	0 12157535
		0 99476003	1 10052399	−2 − 52124821	0 94868746	0 − 40037815	1 10107343	−2 54944144
		0 99476003	1 10052399	−5 − 61166938	0 94645468	0 − 41239039	1 10107408	−5 64627434
		0 99476003	1 10052399	−8 − 98370947	0 94645202	0 − 41240457	1 10107408	−7 10393654
6	2	*0 33162428	1 10010055	3 19708724	4 − 15796064	5 16204306	1 11257754	0 12476984
		0 33162428	1 10010055	−2 − 16664447	0 98345258	0 − 13042055	1 10027000	−2 16944840
		0 33162428	1 10010055	−6 − 20062726	0 98323057	0 − 13163918	1 10027002	−6 20404904

TABLE 6.3. RICHMOND'S ITERATION TO LOCATE ROOTS OF (6.11.3)
Steps with asterisk imply search for root of $f'(T) = 0$

j	i	$\varphi_{i-1,j}$	$\psi_{i-1,j}$	$f(T)$	$f'(T)$	$f''(T)$	$T^{(r+1)}$	Error
1	1	*1 10000000	1 10000000	3 19200007	4 − 15960006	5 16404006	1 13151192	0 31511920
		1 10000000	1 10000000	−2 − 49751225	0 95049629	0 − 39110384	1 10052399	−2 52398792
		1 10000000	1 10000000	−7 − 62456820	0 94841719	0 − 40248704	1 10052399	−7 65853741
2	1	*1 10000000	1 10000000	3 19200007	4 − 15960006	5 16404006	1 13151192	0 31511920
		1 10000000	1 10000000	−2 − 49751225	0 95049629	0 − 39110384	1 10052399	−2 52398792
		1 10000000	1 10000000	−7 − 62456820	0 94841719	0 − 40248704	1 10052399	−7 65853741
3	1	*1 10000000	1 10000000	3 19200007	4 − 15960006	5 16404006	1 13151192	0 31511920
		1 10000000	1 10000000	−2 − 49751225	0 95049629	0 − 39110384	1 10052399	−2 52398792
		1 10000000	1 10000000	−7 − 62456820	0 94841719	0 − 40248704	1 10052399	−7 65853741
4	1	*1 10000000	1 10000000	3 19200007	4 − 15960006	5 16404006	1 13151192	0 31511920
		1 10000000	1 10000000	−2 − 49751225	0 95049629	0 − 39110384	1 10052399	−2 52398792
		1 10000000	1 10000000	−7 − 62456820	0 94841719	0 − 40248704	1 10052399	−7 65853741
5	1	*1 10000000	1 10000000	3 19200007	4 − 15960006	5 16404006	1 13151192	0 31511920
		1 10000000	1 10000000	−2 − 49751225	0 95049629	0 − 39110384	1 10052399	−2 52398792
		1 10000000	1 10000000	−7 − 62456820	0 94841719	0 − 40248704	1 10052399	−7 65853741
6	1	*0 20000000	1 10000000	3 20000008	4 − 15960006	5 16404006	1 13520008	0 35200084
		0 20000000	1 10000000	−3 − 99502450	0 99009926	−1 − 78220721	1 10010050	−2 10050144
		0 20000000	1 10000000	−8 − 56752469	0 99002043	−1 − 78655347	1 10010050	−8 57324543
1	2	*0 99476004	1 10052399	3 18391004	4 − 15127247	5 15393428	1 13239782	0 31873824
		0 99476004	1 10052399	−2 − 52124825	0 94868746	0 − 40037814	1 10107407	−2 55007926
		0 99476004	1 10052399	−7 − 81199686	0 94645206	0 − 41240440	1 10107408	−7 85793768
2	2	*0 99476003	1 10052399	3 18391005	4 − 15127248	5 15393430	1 13239781	0 31873822
		0 99476003	1 10052399	−2 − 52124821	0 94868746	0 − 40037815	1 10107407	−2 55007921
		0 99476003	1 10052399	−7 − 80734026	0 94645206	0 − 41240442	1 10107408	−7 85301760
3	2	*0 99476003	1 10052399	3 18391005	4 − 15127248	5 15393430	1 13239781	0 31873822
		0 99476003	1 10052399	−2 − 52124821	0 94868746	0 − 40037815	1 10107407	−2 55007921
		0 99476003	1 10052399	−7 − 80734026	0 94645206	0 − 41240442	1 10107408	−7 85301760
4	2	*0 99476003	1 10052399	3 18391005	4 − 15127248	5 15393430	1 13239781	0 31873822
		0 99476003	1 10052399	−2 − 52124821	0 94868746	0 − 40037815	1 10107407	−2 55007921
		0 99476003	1 10052399	−7 − 80734026	0 94645206	0 − 41240442	1 10107408	−7 85301760
5	2	*0 99476003	1 10052399	3 18391005	4 − 15127248	5 15393430	1 13239781	0 31873822
		0 99476003	1 10052399	−2 − 52124821	0 94868746	0 − 40037815	1 10107407	−2 55007921
		0 99476003	1 10052399	−7 − 80734026	0 94645206	0 − 41240442	1 10107408	−7 85301760
6	2	*0 33162428	1 10010055	3 19708724	4 − 15796064	5 16204306	1 13475618	0 34655628
		0 33162428	1 10010055	−2 − 16664447	0 98345258	0 − 13042055	1 10027002	−2 16946744
		0 33162428	1 10010055	−7 − 10288204	0 98323053	0 − 13163935	1 10027002	−7 10463674
1	3	*0 98925915	1 10107408	3 16587161	4 − 14307906	5 14408681	1 13332996	0 32255879
		0 98925915	1 10107408	−2 − 54704439	0 94674813	0 − 41012406	1 10165261	−2 57853811
		0 98925915	1 10107408	−7 − 84575731	0 94433868	0 − 42284876	1 10165262	−7 89560806
2	3	*0 98925915	1 10107408	3 17587162	4 − 14307907	5 14408682	1 13332995	0 32255880
		0 98925915	1 10107408	−2 − 54704434	0 94674813	0 − 41012402	1 10165261	−2 57853806
		0 98925915	1 10107408	−7 − 83644408	0 94433868	0 − 42284873	1 10165262	−7 88574588
3	3	*0 98925914	1 10107408	3 17587162	4 − 14307907	5 14408682	1 13332996	0 32255880
		0 98925914	1 10107408	−2 − 54704434	0 94674813	0 − 41012402	1 10165261	−2 57853806
		0 98925914	1 10107408	−7 − 83586201	0 94433869	0 − 42284867	1 10165262	−7 88512949

TABLE 6.4. RICHMOND'S ITERATION TO LOCATE ROOTS OF (6.11.3)
Steps with asterisk imply search for root of $f'(T) = 0$

j	i	$\varphi_{i-1,j}$	$\psi_{i-1,j}$	$f(T)$	$f'(T)$	$f''(T)$	$T^{(r+1)}$	Error
6	31	*0 15798531	1 10030439	3 19563724	4 − 15469822	5 15807996	1 13604292	0 35738532
		0 15798531	1 10030439	−3 − 81008993	0 99198948	−1 − 62830823	1 10038605	−3 81665269
		0 15798531	1 10030439	−8 − 94369170	0 99193805	−1 63111615	1 10038605	−8 95136152
1	32	*0 29821540	1 16845528	2 12446638	2 − 16052449	2 91187413	1 10396389	0 − 64491394
		*0 29821540	1 16845528	3 14682137	4 − 10777964	5 10287428	1 14289813	0 38934247
		*0 29821540	1 16845528	2 21393955	2 − 65257656	3 37144594	1 63239881	1 48950068
		0 29821540	1 16845528	−1 − 67210412	0 81653273	0 − 13728351	1 17674383	−1 82885493
		0 29821540	1 16845528	−4 90484507	0 80854251	−1 − 55921790	1 17673264	−3 − 11191020
		0 29821540	1 16845528	−8 27939677	0 80854877	−1 − 56028842	1 17673264	−8 − 34555339
2	32	*0 34436458	1 16328894	2 12946779	2 − 21396540	3 11703806	0 70895050	0 − 92393888
		*0 34436458	1 16328894	2 98083774	4 − 17135846	5 34554091	0 84430102	0 13535054
		*0 34436458	1 16328894	3 14055094	4 − 16589030	5 23722982	1 10592319	0 21493091
		*0 34436458	1 16328894	3 12707946	3 − 89688765	4 82642789	1 14673130	0 40808108
		*0 34436458	1 16328894	2 18683088	2 − 52611755	3 29217899	2 26936326	2 25469013
		0 34436458	1 16328894	−1 − 66903407	0 79782919	0 − 21599182	1 17177090	−1 84819596
		0 34436458	1 16328894	−3 10363944	0 78351213	0 − 12065776	1 17175767	−3 − 13227412
		0 34436458	1 16328894	−7 13038516	0 78352811	0 − 12080889	1 17175767	−7 − 16640776
3	32	*0 44749140	1 15151070	2 15441156	2 − 40469516	3 22004825	1 − 87093214	2 − 10224428
		*0 44749140	1 15151070	3 14722964	2 − 34837286	1 40000000	1 − 31292425	1 55800789
		*0 44749140	1 15151070	2 15109403	2 − 12516970	1 40000000	1 − 16336682	1 14955743
		*0 44749140	1 15151070	0 86282926	1 − 65346726	1 40000000	1 − 14960689	0 13759925
		*0 44749140	1 15151070	−2 15304088	1 − 59842756	1 40000000	1 − 14958132	−3 25576022
		*0 44749140	1 15151070	−7 59604645	1 − 59832526	1 40000000	1 − 14958132	−8 99619134
		*0 58523742	1 13476699	2 25310334	3 − 10533378	3 64396040	1 22527048	0 90503487
		0 58523742	1 13476699	−1 − 36219540	0 81291874	0 − 62492682	1 13930012	−1 45331261
		0 58523742	1 13476699	−4 − 14053658	0 78442207	0 − 62929190	1 13930191	−4 17916067
		0 58523742	1 13476699	−8 − 74505806	0 78441078	0 − 62929000	1 13930191	−8 94983147
4	32	*0 70546073	1 11731657	2 58606090	3 − 34513749	4 26371983	1 16565839	0 48341820
		0 70546073	1 11731657	−1 − 15103796	0 89260891	0 − 56378785	1 11901776	−1 17011863
		0 70546073	1 11731657	−5 − 17513521	0 88278842	0 − 59058340	1 11901795	−5 19838879
5	32	*0 25666905	1 10155282	3 17650976	4 − 13637426	5 13610234	1 13810080	0 36547985
		0 25666905	1 10155282	−2 − 14867135	0 98566756	0 − 10913825	1 10170366	−2 15084575
		0 25666905	1 10155282	−7 − 13111275	0 98550227	0 − 11000364	1 10170366	−7 13304156

Example 6.3. In Example 5.2 a finite-difference approach was used to solve the problem defined in Example 3.3, which corresponded to determining the concentration distribution of a single reactant flowing in laminar flow through a tubular reactor. The reaction was taken as first-order, $n = 1$, so that a linear set of algebraic simultaneous equations was involved. Proceeding one step further, the present example uses $n = 2$ (a second-order reaction) and the finite-difference representation; the system to solve will now be a nonlinear set of algebraic simultaneous equations.

For $n = 2$, (3.10.11) can be converted to

$$\left(1 - \frac{\text{Pe}\,h}{2}\right) f_{n+1} - 2f_n - R\,\text{Pe}\,h^2 f_n{}^2 + \left(1 + \frac{\text{Pe}\,h}{2}\right) f_{n-1} = 0 \qquad n = 1, 2, \ldots, N \tag{6.11.7}$$

in direct analogy to (5.16.6). The boundary conditions remain as given in (5.16.7), namely,

$$1 = f_0 - \frac{1}{\text{Pe } h}(f_1 - f_0) \qquad z = 0 \text{ (or at } z_0) \tag{6.11.8}$$
$$f_N = f_{N+1} \qquad z = 1 \text{ (or at } z_{N+1})$$

Upon using (6.11.8) in (6.11.7) the result for $n = 1, 2, \ldots, N$ is given by

$$+\left(2 - \frac{1 + \text{Pe } h/2}{1 + \text{Pe } h}\right) f_1 + R \text{ Pe } h^2 f_1^2 - \left(1 - \frac{\text{Pe } h}{2}\right) f_2 = \frac{1 + \text{Pe } h/2}{1 + 1/\text{Pe } h}$$
$$-\left(1 + \frac{\text{Pe } h}{2}\right) f_1 + 2f_2 + R \text{ Pe } h^2 f_2^2 - \left(1 - \frac{\text{Pe } h}{2}\right) f_3 = 0$$
$$-\left(1 + \frac{\text{Pe } h}{2}\right) f_2 + 2f_3 + R \text{ Pe } h^2 f_3^2 - \left(1 - \frac{\text{Pe } h}{2}\right) f_4 = 0 \tag{6.11.9}$$
$$\cdots\cdots\cdots\cdots\cdots\cdots\cdots\cdots$$
$$-\left(1 + \frac{\text{Pe } h}{2}\right) f_{N-1} + \left(1 + \frac{\text{Pe } h}{2}\right) f_N + R \text{ Pe } h^2 f_N^2 = 0$$

Note that (6.11.9) degenerates to (5.16.8) if the power on f_n is changed from 2 to 1.

Equation (6.11.9) involves a set of N nonlinear simultaneous equations with N unknowns $f_1, f_2, \ldots, f_N$. The simplest method of solution is to assume an initial set $f_1^{(0)}, f_2^{(0)}, \ldots, f_N^{(0)}$ and by using (6.11.9) to calculate new estimates $f_1^{(1)}, f_2^{(1)}, \ldots, f_N^{(1)}$. These are then used to generate new improved values, etc. Finally,

$$|f_i^{(r+1)} - f_i^{(r)}| < \epsilon \qquad i = 1, 2, \ldots, N$$

should be satisfied on the assumption that the iteration converges. In the present calculation $\epsilon = 1.0 \times 10^{-7}$ was used.

The question arises as to the means of calculating new estimates $f_1^{(r+1)}, f_2^{(r+1)}, \ldots, f_N^{(r+1)}$ from (6.11.9) and $f_1^{(r)}, f_2^{(r)}, \ldots, f_N^{(r)}$. Since each equation is a quadratic in f_n, some use might be made of this fact. To illustrate, from (6.11.7),

$$f_n^2 + \frac{2}{R \text{ Pe } h^2} f_n - \frac{(1 - \text{Pe } h/2) f_{n+1} + (1 + \text{Pe } h/2) f_{n-1}}{R \text{ Pe } h^2} = 0 \tag{6.11.10}$$

and

$$f_n = \frac{-b + \sqrt{b^2 - 4c}}{2} \tag{6.11.11}$$

where

$$b = \frac{2}{R \text{ Pe } h^2} \tag{6.11.12}$$

$$c = -\frac{(1 - \text{Pe } h/2) f_{n+1} + (1 + \text{Pe } h/2) f_{n-1}}{R \text{ Pe } h^2} \tag{6.11.13}$$

The positive value of the square root must be used for f_n to be positive. Equation (6.11.10) can be used for $f_2, f_3, \ldots, f_{N-1}$ and analogous equations [by using (6.11.9)] for f_1 and f_N.

On this basis it is possible to plunge blindly into the calculations. Table 6.5 presents the results of such a plunge using $h = 0.04$ ($N = 24$), $h = 0.02$ ($N = 49$), $h = 0.01$ ($N = 99$) with $\text{Pe} = 1.0$ and $R = 2.0$. Only the final convergent values are shown, along with the number of iterations required to achieve convergence. Also shown for $h = 0.02$ are the results obtained by substituting the final values back into the original set of equations [(6.11.9)] and the results obtained by integrating the original set of ODE directly. These latter values were used as initial conditions or guesses for the iterations.

TABLE 6.5. FINAL CONVERGENT VALUES OBTAINED FOR (6.11.9), USING DIFFERENT SPACING

z	$h = 0.04$	$h = 0.02$	$h = 0.02$†	$h = 0.01$	Integrating ODE
0	....	....	....	....	0.636757
0.1	....	0.595397	0.02065	0.404724	0.605823
0.2	0.576717	0.564270	0.01839	0.356628	0.575337
0.3	....	0.536987	0.02936	0.313354	0.548622
0.4	0.527275	0.513412	0.01696	0.274658	0.525443
0.5	....	0.493408	0.01955	0.240905	0.505645
0.6	0.491813	0.476852	0.01845	0.213134	0.489153
0.7	....	0.463729	0.03251	0.191345	0.475969
0.8	0.470214	0.454193	0.02294	0.175170	0.466171
0.9	....	0.448410	0.02759	0.165527	0.459921
Number of iterations....	705	927	....	3,876	

† Values substituted back into left side of (6.11.9).

The results reveal a number of interesting items. First, the largest spacing, $h = 0.04$, gives the best approximation to the correct values (on the assumption that the integrated values are correct). The case $h = 0.02$ is not too far different, but $h = 0.01$ yields values which are very far from the correct answers. Such results are the inverse of what would a priori be expected. Second, the number of iterations required to obtain convergence is very large; this is most surprising, especially in view of the fact that the correct values were used to start the iterations. Of course, since the simultaneous equations are only an approximation to the ODE, it would not be expected that the solution would converge to these initial values but it should at least come close. It is apparent that each iteration cycle changes the values of $f_1, f_2, \ldots, f_N$ only slightly. Third, the results of substituting the convergent numbers back into the simultaneous equations reveal significant errors in the second decimal place. Further, data not given here show that the choice of $f_1^{(0)}, f_2^{(0)}, \ldots, f_N^{(0)} = 0.50$ or $= 0.70$ yields roughly the same final results but that the number of iterations required is increased by a significant amount.

It is apparent from these results that something is drastically wrong with the calculations. It is relatively easy, however, to find the reason. By using the case $h = 0.01$, (6.11.10) becomes

$$f_n^2 + 10^4 f_n - 5 \times 10^3(0.995 f_{n+1} + 1.005 f_{n-1}) = 0$$

and thus
$$f_n = \frac{-10^4 + \sqrt{10^8 + (2.01 \times 10^4 f_{n-1} + 1.99 \times 10^4 f_{n+1})}}{2}$$

Since f_{n-1} and f_{n+1} are approximately equal to 0.5, this last equation can be written as

$$f_n \simeq \frac{-10^4 + \sqrt{10^8 + 2 \times 10^4}}{2}$$

and the contribution of f_{n+1} and f_{n-1} to the value of f_n is very small. This is exactly the problem that was mentioned in the introduction to this chapter. When f_n is calculated as above, it involves an addition and subtraction of almost identical numbers, yielding a result in which many significant figures have been lost. This problem is, of course, worse for a small value of h, and for this reason the results in Table 6.5 are best for the large h.

The obvious way to get around this loss in significant figures is to use double- or triple-precision arithmetic. However, since the calculations are so time-consuming in single-precision, it was felt best to attempt another approach. Use was made of the fact that

$$f_{n1} = \frac{-b + \sqrt{b^2 - 4c}}{2} \qquad f_{n2} = \frac{-b - \sqrt{b^2 - 4c}}{2}$$

and

$$f_{n1}f_{n2} = c \tag{6.11.14}$$

Instead of solving for the root f_{n1}, which leads to the loss in significant figures, f_{n2} was solved for and then f_{n1} calculated from (6.11.14). In terms of programming this change involved only a minor correction to the previous program.

Table 6.6 presents the calculated results using this modification. The format

TABLE 6.6. FINAL CONVERGENT VALUES OBTAINED FOR (6.11.9), USING (6.11.14) AND DIFFERENT SPACING

z	$h = 0.04$	$h = 0.02$	$h = 0.02$†	$h = 0.01$‡
0.1	....	0.605174	-0.7049×10^{-4}	0.604097
0.2	0.577406	0.574974	-0.7444×10^{-4}	0.573970
0.3	....	0.548566	-0.8246×10^{-4}	0.547612
0.4	0.528072	0.525723	-0.9341×10^{-4}	0.524795
0.5	....	0.506300	-0.6869×10^{-4}	0.505373
0.6	0.492705	0.490236	-0.9677×10^{-4}	0.489281
0.7	....	0.477544	-0.9718×10^{-4}	0.476529
0.8	0.471155	0.468320	-1.0078×10^{-4}	0.467209
0.9	....	0.462745	-0.9791×10^{-4}	0.461495
Number of iterations	701	3,488	....	5,734‡

† Values substituted back into left side of (6.11.9).
‡ The computation was stopped before complete convergence.

is the same as in Table 6.5. From the cases $h = 0.04$ and $h = 0.02$ it can be seen that the results are quite good when compared with the correct values given in Table 6.5. The error involved in solving the set of simultaneous equations is quite small, as evidenced by the back substitution. The data for $h = 0.01$ are incomplete since the computer was stopped because of excessive computing time before complete convergence occurred. The values, however, are quite good even under these conditions, and it would be expected that, if convergence had occurred, these data would be the best of the three sets. Obviously the difficulties inherent in the first set of calculations have been removed.

The present calculations were performed on the IBM 704 in floating-point mode. The time required for 100 iterations, exclusive of output, was approximately 40 sec.

BIBLIOGRAPHY

1. Aitken, A. C.: *Proc. Roy. Soc. Edinburgh,* **63**: 326 (1951).
2. Amundson, N. R., and R. Aris: *Chem. Eng. Progr.,* **53**: 227 (1957).
3. Bodewig, E.: *Quart. Appl. Math.,* **7**: 325 (1945).
4. Broker, R. A.: *Proc. Cambridge Phil. Soc.,* **52**: 255 (1952).
5. Caldwell, G. C.: *J. Assoc. Comput. Mach.,* **6**: 223 (1959).
6. Curtis, P. C., and W. L. Frank: *J. Assoc. Comput. Mach.,* **6**: 395 (1959).
7. Deans, H. A., and L. Lapidus: *J. AIChE,* **6**: 663 (1960).
8. Derr, J. I.: *Math. Tables Aids Comput.,* **13**: 29 (1959).
9. Dimsdale, B.: *Quart. Appl. Math.,* **6**: 77 (1948).
10. Domb, C.: *Proc. Cambridge Phil. Soc.,* **45**: 237 (1949).
11. Donegan, A. J., and M. Farler: *Jet Propulsion,* March, 1956, p. 164.
12. Flanagan, C., and J. E. Maxfield: *J. SIAM,* **7**: 367 (1959).
13. Frank, W. L.: *J. Assoc. Comput. Mach.,* **5**: 154 (1958).
14. Gill, S.: *Comput. J.,* **1**: 84 (1958).
15. Goldwasser, S. R.: *Ind. Eng. Chem.,* **51**: 595 (1959).
16. Gower, J. C.: *Comput. J.,* **1**: 142 (1958).
17. Greenstadt, J., Y. Bard, and B. Morse: *Ind. Eng. Chem.,* **50**: 1644 (1958).
18. Gross, O., and S. M. Johnson: *Rand Corp. Rept.* P-935, 1956.
19. Hamilton, H. J.: *Am. Math. Monthly,* **57**: 517 (1950).
20. Hartree, D. R.: *Proc. Cambridge Phil. Soc.,* **45**: 230 (1949).
21. Jeeves, T. A.: *Communs. ACM,* **1**: 9 (1958).
22. Koenig, J. F.: *J. Appl. Phys.,* **24**: 476 (1953).
23. Lance, G. N.: *J. Assoc. Comput. Mach.,* **6**: 97 (1958).
24. Longman, I. M.: *Math. Comput.,* **14**: 187 (1960).
25. Marquardt, D. W.: *Chem. Eng. Progr.,* **55**: 65 (1959).
26. McIntire, R. L.: *Chem. Eng. Progr. Symposium Ser.* 21, 1959.
27. Muller, D. E.: *Math. Tables Aids Comput.,* **10**: 208 (1956).
28. Olver, F. W. J.: *Phil. Trans. Roy. Soc. London,* **244**: 385 (1952).
29. Richmond, H. W.: *J. London Math. Soc.,* **19**: 31 (1944).
30. Rose, A., R. E. Stillman, T. J. Williams, and H. C. Carlson: *Chem. Eng. Progr. Symposium Ser.* 21, 1959.
31. Sarafyan, D.: *Communs. ACM,* **2**(11): 23 (1959).
32. Ward, J. A.: *J. Assoc. Comput. Mach.,* **4**: 148 (1957).
33. Wegstein, J. H.: *Communs. ACM,* **1**: 9 (1958).
34. Wensley, J. H.: *Comput. J.,* **1**: 163 (1958).
35. Wilkinson, J. H.: *Numerische Math.,* **1**: 150, 167 (1959).
36. Wolfe, P.: *Communs. ACM,* **2**(12): 12 (1959).
37. Wynn, P.: *Math. Tables Aids Comput.,* **10**: 97 (1956).

CHAPTER 7

FURTHER METHODS OF APPROXIMATION

Chapter 2 was devoted to fitting $N + 1$ tabulated values of $y(x)$ versus x with a suitable approximating polynomial of degree N; the criterion of fit was that the polynomial coincide with the data at the given points. The question immediately arises as to whether there are other criteria for fitting an approximating function to the data which may be better, in some sense, than this previous procedure.

In the present chapter a number of other important types of approximation are investigated. These include a least-square fit in which N tabulated points are represented by a polynomial of degree m, $m < N$, best-fit approximations using Chebyshev polynomials for minimizing the error over the total interval of interest, and a continued-fraction expansion. As will be seen, these lead to approximations which are quite simple to use in terms of digital computation.

The application of these methods to problems of interest to chemical engineers is rather obvious. Approximating experimental data, optimizing steady-state systems, and the construction of suitable models for highly complex systems are typical examples of the use of these techniques.

7.1. The Least-square-error Approach

In the present section it is assumed that $y = y(x)$ and that N discrete values of y are known along with a corresponding number of x. These may be designated as $y_1, y_2, \ldots, y_N$ and $x_1, x_2, \ldots, x_N$.† No particular spacing on the x values is assumed, and some may even be repeated. These values may result from measuring the response of a system or process to an input variation, or they may be specific values from a transcendental function. Instead of requiring that an approximating polynomial $\phi_{N-1}(x)$ pass through the points $y_1, y_2, \ldots, y_N$, a weaker approximation may be used in which a suitable approximating function is made to pass as close as possible, in some sense, to the points. The suitable approximation is herein taken as a linear combination of $m + 1$ linearly independent functions $u_0(x), u_1(x), u_2(x), \ldots, u_m(x)$.

† Note that N rather than $N + 1$ points are used.

Thus

$$\phi_m(x) = a_0u_0(x) + a_1u_1(x) + \cdots + a_mu_m(x) \tag{7.1.1}$$

where the $a_0, a_1, \ldots, a_m$ are constants to be determined from the fit of (7.1.1) to the specified values $y_1, y_2, \ldots, y_N$.

There are a number of possible linearly independent analytical functions which can be used in (7.1.1). Among these are

$$\begin{array}{llll}
u_0(x) = 1 & = 0 & = 1 & = e^{\alpha_0 x} \\
u_1(x) = x & = \sin x & = \cos x & = e^{\alpha_1 x} \\
u_2(x) = x^2 & = \sin 2x & = \cos 2x & = e^{\alpha_2 x} \\
\cdots & \cdots & \cdots & \cdots \\
u_m(x) = x^m & = \sin mx & = \cos mx & = e^{\alpha_m x}
\end{array}$$

Of particular utility are the power functions of x, or

$$\phi_m(x) = a_0 + a_1x + a_2x^2 + \cdots + a_mx^m = \sum_{j=0}^{j=m} a_jx^j \tag{7.1.2}$$

where $\phi_m(x)$ is now a polynomial of degree m. If $m + 1 \geq N$, the approximation becomes one of simple polynomial interpolation with $|y_i - \phi_m(x_i)| = 0$. If, however, $N > m + 1$, an obvious conclusion is that the approximation cannot, in general, coincide with all the tabulated points.

In this latter case the means of determining the coefficients in (7.1.2) such that the resulting expression is the "best" fit to the tabulated points is of importance. When the values $y_1, y_2, \ldots, y_N$ are exact or are subject to random errors, it can be shown that the least-square-error criterion yields the best estimate for $a_0, a_1, \ldots, a_m$. This criterion states merely that if the approximation error at each point is given by

$$\epsilon_i = |y_i - \phi_m(x_i)| \qquad i = 1, 2, \ldots, N$$

then one desires that

$$\epsilon_1^2 + \epsilon_2^2 + \cdots + \epsilon_N^2 = \text{minimum}$$

In other words, the sums of the squares of the approximation errors are to be minimized. With a different nomenclature the residual at any point, R_i, can be defined as

$$\left.\begin{array}{l} R_i = y_i - \phi_m(x_i) \\ R_i^2 = [y_i - \phi_m(x_i)]^2 \end{array}\right\} \qquad i = 1, 2, \ldots, N$$

and

The sum of the squares of the residuals is given by

$$S_m^2 = \sum_{i=1}^{N} R_i^2 \geq 0$$

and, with (7.1.2),

$$S_m{}^2 = \sum_{i=1}^{N} \left(y_i - \sum_{j=0}^{m} a_j x_i{}^j\right)^2 \tag{7.1.3}$$

$R_i{}^2$ is a measure of how well the approximation $\phi_m(x)$ fits the set of points $y_1, y_2, \ldots, y_N$. If $R_i{}^2 = 0$, $\phi_m(x_i)$ coincides with y_i; if $R_i{}^2$ is large, the approximation is not close to the values of y_i.

A detailed discussion of the reason for using the square of the error instead of some other power will not be given here. However, it is obvious that the first power would not be suitable, since errors can be negative as well as positive and hence the sum can be small even though the magnitudes are large. Also, differentiating the square leads to a first power, which can be handled rather easily. For a discussion of this point see Goldstein et al. (18).

There are two important variations on the formulation of (7.1.3). Weighting factors may be included to yield

$$S_{mw}^2 = \sum_{i=1}^{N} w_i R_i{}^2 \geq 0 \tag{7.1.4}$$

Frequently, the weighting factors are related to the precision of the values of $y_1, y_2, \ldots, y_N$ and determined from estimates of the relative accuracy of experimental information. A second variation is to require the integral rather than the sum of the squares of the residuals to be a minimum. This implies

$$\int_a^b \left(y_i - \sum_{j=0}^{m} a_j x_i{}^j\right)^2 dx = \text{minimum} \tag{7.1.5}$$

Actually integration as in (7.1.5) is a more exact expression of the least-square-error criteria, but for purposes of approximation the integral can be replaced with a sum. Both possibilities will be considered in later discussion.

The residual form can be written out for each point i to yield

$$\begin{aligned}
R_1 &= y_1 - (a_0 + a_1 x_1 + a_2 x_1{}^2 + \cdots + a_m x_1{}^m) \\
R_2 &= y_2 - (a_0 + a_1 x_2 + a_2 x_2{}^2 + \cdots + a_m x_2{}^m) \\
&\cdots\cdots\cdots\cdots\cdots\cdots\cdots\cdots \\
R_N &= y_N - (a_0 + a_1 x_N + a_2 x_N{}^2 + \cdots + a_m x_N{}^m)
\end{aligned}$$

This is a set of N simultaneous algebraic equations with $m + 1$ unknowns, $a_0, a_1, \ldots, a_m$. If $N > m + 1$, there are more equations than unknowns. The unknowns may be determined uniquely by imposing the condition that $S_m{}^2$ or S_{mw}^2 be minimized. Using the latter it can be seen that it is necessary that

$$\frac{\partial S^2_{mw}}{\partial a_j} = 0 \qquad j = 0, 1, 2, \ldots, m \tag{7.1.6}$$

With (7.1.4) in the form†

$$S^2_{mw} = \sum_{i=1}^{N} w_i \left(y_i - \sum_{k=0}^{m} a_k x_i^k\right)^2$$

(7.1.6) leads to the minimum form

$$\frac{\partial S^2_{mw}}{\partial a_j} = 0 = 2 \sum_{i=1}^{N} w_i \left(y_i - \sum_{k=0}^{m} a_k x_i^k\right)(-x_i^j) \qquad j = 0, 1, \ldots, m$$

or

$$\sum_{i=1}^{N} w_i y_i x_i^j = \sum_{k=0}^{m} a_k \sum_{i=1}^{N} w_i x_i^k x_i^j \tag{7.1.7}$$

To simplify the nomenclature, let

$$n_{jk} = \sum_{i=1}^{N} w_i x_i^k x_i^j \qquad p_j = \sum_{i=1}^{N} w_i y_i x_i^j$$

and (7.1.7) becomes

$$p_j = \sum_{k=0}^{m} a_k n_{jk} \qquad j = 0, 1, 2, \ldots, m \tag{7.1.8}$$

Expanding this equation results in

$$\begin{aligned} p_0 &= n_{00}a_0 + n_{01}a_1 + \cdots + n_{0m}a_m \\ p_1 &= n_{10}a_0 + n_{11}a_1 + \cdots + n_{1m}a_m \\ &\cdots\cdots\cdots\cdots\cdots\cdots\cdots \\ p_n &= n_{m0}a_0 + n_{m1}a_1 + \cdots + n_{mm}a_m \end{aligned} \tag{7.1.9}$$

Since the p_j's and n_{jk}'s are all known, (7.1.8) or (7.1.9) represents a set of $m + 1$ simultaneous algebraic equations in the $m + 1$ unknowns a_0, a_1, . . . , a_m. These equations are called the normal equations for the least-square formulation. The unknowns can be determined, at least theoretically, by any of the matrix methods previously discussed in Chap. 5, either by inverting the coefficient matrix or by solving the equations directly.

† Note that the index on the second summation has been changed from j to k. This simplifies the following discussion.

From the definition of n_{jk} it can be seen that $n_{jk} = n_{kj}$ and that the coefficient matrix of (7.1.9) is symmetrical. Further, if $w_i = 1.0$, this matrix is striped in the sense that all positive diagonals have the same elements, that is, $n_{m0} = n_{m-1,1} \cdots = n_{0m}$ or $n_{jk} = n_{j-1,k+1}$. Upon recalling the Hilbert matrix of Example 5.1 and its form, it should immediately become apparent that solving the set of normal equations for $m \geq 6$ may present serious computational problems.

Assuming for the moment that the solution of (7.1.9) can be obtained in some way, the resulting $a_0, a_1, \ldots, a_m$ define the approximating polynomial (7.1.2) with a least-square error. This follows from the fact that the solution is unique and does indeed minimize the $S_m{}^2$ or S_{mw}^2 functions (15). It should be pointed out that the entire analysis could have been carried out in terms of the functions $u_j(x)$ of (7.1.1) instead of x^j.

The derivation of (7.1.9) can be obtained in an almost trivial way by using matrix notation. For the case $w_i = 1.0$, let

$$\mathbf{y} = \begin{bmatrix} y_1 \\ y_2 \\ \cdot \\ \cdot \\ \cdot \\ y_N \end{bmatrix} \qquad \mathbf{a} = \begin{bmatrix} a_0 \\ a_1 \\ \cdot \\ \cdot \\ \cdot \\ a_m \end{bmatrix} \qquad \mathbf{X} = \begin{bmatrix} x_1{}^0 & x_1{}^1 & \cdots & x_1{}^m \\ x_2{}^0 & x_2{}^1 & \cdots & x_2{}^m \\ \cdots & \cdots & \cdots & \cdots \\ x_N{}^0 & x_N{}^1 & \cdots & x_N{}^m \end{bmatrix}$$

$\mathbf{X}$ is a matrix of order N times $m + 1$. Premultiplying $\mathbf{Xa}$ and $\mathbf{y}$ by $\mathbf{X}^T$ and setting the results equal to each other yields

$$\mathbf{X}^T\mathbf{X}\mathbf{a} = \mathbf{X}^T\mathbf{y} \tag{7.1.10}$$

Calling

$$\mathbf{X}^T\mathbf{X} = \mathbf{N} \qquad \mathbf{X}^T\mathbf{y} = \mathbf{P}$$

leads to

$$\mathbf{N}\mathbf{a} = \mathbf{P} \tag{7.1.11}$$

which corresponds to the final set (7.1.9). It can be seen that the normal equations of the least-square formulation result from a premultiplication by $\mathbf{X}^T$. The symmetry of the matrix $\mathbf{N}$ results from this multiplication of $\mathbf{X}$ by $\mathbf{X}^T$. The minimization equations can also be written as

$$(\mathbf{y} - \mathbf{Xa})^2 = \text{minimum}$$

If the weighting functions are included, one needs only to handle $(\mathbf{WX})^T$, where $\mathbf{W}$ is a diagonal matrix made up of the weighting functions.

In a subsequent section of this chapter an efficient computational scheme will be illustrated for generating (7.1.11) in an especially convenient manner. For the case where there are a number of independent variables or inputs and a number of responses the reader is referred to Amara (1).

7.2. Computational Aspects of Least-square Analysis

It is important to note the flexible nature of the functions $u_0(x)$, $u_1(x)$, . . . , $u_m(x)$ in (7.1.1). In addition to those already presented an analysis of a physical system may lead to such diverse items as $u_0(x) = x_1/x_2$, $u_1(x) = \log x_1x_2$, $u_2(x) = e^{-(x_1+x_2)}$, $u_3(x) = x_1^n$, . . . , where the x_1's and x_2's could be any functionality desired. The only restriction for a least-square analysis is that $\phi_m(x)$ is a linear function of the parameters a_0, a_1, . . . , a_m or that the approximating equation can be reduced to a form linear in the parameters. As an illustration of this latter case, consider the equation

$$\phi = K_0e^{K_1x}$$

where K_0 and K_1 are to be determined according to a least-square fit. Rewriting in the form

$$\log \phi = K_1x + \log K_0$$

and defining

$$\phi_m(x) = \log \phi \qquad a_0 = \log K_0 \qquad a_1 = K_1 \qquad u_1(x) = x$$

results in

$$\phi_m(x) = a_0 + a_1u_1(x)$$

This equation is now linear in the unknown coefficients a_0 and a_1. In the same way an equation of the form

$$\phi = K_0x^{K_1} \tag{7.2.1}$$

can be rewritten by defining

$$\phi_m(x) = \log \phi \qquad a_0 = \log K_0 \qquad a_1 = K_1 \qquad u_1(x) = \log x$$

This yields

$$\phi_m(x) = a_0 + a_1u_1(x)$$

Equation (7.2.1) is commonly used in dimensional analysis, as has been discussed by Levenspiel (25). A word of caution is necessary, however. The least-square error of the original functions is not determined, but instead that for the transformed variables [see Chou (6)]. When the unknowns are not linear or cannot be transformed into linear form by a transformation, the linear least-square technique above cannot be used directly. Instead it is necessary to resort to an iteration procedure in which the parameters are linearized by expanding in a Taylor series and truncating after the second term. Further details of this "nonlinear" least-square approach will not be discussed here.

It is necessary to have some way of estimating the precision of the determined coefficients a_0, a_1, . . . , a_m. A convenient measure which finds wide usage is the error variance. On the assumption that the $y_i(x)$'s are normally distributed and with an error variance σ^2 independent of m, an unbiased estimate of the error variance is given by

$$\sigma^2 = \frac{S_m{}^2}{N - (m + 1)} = \frac{\sum_{i=1}^{N} [y_i - \phi_m(x_i)]^2}{N - (m + 1)} \qquad (7.2.2)$$

where $N - (m + 1)$ is the degrees of freedom. The variance is a measure of the spread of the error distribution, and the smaller the value, the better the least-square approximation to the given data points.

Unfortunately, there are a number of practical problems associated with the implementation of the least-square analysis. First, it is necessary to decide what degree of polynomial to use to represent the data; i.e., should m be 2, or 5, or what? The answer to this question is usually obtained by starting with $m = 1$, calculating a_0 and a_1, and finally $\sigma_1{}^2$. (The subscript on σ^2 is used to indicate the corresponding value of m.) Then, with $m = 2$, a_0, a_1, a_2, and $\sigma_2{}^2$ are calculated. This procedure is continued for $m = 3, 4, \ldots$ until the variance becomes approximately a constant or very small. At this point the least-square fit is considered adequate. Since it can readily be determined that the $a_0, a_1, a_2, \ldots$ determined for one m bear no relation to those determined for another m, it follows that the entire least-square analysis must be repeated over and over. This may be quite time-consuming for m large unless there is an a priori reason for estimating the final value of m to use.

A second serious problem occurs when $m \geq 6$. While the matrix of coefficients $\mathbf{X}^T\mathbf{X}$ in (7.1.10) is symmetric, it has all the problems associated with a Hilbert matrix. The actual form of the Hilbert matrix occurs, of course, only when the polynomial form is used [(7.1.2)]. The inverse $(\mathbf{X}^T\mathbf{X})^{-1}$ has elements which are very large, and a small error in $y_1, y_2, \ldots, y_N$ can lead to large differences in the final values of $a_0, a_1, \ldots, a_m$. Another way of looking at this problem is in terms of the determinant of $\mathbf{X}^T\mathbf{X}$. The determinant is equal to the product of all the eigenvalues

$$|\mathbf{X}^T\mathbf{X}| = \lambda_0\lambda_1 \cdots \lambda_m$$

and as m increases $|\mathbf{X}^T\mathbf{X}| \to 0$. This results from the widespread magnitude of the eigenvalues, that is, $\lambda_{\text{largest}} \gg \lambda_{\text{smallest}}$, and the solution of the set of simultaneous equations is equal to a determinant divided by an almost zero determinant. This, of course, indicates an ill-conditioned matrix.

The problems mentioned severely limit the applicability of the least-square fit when $m \geq 6$. In the next section of this chapter, however, it will be shown that the use of orthogonal polynomials alleviates the computational difficulties.

Of interest is a simple computational technique for generating the least-square-fit coefficients. The procedure to be described is particularly suitable for updating the fit as new experimental data are obtained. Consider that (7.1.1) is written in the form

$$\phi_m(x) = a_0 + a_1u_1(x) + a_2u_2(x) + a_3u_3(x)\dagger \tag{7.2.3}$$

and that it is desired to calculate a_0, a_1, a_2, and a_3 such that this equation exhibits a least-square fit to data of $y_1, y_2, \ldots, y_N$ at $x_1, x_2, \ldots, x_N$. For each x_r, (7.2.3) leads to

$$\phi_m(x_r) = a_0 + a_1u_1(x_r) + a_2u_2(x_r) + a_3u_3(x_r) \tag{7.2.4}$$

Upon defining the two vectors

$$\mathbf{M}(x_r) = \begin{bmatrix} 1 \\ u_1(x_r) \\ u_2(x_r) \\ u_3(x_r) \end{bmatrix} \qquad \mathbf{a} = \begin{bmatrix} a_0 \\ a_1 \\ a_2 \\ a_3 \end{bmatrix}$$

(7.2.4) can be written as

$$\phi_m(x_r) = \mathbf{M}(x_r)^T\mathbf{a}$$

The least-square formulation for **a** becomes merely

$$\sum_{r=1}^{N} \mathbf{M}(x_r)y(x_r) = \sum_{r=1}^{N} \mathbf{M}(x_r)\mathbf{M}(x_r)^T\mathbf{a}$$

or

$$\mathbf{a} = \left[\sum_{r=1}^{N} \mathbf{M}(x_r)\mathbf{M}(x_r)^T\right]^{-1} \sum_{r=1}^{N} \mathbf{M}(x_r)y(x_r) \tag{7.2.5}$$

The proof that (7.2.5) actually represents the least-square formulation will be given shortly, but for now it is sufficient to point out some virtues of this equation. For the problem as written with $m = 3$, only four sets of y versus x data are required to obtain an initial estimate for **a**. If new data are then made available, (7.2.5) can be made self-sustaining by defining

$$\mathbf{B}_N = \sum_{1}^{N} \mathbf{M}(x_r)\mathbf{M}(x_r)^T \tag{7.2.6}$$

and noting that

$$\mathbf{B}_{N+1} = \mathbf{B}_N + \mathbf{M}(x_{N+1})\mathbf{M}(x_{N+1})^T \tag{7.2.7}$$

In the form of (7.2.5) to (7.2.7) only a minimum amount of computation is required to incorporate the new data as they become available. Proceeding a step further, suppose that the new data obtained are felt to be

† The choice of $m = 3$ here is purely arbitrary and taken only for illustrative purposes.

more accurate than the older data. Thus the new data should be given more weight than the older data. In the present formulation this can be done by introducing α, $0 \leq \alpha \leq 1$, such that

$$\mathbf{a} = \Big[\sum_{r=1}^{N} \alpha^{N-r}\mathbf{M}(x_r)\mathbf{M}(x_r)^T\Big]^{-1}\Big[\sum_{r=1}^{N} \alpha^{N-r}\mathbf{M}(x_r)y(x_r)\Big]$$

and

$$\mathbf{B}_N = \Big[\sum_{r=1}^{N} \alpha^{N-r}\mathbf{M}(x_r)\mathbf{M}(x_r)^T\Big] \qquad \mathbf{B}_{N+1} = \alpha\mathbf{B}_N + \mathbf{M}(x_{N+1})\mathbf{M}(x_{N+1})^T$$

By changing the numerical value of α any desired weighting of new data with respect to the old data can be obtained. Note that as before $u_1(x)$, $u_2(x)$, . . . could be such items as flow rates, concentrations, temperatures, etc.

To illustrate the validity of (7.2.5), consider (7.2.3) in the simple form

$$\phi_m(x) = a_0 + a_1u_1(x)$$

The least-square formulation becomes, corresponding to (7.1.10),

$$\mathbf{X}^T\mathbf{X}\mathbf{a} = \mathbf{X}^T\mathbf{y} \qquad \text{and} \qquad \mathbf{a} = (\mathbf{X}^T\mathbf{X})^{-1}\mathbf{X}^T\mathbf{y}$$

where $\mathbf{y} = \begin{bmatrix} y_1 \\ y_2 \end{bmatrix} \qquad \mathbf{X} = \begin{bmatrix} 1 & u_1(x_1) \\ 1 & u_1(x_2) \end{bmatrix} \qquad \mathbf{a} = \begin{bmatrix} a_0 \\ a_1 \end{bmatrix}$

But

$$\mathbf{X}^T\mathbf{X} = \begin{bmatrix} 1 & 1 \\ u_1(x_1) & u_1(x_2) \end{bmatrix}\begin{bmatrix} 1 & u_1(x_1) \\ 1 & u_1(x_2) \end{bmatrix} = \begin{bmatrix} 2 & u_1(x_1) + u_1(x_2) \\ u_1(x_1) + u_1(x_2) & u_1(x_1)^2 + u_1(x_2)^2 \end{bmatrix} \qquad (A)$$

and

$$\mathbf{A}^T\mathbf{y} = \begin{bmatrix} 1 & 1 \\ u_1(x_1) & u_1(x_2) \end{bmatrix}\begin{bmatrix} y_1 \\ y_2 \end{bmatrix} = \begin{bmatrix} y_1 + y_2 \\ u_1(x_1)y_1 + u_1(x_2)y_2 \end{bmatrix} \qquad (B)$$

In the formulation of (7.2.5)

$$\phi_m(x_r) = \begin{bmatrix} 1 \\ u_1(x_r) \end{bmatrix}^T \mathbf{a} = \mathbf{M}(x_r)^T\mathbf{a}$$

with

$$\mathbf{M}(x_1) = \begin{bmatrix} 1 \\ u_1(x_1) \end{bmatrix} \qquad \mathbf{M}(x_2) = \begin{bmatrix} 1 \\ u_1(x_2) \end{bmatrix}$$

As a result, with $y_1 = y(x_1)$ and $y_2 = y(x_2)$,

$$\sum_{r=1}^{2} \mathbf{M}(x_1)y(x_r) = \mathbf{M}(x_1)y(x_1) + \mathbf{M}(x_2)y(x_2)$$

$$= \begin{bmatrix} 1 \\ u_1(x_1) \end{bmatrix} y(x_1) + \begin{bmatrix} 1 \\ u_1(x_2) \end{bmatrix} y(x_2) = \begin{bmatrix} y(x_1) + y(x_2) \\ u_1(x_1)y(x_1) + u_2(x_2)y(x_2) \end{bmatrix} \qquad (C)$$

and

$$\sum_{r=1}^{2} \mathbf{M}(x_r)\mathbf{M}(x_r)^T = \mathbf{M}(x_1)\mathbf{M}(x_1)^T + \mathbf{M}(x_2)\mathbf{M}(x_2)^T$$

$$= \begin{bmatrix} 1 \\ u_1(x_1) \end{bmatrix} [1 \quad u_1(x_1)] + \begin{bmatrix} 1 \\ u_1(x_2) \end{bmatrix} [1 \quad u_1(x_2)]$$

$$= \begin{bmatrix} 2 & u_1(x_1) + u_1(x_2) \\ u_1(x_1) + u_1(x_2) & u_1(x_1)^2 + u_1(x_2)^2 \end{bmatrix} \qquad (D)$$

A comparison of (A) with (D) and (B) with (C) indicates that the two procedures lead to identical results.

7.3. Orthogonal Polynomials and Least Squares

To remove the computational difficulties mentioned above, it is possible to turn to the use of orthogonal polynomials. Let

$$\phi_m(x) = b_0P_0(x) + b_1P_1(x) + \cdots + b_mP_m(x) = \sum_{j=0}^{j=m} b_jP_j(x) \qquad (7.3.1)$$

where $P_j(x)$ is a polynomial of degree j. Rearrangement of (7.3.1) followed by the condensation of the constants leads to (7.1.2). In the same manner as before, the least-square minimization of (7.3.1) with $w_i = 1.0$ leads to

$$\sum_{i=1}^{N} \Big[y_i - \sum_{j=0}^{m} b_jP_j(x) \Big]^2 = \text{minimum}$$

$$r_{jk} = \sum_{i=1}^{N} P_j(x_i)P_k(x_i) \qquad s_j = \sum_{i=1}^{N} y_iP_j(x_i)$$

and a set of normal equations

$$s_j = \sum_{k=0}^{m} b_kr_{jk} \qquad j = 0, 1, 2, \ldots, m$$

In expanded form the normal equations are

$$\begin{aligned} s_0 &= r_{00}b_0 + r_{01}b_1 + \cdots + r_{0m}b_m \\ s_1 &= r_{10}b_0 + r_{11}b_1 + \cdots + r_{1m}b_m \\ &\cdots\cdots\cdots\cdots\cdots\cdots \\ s_m &= r_{m0}b_0 + r_{m1}b_1 + \cdots + r_{mm}b_m \end{aligned} \qquad (7.3.2)$$

Equation (7.3.2) is a set of $m + 1$ simultaneous equations with an equal number of unknowns. The form is exactly as before, (7.1.9), and nothing seems to have been achieved by this method. However, suppose that the polynomials $P_j(x)$ can be chosen to be orthogonal in the summation sense, i.e.,

$$r_{jk} = \begin{cases} 0 & j \neq k \\ \sum_{i=1}^{N} P_j^2(x_i) & j = k \end{cases} \tag{7.3.3}$$

Under this condition all the r_{jk}'s except those of the main diagonal of (7.3.2) become zero, leading to

$$\begin{aligned} s_0 &= r_{00}b_0 \\ s_1 &= \qquad r_{11}b_1 \\ s_2 &= \qquad\qquad r_{22}b_2 \\ &\cdot \\ &\cdot \\ &\cdot \\ s_m &= \qquad\qquad\qquad r_{mm}b_m \end{aligned}$$

The unknowns may now be evaluated directly without solving a set of simultaneous equations. Thus

$$\begin{aligned} b_0 &= \frac{s_0}{r_{00}} \\ b_1 &= \frac{s_1}{r_{11}} \\ b_2 &= \frac{s_2}{r_{22}} \\ &\cdot\ \cdot\ \cdot\ \cdot\ \cdot \\ b_m &= \frac{s_m}{r_{mm}} \end{aligned}$$

In effect, the use of orthogonal polynomials makes the least-square analysis appear as if each parameter were the only one used. Since simultaneous equations are not solved, the case of $m \geq 6$ no longer presents any computational problem. A further feature of the orthogonal polynomial least-square fit is that the coefficients $b_0, b_1, \ldots$ are independent of each other; as m is increased, the previously calculated $b_0, b_1, \ldots, b_{m-1}$ do not change. Thus calculating the coefficients for m large yields all the necessary information for all the lower values of m. From this single calculation it is possible to determine all the $\sigma_1^2, \sigma_2^2, \ldots$ and the $b_0, b_1, \ldots$. As a result the least-square fit can be decided upon immediately. Thus the method is one of a step-by-step nature, with a provision for measuring the degree of improvement as each new term is added.

The question now arises of how to generate or obtain the necessary orthogonal polynomials to use in (7.3.1). To illustrate the procedure, it seems appropriate to consider first the least-square criterion in terms of integration rather than summation. This means that the integral

$$\int_a^b \left[y(x) - \sum_{j=0}^{m} b_j P_j(x) \right]^2 dx \tag{7.3.4}$$

is to be minimized (with unit weighting function) over the interval (a,b). The condition of orthogonality can be stated as

$$\int_a^b P_j(x)P_k(x)\,dx = \begin{cases} 0 & j \neq k \\ \int_a^b P_j(x)^2\,dx & j = k \end{cases} \tag{7.3.5}$$

Upon differentiating (7.3.4) with respect to the b_j and using (7.3.5) the normal equations become

$$\int_a^b P_0(x)y(x)\,dx = b_0 \int_a^b P_0(x)^2\,dx$$

$$\int_a^b P_1(x)y(x)\,dx = b_1 \int_a^b P_1(x)^2\,dx$$

$$\vdots$$

$$\int_a^b P_m(x)y(x)\,dx = b_m \int_a^b P_m(x)^2\,dx$$

Thus
$$b_j = \frac{\int_a^b P_j(x)y(x)\,dx}{\int_a^b P_j(x)^2\,dx} \qquad j = 0, 1, 2, \ldots, m \tag{7.3.6}$$

Now, upon recalling the Legendre polynomials with the property

$$\int_{-1}^{+1} P_j(x)P_k(x)\,dx = \begin{cases} 0 & j \neq k \\ \dfrac{2}{2j+1} & j = k \end{cases}$$

it is apparent that if $a = -1$ and $b = +1$ in (7.3.5) the Legendre polynomials satisfy the requirements for the orthogonal polynomials. Thus for the special case of $a = -1$ and $b = +1$, (7.3.6) becomes

$$b_j = \frac{2j+1}{2} \int_{-1}^{+1} P_j(x)y(x)\,dx \qquad j = 0, 1, 2, \ldots, m \tag{7.3.7}$$

where the $P_j(x)$'s are now the Legendre polynomials. If the interval (a,b) is not $(-1,+1)$, it can be mapped to the desired spacing by the change of variable

$$z = \frac{2x - (a+b)}{b-a}$$

on the assumption that a and b are both finite. In this case a new set of orthogonal polynomials $R(z)$ are obtained from the Legendre polynomials with the property

$$\int_a^b R_j(z)R_k(z)\,dz = \begin{cases} 0 & j \neq k \\ \dfrac{b-a}{2j+1} & j = k \end{cases}$$

In exactly the same manner the Laguerre orthogonal polynomials can be used with (a,b) as $(0,+\infty)$ and with $w(x) = e^{-x}$, the Hermite polynomials with (a,b) as $(-\infty,+\infty)$ and with $w(x) = e^{-x^2}$.

Unfortunately, it is not always possible to evaluate the integrals in (7.3.7). If $y(x)$ is not an analytical function but is given only as discrete data points, a numerical technique is required. Since the spacing on the $x_0, x_1, \ldots, x_N$ is not assumed to have any regular pattern, such a numerical process is not easy. If, however, the integration is replaced by summation, the evaluation of the b_j becomes quite simple. While there are a number of orthogonal polynomials which can be used under summation the method of Forsythe (15) seems to be the best. The polynomials $P_j(x)$ are defined by the set

$$\begin{aligned} P_{-1}(x) &= 0 \\ P_0(x) &= 1 \\ P_1(x) &= (x-\alpha_1)P_0(x) - \beta_0 P_{-1}(x) \\ P_2(x) &= (x-\alpha_2)P_1(x) - \beta_1 P_0(x) \\ &\cdots\cdots\cdots\cdots \\ P_{j+1}(x) &= (x-\alpha_{j+1})P_j(x) - \beta_j P_{j-1}(x) \end{aligned} \tag{7.3.8}$$

with $\beta_0 = 0$. The α and β are to be chosen in such a way that

$$\sum_{i=1}^{N} P_j(x_i)P_k(x_i) = 0 \qquad j \neq k$$

namely, as orthogonal under summation. As a first step in obtaining the desired α and β, assume that $P_0(x), P_1(x), \ldots, P_j(x)$ are all orthogonal to each other. Using the final recurrence relation (7.3.8), multiply each term by $P_k(x)$, and sum the x from $i = 1$ to N.

$$\sum_{i=1}^{N} P_k(x_i)P_{j+1}(x_i) = \sum_{i=1}^{N} P_k(x_i)(x_i - \alpha_{j+1})P_j(x_i) - \sum_{i=1}^{N} P_k(x_i)\beta_j P_{j-1}(x_i) \tag{7.3.9}$$

where $k \leq j$. For the particular case $k = j$, (7.3.9) becomes

$$\sum_{i=1}^{N} P_j(x_i)P_{j+1}(x_i) = \sum_{i=1}^{N} x_i P_j(x_i)^2 - \alpha_{j+1}\sum_{i=1}^{N} P_j(x_i)^2 - \beta_j \sum_{i=1}^{N} P_j(x_i)P_{j-1}(x_i)$$

From the assumed orthogonality of $P_j(x)$ and $P_{j-1}(x)$ the third term on the right is zero. The choice of

$$\alpha_{j+1} = \frac{\sum_{i=1}^{N} x_i P_j(x_i)^2}{\sum_{i=1}^{N} P_j(x_i)^2} \tag{7.3.10}$$

then means that the left-hand side is zero, or

$$\sum_{i=1}^{N} P_j(x_i) P_{j+1}(x_i) = 0$$

and $P_{j+1}(x)$ and $P_j(x)$ are orthogonal. Letting $k = j - 1$ in (7.3.9) yields

$$\sum_{i=1}^{N} P_{j-1}(x_i)P_{j+1}(x_i) = \sum_{i=1}^{N} x_i P_{j-1}(x_i)P_j(x_i) - \alpha_{j+1} \sum_{i=1}^{N} P_{j-1}(x_i)P_j(x_i) - \beta_j \sum_{i=1}^{N} P_{j-1}(x_i)^2$$

Since the second term on the right-hand side is zero from the orthogonality of $P_{j-1}(x)$ and $P_j(x)$, the choice of β as

$$\beta_j = \frac{\sum_{i=1}^{N} x_i P_{j-1}(x_i)P_j(x_i)}{\sum_{i=1}^{N} P_{j-1}(x_i)^2} \tag{7.3.11}$$

means that the left-hand side is zero. Thus

$$\sum_{i=1}^{N} P_{j-1}(x_i)P_{j+1}(x_i) = 0$$

and $P_{j+1}(x)$ and $P_{j-1}(x)$ are orthogonal. As a result $P_{j+1}(x)$, $P_j(x)$, and $P_{j-1}(x)$ are orthogonal under summation if α_{j+1} is calculated from (7.3.10) and β_j from (7.3.11). Thus all the $P_r(x)$, $r = 0, 1, 2, \ldots, j + 1$, are orthogonal to each other when the recurrence relation (7.3.8) and the two equations (7.3.10) and (7.3.11) are used successively.

Starting with the first two terms $P_{-1}(x)$ and $P_0(x)$, (7.3.8) can be used to generate a sequence of orthogonal polynomials (with respect to summation). On this basis all the desired properties of orthogonal polynomials for least-square estimation are obtained, and the b_j of (7.3.7) (with a summation and not integration) can be evaluated directly.

If the points $x_1, x_2, \ldots, x_N$ happen to be equally spaced the orthogonal polynomials assume a particular form called the Gram-Chebyshev polynomials. For further details of this procedure see Pings and Sage (32).

7.4. Approximation by Chebyshev Polynomials

The reader recalls that one of the more efficient numerical-integration methods involved the use of orthogonal polynomials as an approximating function (Chap. 2). Instead of using a specified set of independent variable points for the integration, this procedure, in effect, generated its own points, i.e., such that they were roots of the appropriate orthogonal polynomial. In other words a polynomial of degree m, $\phi_m(x)$, was chosen to approximate $y(x)$ at $m + 1$ points. The requirement placed upon the approximation was, as pointed out previously,

$$\phi_m(x_r) = y(x_r) \qquad r = 0, 1, 2, \ldots, m$$

In the present section the requirement above will be discarded, and instead an attempt made to find the "best" fit in the sense that the error $\epsilon(x)$,

$$\epsilon(x) = y(x) - \phi_m(x)$$

is minimized over the entire interval (a,b). Thus

$$\max_{(a,b)} |\epsilon(x)| = \text{minimum}$$

As will be seen shortly the Chebyshev orthogonal polynomials, when used as the approximating function, satisfy this last requirement.

While the Chebyshev polynomials have already been mentioned in Sec. 2.11, it is worthwhile here to examine some of their properties. The most common definition is given by the sequence, $-1 \le x \le 1$,

$$\begin{aligned} T_0(x) &= 1 \\ T_1(x) &= x \\ T_2(x) &= 2x^2 - 1 \\ T_3(x) &= 4x^3 - 3x \qquad\qquad -1 \le x \le 1 \qquad (7.4.1) \\ T_4(x) &= 8x^4 - 8x^2 + 1 \\ T_5(x) &= 16x^5 - 20x^3 + 5x \\ &\cdots\cdots\cdots \end{aligned}$$

with higher-order terms generated by the recurrence relation

$$T_{m+1}(x) = 2xT_m(x) - T_{m-1}(x) \qquad m = 1, 2, 3, \ldots \qquad (7.4.2)$$

Note in (7.4.1) that the successive terms alternate in sign and that only even or odd powers of x are included. The coefficients of the polynomials have been tabulated by Lanczos (23) as

$$T_m(x) = t_{m,0}x^m - t_{m,2}x^{m-2} + t_{m,4}x^{m-4} \cdots$$

such that
$$t_{m,2p} = \begin{cases} \dfrac{m}{2^{(1+2p-m)}} \dfrac{[m - (p+1)]!}{p!(m-2p)!} & m \geq 2p \geq 0 \\ 0 & 2p > m \end{cases} \qquad (7.4.3)$$

As an example, if $m = 2$ and $p = 0$,

$$t_{2,0} = 2$$

which agrees with the coefficient of x^2 in $T_2(x)$ as given in (7.4.1). With the aid of $T_0(x) = 1$, $T_1(x) = x$, and (7.4.2) and (7.4.3), any Chebyshev polynomial can be quickly computed. Of practical importance is the fact that $t_{m,0}$ [$m \neq 0$, $p = 0$ in (7.4.3)] always leads to 2^{m-1} as the coefficient of the highest-order term.

The variable x in (7.4.1) is defined by

$$x = \cos\theta \qquad 0 \leq \theta \leq \pi$$

such that
$$T_m(x) = \cos(m \cos^{-1} x) \qquad (7.4.4)$$

For future usage the relations in (7.4.1) can be inverted or solved for x sequentially. This yields

$$\begin{aligned} 1 &= T_0(x) \\ x &= T_1(x) \\ x^2 &= \tfrac{1}{2}(T_0 + T_2) \\ x^3 &= \tfrac{1}{4}(3T_1 + T_3) \\ x^4 &= \tfrac{1}{8}(3T_0 + 4T_2 + T_4) \\ x^5 &= \tfrac{1}{16}(10T_1 + 5T_3 + T_5) \\ &\cdots\cdots \end{aligned} \qquad (7.4.5)$$

where $T_0 = T_0(x)$, $T_1 = T_1(x)$, ...

Lanczos also defines the shifted Chebyshev polynomial $T_m^*(x)$ in the interval $0 \leq x \leq 1$ such that

$$\begin{aligned} T_m^*(x) &= T_m(2x - 1) \\ &= \cos[m \cos^{-1}(2x-1)] \qquad 0 \leq x \leq 1 \end{aligned}$$

Further,
$$2x - 1 = \cos\theta$$

and
$$x = \cos^2\frac{\theta}{2} \qquad 0 \leq \theta \leq \pi$$

The first six shifted Chebyshev polynomials are given by

$$\begin{aligned} T_0^*(x) &= 1 \\ T_1^*(x) &= 2x - 1 \\ T_2^*(x) &= 8x^2 - 8x + 1 \\ T_3^*(x) &= 32x^3 - 48x^2 + 18x - 1 \\ T_4^*(x) &= 128x^4 - 256x^3 + 160x^2 - 32x + 1 \\ T_5^*(x) &= 512x^5 - 1280x^4 + 1120x^3 - 400x^2 + 50x - 1 \end{aligned} \qquad 0 \leq x \leq 1 \quad (7.4.6)$$

Additional terms follow from the recurrence relation

$$T^*_{m+1}(x) = (4x - 2)T^*_m(x) - T^*_{m-1}(x) \qquad m = 1, 2, 3, \ldots$$

and the coefficients from

$$T^*_m(x) = t_{2m,0}x^m - t_{2m,2}x^{m-1} + t_{2m,4}x^{m-2} - \cdots$$

with
$$t_{2m,p} = \frac{2m}{2^{1+2p-2m}} \frac{[2m - (p+1)]!}{p!(2m-2p)!}$$

For $m = 2$, $p = 0$,

$$t_{4,0} = 8$$

which agrees with the leading coefficient of $T^*_2(x)$ in (7.4.6). In the present case the leading coefficient of $T^*_m(x)$ is given by $t_{2m,0} = 2^{2m-1}$. Inversion of (7.4.6) leads to the set

$$\begin{aligned} 1 &= T^*_0(x) \\ x &= \tfrac{1}{2}(T^*_0 + T^*_1) \\ x^2 &= \tfrac{1}{8}(3T^*_0 + 4T^*_1 + T^*_2) \\ x^3 &= \tfrac{1}{32}(10T^*_0 + 15T^*_1 + 6T^*_2 + T^*_3) \\ x^4 &= \tfrac{1}{128}(35T^*_0 + 56T^*_1 + 28T^*_2 + 8T^*_3 + T^*_4) \\ x^5 &= \tfrac{1}{412}(252T^*_0 + 210T^*_1 + 120T^*_2 + 45T^*_3 + 10T^*_4 + T^*_5) \end{aligned} \tag{7.4.7}$$

It should be noted that the restriction $-1 \leq x \leq 1$ or $0 \leq x \leq 1$ is not important, since a linear transformation can map any finite interval (a,b) into the desired interval.

The behavior of the function $T_m(x)$ in the interval $-1 \leq x \leq 1$ [or $T^*_m(x)$ in $0 \leq x \leq 1$] is of considerable interest. From (7.4.4) it can be seen that $T_m(x)$ is a cosine function, oscillatory in form and with constant amplitude. Two factors of this oscillation are important, the magnitude of the amplitude and the location of the roots corresponding to crossing the x axis. The latter can be ascertained quite easily. From (7.4.1) it is observed that $T_m(x)$ is merely a polynomial of degree m and thus has m roots. These roots occur at values of x such that $\cos\theta = 0$ or at factors of $\pi/2$ and may be located from

$$m\theta_r = \frac{2r+1}{2}\pi \qquad r = 0, 1, 2, \ldots, m-1$$

or at
$$x_r = \cos\left(\frac{2r+1}{2m}\pi\right) \qquad r = 0, 1, 2, \ldots, m-1$$

Since there are m roots and noting from (7.4.1) that at the extremities of the interval $(-1,+1)T_m(x) = \pm 1.0$, one concludes that $T_m(x)$ must have $m + 1$ maximum or minimum values. Thus $T_1(x)$ is a straight line and is equal to -1.0 at $x = 1.0$, $+1.0$ at $x = +1.0$, and crosses the x axis once; $T_2(x)$ is a curved function equal to $+1.0$ at $x = -1.0$, $+1.0$ at $x = +1.0$, and crosses the x axis twice; $T_3(x)$ is equal to -1.0

at $x = -1.0$, $+1.0$ at $x = +1.0$, and crosses the x axis three times, and so on. At $x = -1.0$, $T_m(x) = (-1)^m$, and at $x = +1.0$, $T_m(x) = +1.0$. The intermediate minimum and maximum are located at values of x such that $\cos\theta = 1.0$ or at factors of π. This may be expressed as

$$\left.\begin{aligned} \theta_r &= \frac{r\pi}{m} \\ \text{or} \qquad x_r &= \cos\frac{r\pi}{m} \end{aligned}\right\} \qquad r = 0, 1, 2, \ldots, m \tag{7.4.8}$$

where the end points have been included. Of special importance is it that (7.4.4) or (7.4.8) shows that the maximum values of $T_m(x)$ are ± 1. Thus, in the interval $-1 \le x \le 1$,

$$|T_m(x)| \le 1.0 \tag{7.4.9}$$

Of course the same type of analysis can be applied to $T_m^*(x)$ when desired.

Another important feature of the Chebyshev polynomials is that of all polynomials of degree m and with coefficient unity on x^m these particular polynomials have the least deviation or upper bound in the interval $-1 \le x \le 1$. To prove this point, assume that $S_m(x)$ is another polynomial of degree m with leading coefficient unity which has a smaller deviation than $T_m(x)$. At the maximum or minimum points of (7.4.8) it follows that

$$\begin{aligned} T_m(x_0) - S_m(x_0) &\ge 0 \\ T_m(x_1) - S_m(x_1) &\le 0 \\ T_m(x_2) - S_m(x_2) &\ge 0 \\ T_m(x_3) - S_m(x_3) &\le 0 \\ \cdots\cdots\cdots\cdots \end{aligned}$$

The function $T_m(x_r) - S_m(x_r)$ alternates in sign depending on a maximum or minimum. On this basis there must be m roots of $T_m(x) - S_m(x)$ in $(-1,+1)$. However, in the subtraction of $S_m(x)$ from $T_m(x)$ the leading term x^m cancels out, leaving a polynomial of degree $m - 1$. Since these two facts contradict each other, the original assumption on $S_m(x)$ is incorrect and $T_m(x)$ is the polynomial with leading coefficient unity which has the least upper bound in $-1 \le x \le 1$.

Consider now the representation of a function $y = y(x)$ in $(-1,+1)$ by a sum of orthogonal polynomials $Q_0(x), Q_1(x), \ldots, Q_m(x)$,

$$\phi_m(x) = a_0Q_0(x) + a_1Q_1(x) + \cdots + a_mQ_m(x) \tag{7.4.10}$$

where $\phi_m(x)$ is also an orthogonal polynomial of degree m. For any polynomial of degree m, however, it follows from the Lagrangian remainder formula that

$$|y(x) - \phi_m(x)| = R(x) = \frac{\phi_{m+1}(x)y^{[m+1]}(\xi)}{(m+1)!} \tag{7.4.11}$$

where $\phi_{m+1}(x)$ is a polynomial of degree $m + 1$ and $-1 < \xi < +1$. But if (7.4.10) is thought of as a truncated version of an infinite series of $Q(x)$, the first truncated term would be $a_{m+1}Q_{m+1}(x)$. Since both $Q_{m+1}(x)$ and $\phi_{m+1}(x)$ are polynomials of degree $m + 1$, the error associated with using (7.4.10) can be visualized by observing the behavior of $Q_{m+1}(x)$. If the points at which the approximation is fitted are the roots of $Q_{m+1}(x) = 0$, the first truncated term, that is, $a_{m+1}Q_{m+1}(x)$, will be zero at the specified points. Between these points the approximation error will oscillate back and forth. In the particular case of

$$Q_{m+1}(x) = T_{m+1}(x)$$

this oscillation will occur with constant maximum or minimum amplitude; if $Q_{m+1}(x) = P_{m+1}(x)$, where $P_{m+1}(x)$ is the Legendre polynomial, the amplitude increases as x goes from zero to $|1.0|$. In other words, the amplitude of the error is fixed for $T_m(x)$ used in (7.4.10), whereas when $P_m(x)$ is used, the amplitude varies. Thus, if the approximation is to remain within some predetermined error bound over the entire interval $(-1,+1)$, more terms must be used in (7.4.10) when $Q_{m+1}(x) = P_{m+1}(x)$ than when $Q_{m+1}(x) = T_{m+1}(x)$. While the average error may be less with some other orthogonal polynomial expansion, the use of the Chebyshev polynomial leads to the minimum absolute error over the entire interval. As a result it may be stated that if the approximating function is to represent $y(x)$ with the smallest error over the entire interval the use of Chebyshev polynomials represents the optimum arrangement. This implies also that the discrete data to be fitted should be taken to correspond to the roots of $T_{m+1}(x)$, rather than at equal intervals. As a result of this discussion it becomes apparent that the optimum type of interpolation formula is one which employs Chebyshev polynomials.

Because the Chebyshev polynomials are merely cosine functions, they exhibit a twofold orthogonality. This means that they are orthogonal with respect to both integration and summation. The $T_m(x)$ are orthogonal under integration with a weighting factor $1/\sqrt{1 - x^2}$ and in the interval $(-1,+1)$. This may be illustrated by

$$\int_{-1}^{+1} \frac{T_j(x)T_k(x)}{\sqrt{1 - x^2}}\, dx = \begin{cases} 0 & j \neq k \\ \dfrac{\pi}{2} & j = k \end{cases}$$

In addition the Chebyshev polynomials are orthogonal under summation in $(-1,+1)$ with respect to a unit weighting function if the summation index is chosen to correspond to the roots of the first neglected polynomial. Thus

$$\sum_{i=1}^{m} T_j(x_i)T_k(x_i) = \begin{cases} 0 & i \neq j \\ \dfrac{m}{2} & i = j \end{cases}$$

where $x_i = \cos\left(\dfrac{2i+1}{i+1}\dfrac{\pi}{2}\right)$ and $i = 0, 1, 2, \ldots, m$. Obviously both types of orthogonality can be used in a suitable least-square expansion.

7.5. Telescoping a Power Series

It has already been pointed out that the Chebyshev polynomial leads to an optimum type of interpolation arrangement. Since a power-series expansion is basically an inefficient process for representation (this is especially true as one proceeds further from the origin of interest), it would seem appropriate to try to replace such a function with an equivalent series of Chebyshev polynomials. This transformation is referred to as telescoping a power series and is due to the brilliant work of Lanczos (23). As will be seen, this replacement tends to "tailor" the Chebyshev series to fit the interval of interest within the permissible error. It can be used for transcendental functions such as $\sin x$, $\cos x$, e^x, or any analytical function with an infinite Taylor series expansion.

The method to be described will use the shifted Chebyshev polynomials $T_m^*(x)$ because of general applicability. Given an initial power series, the values $x, x^2, x^3, \ldots$ are replaced by the equivalent $T_1^*(x)$, $T_2^*(x)$, $T_3^*(x)$, $\ldots$, the inverted series (7.4.7) being used. This new series of Chebyshev polynomials converges faster for any x, $0 \leq x \leq 1$, than the original power series. Thus some terms can be truncated without reducing the error. In turn this truncated series can be rearranged by using (7.4.6), to yield a final polynomial with the desired accuracy but with fewer terms than in the original series. The coefficients of this final polynomial are, of course, not the same as those in the original series. In summary a polynomial is obtained after transformation with Chebyshev polynomials with fewer terms than the original power series but with the same accuracy.

To illustrate the technique, consider a power series of the form

$$\phi_m(x) = \sum_{j=0}^{m} a_j x^j + E(x) \qquad 0 \leq x \leq 1 \tag{7.5.1}$$

$E(x)$ is the portion of the series corresponding to $j > m$. From previous calculations on this series let us say that it has been found that the maximum value of $E(x)$ in (0,1) is less than a tolerable error ϵ. However, the term $j = m$ (or $a_m x^m$) cannot be truncated, because $a_m x^m + E(x) > \epsilon$. Thus (7.5.1) is a finite polynomial when $E(x)$ is truncated, which always approximates the desired function within the desired accuracy. Expanding (7.5.1), after truncating $E(x)$,

$$\phi_m(x) = a_0 x^0 + a_1 x^1 + a_2 x^2 + \cdots + a_m x^m \qquad |\phi_m(x)| < \epsilon \qquad (7.5.2)$$

and then replacing $x^0, x^1, x^2, \ldots, x^m$ with the corresponding Chebyshev polynomials from (7.4.7) leads to

$$\phi_m(x) = b_0 T_0^*(x) + b_1 T_1^*(x) + b_2 T_2^*(x) + \cdots + b_m T_m^*(x) \qquad (7.5.3)$$

This last equation has the same number of terms, $m + 1$, as the original series (7.5.2). The b_j's are related, of course, to the a_j's. As an example of the process to this point, consider the simple case $m = 2$.

$$\phi_2(x) = a_0 + a_1 x + a_2 x^2$$

But from (7.4.7)

$$1 = T_0^*$$
$$x = \tfrac{1}{2}(T_0^* + T_1^*)$$
$$x^2 = \tfrac{1}{8}(3T_0^* + 4T_1^* + T_2^*)$$

so that

$$\phi_2(x) = a_0 T_0^*(x) + \frac{a_1}{2}(T_0^* + T_1^*) + \frac{a_2}{8}(3T_0^* + 4T_1^* + T_2^*)$$

Collecting coefficients,

$$\phi_2(x) = \left(a_0 + \frac{a_1}{2} + \tfrac{3}{8}a_2\right) T_0^* + \left(\frac{a_1}{2} + \frac{a_2}{2}\right) T_1^* + \frac{a_2}{8} T_2^*$$

and thus $\quad b_0 = a_0 + \dfrac{a_1}{2} + \tfrac{3}{8}a_2 \qquad b_1 = \dfrac{a_2}{2} + \dfrac{a_3}{2} \qquad b_2 = \dfrac{a_2}{8}$

Note that in performing this transformation to a series of Chebyshev polynomials the coefficient in the mth term has been decreased. In this example it has gone from a_2 to $a_2/8$; in the general form, a_m goes to $b_m = (1/2^{2m-1})a_m$. When m is large, this difference becomes significant; further, it penetrates back to the lower-order coefficients. Not only b_m but also $b_{m-1}, b_{m-2}, \ldots, b_{m-r}$, where r is a positive integer, may be smaller than the corresponding $a_m, a_{m-1}, a_{m-2}, \ldots, a_{m-r}$. Thus the ratio b_m/a_m is very small, b_{m-1}/a_{m-1} is larger but still small, . . . , until at b_{m-r}/a_{m-r} the ratio becomes almost 1.0. The higher the value of m, the larger will be r; if $m = 3$, then r may be 1, while if $m = 10$, r may be 3.

The transformed series (7.5.3) having been obtained, the next step is to investigate the possibility of truncating the mth, $(m - 1)$st, . . . terms. Since $|T_j^*(x)| \leq 1.0$, $j = 0, 1, 2, \ldots$, the convergence of the series is determined by the absolute values of the coefficients $b_0, b_1, \ldots,$

b_m. The new series (7.5.3) may be truncated after the b_{m-r} term if

$$\sum_{j=r+1}^{m} |b_j| + E(x) \leq \epsilon$$

to yield

$$\phi_m(x) = \sum_{j=0}^{r} b_j T_j^*(x) \qquad r < m \tag{7.5.4}$$

This equation still yields values of $\phi_m(x)$ within the prescribed error bound. Another way of visualizing what has happened is to consider the expansion for $T_5^*(x)$.

$$T_5^* = 512x^5 - 1{,}280x^4 + 1{,}120x^3 - 400x^2 + 50x - 1$$

Solving for x^5,

$$x^5 = \frac{1{,}280x^4 - 1{,}120x^3 + 400x^2 - 50x + 1}{512} + \frac{T_5^*}{512} \tag{7.5.5}$$

If the original polynomial was fifth-degree, the substitution of (7.5.5) for x^5 and the subsequent truncation of T_5^* yields a polynomial of degree 4. The maximum error committed in the truncation is seen to be $a_5/512$, which is much smaller than if the a_5x^5 term were truncated in the original polynomial.

Having the new truncated equation in $T_j(x)$ [(7.5.4)], which still meets the necessary accuracy requirement, one can reverse the process with (7.4.6) to replace the $T_j(x)$ with x^j. This converts (7.5.4) to the form

$$\phi_m(x) = \sum_{j=0}^{r} c_j x^j \qquad 0 \leq x \leq 1 \tag{7.5.6}$$

still with the required accuracy. This final form has fewer terms than the original (7.5.2).

The implications associated with this telescoping of the polynomial are obvious. A polynomial of lower degree is obtained which meets the accuracy requirement. The new polynomial requires less computing time and less storage to evaluate a specific $\phi_m(x)$.

Actually, once the truncated Chebyshev form (7.5.4) is known, $\phi_m(x)$ can be evaluated at the desired x without requiring the inversion to (7.5.6). Clenshaw (8) has outlined a recurrence process which yields the desired $\phi_m(x)$. The sequence $B_r, B_{r-1}, B_{r-2}, \ldots, B_0$ is first constructed by using $B_{r+1} = B_{r+2} = 0$ and

$$B_j - (4x - 2)B_{j+1} + B_{j+2} = b_j \qquad j = r, r-1, r-2, \ldots, 1, 0$$

The b_j's are the known coefficients in (7.5.4). The value of $\phi_m(x)$ follows directly from

$$\phi_m(x) = B_0 - (2x - 1)B_1$$

In a second paper Clenshaw (10) has tabulated the coefficients b_j of (7.5.4) for a number of well-known functions. These include sin $(\pi x/2)$, cos $(\pi x/2)$, arctan x, arcsin x, arccos x, e^x, e^{-x}, log $(1 + x)$, $\Gamma(1 + x)$, $J_0(x)$, and $J_1(x)$. The coefficients were obtained by using the known Taylor series expansions for the particular function and then converting to the Chebyshev form. As an example, the expansion of e^{-x} in $(0,+1)$ yields the coefficients

$$
\begin{aligned}
b_0 &= 0.645035270 \\
b_1 &= -0.312841606 \\
b_2 &= 0.038704116 \\
b_3 &= -0.003208683 \\
b_4 &= 0.000199919 \\
b_5 &= -0.000009975 \\
b_6 &= 0.000000415
\end{aligned}
$$

Note how the coefficients decrease in magnitude in an extremely rapid manner. If one desired to calculate e^{-x} within an error limit of $+0.005$, the following could be used: Since $|T_j^*(x)| \leq 1.0$, it is necessary only to look at the absolute sum of the various coefficients. Using b_3 to b_6,

$$\sum_{b=3}^{b=6} |b_j| = 0.003418992$$

which is less than $+0.005$. As a result the equation

$$\phi_2(x) = b_0 T_0^*(x) + b_1 T_1^*(x) + b_2 T_2^*(x)$$

or its counterpart in terms of 1, x, and x^2 will yield values of $\phi_2(x)$ which are always within $+0.005$ of the true value of e^{-x} in the interval $(0,+1)$.

Along these same lines Lanczos (23) has presented a classic case in which the Taylor series expansion of sin $2\pi x$ required a polynomial of degree 19 to achieve a predetermined accuracy, whereas the Chebyshev polynomial was only of the fifth degree. Many further examples can be quoted of this increased efficiency.

There is also another interesting and important feature of the Chebyshev telescoping of a polynomial. Since all previous interpolation formulas (Chap. 2) had the form of (7.5.2), this seems like a natural area for increased efficiency of interpolation. Kopal (Chap. 1, 23) has investigated the replacement of the Everett and Bessel interpolation formulas with the corresponding Chebyshev polynomials, and Chisnall (5) has extended this treatment. These lead to what might be termed the most optimum and economic interpolation formulas. However, it should be pointed out that interpolation directly in terms of Chebyshev polynomials (Sec. 7.4) is also a very efficient process.

It is also possible to use other orthogonal polynomials, such as the Legendre polynomials, for performing the telescoping of a polynomial. When another orthogonal set is used, however, it will never yield as few terms in the final expansion as when Chebyshev polynomials are used. If the full accuracy of the machine word is required, the Chebyshev formulation is the best to use. For only half word accuracy, it may actually be better to use the Legendre formulation, since the average error may be smaller.

7.6. Continued-fraction Expansions

In addition to the previously discussed methods for approximating a function in a computationally efficient manner, there also exists the technique of continued-fraction expansions. In general the method is useful for any function which can be represented by a power series.

The notation used is that the continued-fraction expansion of a function $\phi(x)$ is given by

$$\phi(x) = b_0 + \cfrac{a_1}{b_1 + \cfrac{a_2}{b_2 + \cfrac{a_3}{b_3 + \cfrac{a_4}{b_4 + \cdots}}}} \tag{7.6.1}$$

or in a simpler notation

$$\phi(x) = b_0 + \frac{a_1}{b_1 +} \frac{a_2}{b_2 +} \frac{a_3}{b_3 +} \frac{a_4}{b_4 +} \cdots \tag{7.6.2}$$

Note that the addition signs in (7.6.2) are lowered so that they do not indicate straight addition of the fractions. The a_r and b_r, $r = 0, 1, 2, \ldots$, are possible functions of x with r extending to infinity. In much the same way as an ordinary power series is truncated after the mth term to yield an approximate polynomial, (7.6.1) or (7.6.2) can be truncated to yield the mth approximant or convergent.

$$\phi_m(x) = b_0 + \frac{a_1}{b_1 +} \frac{a_2}{b_2 +} \frac{a_3}{b_3 +} \cdots \frac{a_m}{+ b_m} \tag{7.6.3}$$

The zeroth approximant is merely b_0. In (7.6.3) a_r and b_r are called the rth partial numerator and denominator, respectively.

A convergent continued fraction is one in which $\phi(x)$ is finite for $m = \infty$. This is termed the limit on the sequence of approximants; that is, $\phi_m(x)$ as $m \to \infty$. In the present discussion only those cases in which m is held finite will be considered.

The first question which arises in the use of continued-fraction expansions is how to generate the expansion for a particular function. There are many techniques which can be used, but the classical method of Gauss is discussed here. For other general methods see Wall (42). Before outlining this method, however, it should be realized that one can frequently determine the expansion of a particular function by merely examining the function. As an illustration, consider the square root of a real number A. Writing

$$a = A - 1$$

it follows that

$$\sqrt{A} = 1 + \frac{a}{1 + \sqrt{A}} \tag{7.6.4}$$

This result can be verified by cross multiplication. But using the result in (7.6.4) for $\sqrt{A}$ and resubstituting,

$$\sqrt{A} = 1 + \frac{a}{1 + 1 + a/(1 + \sqrt{A})} = 1 + \frac{a}{2 + a/(1 + \sqrt{A})}$$

By using (7.6.4) sequentially the continued-fraction expansion of $\sqrt{A}$ becomes

$$\sqrt{A} = 1 + \frac{a}{2 +}\,\frac{a}{2 +}\,\frac{a}{2 +}\,\cdots$$

The solution of Gauss' ordinary differential equation

$$(x - x^2)y'' + [\gamma - (\alpha + \beta + 1)]y' - \alpha\beta y = 0$$
$$\alpha,\ \beta,\ \gamma = \text{real or complex constants}$$

is written in terms of the hypergeometric series or function $F(\alpha,\beta,\gamma;x)$ such that

$$F(\alpha,\beta,\gamma;x) = 1 + \frac{\alpha\beta}{1!\gamma}x + \frac{\alpha(\alpha+1)\beta(\beta+1)}{2!\gamma(\gamma+1)}x^2 + \frac{\alpha(\alpha+2)(\alpha+2)\beta(\beta+1)(\beta+2)}{3!\gamma(\gamma+1)(\gamma+2)}x^3 \cdots \tag{7.6.5}$$

(7.6.5) is an infinite series with many interesting and important properties depending on the choice of α, β, and γ. Of general interest is it that (7.6.5) converges for all $|x| < 1.0$ but diverges outside this interval. For negative integer values of α or β the series terminates after a finite number of terms; i.e., if α or β is equal to -2, the series terminates after x^2. The only restriction on the use of the hypergeometric function is that $\gamma \neq 0, -1, -2, -3, \ldots$.

It is of particular interest in the present discussion that a suitable choice of α, β, and γ will degenerate (7.6.5) to many well-known functions.

For $\alpha = 1$ and $\beta = \gamma$,

$$F(1,\beta,\beta;x) = 1 + x + x^2 + x^3 + \cdots + x^m + \cdots = \frac{1}{1-x}$$

Other special functions are

$$\begin{aligned}
F(\alpha,\beta,\beta;x) &= \frac{1}{(1-x)^\alpha} \\
F(-\alpha,1,1;x) &= (1+x)^\alpha \\
xF(1,1,2;x) &= \log(1-x) \\
xF(1,1,2;-x) &= \log(1+x) \\
2xF\left(\frac{1}{2},1,\frac{3}{2};x^2\right) &= \log\frac{1+x}{1-x} \\
xF\left(\frac{1}{2},\frac{1}{2},\frac{3}{2};x^2\right) &= \arcsin x \\
xF\left(\frac{1}{2},1,\frac{3}{2};-x^2\right) &= \arctan x
\end{aligned} \tag{7.6.6}$$

The hypergeometric function is also related to many polynomial functions such as the Legendre and Chebyshev polynomials. Letting $x = \frac{1}{2}(1-\lambda)$ maps the variable x from 0 to 1 to the new range in λ of -1 to $+1$. As a result

$$F\left(m+1,\ -m,\ 1;\ \frac{1-\lambda}{2}\right) = P_m(\lambda)$$
$$F\left(m,\ -m,\ \frac{1}{2};\ \frac{1-\lambda}{2}\right) = T_m(\lambda)$$

Variations on the standard form of the hypergeometric series (7.6.5) are also possible. As an example,

$$F_1(\beta,\gamma;x) = 1 + \frac{\beta x}{\gamma} + \frac{\beta(\beta+1)}{2!\gamma(\gamma+1)}x^2 + \frac{\beta(\beta+1)(\beta+2)}{3!\gamma(\gamma+1)(\gamma+2)}x^3 + \cdots \tag{7.6.7}$$

corresponds to the case of replacing x by x/α in (7.6.5) and letting $\alpha \to \infty$. In the same way (7.6.7) can be degenerated by replacing x with x/β and letting $\beta \to \infty$. This yields

$$F_2(\gamma;x) = 1 + \frac{x}{\gamma} + \frac{x^2}{2!\gamma(\gamma+1)} + \frac{x^3}{3!\gamma(\gamma+1)(\gamma+2)} + \cdots \tag{7.6.8}$$

Equations (7.6.7) and (7.6.8) are equivalent to removing first α in (7.6.5) and then β. Both $F_1(\beta,\gamma;x)$ and $F_2(\gamma;x)$ can be related to certain well-known functions. As an illustration,

$$F_1(1,1;x) = e^x \tag{7.6.9}$$

Taking the hypergeometric series defined by $F(\alpha, \beta + 1, \gamma + 1; x)$ and dividing by $F(\alpha,\beta,\gamma; x)$ leads to the continued-fraction expansion of Gauss.

$$\frac{F(\alpha, \beta + 1, \gamma + 1; x)}{F(\alpha,\beta,\gamma;x)} = \cfrac{1}{1 - \cfrac{\frac{\alpha(\gamma-\beta)}{\gamma(\gamma+1)}x}{1 - \cfrac{\frac{(\beta+1)(\gamma-\alpha+1)}{(\gamma+1)(\gamma+2)}x}{1 - \cfrac{\frac{(\alpha+1)(\gamma-\beta+1)}{(\gamma+2)(\gamma+3)}x}{1 - \cfrac{\frac{(\beta+2)(\gamma-\alpha+2)}{(\gamma+3)(\gamma+4)}x}{1 - \cdots}}}}} \tag{7.6.10}$$

By specifying a choice of α, β, and γ it is now possible to use (7.6.10) to obtain the continued-fraction expansion of many functions. To illustrate, from (7.6.6) note that

$$F\left(\frac{1}{2},1,\frac{3}{2};-x^2\right) = \frac{1}{x}\arctan x$$

The left side of (7.6.10) may be written as

$$\frac{F\left(\frac{1}{2},1,\frac{3}{2};-x^2\right)}{F\left(\frac{1}{2},0,\frac{1}{2};-x^2\right)}$$

and upon noting that $\beta = 0$ leads to

$$F\left(\frac{1}{2},0,\frac{1}{2};-x^2\right) = 1.0$$

there finally results

$$\frac{F\left(\frac{1}{2},1,\frac{3}{2};-x^2\right)}{1} = \frac{1}{x}\arctan x$$

Substituting the parameters $\alpha = \frac{1}{2}$, $\beta = 0$, $\gamma = \frac{1}{2}$, and $x = -x^2$ in the right-hand side of (7.6.10) thus leads to

$$F\left(\frac{1}{2},1,\frac{3}{2};-x^2\right) = \frac{1}{x}\arctan x = \cfrac{1}{1+\cfrac{\frac{1}{3}x^2}{1+\cfrac{\frac{4}{15}x^2}{1+\cfrac{\frac{9}{35}x^2}{1+\cfrac{\frac{16}{32}x^2}{\ddots}}}}}$$

or

$$F\left(\frac{1}{2},1,\frac{3}{2};-x^2\right) = \cfrac{1}{1+\cfrac{x^2}{3+\cfrac{4x^2}{5+\cfrac{9x^2}{7+\cfrac{16x^2}{\ddots}}}}}$$

This result may be written as

$$\arctan x = \cfrac{x}{1+\cfrac{x^2}{3+\cfrac{4x^2}{5+\cfrac{9x^2}{7+\cfrac{16x^2}{\ddots}}}}}$$

$$= \frac{x}{1+}\,\frac{x^2}{3+}\,\frac{(2x)^2}{5+}\,\frac{(3x)^2}{7+}\,\frac{(4x)^2}{9+}\cdots$$

In the same way, using (7.6.5) and (7.6.6) to (7.6.8) leads to the following continued-fraction expansions:

$$(1+x)^k = \frac{1}{1-}\,\frac{kx}{1+}\,\frac{\frac{(1+k)}{2}x}{1+}\,\frac{\frac{(1-k)}{2\times 3}x}{1+}\,\frac{\frac{2(2+k)}{3\times 4}x}{1}$$
$$+\frac{\frac{2(2-k)}{4\times 5}x}{1+}\cdots$$

$$\ln x = \frac{x-1}{1+}\;\frac{1^2(x-1)}{2+}\;\frac{1^2(x-1)}{3+}\;\frac{2^2(x-1)}{4+}\;\frac{2^2(x+1)}{5+}\;\cdots$$

$$e^x = \frac{1}{1-}\;\frac{x}{1+}\;\frac{x}{2-}\;\frac{x}{3+}\;\frac{x}{4-}\;\frac{x}{5+}\;\cdots$$

$$\tanh x = \frac{x}{1+}\;\frac{x^2}{3+}\;\frac{x^2}{5+}\;\frac{x^2}{7+}\;\cdots$$

$$\log\frac{1+x}{1-x} = \frac{2x}{1-}\;\frac{x^2}{3-}\;\frac{4x^2}{5-}\;\frac{9x^2}{7-}\;\cdots$$

$$\tan x = \frac{x}{1-}\;\frac{x^2}{3-}\;\frac{x^2}{5-}\;\frac{x^2}{7-}\;\cdots$$

These formulas are only representative samples of those which can be developed using this approach.

Once the continued-fraction expansion of a function has been obtained, the question of how to evaluate this expansion in an efficient manner arises. The most obvious procedure is to use the definition given by (7.6.3). A value of m to terminate the infinite expansion having been chosen, the method works backward by calculating the sequence c_{m-r} and d_{m-r} such that

$$\begin{aligned} d_m &= b_m & c_m &= \frac{a_m}{d_m} \\ d_{m-1} &= b_{m-1} + c_m & c_{m-1} &= \frac{a_{m-1}}{d_{m-1}} \\ d_{m-2} &= b_{m-2} + c_{m-1} & c_{m-2} &= \frac{a_{m-2}}{d_{m-2}} \\ &\cdots\cdots\cdots\cdots\cdots\cdots \end{aligned}$$

This may be written simply as

$$\begin{aligned} c_{m+1} &= 0 \\ \left.\begin{aligned} d_{m-r} &= b_{m-r} + c_{m-r+1} \\ c_{m-r} &= \frac{a_{m-r}}{d_{m-r}} \end{aligned}\right\} & \qquad r = 0, 1, 2, \ldots, m-1 \end{aligned}$$

and finally

$$\phi_m(x) = b_0 + c_1$$

Unfortunately, this procedure requires the a priori fixing of the m to use. To repeat the process for a new m requires that the entire computation be repeated. Thus this method is really an inefficient one.

An alternative method is to compute successive approximants $\phi_0(x)$, $\phi_1(x)$, $\phi_2(x)$, . . . This does not require any a priori choice of m, and the proper m can be chosen during the single computation. By letting

$$\phi_m(x) = \frac{A_m}{B_m}$$

and using

$$A_0 = b_0 \qquad B_0 = 1$$
$$A_1 = b_0 b_1 + a_1 \qquad B_1 = b_1$$

the two recurrence relations

$$\left.\begin{aligned} A_r &= b_r A_{r-1} + a_r A_{r-2} \\ B_r &= b_r A_{r-1} + a_r B_{r-2} \end{aligned}\right\} \qquad r = 2, 3, \ldots, m \tag{7.6.11}$$

can be used to evaluate the successive approximants. As a general rule each additional approximant will yield approximately one more correct decimal place than the previous approximant.

In the manner outlined it is possible to derive the continued-fraction expansion for many analytic functions. Since the evaluation of the expansion is relatively simple and since it converges at least as fast as the corresponding power-series representation, this is a most efficient approximation. The applicability of the continued fraction can frequently be ascertained by merely looking at the power series. As pointed out by Teichroew (41), a function whose power series is rapidly convergent or has the form $x^r/r!$ is not too amenable to continued-fraction expansion, since both approximations converge at about the same rate. If, however, the power series converges slowly or has the form x^r/r, the continued-fraction expansion will be quite superior and will converge much faster. As an example, the evaluation of $\ln x$ to nine decimal places requires approximately 95,000 terms of the power series and 550 of the continued-fraction expansion for $x = 0.001$. In this case an attempt to use the power series close to a singular point $x = 0$ is not feasible; on the other hand the circle of convergence for the fraction expansion is larger, and thus the technique works adequately. In the same way the power series cannot be used for $\arctan x$, $x > 1.0$, whereas the continued-fraction expansion will yield valid results.

The error problems associated with the use of continued fractions are usually negligible. The round-off error is usually small, and the truncation error (resulting from the finite approximant) can be minimized by making m sufficiently large. It should also be pointed out that it is possible to have a number of different continued-fraction expansions for the same function. To illustrate, the expansion for e^x by Gauss' approach has been shown to be

$$e^x = \frac{1}{1-}\,\frac{x}{1+}\,\frac{x}{2-}\,\frac{x}{3+}\,\frac{x}{4-}\,\frac{x}{5+}\cdots$$

However, upon noting that

$$e^x = \frac{1 + \tanh (x/2)}{1 - \tanh (x/2)} = 1 + \frac{x}{-\frac{x}{2} + \frac{x}{2} \coth \frac{x}{2}}$$

there results

$$e^x = \frac{1}{1 +} \frac{2x}{2 - x +} \frac{x^2}{6 +} \frac{x^2}{10 +} \frac{x^2}{14 +} \cdots$$

which converges faster than the previous formula. In the same way Macon (27) has shown that

$$e^x = 1 + \frac{x}{1 - x/2 + F}$$

where $$F = \frac{x^2/4 \cdot 3}{1} + \frac{x^2/4 \cdot 15}{1} + \frac{x^2/4 \cdot 35}{1} + \cdots$$

is a better expansion than the original one.

Since it has already been pointed out that any polynomial (a truncated power series) may be converted to a more efficient, or "best-fit," form by means of the Chebyshev polynomial, the question arises as to whether or not the coefficients of a continued fraction cannot also be "best fitted." In other words, if

$$\phi_m(x) = b_0 + \frac{a_1 x}{b_1 +} \frac{a_2 x}{b_2 +} \frac{a_3 x}{b_3 +} \cdots$$

can an analogous expression

$$\phi_m^*(x) = b_0^* + \frac{a_1^* x}{b_1^* +} \frac{a_2^* x}{b_2^* +} \frac{a_3^* x}{b_3^* +} \cdots$$

be written in which the b_0^*, b_1^*, . . . and a_1^*, a_2^*, . . . are adjusted coefficients such that $\phi_m^*(x)$ is a better fit than $\phi_m(x)$? The motivation for asking this question lies in the fact that the mth approximant of a continued fraction can be expressed as the ratio of two polynomials

$$\phi_m(x) = \frac{c_0 + c_1 x + \cdots + c_n x^n}{d_0 + d_1 x + \cdots + d_{n-1} x^{n-1}} \qquad m = 2n$$
$$= \frac{P_n(x)}{Q_{n-1}(x)}$$

where m = even and $P_n(x)$ and $Q_n(x)$ are nth- and $(n - 1)$st-degree polynomials. The answer to the question posed is "yes," and a best-fit continued fraction can actually be obtained. However, it is felt that the details of this manipulation go beyond the present discussion. All that is desired at this point is to bring the possibility of such an approach to the reader's attention. For further details see Maehly (28).

7.7. Numerical Examples

Example 7.1. Dow and Jacob (14) proposed the following dimensionless equation as a suitable representation for experimental data dealing with heat transfer between a vertical tube and a fluidized air-solid mixture,

$$\frac{h_m D_t}{k_g} = a_1 \left(\frac{D_t}{L}\right)^{a_2} \left(\frac{D_t}{D_p}\right)^{a_3} \left(\frac{1 - \epsilon}{\epsilon} \frac{\rho_s C_s}{\rho_g C_g}\right)^{a_4} \left(\frac{D_t G}{\mu_g}\right)^{a_5} \tag{7.7.1}$$

where h_m = heat-transfer coefficient
D_t = tube diameter
D_p = solid-particle diameter
L = heated fluidized bed length
ϵ = void fraction of fluid bed
G = gas mass velocity
k_g, ρ_g, C_g, μ_g = properties of gas phase
C_s, ρ_s = properties of solid phase

The constants $a_1, a_2, \ldots, a_5$ must be fitted to the experimental data. Eighteen sets of data are available, and these may be summarized as in Table 7.1.

TABLE 7.1

$\frac{h_m D_t}{k_g}$	$\frac{D_t}{L}$	$\frac{D_t}{D_p}$	$\frac{1-\epsilon}{\epsilon}\frac{\rho_s C_s}{\rho_g C_g}$	$\frac{D_t G}{\mu_g}$
469	0.636	309	833	256
913	0.636	309	868	555
1,120	0.641	309	800	786
234	0.285	309	800	255
487	0.285	309	800	555
709	0.283	309	767	850
581	0.518	683	795	254
650	0.521	683	795	300
885	0.524	683	795	440
672	0.455	1,012	867	338
986	0.451	1,012	867	565
1,310	0.455	1,012	867	811
1,190	0.944	1,130	1,608	343
1,890	0.974	1,130	1,608	573
2,460	0.985	1,130	1,608	814
915	0.602	1,130	1,673	343
1,260	0.602	1,130	1,673	485
1,690	0.617	1,130	1,673	700

Equation (7.7.1) is equivalent to (7.2.1) and may be written as

$$\ln y = \ln a_1 + a_2 \ln N_1 + a_3 \ln N_2 + a_4 \ln N_3 + a_5 \ln N_4$$

or

$$\phi = b_1x_1 + b_2x_2 + b_3x_3 + b_4x_4 + b_5x_5 \tag{7.7.2}$$

In these equations

$$\phi = \ln y \qquad x_1 = 1.0 \qquad y = \frac{h_m D_t}{k_g}$$

$$b_1 = \ln a_1 \qquad x_2 = \ln N_1 \qquad N_1 = \frac{D_t}{L}$$

$$b_2 = a_2 \qquad x_3 = \ln N_2 \qquad N_2 = \frac{D_t}{D_p}$$

$$b_3 = a_3 \qquad x_4 = \ln N_3 \qquad N_3 = \frac{1-\epsilon}{\epsilon}\,\frac{\rho_s C_s}{\rho_g C_g}$$

$$b_4 = a_4 \qquad x_5 = \ln N_4 \qquad N_4 = \frac{D_t G}{\mu_g}$$

$$b_5 = a_5$$

In the form (7.7.2) the coefficients $b_1, b_2, \ldots, b_5$ can be determined by a least-square fit to the experimental data. The $a_1, a_2, \ldots, a_5$ can then be evaluated. Let

$$\mathbf{b} = \begin{bmatrix} b_1 \\ b_2 \\ \cdot \\ \cdot \\ \cdot \\ b_5 \end{bmatrix} \qquad \mathbf{y} = \begin{bmatrix} \ln y(1) \\ \ln y(2) \\ \cdot \\ \cdot \\ \cdot \\ \ln y(N) \end{bmatrix} \qquad \mathbf{X} = \begin{bmatrix} x_1(1) & x_2(1) & \cdots & x_5(1) \\ x_1(2) & x_2(2) & \cdots & x_5(2) \\ \cdot & \cdot & \cdots & \cdot \\ x_1(N) & x_2(N) & \cdots & x_5(N) \end{bmatrix}$$

where $\mathbf{y}$ represents the experimental N sets of response data. In the present case $N = 18$. The least-square determination of $b_1, b_2, \ldots, b_5$ follows now from a premultiplication by $\mathbf{X}^T$ of $\mathbf{Xb}$ and $\mathbf{y}$,

$$\mathbf{X}^T\mathbf{X}\mathbf{b} = \mathbf{X}^T\mathbf{y} \tag{7.7.3}$$

and an inversion and multiplication,

$$\mathbf{b} = (\mathbf{X}^T\mathbf{X})^{-1}\mathbf{X}^T\mathbf{y} \tag{7.7.4}$$

Upon performing the indicated matrix operations above, the final values of $a_1, a_2, \ldots, a_5$ are given by

$$a_1 = 1.449$$
$$a_2 = 0.7571$$
$$a_3 = 0.3319$$
$$a_4 = -0.001875$$
$$a_5 = 0.7733$$

These values correspond approximately to the numbers proposed by Dow and Jakob. Table 7.2 lists the actual numerical values of the various matrices and vectors of (7.7.3) and (7.7.4). Note that the matrix $(\mathbf{X}^T\mathbf{X})$ is matrix I of Example 5.1; many features of this matrix, including the inverse, were discussed in this previous example.

This problem was carried out on the IBM 704 in floating-point mode. The calculation is quite straightforward and required only about 2 sec of machine time exclusive of input and output.

TABLE 7.2. THE VARIOUS MATRICES AND VECTORS ASSOCIATED WITH THE LEAST-SQUARE FIT OF HEAT-TRANSFER DATA

X

1.0000000	−0.4525567	5.7333412	6.7250336	5.4595855
1.0000000	−0.4525567	5.7333412	6.7661917	6.3189681
1.0000000	−0.4447258	5.7333412	6.6846117	6.6669567
1.0000000	−1.2552661	5.7333412	6.6846117	5.5412635
1.0000000	−1.2552661	5.7333412	6.6846117	6.3189681
1.0000000	−1.2623084	5.7333412	6.6424868	6.7452363
1.0000000	−0.6577800	6.5264948	6.6783420	5.5373343
1.0000000	−0.6520052	6.5264948	6.6783420	5.7037824
1.0000000	−0.6462636	6.5264948	6.6783420	6.0867746
1.0000000	−0.7874579	6.9196838	6.7650389	5.8230458
1.0000000	−0.7962879	6.9196838	6.7650389	6.3368257
1.0000000	−0.7874579	6.9196838	6.7650389	6.6982680
1.0000000	−0.0576291	7.0299729	7.3827464	5.8377303
1.0000000	−0.0263440	7.0299729	7.3827464	6.3508856
1.0000000	−0.0151136	7.0299729	7.3827464	6.7019603
1.0000000	−0.5074978	7.0299729	7.4223737	5.8377303
1.0000000	−0.5074978	7.0299729	7.4223737	6.1841488
1.0000000	−0.4828863	7.0299729	7.4223737	6.5510803

$\mathbf{X}^T\mathbf{X}$

18.0000000	−11.0469009	116.9184217	124.9330502	110.7005453
−11.0469009	9.2544317	−69.7708397	−75.1989851	−67.7681227
116.9184217	−69.7708397	765.1817856	813.8419876	719.3762970
124.9330502	−75.1989851	813.8419876	869.0698929	768.7408600
110.7005453	−67.7681227	719.3762970	768.7408600	684.0605316

$[\mathbf{X}^T\mathbf{X}]^{-1}$

56.0077229	4.1650779	0.2768109	−6.7956548	−1.3052348
4.1650800	0.7478976	−0.0514011	−0.5112006	0.0286004
0.2768260	−0.0514001	0.3472523	−0.3826930	0.0149967
−6.7956818	−0.5112020	−0.3826916	1.3850333	−0.1049467
−1.3052202	0.0286014	0.0149974	−0.1049495	0.3176868

$\mathbf{X}^T\mathbf{y}$	**b**
122.2291040	0.3566895
−72.3527756	0.7570875
797.5894547	0.3318896
850.5574417	−0.0018749
754.4610748	0.7732735

Example 7.2. In an analysis of the fluidization of solid glass spheres in water by Struve, Lapidus, and Elgin (39) data were reported for the fraction holdup of the solid phase, $1 - \epsilon$, versus the slip velocity V_s. The slip velocity is the vectorial difference between the fluid and the solids velocity. The data are available for two different modes of operating a fluidized bed; a batch-fluidized system in which there is no continuous addition or removal of solids and the cocurrent-countergravity system in which there is a continuous addition and removal of both solids and liquid at the bottom and top of the fluidized bed. The explicit data are given in Table 7.3.

TABLE 7.3

Batch fluidization		Cocurrent-countergravity fluidization			
$1 - \epsilon$	V_s	$1 - \epsilon$	V_s	$1 - \epsilon$	V_s
0.455	0.127	0.519	0.02	0.254	0.55
0.404	0.184	0.422	0.10	0.247	0.57
0.364	0.239	0.467	0.13	0.221	0.58
0.336	0.304	0.411	0.24	0.240	0.60
0.308	0.370	0.341	0.26	0.221	0.61
0.278	0.426	0.343	0.27	0.244	0.61
0.256	0.484	0.343	0.30	0.211	0.62
0.236	0.538	0.357	0.32	0.221	0.63
0.216	0.588	0.335	0.34	0.226	0.63
0.196	0.643	0.276	0.35	0.230	0.63
0.180	0.694	0.282	0.44	0.137	0.84
0.149	0.787	0.285	0.46	0.111	0.88
0.122	0.878	0.267	0.47	0.104	1.04
0.098	0.970	0.294	0.48	0.0679	1.07
0.075	1.059	0.237	0.49	0.0456	1.12

According to the theoretical postulates of the authors the plot of V_s versus $1 - \epsilon$ should be identical for both modes of operating the fluidized bed. To test this hypothesis each set of data is to be fitted with a least-square polynomial and the resulting two polynomials compared. The form of the least-square polynomial is

$$\phi_m = \sum_{i=0}^{m} a_i(1 - \epsilon)^i \qquad m = 1, 2, \ldots \tag{7.7.5}$$

with the variance of (7.2.2),

$$\sigma_m{}^2 = \frac{S_m{}^2}{N - (m + 1)}$$

used as a criterion for deciding on the upper limit of m.

The basic procedure is straightforward. Using the batch-fluidization data with $m = 5$ and $N = 15$ as an example, the matrix system

$$\mathbf{X}^T\mathbf{X}\mathbf{a} = \mathbf{X}^T\mathbf{v} \tag{7.7.6}$$

is first formed, where

$$\mathbf{a} = \begin{bmatrix} a_0 \\ a_1 \\ \cdot \\ \cdot \\ \cdot \\ a_5 \end{bmatrix} = 6 \times 1 \qquad \mathbf{v} = \begin{bmatrix} V_s(1) \\ V_s(2) \\ \cdot \\ \cdot \\ \cdot \\ V_s(15) \end{bmatrix} = 15 \times 1$$

$$\mathbf{X} = \begin{bmatrix} 1.0 & (1-\epsilon)_1 & (1-\epsilon)_1{}^2 & \cdots & (1-\epsilon)_1{}^5 \\ 1.0 & (1-\epsilon)_2 & (1-\epsilon)_2{}^2 & \cdots & (1-\epsilon)_2{}^5 \\ \cdots & \cdots & \cdots & \cdots & \cdots \\ 1.0 & \cdots & \cdots & \cdots & (1-\epsilon)_{15}{}^5 \end{bmatrix} = 15 \times 6$$

$V_s(2)$ indicates that this is the experimental value of V_s corresponding to the experimental $(1 - \epsilon)_2$. The **X** matrix is formed from successive powers of $1 - \epsilon$. It then follows that

$$\mathbf{a} = [\mathbf{X}^T\mathbf{X}]^{-1}\mathbf{X}^T\mathbf{v}$$

yields the vector containing the values $a_0, a_1, \ldots, a_5$. The residuals R_i can be calculated by back substitution into (7.7.5) and in turn $\sigma_m{}^2$ calculated by using

$$S_m{}^2 = \sum_{i=1}^{15} R_i{}^2$$

To illustrate, Table 7.4 shows the **X** matrix for this case, the upper elements of $\mathbf{X}^T\mathbf{X}$, and the values of $\mathbf{X}^T\mathbf{v}$. The same procedure, of course, follows for the cocurrent-countergravity data except that $N = 30$.

Table 7.5 lists the calculated values of $a_0, a_1, \ldots, a_m$ for both modes of fluidization and the associated variance. It can be seen that the variance is smaller for the batch data than for the cocurrent data; this is to be expected, since the former are obtained experimentally with greater accuracy. In the case of the batch fluidization the values for $a_0, a_1, \ldots$ remain essentially constant through $m = 3$, but for $m = 4$ and 5 the values begin to deviate widely; that is, $a_2 = 3.5995$, 3.5225, 15.2635, and 10.0784 as $m = 2$, 3, 4, and 5. At the same time, however, $\sigma_m{}^2$ for $m = 4$ and 5 is lower than any of the others. Unfortunately, there does not seem any clean-cut way to make a decision on whether to pick $m = 2$ or $m = 4$ as the best approximation to the data (the case $m = 3$ is essentially equivalent to $m = 2$ because of the small value of a_3). Thus the two possibilities

$$V_s = 1.3618 - 4.3615(1-\epsilon) + 3.5995(1-\epsilon)^2 \qquad (A)$$

$$V_s = 1.4405 - 6.0441(1-\epsilon) + 15.2635(1-\epsilon)^2 - 32.1454(1-\epsilon)^2 + 30.4430(1-\epsilon)^4 \qquad (B)$$

exist for the batch-fluidization data.

Actually it is possible at this point to surmise that (A) is the better fit to the experimental data. The large decrease in the variance occurs in going from $m = 1$ to $m = 2$; after this point the variance merely fluctuates in value but never decreases by any significant amount. Since rounding errors probably affect the calculation as the degree of the polynomial increases, this fluctuation is really expected.

TABLE 7.4. MATRICES AND VECTORS INVOLVED IN LEAST-SQUARE FIT OF BATCH-FLUIDIZATION DATA, $m = 5$

X

1 10000000	0 45499999	0 20702500	−1 94196372	−1 42859349	−1 19501004
1 10000000	0 40400000	0 16321600	−1 65939262	−1 26639462	−1 10762343
1 10000000	0 36399999	0 13249600	−1 48228542	−1 17555189	−2 63900886
1 10000000	0 33600000	0 11289600	−1 37933055	−1 12745506	−2 42824901
1 10000000	0 30800000	−1 94863998	−1 29218111	−2 89991781	−2 27717468
1 10000000	0 27800000	−1 77283998	−1 21484951	−2 59728163	−2 16604429
1 10000000	0 25600000	−1 65535998	−1 16777215	−2 42949670	−2 10995115
1 10000000	0 23600000	−1 55695999	−1 13144256	−2 31020443	−3 73208246
1 10000000	0 21600000	−1 46655999	−1 10077695	−2 21767822	−3 47018495
1 10000000	0 19600000	−1 38415999	−2 75295357	−2 14757890	−3 28925463
1 10000000	0 18000000	−1 32399999	−2 58319998	−2 10497600	−3 18895679
1 10000000	0 14900000	−1 22200999	−2 33079488	−3 49288437	−4 73439770
1 10000000	0 12200000	−1 14884000	−2 18158479	−3 22153345	−4 27027080
1 10000000	−1 97999999	−2 96039997	−3 94119196	−4 92236812	−5 90392073
1 10000000	−1 74999999	−2 56249998	−3 42187498	−4 31640623	−5 23730467

$\mathbf{X}^T\mathbf{X}$

15.00000	3.67299	1.07880	0.35685	0.12770	0.048260
	1.07880	0.35685	0.12770	0.048260	0.018963
		0.12770	0.048260	0.018963	0.007669
			0.018963	0.007669	0.003170
				0.003170	0.001333
					0.000567

$\mathbf{X}^T\mathbf{v}$
8.29099
1.58134
0.37245
0.102681
0.031699
0.010631

The changes in the a_i for the cocurrent-countergravity fluidization start at $m = 3$; from the variance values the logical choice is $m = 2$. Thus

$$V_s = 1.3164 - 3.7289(1 - \epsilon) + 2.3710(1 - \epsilon)^2 \qquad (C)$$

is the best approximation.

A comparison of (A) and (B) with (C) indicates that (A) and (C) are quite similar, with the coefficients of almost the same magnitude. The final choice of a suitable approximation to the data is thus (A) and/or (C).

This problem was run on the IBM 704 in floating-point mode. Exclusive of output, the computation time for all the calculations was less than 1 min.

TABLE 7.5. LEAST-SQUARE COEFFICIENTS AND VARIANCE FOR TWO MODES OF FLUIDIZATION

Batch Fluidization

	m = 1	2	3	4	5
a_0	1.1654	1.3618	1.3607	1.4405	1.4206
a_1	−2.5019	−4.3615	−4.3437	− 6.0441	− 5.5066
a_2	....	3.5995	3.5225	15.2635	10.0784
a_3	....	....	0.09779	−32.1454	− 9.3871
a_4	....	....	....	30.4430	−15.7255
a_5	....	....	....	....	35.0779
σ_m^2	2.448×10^{-3}	3.557×10^{-5}	3.911×10^{-5}	2.209×10^{-5}	2.429×10^{-5}

Cocurrent-countergravity Fluidization

	m = 1	2	3	4	5
a_0	1.1680	1.3164	1.2742	1.2157	1.2778
a_1	−2.4362	−3.7289	−3.0200	− 1.6302	− 3.5788
a_2	....	2.3710	−0.6607	−10.1630	9.6185
a_3	....	....	3.6560	28.4583	− 58.2696
a_4	....	....	....	−21.7899	148.3813
a_5	....	....	....	....	−122.3426
σ_m^2	4.040×10^{-3}	2.409×10^{-3}	2.444×10^{-3}	2.512×10^{-3}	2.603×10^{-3}

Example 7.3. This example repeats part of Example 7.2, but using the orthogonal polynomial representation of Forsythe, (7.3.8). Only the cocurrent-countergravity fluidization data are used. From (7.3.1) it can be seen that an equation of the form

$$V_s = b_0P_0 + b_1P_1 + \cdots + b_mP_m \tag{7.7.7}$$

is used to fit the experimental data. The $b_0, b_1, \ldots, b_m$ are to be determined with $P_i = P_i(1 - \epsilon)$.

The method of calculation is quite direct. For $m = 5$ and

$$r_{00} = \sum_1^{30} P_0(x)P_0(x) = \sum_1^{30} 1.0 = 30.0$$

the values α_1, s_0, r_{11}, and β_1 are evaluated in order. Thus, from (7.3.10),

$$\alpha_1 = \frac{\sum_1^{30} x_iP_0(x_i)^2}{\sum_1^{30} P_0(x_i)^2} = \frac{\sum_1^{30} x_i}{30}$$

since $P_0(x_i) = 1.0$. The x_i's are interpreted, of course, as $(1 - \epsilon)_i$. s_0 is obtained from

$$s_0 = \sum_1^{30} V_s(i)P_0(x_i) = \sum_1^{30} V_s(i)$$

and r_{11} from

$$r_{11} = \sum_1^{30} P_1(x_i)P_1(x_i)$$

Finally, β_1 is calculated by using (7.3.11) in the form

$$\beta_1 = \frac{\sum_1^{30} x_iP_1(x_i)P_0(x_i)}{\sum_1^{30} P_0(x_i)^2} = \frac{\sum_1^{30} x_iP_1(x_i)}{30}$$

The entire sequence is repeated for α_2, s_1, . . . until finally s_5 and r_{55} are known. At this point b_0, b_1, . . . , b_5 and σ_0^2, σ_1^2, . . . , σ_5^2 can be calculated. All the pertinent formulas are listed in Sec. 7.3. In performing the calculations simple subroutines for $P_1(x)$, $P_2(x)$, . . . are quite useful.

TABLE 7.6. RESULTS OF ORTHOGONAL POLYNOMIAL FIT OF COCURRENT-COUNTERGRAVITY FLUIDIZATION DATA

$\alpha_1, \ldots, \alpha_5$	$\beta_1, \ldots, \beta_4$	$s_0, \ldots, s_5$	$r_{00}, \ldots, r_{55}$	$b_0, \ldots, b_5$	$\sigma_0^2, \ldots, \sigma_5^2$
0.265317	1.170052×10^{-2}	15.650000	30.0	0.521667	7.560059×10^{-2}
0.279893	2.352848×10^{-2}	−0.855150	0.351015	−2.436217	3.895906×10^{-3}
0.284022	1.403898×10^{-2}	1.958208×10^{-2}	8.258866×10^{-3}	2.371037	2.320576×10^{-3}
0.308956	1.485243×10^{-2}	4.239953×10^{-4}	1.159460×10^{-4}	3.656834	2.350195×10^{-3}
0.251813		-3.750691×10^{-5}	1.722080×10^{-6}	− 21.780004	2.411527×10^{-3}
		-3.477278×10^{-6}	2.864277×10^{-8}	−121.4016	2.494418×10^{-3}

The results of this calculation are listed in Table 7.6. Note that the values σ_1^2, σ_2^2, . . . , σ_5^2 show a marked similarity to the equivalent values in Table 7.4. From these data the case $m = 2$, $\sigma_2^2 = 2.3205 \times 10^{-3}$, gives the best fit. Thus

$$V_s = 0.5217P_0 - 2.4362P_1 + 2.3710P_2 \tag{7.7.8}$$

is the appropriate least-square approximation. Equation (7.7.8) can be converted in terms of $1 - \epsilon$ by using the data in Table 7.6 and

$$P_0 = 1.0$$
$$P_1 = x - \alpha_1 = x - 0.265$$
$$P_2 = (x - \alpha_2)P_1 - \beta_1 = (x - 0.280)(x - 0.265) - 0.0170$$

On this basis (numbers rounded to three significant figures), (7.7.8) becomes

$$V_s = 1.31 - 3.73(1 - \epsilon) + 2.37(1 - \epsilon)^2$$

Comparison with (C) of Example 7.2 shows complete agreement.

Note that the present method yielded all the $b_0, b_1, \ldots, b_m$ without any matrix manipulations. The computation time on the IBM 704 was about 10 sec.

Example 7.4. One of the more important problems which the chemical engineer is called upon to solve involves the static, or steady-state, optimization of chemical processes. This implies the determination of the specific values of the independent variables (flow rates, temperatures, etc.) which optimize the response of the process, i.e., maximize the yield or minimize the cost (see Chap. 8). This operation may be stated in a more quantitative fashion as given,

$$y = f(x_1,x_2, \ldots ,x_m) \tag{7.7.9}$$

to minimize (or maximize) the response function y by a systematic manipulation of the independent variables $x_1, x_2, \ldots, x_m$; y and the $x_1, x_2, \ldots, x_m$ may or may not be constrained. The functional relationship $f(x_1,x_2, \ldots ,x_m)$ is usually highly nonlinear, with the exact form unknown.

The use of steepest-descent (ascent) and gradient techniques has found wide applicability in locating the optimum condition; one approach using a least-square formulation is illustrated here. Consider a chemical process with a single optimum (minimum or maximum) value, with the requirement that the process be "moved" to this point from a current nonoptimum point. This may be accomplished by changing the independent variables a small amount and noting the corresponding response of the system. From a number of such changes around the current nonoptimum point it is possible to calculate a direction in which to move the process so as to decrease (or increase) the response most rapidly toward the optimum point. After determining the direction, a step is taken in this direction. The term step indicates that the process is moved from one set of values of the independent variables to a different set. The difference between the new and old set of values is known as the step size. After moving this one step a new estimate of best direction is made and another step taken along this direction. This procedure is continued until either the optimum or the neighborhood of the optimum is reached.

A least-square approach to this gradient technique may be achieved by fitting a linear approximation to the response surface (y versus $x_1, x_2, \ldots, x_m$) in the form

$$\phi(t_r) = a_0 + a_1x_1(t_r) + a_2x_2(t_r) + \cdots + a_mx_m(t_r) \tag{7.7.10}$$

[Note that this equation has the form of (7.2.4).] In (7.7.10), t_r represents the rth experiment or set of values of the independent variables, which may be flow rates, concentrations, temperatures, etc. The coefficients $a_0, a_1, \ldots, a_m$ are taken as $a_i = \partial\phi/\partial x_i$, $i = 1, 2, \ldots, m$, or as partial derivatives of the response function to changes in an independent variable. This results from a multivariable Taylor series expansion of ϕ in terms of the x_i and a truncation after the first derivative. If the $a_0, a_1, \ldots, a_m$ can be estimated in some manner, they will yield the direction that will minimize (maximize) y for changes in the x_i. Equation (7.7.10) can be written in matrix form as

$$\phi(t_r) = \mathbf{x}(t_r)^T\mathbf{a}$$

where

$$\mathbf{x}(t_r) = \begin{bmatrix} x_1 \\ x_2 \\ \cdot \\ \cdot \\ \cdot \\ x_m \end{bmatrix} \qquad \mathbf{a} = \begin{bmatrix} a_0 \\ a_1 \\ \cdot \\ \cdot \\ \cdot \\ a_m \end{bmatrix}$$

and following (7.2.5) the least-square fit for **a** can be obtained from

$$\mathbf{a} = \Big[\sum_{r=1}^{N} \mathbf{x}(t_r)\mathbf{x}(t_r)^T \Big]^{-1} \Big[\sum_{r=1}^{N} \mathbf{x}(t_r)y(t_r) \Big] \tag{7.7.11}$$

or, with the weighting factor α, $0 \leq \alpha \leq 1$, introduced,

$$\mathbf{a} = \Big[\sum_{r=1}^{N} \alpha^{N-r}\mathbf{x}(t_r)\mathbf{x}(t_r)^T \Big]^{-1} \Big[\sum_{r=1}^{N} \alpha^{N-r}\mathbf{x}(t_r)y(t_r) \Big] \tag{7.7.12}$$

If a set of $m + 1$ experiments is made around the current nonoptimum point, sufficient information is available to estimate **a** and a step is made toward the optimum value. This may be accomplished by using the gradient equation

$$\mathbf{x}(t_{r+1}) = \mathbf{x}(t_r) - \lambda(t_r)\mathbf{a} \tag{7.7.13}$$

where $\lambda(t_r)$ is a positive scalar representing the magnitude of the step size. Once the initial $m + 1$ experiments have been performed, the least-square procedure becomes self-perpetuating as given by (7.2.6) and (7.2.7) in the form

$$\begin{aligned} \mathbf{B}_N &= \sum_{r=1}^{N} \mathbf{x}(t_r)\mathbf{x}(t_r)^T \\ \mathbf{B}_{N+1} &= \mathbf{B}_N + \mathbf{x}(t_{N+1})\mathbf{x}(t_{N+1})^T \end{aligned} \tag{7.7.14}$$

or, with the weighting factor,

$$\begin{aligned} \mathbf{B}_N &= \sum_{r=1}^{N} \alpha^{N-r}\mathbf{x}(t_r)\mathbf{x}(t_r)^T \\ \mathbf{B}_{N+1} &= \alpha\mathbf{B}_N + \mathbf{x}(t_{N+1})\mathbf{x}(t_{N+1})^T \end{aligned} \tag{7.7.15}$$

To illustrate the use of these equations, the simple nonlinear equation

$$y = 1 + x_1 + x_2 + x_3 + \frac{4}{x_1} + \frac{9}{x_2} + \frac{16}{x_3} \tag{7.7.16}$$

is used for a hypothetical process (35). Note that $m = 3$. The optimum condition for (7.7.16) is $y_{\text{optimum}} = 19$ with $x_1 = 2$, $x_2 = 3$, and $x_3 = 4$ and the x_i constrained as $x_i > 0$. Further, the value of $\lambda(t_r)$ in (7.7.13) is taken as a constant $\lambda(t_r) = 1.0$ and $\alpha = 0.90$. These values are used for convenience. It is important to realize that so far as the gradient calculation is concerned (7.7.16) is used only to yield a y for any set of x_1, x_2, and x_3, that is, to behave as if it were a real process.

To start the calculation, four random sets of values of x_1, x_2, and x_3 are used in (7.7.16) to calculate $y(t_r)$. From these values (7.7.12) can be used with $N - r = 0$ to calculate **a**. From (7.7.13), using $\mathbf{x}(t_4)$ and $\lambda = 1.0$, a new value of $\mathbf{x}(t_5)$ can be calculated in the direction of the optimum. This is followed by $y(t_5)$. Some of these intermediate values and results are given in Table 7.7. Note that the square 4×4 matrix $\mathbf{x}(t_r)\mathbf{x}(t_r)^T$ must be evaluated. Because of the random initial guess for the $\mathbf{x}(t_1)$, $\mathbf{x}(t_2)$, $\mathbf{x}(t_3)$, and $\mathbf{x}(t_4)$ the first value obtained is $y(t_5) = 45.805081$. In actual

TABLE 7.7. FIRST SET OF INITIAL EXPERIMENTS FOR GRADIENT METHOD TOWARD AN OPTIMUM OF (7.7.16)

$\mathbf{x}(t_1)$	$\mathbf{x}(t_2)$	$\mathbf{x}(t_3)$	$\mathbf{x}(t_4)$
1.000000	1.000000	1.000000	1.000000
12.615851	18.580017	7.051682	17.793737
23.137424	21.875897	9.886950	15.962744
16.134773	22.507295	10.345803	11.560760
$\mathbf{x}(t_r)\mathbf{x}(t_r)^T$			
3.439000	48.387020	59.447658	50.865141
48.387020	757.023887	888.806565	758.490290
59.447658	888.806565	1,120.678386	947.566686
50.865141	758.490290	947.566686	830.092919

$\mathbf{a}$	$\mathbf{x}(t_5)$
5.338877	1.000000
0.963881	16.829856
0.930932	15.031812
0.963587	10.597173

$y(t_5)$
45.805081

practice knowledge about the process would allow much better first estimates. Table 7.8 shows some further results as the procedure is continued. After the initial value has gone above the correct optimum, the succeeding values are proceeding toward the optimum of $y = 19.0$. Further calculations (data not shown) reveal that after 36 steps the value of $y(t_{36})$ was equal to the known optimum value within three decimal places.

Actually only the simplest details of the gradient method have been presented here. Equation (7.7.13) may be written in more general form as

$$\mathbf{x}(t_{r+1}) = \mathbf{x}(t_r) - \lambda(t_r)\mathbf{G}(t_r)$$

where $\mathbf{G}(t_r)$ is a general direction vector. Choosing $G(t_r) = \mathbf{a}$ (equal to the vector of first partial derivatives) is the most obvious method for estimating $\mathbf{G}(t_r)$ and was proposed by Cauchy many years ago. Another possibility is due to Newton and sets $\mathbf{G}(t_r)$ equal to a vector whose elements compose various mixed second partial derivatives. Further, one might use different values for $\lambda(t_r)$ instead of the constant in the present example. These might be determined by consideration of the magnitude of the angle θ between successive evaluations of $\mathbf{G}(t_r)$.

There is one further point of interest to be mentioned before leaving this example. The reader will note that a linear approximation (7.7.10) was fitted to the nonlinear process; on this basis a "look and then step" procedure is necessary to move to the optimum condition. If, however, the process is actually linear, then theoretically, at least, the optimum can be located in a much more direct fashion (the gradient vector is now a constant and does not change from step to step). Details for this linear approach are given in Chap. 8 under the heading Linear Programming.

TABLE 7.8. FURTHER SETS OF EXPERIMENTS FOR GRADIENT METHOD

a	$\mathbf{x}(t_6)$	$y(t_6)$
5.350806	1.000000	43.151609
0.965836	15.864020	
0.930892	14.100920	
0.961378	9.635794	
a	$\mathbf{x}(t_7)$	$y(t_7)$
5.384303	1.000000	40.539721
0.968235	14.895785	
0.930955	13.169965	
0.957384	8.678410	
a	$\mathbf{x}(t_8)$	$y(t_8)$
5.462778	1.000000	37.985119
0.970122	13.925662	
0.931249	12.238715	
0.950769	7.727640	
a	$\mathbf{x}(t_9)$	$y(t_9)$
5.621175	1.000000	35.511963
0.968659	12.956003	
0.931825	11.306890	
0.940780	6.786861	

The preceding calculations were run on the IBM 704 in floating-point mode. Exclusive of output, the entire set of calculations leading into the optimum value required about 1 min.

Example 7.5. As part of an initial phase of installing a digital computer the need has arisen for subroutines to generate e^x, exact to five significant figures and arctan x, $|x| < 1$, exact to six significant figures. To ascertain the optimum computational procedure, the method of power series, the continued fraction expansion, and the power series converted with Chebyshev polynomials are to be considered.

The power-series representation for each function is given by

$$e^x = 1 + x + \frac{x^2}{2!} + \frac{x^3}{3!} + \cdots \tag{7.7.17}$$

$$\arctan x = x - \frac{x^3}{3} + \frac{x^5}{5} - \frac{x^7}{7} + \cdots \tag{7.7.18}$$

and the continued-fraction expansions by

$$e^x = \frac{1}{1 -}\,\frac{x}{1 +}\,\frac{x}{2 -}\,\frac{x}{3 +}\,\frac{x}{4 -}\,\cdots \tag{7.7.19}$$

$$\arctan x = \frac{x}{1 +}\,\frac{x^2}{3 +}\,\frac{(2x)^2}{5 +}\,\frac{(3x)^2}{7 +}\,\frac{(4x)^2}{9 +}\,\cdots \tag{7.7.20}$$

From the tables of Clenshaw (10) it follows that the Chebyshev expansion of e^x in the form

$$e^x = \sum_{r=0}^{\infty} A_r T_r^*(x) \qquad 0 \leq x \leq 1 \tag{7.7.21}$$

has the coefficients

$$\begin{aligned}
A_0 &= 1.753387654\\
A_1 &= 0.850391654\\
A_2 &= 0.105208694\\
A_3 &= 0.008722105\\
A_4 &= 0.000543437\\
A_5 &= 0.000027115\\
A_6 &= 0.000001128\\
A_7 &= 0.000000040\\
A_8 &= 0.000000001
\end{aligned}$$

In the same way for

$$\arctan x = x \sum_{r=0}^{\infty} A_r T_r^*(x^2) \qquad 1 \leq x \leq 1 \tag{7.7.22}$$

the coefficients are given by

$$\begin{aligned}
A_0 &= 0.881373587\\
A_1 &= -0.105892925\\
A_2 &= 0.011135843\\
A_3 &= -0.001381195\\
A_4 &= 0.000185743\\
A_5 &= -0.000026215\\
A_6 &= 0.000003821\\
A_7 &= -0.000000570\\
A_8 &= 0.000000086\\
A_9 &= -0.000000013\\
A_{10} &= 0.000000002
\end{aligned}$$

For e^x the two values $x = 0.90$ and $x = 10.0$ were chosen for comparing the different methods, i.e., the power series of (7.7.17), the continued-fraction expansion of (7.7.19), and the Chebyshev expansion of (7.7.21). The last values required to achieve five-place accuracy are tabulated as follows:

	Power series	Continued fraction	Chebyshev polynomial
$e^{0.90} = 2.459603$	$\dfrac{x^8}{8!}$	$\dfrac{x}{9}$	A_5
$e^{10.0} = 22{,}026.08$	$\dfrac{x^{25}}{25!}$	$\dfrac{x}{25}$	

As was expected from the form of the power series for e^x, convergence is obtained at about the same rate as with the continued-fraction expansion. In contrast, the Chebyshev expansion requires only about two-thirds as many terms and thus is the most efficient.

For arctan x, $|x| < 1.0$, the three values $x = 0.10$, $x = 0.80$, and $x = 0.99$ were chosen for comparing the different methods. The pertinent results from these calculations are tabulated as follows:

	No. of terms required		
	Power series	Continued fraction	Chebyshev polynomial
arctan 0.1 = 0.09966865	4	3	7
arctan 0.80 = 0.6747409	23	8	7
arctan 0.99 = 0.7803731	361	9	7

In this case the continued-fraction expansion is decidedly superior to the power series. This is especially true as the value $x = 1.0$ is approached. However, once again the Chebyshev polynomial expansion is the best when the entire region of $0 \leq x \leq 1$ is considered.

These results were obtained with the IBM 650 in the Bell I interpretive mode. Approximately 15 sec was required for any one of the computations.

BIBLIOGRAPHY

1. Amara, R. C.: *J. Franklin Inst.*, **268** (1): 1 (1959).
2. Ascher, M., and G. E. Forsythe: *J. Assoc. Comput. Mach.*, **5**: 9 (1958).
3. Box, G. E. P., and J. S. Hunter: *Ann. Math. Statistics*, **28**: 195 (1957).
4. Brough, H. W., W. G. Schlinger, and B. H. Sage: *Ind. Eng. Chem.*, **43**: 2442 (1951).
5. Chisnall, G. A.: *Math. Tables Aids Comput.*, **10**: 66 (1956).
6. Chou, C.: *Ind. Eng. Chem.*, **50**: 799 (1958).
7. Chow, W. M.: *Communs. ACM*, **2**(7): 28 (1959).
8. Clenshaw, C. W.: *Math. Tables Aids Comput.*, **8**: 143 (1954).
9. Clenshaw, C. W.: *Math. Tab., Wash.*, **8**: 143 (1954).
10. Clenshaw, C. W.: *Math. Tables Aids Comput.*, **9**: 118 (1955).
11. Clenshaw, C. W.: *Math. Tab., Wash.*, **9**: 118 (1955).
12. Clenshaw, C. W., and F. W. J. Olver: *Proc. Cambridge Phil. Soc.*, **51**: 614 (1955).
13. De Vogelaere, R.: *J. Assoc. Comput. Mach.*, **6**: 111 (1959).
14. Dow, W. M., and M. Jacob: *Chem. Eng. Progr.*, **47**: 637 (1951).
15. Forsythe, G. E.: *J. SIAM*, **5**: 74 (1957).
16. Forsythe, G. E.: *Am. Math. Monthly*, **65**: 229 (1958).
17. Frank, W. L.: The Solution of Linear Systems by Richardson's Method, *Ramo-Wooldridge Tech. Note* 2, September, 1959.
18. Goldstein, A. A., N. Levine, and J. B. Hereshoff: *J. Assoc. Comput. Mach.*, **4**: 43 (1957).
19. Gordon, E., J. J. Goodwill, and J. W. Paylor: *Chem. Eng. Progr. Symposium Ser.* 21, 1959.
20. Hastings, C.: "Approximations for Digital Computers," Princeton University Press, Princeton, N.J., 1955.
21. Henrici, P.: *J. Assoc. Comput. Mach.*, **3**: 10 (1956).

22. Jones, C. W., J. C. P. Miller, J. F. C. Conn, and R. C. Pankhurst: *Proc. Roy. Soc. Edinburgh*, sec. A, pt. II, p. 187, 1944.
23. Lanczos, C.: Tables of Chebyshev Polynomials, *Natl. Bur. Standards Appl. Math. Ser.* 9, 1952.
24. Lesh, F. H.: *Communs. ACM*, **2**(9): 29 (1959).
25. Levenspiel, O., N. J. Weinstein, and J. C. R. Li: *Ind. Eng. Chem.*, **48**: 324 (1956).
26. Levy, R.: *Proc. Inst. Elec. Engrs. (London)*, pt. C, June, 1959.
27. Macon, N.: *J. Assoc. Comput. Mach.*, **2**: 262 (1955).
28. Maehly, H. J.: *J. Assoc. Comput. Mach.*, **7**: 150 (1960).
29. Minnick, R. C.: *J. Assoc. Comput. Mach.*, **4**: 487 (1957).
30. Murnaghan, F. D., and J. W. Wrench: *Math. Tables Aids Comput.*, **13**: 185 (1959).
31. Opfell, J. B., and B. H. Sage: *Ind. Eng. Chem.*, **50**: 803 (1958).
32. Pings, C. J., Jr., and B. H. Sage: *Ind. Eng. Chem.*, **49**: 1315, 1321 (1957).
33. Price, A. R., T. W. Leland, and R. Kobayashi: *Chem. Eng. Progr. Symposium Ser.* 21, 1959.
34. Rice, J. R.: *J. SIAM*, **7**: 133 (1959).
35. Shapiro, E., S. Shapiro, R. Stillman, and L. Lapidus: *J. AIChE*, **7**: 288 (1961).
36. Shortley, G.: *J. Appl. Phys.*, **24**: 392 (1953).
37. Spitzbart, A., and D. L. Shell: *J. Assoc. Comput. Mach.*, **5**: 22 (1958).
38. Stoller, D. S., and L. C. Stoller: *Math. Tables Aids Comput.*, **13**: 122 (1959).
39. Struve, D., L. Lapidus, and J. C. Elgin: *Can. J. Chem. Eng.*, **36**: 141 (1958).
40. Szego, G.: *J. SIAM*, **7**: 311 (1959).
41. Teichroew, D.: *Math. Tables Aids Comput.*, **6**: 127 (1952).
42. Wall, H. S.: "The Analytical Theory of Continued Fractions," D. Van Nostrand Company, Inc., Princeton, N.J., 1948.

CHAPTER 8

OPTIMIZATION AND CONTROL

Of increasing interest and importance to chemical engineers is the automatic optimization and closed-loop control of chemical and petroleum processes. Since the digital computer can perform many of the complex computations and operations required for this optimization and control, the present chapter will delineate certain of the basic theoretical details required for implementing the over-all concepts.

8.1. Concepts and Definitions

To aid the discussion, consider a chemical process which has m inputs x_i, $i = 1, 2, \ldots, m$ and n outputs y_i, $i = 1, 2, \ldots, n$. These may be considered as vectors $\mathbf{x}$ and $\mathbf{y}$. The inputs and outputs may be such diverse items as concentrations, temperatures, flow rates, etc. The inputs are assumed to be available for physical manipulation, and both the inputs and outputs are assumed measurable in the sense that analytical devices exist which can identify the variables under consideration.

Optimization is the first concept which must be defined and is here taken to mean the determination of conditions which result in the "best" operation of the system or process. This may involve either maximizing the profit, minimizing the cost, maximizing the throughput, or minimizing the impurities of the process product. A variety of other "best" conditions are, of course, also possible. In more quantitative terms the process under consideration can be regarded, for the moment, as defined by

$$\mathbf{A}\mathbf{x} = \mathbf{y} \tag{8.1.1}$$

where $\mathbf{A}$ is some linear or nonlinear operator which transforms the inputs $\mathbf{x}$ to the outputs $\mathbf{y}$. Further, there exists some function z such that

$$z = z(\mathbf{x},\mathbf{y},\mathbf{u},\mathbf{v},\mathbf{w}, \ldots ;t) \tag{8.1.2}$$

z may be the profit of the process operation in terms of the inputs and outputs and other items such as market conditions, catalyst cost, ambient temperature, and uncontrollable variables. These latter quantities are indicated in (8.1.2) by the vectors **u**, **v**, **w**, ... The possible influence of time is indicated by t. Note that the process model enters implicitly in (8.1.2) by the inclusion of **x** and **y**. Using (8.1.1), the **y** functionality could be removed if desired. Because the process is a real one, it is necessary to add constraints on some of the variables, i.e.,

$$c_j(\mathbf{x},\mathbf{y}) \leq 0 \tag{8.1.3}$$

Optimization may now be defined as locating the operating condition **x** which for given **u**, **v**, **w**, . . . maximizes (or minimizes) z and satisfies the constraints. For static or steady-state conditions (time not considered as a variable) this means that

$$\max_{\mathbf{x}} z(\mathbf{x},\mathbf{y},\mathbf{u},\mathbf{v},\mathbf{w}, \ldots)$$

subject to $\quad \mathbf{Ax} = \mathbf{y} \qquad c_j(\mathbf{x},\mathbf{y}) \leq 0$

For z a function of only one or two variables static optimization can be visualized as finding a peak or valley on a curve or surface; for more than two variables the geometric visualization quickly becomes impossible.

When the optimum point of operation of the process is known or has been calculated, control action may be applied. This implies moving the process from point 1 (a nonoptimum condition) to point 2 (the optimum condition) by suitable changes in **x**. In this sense **x** may be termed the control variable. It should be pointed out, however, that in some cases optimization and control are carried out concurrently; when the optimum condition is located, the process is already at this point. This will occur when the actual physical process is used to locate the optimum point. When, however, a mathematical model is used, control will follow after the independent location of the optimum.

There are, of course, a number of possible variations to the system and method above. In a more general case some of the inputs may be uncontrollable in the sense that it is impossible to make any direct changes in their magnitude. In this case **x** includes only those inputs which are subject to actual control. Control may also be applied merely to regulate the process which has already been established at its optimum operating point but which is subject to random fluctuations. Although these alternative formulations are important, we shall confine ourselves to the problem as originally stated.

The control action applied may be divided into two possible types, static and dynamic. In static control, time is excluded from consideration, whereas in dynamic control, time becomes an important variable.

A convenient classification of the two types of control can be made by calling

t_D = average time between input disturbances or changes

t_R = average time for system to reach a stationary, or equilibrium, point after a disturbance (a stationary point is merely a static time-invariant condition)

If $t_D \gg t_R$, the dynamic, or time, effects of an input change are over so soon that they can be ignored. The control is then of a static type in which the inputs $\mathbf{x}$ are merely set to the values which yield the desired z. The process moves from point 1 to point 2 under its normal transient behavior. Equation (8.1.1) serves as an adequate definition of the process model since time is neglected.

If $t_D \approx t_R$, the dynamic effects cannot be ignored and a dynamic control scheme must be employed. Now a sequence $\mathbf{x}(t)$ must be found instead of a single $\mathbf{x}$. Equation (8.1.1) no longer serves as an adequate definition of the process, since it does not specify the time variation of the process.

If $t_D \ll t_R$, then there is probably no control scheme which can be applied.

The question now arises as to how to implement these concepts of locating an optimum condition and performing static or dynamic control. In the present chapter one method for locating the optimum, linear programming, and one method for dynamic control will be discussed.

8.2. Linear Programming

Linear programming is a technique for static optimization which has evolved into a useful procedure because of the availability of digital computers. The title results from a basic assumption inherent in the method that linear relationships describe the system under consideration. Thus each ton per day increase in throughput in a process produces a fixed profit increase per day. However, there are many cases where this linear model is inadequate in terms either of not being precise enough or of being misleading as to trends. It is thus necessary to resort to alternative procedures such as iterative linear programming or nonlinear programming. In a later section some brief details will be presented for handling the nonlinear problem and its simplification to the presently assumed linear situation.

Some of the important features of linear programming can be developed by using a simple classical example called the diet problem. Consider the following statements and subsequent question:

Two foods x_1 and x_2 are to be used in a daily diet which requires a minimum of b_1 cal and b_2 g of protein.

Food x_1 costs c_1 cents per pound and contains a_{11} cal and a_{21} g of protein per pound. Food x_2 cost c_2 cents per pound and contains a_{21} cal and a_{22} g protein.

What is the optimal choice of the amounts of x_1 and x_2 which meet the minimum diet requirements and minimizes the cost?

Mathematically this problem may be stated as minimizing the cost C

$$C = c_1x_1 + c_2x_2 \tag{8.2.1}$$

subject to $$a_{11}x_1 + a_{12}x_2 \geq b_1 \qquad a_{21}x_1 + a_{22}x_2 \geq b_2 \tag{8.2.2}$$

Further it is obvious that

$$x_1 \geq 0 \qquad x_2 \geq 0 \tag{8.2.3}$$

since negative amounts cannot be used. Note that these equations are particular forms of (8.1.2) and (8.1.3).

The geometric significance to this problem can be seen by plotting

$$a_{11}x_1 + a_{12}x_2 = b_1 \qquad a_{21}x_1 + a_{22}x_2 = b_2$$

in Fig. 8.1. Only the first quadrant need be considered, because (8.2.3) must hold. It is apparent that the only values of x_1 and x_2 which will satisfy (8.2.2) lie *above* the solid lines (the shaded area). This shaded area is termed the constraint set. Now place on Fig. 8.1 a series of straight lines or contours corresponding to the cost equation (8.2.1), with a different value of C used for each line. Of all these lines the smallest C for which x_1 and x_2 remain in the specified region will be the minimum cost. This will yield that proportion of x_1 and x_2 which minimizes the cost. Stated in other words, one desires the lowest-value contour having some point in common with the constraint set. For the particular value of slope chosen for (8.2.1) the minimum point is seen to correspond to B or $C = C_1$. Further, if the constants c_1 and c_2 in (8.2.1) are changed, it is possible that the minimum point occurs at either D or A. Which of the three points A, B, or D is the minimum is determined by the constants of the problem. While Fig. 8.1 is available, it should be pointed out that if the cost equation were nonlinear the contour lines would be curved and if the constraint equations were nonlinear the constraint lines would not be straight. It is intuitively obvious that locating the minimum point is more complicated in this case.

A number of important points can now be ascertained. First, there is a unique solution to the problem, and second, the optimal cost is situated at one of the corners of the convex polygon formed by the constraints. This latter condition is always true for problems of this type.

The problem of maximizing the profit P can also be considered by using

$$P = p_1y_1 + p_2y_2 \tag{8.2.4}$$

subject to $\quad d_{11}y_1 + d_{12}y_2 \leq f_1 \qquad d_{21}y_1 + d_{22}y_2 \leq f_2 \qquad (8.2.5)$

and $\quad y_1 \geq 0 \qquad y_2 \geq 0 \qquad (8.2.6)$

Proceeding as in the minimization case, the equations

$$d_{11}y_1 + d_{12}y_2 = f_1 \qquad d_{21}y_2 + d_{22}y_2 = f_2$$

can be plotted in the first quadrant (Fig. 8.2). The desired values of y_1

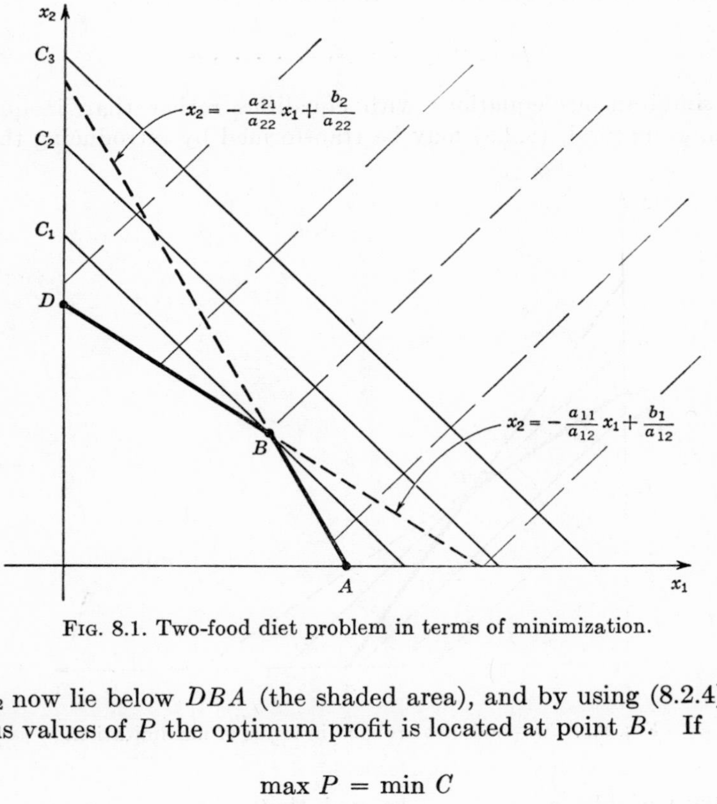

Fig. 8.1. Two-food diet problem in terms of minimization.

and y_2 now lie below DBA (the shaded area), and by using (8.2.4) with various values of P the optimum profit is located at point B. If

$$\max P = \min C$$

although the $x_i \neq y_i$, the two problems are termed "duals" of each other.

It is now possible to phrase a general statement for linear programming in which one maximizes a linear function of n variables,

$$P = p_1y_1 + p_2y_2 + \cdot \cdot \cdot + p_ny_n \tag{8.2.7}$$

subject to the linear inequalities

$$\begin{aligned} d_{11}y_1 + d_{12}y_2 + \cdots + d_{1n}y_n &\leq f_1 \\ d_{21}y_2 + d_{22}y_2 + \cdots + d_{2n}y_n &\leq f_2 \\ \cdots\cdots\cdots\cdots\cdots\cdots \\ d_{m1}y_1 + d_{m2}y_2 + \cdots + d_{mn}y_n &\leq f_m \end{aligned} \tag{8.2.8}$$

and the constraints

$$y_i \geq 0, \; i = 1, 2, \ldots, n \tag{8.2.9}$$

The profit terminology has been used here, but this is optional. The coefficients of (8.2.7) are assumed to be nonnegative, i.e.,

$$p_i \geq 0 \qquad i = 1, 2, \ldots, n$$

Since simultaneous equations with equalities rather than inequalities seem more natural, (8.2.8) may be transformed by introducing the new

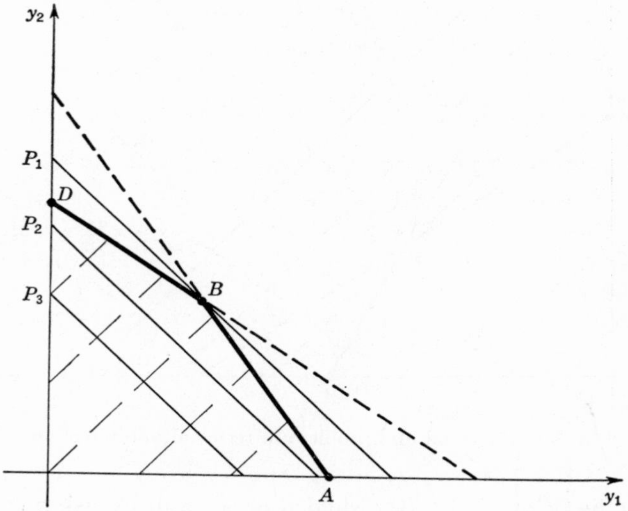

FIG. 8.2. Two-food diet problem in terms of maximization.

arbitrary variables $q_1, q_2, \ldots, q_m$ such that

$$\begin{aligned} d_{11}y_1 + d_{12}y_2 + \cdots + d_{1n}y_n + q_1 &= f_1 \\ d_{21}y_1 + d_{22}y_2 + \cdots + d_{2n}y_n + q_2 &= f_2 \\ \cdots\cdots\cdots\cdots\cdots\cdots \\ d_{m1}y_1 + d_{m2}y_2 + \cdots + d_{mn}y_n + q_m &= f_m \end{aligned}$$

The entire system can now be consolidated by changing variables once more. Let

$$y_i = u_i \qquad i = 1, 2, \ldots, n$$
$$q_i = u_{i+n} \qquad i = 1, 2, \ldots, m$$

and upon calling $N = n + m$ there results

$$\left.\begin{array}{l} P = p_1u_1 + p_2u_2 + \cdots + p_Nu_N \\ d_{11}u_1 + d_{12}u_2 + \cdots + d_{1N}u_N = f_1 \\ d_{21}u_1 + d_{22}u_2 + \cdots + d_{2N}u_N = f_2 \\ \cdots\cdots\cdots\cdots\cdots\cdots\cdots \\ d_{m1}u_1 + d_{m2}u_2 + \cdots + d_{mN}u_N = f_m \end{array}\right\} \quad u_i \geq 0; i = 1, 2, \ldots, N \tag{8.2.10}$$

Actually many of the parameters in (8.2.10) have the simple form zero or 1.0. In particular,

$$\begin{aligned} p_{n+1} &= p_{n+2} = \cdots = p_N = 0 \\ d_{1,n+1} &= d_{2,n+2} = \cdots = d_{m,N} = 1 \\ d_{1,n+2} &= d_{1,n+3} = \cdots = d_{1,N} = 0 \\ d_{2,n+1} &= d_{2,n+3} = \cdots = d_{2,N} = 0 \\ &\cdots\cdots\cdots\cdots\cdots\cdots \\ d_{m,n+1} &= d_{m,n+2} = \cdots = d_{m,N-1} = 0 \end{aligned}$$

In linear-programming terminology the u_i's introduced to produce the equality equations, $i = n + 1, n + 2, \ldots, N$, are termed slack variables. The reason for introducing these variables will be detailed later. Values of y_i (or u_i) which satisfy (8.2.8) or (8.2.10) are called feasible solutions, and the desired optimal set which maximizes P is called an optimal feasible solution. The feasible solutions satisfy the inequality equations but not the maximum equation.

It is also possible to write the system of (8.2.8) or (8.2.10) in a number of different forms. Letting

$$\mathbf{p} = \begin{bmatrix} p_1 \\ p_2 \\ \cdot \\ \cdot \\ \cdot \\ p_n \end{bmatrix} \qquad \mathbf{y} = \begin{bmatrix} y_1 \\ y_2 \\ \cdot \\ \cdot \\ \cdot \\ y_n \end{bmatrix} \qquad \mathbf{f} = \begin{bmatrix} f_1 \\ f_2 \\ \cdot \\ \cdot \\ \cdot \\ f_m \end{bmatrix} \qquad \mathbf{u} = \begin{bmatrix} u_1 \\ u_2 \\ \cdot \\ \cdot \\ \cdot \\ u_N \end{bmatrix}$$

$$\mathbf{D} = \begin{bmatrix} d_{11} & d_{12} & \cdots & d_{1n} \\ d_{21} & d_{22} & \cdots & \cdots \\ \cdots & \cdots & \cdots & \cdots \\ d_{m1} & d_{m2} & \cdots & d_{mn} \end{bmatrix}$$

and

$$\mathbf{p}_0 = \begin{bmatrix} f_1 \\ f_2 \\ \cdot \\ \cdot \\ \cdot \\ f_m \end{bmatrix} \qquad \mathbf{p}_1 = \begin{bmatrix} d_{11} \\ d_{21} \\ \cdot \\ \cdot \\ \cdot \\ d_{m1} \end{bmatrix} \qquad \mathbf{p}_2 = \begin{bmatrix} d_{12} \\ d_{22} \\ \cdot \\ \cdot \\ \cdot \\ d_{m2} \end{bmatrix} \qquad \cdots \qquad \mathbf{p}_N = \begin{bmatrix} d_{1N} \\ d_{2N} \\ \cdot \\ \cdot \\ \cdot \\ d_{mN} \end{bmatrix}$$

Equations (8.2.7) to (8.2.9) may be written as

$$\begin{gathered} P = \max \mathbf{p}^T\mathbf{y} \\ \mathbf{D}\mathbf{y} \leq \mathbf{f} \qquad \mathbf{y} \geq 0 \end{gathered} \tag{8.2.11}$$

and (8.2.10) as

$$\begin{gathered} P = \max \mathbf{u}^T\mathbf{p} \\ u_1\mathbf{p}_1 + u_2\mathbf{p}_2 + \cdots + u_N\mathbf{p}_N = \mathbf{p}_0 = \sum_1^N u_i\mathbf{p}_i \qquad u_i \geq 0 \end{gathered} \tag{8.2.12}$$

The dual problem may be defined with the same type of operations.

Before outlining an efficient method for solving (8.2.12), it seems appropriate to mention one or two examples of complex systems for which linear programming is suitable as an optimizing procedure. As an illustration, a refinery has different crudes available in stated quantities and wishes to use these crudes for a variety of different products. If product yields and the profit associated with each crude operation are known, linear programming will indicate how to distribute the crudes so that a maximum profit is achieved. To state this in a different way, the refinery has reactants $A_1, A_2, \ldots, A_m$ which can be used to form $B_1, B_2, \ldots, B_n$ in various combinations. Given the maximum available supply and cost of each A_i and the selling price of each B_i, linear programming will show how to obtain the products with maximum profit. The minimization approach is called a transportation problem. If a refinery has m crudes in stated quantity per day to distribute to n total refineries with stated total requirements, linear programming will show how to minimize the total cost of shipping if the individual shipping costs are known.

However, it must be pointed out that these systems are ideal in many respects. In most practical refinery operations (as an example) nonlinear profit functions or constraints are involved. As an illustration, the American Oil Co. and IBM have recently announced preliminary details of a digital-computer optimization scheme for a 140,000 barrel per day crude-distillation unit. The technique used for optimizing this system is a variation on the linear-programming approach and evolves in the following manner: First the nonlinear functions, let us say that both the profit function and the constraint set are of this form, are linearized about some small region B_1. This is accomplished by expanding the desired functions in Taylor series and truncating to retain only the linear terms. Now the system equations are suitable for direct linear programming, and an optimum is sought in the region B_1. In general, however, the solution to the original problem is not in B_1, and the computations are stopped when the border of B_1 is reached. Now a new linearization is made for a region B_2 next to B_1 and the optimization continued. This procedure is repeated until finally an optimum is found. To ensure that this is a true optimum (in, say, B_r), a new linearization is made within B_r, but for a region smaller than B_r. However, this procedure is guaranteed to converge to the true optimum only under certain specialized restrictions; these seem to be met in the above crude-distillation unit. Obviously the computer program for such a procedure is far from trivial; in fact it may be overpowering in terms of man-hours and computation time. As an illustration the above-mentioned operation took eight programmers and four process engineers a total of 1 year and considerable IBM 704 time to obtain a properly working program. Because of these difficulties it is probably desirable in cases of extreme nonlinearities and multidimensions to turn to nonlinear programming. However, in other less difficult or complex problems the linear-programming procedure is quite adequate.

8.3. Convex Sets

Convex sets of points are quite important in linear programming. To start the discussion, consider Fig. 8.3, and call the points within either

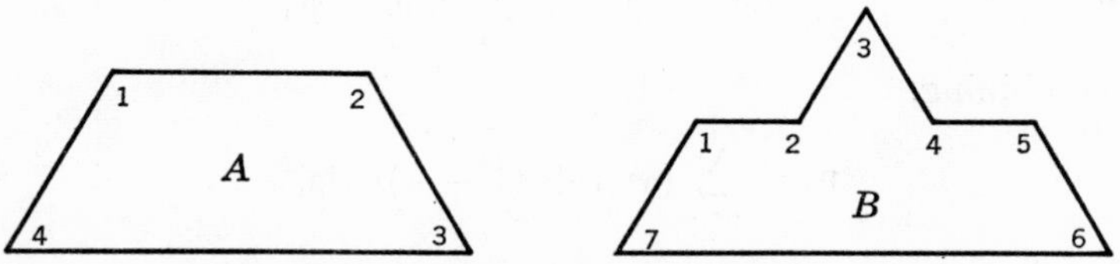

FIG. 8.3. Convex and nonconvex sets.

two-dimensional drawing the set S. If $\mathbf{u}_1$ and $\mathbf{u}_2$ (vector notation being used to cover m-dimensional space) are points in the set S and the line joining these two points is also in the set, then the set is said to be convex. Further, any point $\mathbf{u}$ within the set S can be related to $\mathbf{u}_1$ and $\mathbf{u}_2$ by

$$\mathbf{u} = \alpha\mathbf{u}_1 + (1 - \alpha)\mathbf{u}_2 \qquad 0 \leq \alpha \leq 1 \tag{8.3.1}$$

From this definition it can be seen that A in Fig. 8.3 is convex but that B is not. In the latter case it is possible to find points which do not satisfy (8.3.1). An extreme point of a convex set is a point which does not fulfill (8.3.1), i.e., which does not lie on a segment between any other two points in the set. In A of Fig. 8.3 the points 1, 2, 3, and 4 are each an extreme point. It is further apparent from simple geometrical conditions that any point in a convex set $\mathbf{u}$ which is generated from (or results from the combination of) a finite number of points $\mathbf{u}_1, \mathbf{u}_2, \ldots, \mathbf{u}_r$ may be expressed as

$$\mathbf{u} = \alpha_1\mathbf{u}_1 + \alpha_2\mathbf{u}_2 + \alpha_3\mathbf{u}_3 + \cdots + \alpha_r\mathbf{u}_r \tag{8.3.2}$$

with

$$\alpha_i \geq 0 \qquad \sum_{i=1}^{r} \alpha_i = 1.0$$

These points $\mathbf{u}_1, \mathbf{u}_2, \ldots, \mathbf{u}_r$ can, of course, be extreme points of the convex set.

It now becomes evident that the feasible solutions to the two-food diet problem form convex sets (Figs. 8.1 and 8.2) and that the optimal feasible points are at the extreme points of the convex sets. This is a truism for all properly stated linear-programming problems, as will now be shown. Let $\mathbf{u}_1$ and $\mathbf{u}_2$ be two different feasible solutions with

$$\mathbf{u}_1 = \begin{bmatrix} u_{11} \\ u_{21} \\ \cdot \\ \cdot \\ \cdot \\ u_{n1} \end{bmatrix} \qquad \mathbf{u}_2 = \begin{bmatrix} u_{12} \\ u_{22} \\ \cdot \\ \cdot \\ \cdot \\ u_{n2} \end{bmatrix}$$

If these are each a feasible solution, then from (8.2.12)

$$\sum_{i=1}^{n} u_{r1}\mathbf{p}_i = \mathbf{p}_0 \qquad \sum_{i=1}^{n} u_{i2}\mathbf{p}_i = \mathbf{p}_0$$

or, by combining,

$$\mathbf{p}_0 = \sum_{i=1}^{n} [\alpha u_{i1} + (1 - \alpha)u_{i2}]\mathbf{p}_i$$

From (8.3.1) this last equation may be written as

$$\mathbf{p}_0 = \sum_{i=1}^{n} u_i\mathbf{p}_i$$

and it follows that

$$\mathbf{u} = \alpha\mathbf{u}_1 + (1 - \alpha)\mathbf{u}_2 = \begin{bmatrix} u_1 \\ u_2 \\ \cdot \\ \cdot \\ \cdot \\ u_n \end{bmatrix}$$

But if $u_1, u_2, \ldots, u_n$ are all nonnegative, that is, $u_i \geq 0$ from (8.2.12), then the set $\mathbf{u}$ is convex and feasible. Thus the feasible solutions form a convex set.

Now consider a point $\mathbf{u}$ in a convex set of feasible solutions, and assume that this point is a maximum but is not an extreme point. This means that $\mathbf{u}$ satisfies the inequality equations and the maximum-profit equation but is an interior point of the convex set. This point may be expressed as a linear combination of the extreme points as given in (8.3.2).

$$\mathbf{u} = \sum_{j=1}^{r} \alpha_j \mathbf{u}_j$$

$$\alpha_j \geq 0 \qquad \sum_{j=1}^{r} \alpha_j = 1.0$$

where $\mathbf{u}_1, \mathbf{u}_2, \ldots, \mathbf{u}_r$ are the extreme points. Further, the ith element of $\mathbf{u}$ can be expressed as

$$u_i = \sum_{j=1}^{r} \alpha_j u_{ij}$$

where u_{ij} is the ith element of $\mathbf{u}_j$. If $\mathbf{u}$ is an optimal feasible solution, it must satisfy a linear function of the form

$$f(\mathbf{u}) = \beta_1 u_1 + \beta_2 u_2 + \cdots + \beta_n u_n = \sum_{i=1}^{n} \beta_i u_i$$

corresponding to the profit equation. It follows that

$$f(\mathbf{u}) = \sum_{i=1}^{n} \beta_i \sum_{j=1}^{r} \alpha_j u_{ij} = \sum_{j=1}^{r} \alpha_j \sum_{i=1}^{n} \beta_i u_{ij} = \sum_{j=1}^{r} \alpha_j f(\mathbf{u}_j)$$

Now consider that $f(\mathbf{u}_p)$ is the largest of the $f(\mathbf{u}_j)$'s, $j = 1, 2, \ldots, n$, and since max $f(\mathbf{u})$ implies an optimal feasible solution,

$$\max f(\mathbf{u}) \leq \sum_{j=1}^{r} \alpha_j f(\mathbf{u}_p) \leq f(\mathbf{u}_p) \sum_{j=1}^{r} \alpha_j \leq f(\mathbf{u}_p)$$

by using $\sum_{1}^{r} \alpha_j = 1.0$. But this condition says that max $f(\mathbf{u})$ for an interior point is less than or equal to one of the $f(\mathbf{u}_p)$'s. Thus $f(\mathbf{u})$ cannot be a maximum if it is an interior point, and this contradicts the original assumption. This means that the linear function $f(\mathbf{u})$ must have a maximum at an extreme point of the convex set; further, the profit function assumes its maximum value at the extreme points of the convex set of feasible solutions, and the optimal feasible solution occurs at one of the extreme points.

A number of other important points regarding convex sets can be proved, but only one will be quoted here, and without the necessary proof. A point **u** is an extreme point of the convex set of feasible solutions if and only if those $\mathbf{p}_i$'s in (8.2.12) whose coefficients are positive, $u_i > 0$, form a linearly independent set. All the other u_i's are zero. But since there cannot be more than m linearly independent vectors for the inequality equations under consideration, each extreme point has m linearly independent vectors from among the n associated with it.

The important point of the discussion of this section has been to show that the optimum feasible solution must occur at an extreme point of the convex set. Thus the system of equations need be solved only at the extreme points, and one of these will yield the desired answer. The question immediately arises as to an efficient method for scanning the extreme points. The method to be described is called the "simplex" method as developed by Dantzig (11, 12). In effect this is an iterative technique which uses an initial feasible solution as a start and in a finite number of steps calculates the optimal feasible solution (if it exists). In geometric terms the method of solution is easily visualized. If there are r constraint equations, then because of linearity the faces of the constraint set are planes. Thus the r constraint planes intersect to form a closed volume, and the solution of the problem is on one of the vertices of these planes. Starting at one vertex the simplex method progressively looks at other vertices to locate that one which yields the optimal profit or cost. Consideration of any point on the face of the planes is not required.

8.4. Vector Manipulations for the Simplex Method

In very simple terms the steps in the simplex method for solving a linear-programming problem may be listed as:

1. Pick a starting feasible solution (one vertex of the intersecting planes above).
2. Replace this first starting solution by another solution in which the profit obtained is greater (find another vertex).
3. Continue the replacement of one solution with another until no further increase in the profit is possible.

The result of steps 1 to 3 is to find a set of values $u_1, u_2, \ldots, u_n, u_{n+1}, \ldots, u_N$, $u_i \geq 0$, among all possible sets of values which satisfy Eqs. (8.2.12). From this set the subset $u_1, u_2, \ldots, u_n$ represent the optimal feasible solution, with the slack variables $u_{n+1}, \ldots, u_N$ set equal to zero.

In the present section two items involved in the above sequence are discussed. These include the means of picking a starting feasible solution and the way to progress from one feasible solution to another. Actually the slack variables $u_{n+1}, \ldots, u_N$ were introduced so that an initial feasible solution could be obtained. To show this, note that

$$\mathbf{u}^T = [0 \quad 0 \quad \cdots \quad 0 \quad f_1 \quad f_2 \quad \cdots \quad f_m] \tag{8.4.1}$$

satisfies
$$\sum_{i=n+1}^{N} u_i \mathbf{p}_i = \mathbf{p}_0 \tag{8.4.2}$$

but that $P = \mathbf{u}^T \mathbf{p}$

$$= [0 \quad 0 \quad \cdots \quad 0 \quad f_1 \quad f_2 \quad \cdots \quad f_m] \begin{bmatrix} p_1 \\ p_2 \\ \cdot \\ \cdot \\ \cdot \\ p_n \\ 0 \\ 0 \\ \cdot \\ \cdot \\ \cdot \\ 0 \end{bmatrix}$$

$$= 0$$

Thus $\mathbf{u}$ as given in (8.4.1) (all the elements are set to zero except the slack elements, which are set equal to $f_1, f_2, \ldots, f_m$) is a feasible solution, but the profit is zero. Since the $\mathbf{p}_i$ in (8.4.2) are unit vectors (the reader can quickly check this), they form a set of linearly independent vectors. From the discussion in Sec. 8.3 this means that $\mathbf{u}^T$ in (8.4.1) is an extreme point. Thus the simple procedure using (8.4.1) leads to an extreme point or feasible solution with zero profit; any other feasible solution would be expected to increase the profit. Equation (8.4.1) fulfills all the necessary criteria for an initial, or starting, solution to the linear-programming problem and is termed a basic solution, or basis, since there are at most m nonzero u_i's.

Next consider that there are m linearly independent vectors $\mathbf{p}_i$ such that

$$\mathbf{p}_0 = \sum_{i=1}^{m} u_i \mathbf{p}_i \tag{8.4.3}$$

where $\mathbf{p}_0^T = [f_1 f_2 \cdots f_m] \qquad \mathbf{p}_i^T = [d_{1i} d_{2i} \cdots d_{mi}] \qquad u_i \geq 0$

Equation (8.4.3) corresponds to the vector formulation of m simultaneous equations with a coefficient matrix of rank m. Note that if desired $\mathbf{p}_0$ and the $\mathbf{p}_i$'s can be expressed in terms of the unit vectors $\mathbf{e}_i$,

$$\mathbf{p}_0 = f_1\mathbf{e}_1 + f_2\mathbf{e}_2 + \cdots + f_m\mathbf{e}_m$$
$$\mathbf{p}_i = d_{1i}\mathbf{e}_1 + d_{2i}\mathbf{e}_2 + \cdots + d_{mi}\mathbf{e}_m$$

Thus $\mathbf{p}_0$ can be expressed as a linear combination of either the vectors $\mathbf{p}_i$ or $\mathbf{e}_i$; that is, either set of vectors forms a basis for $\mathbf{p}_0$. But suppose that what is really desired is to express $\mathbf{p}_0$ as a linear function of some of the $\mathbf{p}_i$'s and some of the $\mathbf{e}_i$'s; the question arises how some of the $\mathbf{p}_i$'s in (8.4.3) can be replaced by some of the $\mathbf{e}_i$'s. To illustrate the necessary procedure, consider that $\mathbf{w}_1, \mathbf{w}_2, \ldots, \mathbf{w}_m$ are m linearly independent vectors (these could be any desired combination of the $\mathbf{p}_i$'s and $\mathbf{e}_i$'s). Since any vector can be expanded in terms of the m vectors, it is possible to write

$$\mathbf{s} = s_1\mathbf{w}_1 + s_2\mathbf{w}_2 + \cdots + s_k\mathbf{w}_k + \cdots + s_m\mathbf{w}_m \tag{8.4.4}$$
$$\mathbf{t} = t_1\mathbf{w}_1 + t_2\mathbf{w}_2 + \cdots + t_k\mathbf{w}_k + \cdots + t_m\mathbf{w}_m \tag{8.4.5}$$
$$\mathbf{q} = q_1\mathbf{w}_1 + q_2\mathbf{w}_2 + \cdots + q_k\mathbf{w}_k + \cdots\ q_m\mathbf{w}_m \tag{8.4.6}$$

where $\mathbf{s}$, $\mathbf{t}$, and $\mathbf{q}$ are vectors and the s_i's, t_i's, and q_i's are scalars. It is desired to replace the vector $\mathbf{w}_k$ with $\mathbf{q}$ in the linear expansions of $\mathbf{s}$ and $\mathbf{t}$. Adding and subtracting $\mathbf{q}$ to and from (8.4.4) and (8.4.5) yields

$$\mathbf{s} = s_1\mathbf{w}_1 + s_2\mathbf{w}_2 + \cdots + s_k\mathbf{w}_k + \cdots + s_m\mathbf{w}_m + \alpha\mathbf{q} - \alpha\mathbf{q}$$
$$\mathbf{t} = t_1\mathbf{w}_1 + t_2\mathbf{w}_2 + \cdots + t_k\mathbf{w}_k + \cdots + t_m\mathbf{w}_m + \beta\mathbf{q} - \beta\mathbf{q}$$

where α and β are constants. Using (8.4.6) and grouping terms

$$\mathbf{s} = \sum_{i=1}^{m} (s_i - \alpha q_i)\mathbf{w}_i + \alpha\mathbf{q} \qquad \mathbf{t} = \sum_{i=1}^{m} (t_i - \beta q_i)\mathbf{w}_i + \beta\mathbf{q} \tag{8.4.7}$$

and if we choose

$$\alpha = \frac{s_k}{q_k} \qquad \beta = \frac{t_k}{q_k}$$

then

$$\mathbf{s} = \sum_{i=1}^{m} \left(s_i - \frac{s_k}{q_k} q_i\right) \mathbf{w}_i + \frac{s_k}{q_k}\mathbf{q} \qquad \mathbf{t} = \sum_{i=1}^{m} \left(t_i - \frac{t_k}{q_k} q_i\right) \mathbf{w}_i + \frac{t_k}{q_k}\mathbf{q} \tag{8.4.8}$$

Now the $\mathbf{q}$ vector has replaced the $\mathbf{w}_k$ vector in the expansion of both $\mathbf{s}$ and $\mathbf{t}$. Further, if the α's and β's are chosen so that

$$\alpha = \frac{s_k}{q_k} > 0 \qquad \beta = \frac{t_k}{q_k} > 0$$
$$s_i - \frac{s_k}{q_k} q_i > 0 \qquad t_i - \frac{t_k}{q_k} q_i > 0$$

the coefficients of the new expansions are positive and the new vectors are linearly independent.

The entire process can be conveniently illustrated by means of a tableau as shown in the first part of Fig. 8.4. The vectors $\mathbf{w}_1, \mathbf{w}_2, \ldots, \mathbf{w}_k, \ldots, \mathbf{w}_m$ in the initial basis are listed in the left vertical column.

Along the top row all vectors are listed. The elements in the table are the coefficients of the expansion of a vector in the top row in terms of the basis vectors [as given, for example, by (8.4.4) to (8.4.6)]. To replace $\mathbf{w}_k$ in the starting set of m linearly independent vectors with $\mathbf{q}$, subtract row k after multiplying by q_i/q_k from row i in accordance with (8.4.8). This leads to the second tableau of Fig. 8.4. It is immediately apparent that any vector in the basis can be replaced by any other vector in exactly the same way. Note from the second tableau of Fig. 8.4 that the manipulation performed is really a form of Gaussian elimination.

	$\mathbf{s}$	$\mathbf{t}$	$\mathbf{w}_1$	$\mathbf{w}_2$	$\cdots$	$\mathbf{w}_k$	$\cdots$	$\mathbf{w}_m$	$\mathbf{q}$
$\mathbf{w}_1$	s_1	t_1	1	0	$\cdots$	0	$\cdots$	0	q_1
$\mathbf{w}_2$	s_2	t_2	0	1	$\cdots$	0	$\cdots$	0	q_2
$\cdots$	$\cdots$	$\cdots$	$\cdots$	$\cdots$	$\cdots$	$\cdots$	$\cdots$	$\cdots$	$\cdots$
$\rightarrow \mathbf{w}_k$	s_k	t_k	0	0	$\cdots$	1	$\cdots$	0	q_k
$\cdots$	$\cdots$	$\cdots$	$\cdots$	$\cdots$	$\cdots$	$\cdots$	$\cdots$	$\cdots$	$\cdots$
$\mathbf{w}_m$	s_m	t_m	0	0	$\cdots$	0	$\cdots$	1	q_m
									$\uparrow$

	$\mathbf{s}$	$\mathbf{t}$	$\mathbf{w}_1$	$\mathbf{w}_2$	$\cdots$	$\mathbf{w}_k$	$\cdots$	$\mathbf{w}_m$	$\mathbf{q}$
$\mathbf{w}_1$	$s_1 - \frac{q_1}{q_k} s_k$	$t_1 - \frac{q_1}{q_2} t_k$	1	0	$\cdots$	$-\frac{q_1}{q_k}$	$\cdots$	0	0
$\mathbf{w}_2$	$s_2 - \frac{q_2}{q_k} s_k$	$t_2 - \frac{q_2}{q_k} t_k$	0	1	$\cdots$	$-\frac{q_2}{q_k}$	$\cdots$	0	0
$\cdots$	$\cdots$	$\cdots$	$\cdots$	$\cdots$	$\cdots$	$\cdots$	$\cdots$	$\cdots$	$\cdots$
$\mathbf{q}$	$\frac{s_k}{q_k}$	$\frac{t_k}{q_k}$	0	0	$\cdots$	$\frac{1}{q_k}$	$\cdots$	0	1
$\cdots$	$\cdots$	$\cdots$	$\cdots$	$\cdots$	$\cdots$	$\cdots$	$\cdots$	$\cdots$	$\cdots$
$\mathbf{w}_m$	$s_m - \frac{q_m}{q_k} s_k$	$t_m - \frac{q_m}{q_k} t_k$	0	0	$\cdots$	$-\frac{q_m}{q_k}$	$\cdots$	1	0

FIG. 8.4. A tableau arrangement for replacing $\mathbf{w}_k$ with $\mathbf{q}$.

To return to the original system (8.4.3), it is now possible to form a tableau which has the unit vectors $\mathbf{e}_1, \mathbf{e}_2, \ldots, \mathbf{e}_m$ on the outside column and the unit vectors, the vectors $\mathbf{p}_1, \mathbf{p}_2, \ldots, \mathbf{p}_m$ and $\mathbf{p}_0$, on the outside row. If the $\mathbf{e}_i$'s are replaced one by one with the $\mathbf{p}_i$'s, the final result will have $\mathbf{p}_1, \mathbf{p}_2, \ldots, \mathbf{p}_m$ on the outside column. But from (8.4.3) it can also be seen that the resulting elements under $\mathbf{p}_0$ will represent those values of u_i which satisfy the m simultaneous equations.

8.5. The Simplex Algorithm

By using the material of the previous section it is now possible to describe the computational details of the simplex algorithm. Obtaining the initial feasible solution with zero profit and replacing one vector in the basis with another can be readily accomplished as outlined above.

The only remaining questions are how to check the profit made at each step and how to decide which vectors to change to increase the profit from step to step in the iteration cycle.

Consider that a point has been reached in the calculation where N vectors $\mathbf{w}_1, \mathbf{w}_2, \ldots, \mathbf{w}_k, \ldots, \mathbf{w}_m, \mathbf{w}_{m+1}, \ldots, \mathbf{w}_q, \ldots, \mathbf{w}_N$ are available. Of this total group $\mathbf{w}_1, \ldots, \mathbf{w}_m$ are the linearly independent ones (in the basis). $\mathbf{w}_k$ is a vector in the basis, and $\mathbf{w}_q$ is not. The profit at this point in the calculation is given by $P = \sum_{i=1}^{N} u_i p_i$. Using (8.4.3) and (8.4.6),

$$\mathbf{p}_0 = \sum_{i=1}^{m} u_i \mathbf{w}_i$$

and

$$\mathbf{w}_q = \sum_{i=1}^{m} \gamma_{iq} \mathbf{w}_i = \gamma_{1q}\mathbf{w}_1 + \gamma_{2q}\mathbf{w}_2 + \cdots + \gamma_{mq}\mathbf{w}_m \tag{8.5.1}$$

The terminology in (8.5.1) is that any of the vectors $\mathbf{w}_{m+1}, \ldots, \mathbf{w}_N$ not in the basis can be expanded in terms of $\mathbf{w}_1, \ldots, \mathbf{w}_m$. To identify the appropriate vector being expanded, the coefficients of the expansion are given two subscripts, the first to indicate the point in the expansion and the second to identify the vector. If the vector $\mathbf{w}_q$ is used to replace $\mathbf{w}_k$ in the basis, it follows immediately from (8.4.7) that

$$\mathbf{p}_0 = \sum_{i=1}^{m} (u_i - \alpha\gamma_{iq})\mathbf{w}_i + \alpha\mathbf{w}_q$$

and using (8.5.1) with

$$\alpha = \frac{u_k}{\gamma_{kq}} > 0 \qquad u_i - \frac{u_k}{\gamma_{kq}}\gamma_{iq} > 0 \tag{8.5.2}$$

$$\mathbf{p}_0 = \sum_{i=1}^{m} \left(u_i - \frac{u_k}{\gamma_{kq}}\gamma_{iq} \right) \mathbf{w}_i + \frac{u_k}{\gamma_{kq}}\mathbf{w}_q \tag{8.5.3}$$

Thus the $\mathbf{w}_q$ vector has replaced the $\mathbf{w}_k$ vector, leaving a linearly independent set. The coefficients of the new vector set in (8.5.3) form a new feasible solution which can be designated $u_1, u_2, \ldots, u_m$. The profit function now is

$$P_{\text{new}} = \sum_{i=1}^{N} u_i p_i = \sum_{i=1}^{m} u_i p_i$$

since all the p_i's except the first m can be set equal to zero. This last equation can be written as

$$P_{\text{new}} = \sum_{i=1}^{m} \left(u_i - \frac{u_k}{\gamma_{kq}} \gamma_{iq} \right) p_i + \frac{u_k}{\gamma_{kq}} p_q = \sum_{i=1}^{m} u_i p_i + \frac{u_k}{\gamma_{kq}} \left(p_q - \sum_{i=1}^{m} \gamma_{iq} p_i \right) \tag{8.5.4}$$

by using (8.5.3). Upon defining a new term

$$z_q = \sum_{i=1}^{m} \gamma_{iq} p_i$$

(8.5.4) becomes

$$P_{\text{new}} = P_{\text{old}} + \frac{u_k}{\gamma_{kq}} (p_q - z_q) \tag{8.5.5}$$

P_{old} represents the profit corresponding to the basis which included $\mathbf{w}_k$. But since $u_k/\gamma_{kq} > 0$ from (8.5.2), the new profit will be greater than the old profit if $p_q - z_q > 0$. It thus becomes apparent that in the iteration cycles the $\mathbf{w}_q$ vector to be substituted is the one for which $p_q - z_q$ is the largest. The $\mathbf{w}_k$ to be removed also follows directly by picking the minimum $u_k/\gamma_{kq} > 0$. Note that this last condition implies that $\gamma_{kq} > 0$ since u_k is positive.

The entire simplex algorithm can now be summarized by the following steps:

1. Pick an initial feasible solution [(8.4.1)].
2. Replace one vector in this basis with a new one, using the principles above (see later).
3. The iteration will terminate with the optimal feasible solution when $p_q = z_q$ or when all $\gamma_{iq} \leq 0$, since the conditions listed above can no longer be satisfied.

The procedure can be illustrated with the tableau of Fig. 8.5. The outside column contains the vectors $\mathbf{w}_1, \mathbf{w}_2, \ldots, \mathbf{w}_m$ plus the values p_q, z_q, and $p_q - z_q$. The outside row contains $\mathbf{w}_1, \ldots, \mathbf{w}_N$, $\mathbf{p}_0$, and p_i. Initially $\mathbf{w}_1, \mathbf{w}_2, \ldots, \mathbf{w}_m$ are unit vectors following from the use of the slack variables as the starting solution, and all the elements in the z_q row are zero; all the p_i's, $i > m$, are also zero. The iteration now becomes as follows:

1. Choose the value of $p_q - z_q$ which is the largest positive number. This fixes the $\mathbf{w}_q$ column and indicates the vector to be substituted into the new basis.
2. Look over the elements in the $\mathbf{w}_q$ column, and for all $\gamma_{iq} > 0$ calculate u_i/γ_{iq}. The smallest of these values picks the k row which is to be removed from the basis.

3. Replace the $\mathbf{w}_k$ vector with the $\mathbf{w}_q$ vector, using the procedure outlined above. This means dividing the k row by γ_{kq}, multiplying the k row by γ_{iq}/γ_{kq}, and subtracting from the ith row.

4. Calculate a new set of z_q and $p_q - z_q$.

5. Check on whether or not all $p_q - z_q \leq 0$. If they are not, repeat the iteration. If they are, then the elements under the $\mathbf{p}_0$ column represent the optimal feasible solution values $u_1, u_2, \ldots, u_m$.

	$\mathbf{w}_1$	$\mathbf{w}_2$	$\cdots$	$\mathbf{w}_k$	$\cdots$	$\mathbf{w}_m$	$\cdots$	$\mathbf{w}_q$	$\cdots$	$\mathbf{w}_N$	p_0	p_i
$\mathbf{w}_1$	1	0	$\cdots$	0	$\cdots$	0	$\cdots$	γ_{1q}	$\cdots$	γ_{1N}	u_1	p_1
$\mathbf{w}_2$	0	1	$\cdots$	0	$\cdots$	0	$\cdots$	γ_{2q}	$\cdots$	γ_{2N}	u_2	p_2
$\cdots$	$\cdots$	$\cdots$	$\cdots$	$\cdots$	$\cdots$	$\cdots$	$\cdots$	$\cdots$	$\cdots$	$\cdots$	$\cdots$	$\cdots$
$\mathbf{w}_k$	0	0	$\cdots$	1	$\cdots$	0	$\cdots$	γ_{kq}	$\cdots$	γ_{kN}	u_k	p_k
$\cdots$	$\cdots$	$\cdots$	$\cdots$	$\cdots$	$\cdots$	$\cdots$	$\cdots$	$\cdots$	$\cdots$	$\cdots$	$\cdots$	$\cdots$
$\mathbf{w}_m$	0	0	$\cdots$	0	$\cdots$	1	$\cdots$	γ_{mq}	$\cdots$	γ_{mN}	u_m	p_m
p_q	p_1	p_2	$\cdots$	p_k	$\cdots$	p_m	$\cdots$	p_q	$\cdots$	p_N		
z_q	z_1	z_2	$\cdots$	z_k	$\cdots$	z_m	$\cdots$	z_q	$\cdots$	z_N		
$p_q - z_q$												

FIG. 8.5. Tableau for the simplex method.

To illustrate the procedure further, a set of equations which comprise a linear programming arrangement are listed below. These have no physical significance.

$$\max P = y_1 + 2y_2 + 3y_3 + 5y_4$$

subject to

$$4y_1 + 3y_2 + y_4 \leq 5$$
$$2y_1 + 4y_2 + y_3 + y_4 \leq 2$$
$$y_2 + 3y_3 + 4y_4 \leq 4$$

and

$$y_i \geq 0$$

The new variables u_i are defined as

$$u_1 = y_1 \qquad u_2 = y_2 \qquad u_3 = y_3 \qquad u_4 = y_4$$

with u_5, u_6, and u_7 added as slack variables. Thus

$$p_1 = 1 \qquad p_2 = 2 \qquad p_3 = 3 \qquad p_4 = 5 \qquad p_5 = 0 \qquad p_6 = 0 \qquad p_7 = 0$$

and

$$\mathbf{p}_0 = \begin{bmatrix} 5 \\ 2 \\ 4 \end{bmatrix} \quad \mathbf{p}_1 = \begin{bmatrix} 4 \\ 2 \\ 0 \end{bmatrix} \quad \mathbf{p}_2 = \begin{bmatrix} 3 \\ 4 \\ 1 \end{bmatrix} \quad \mathbf{p}_3 = \begin{bmatrix} 0 \\ 1 \\ 3 \end{bmatrix} \quad \mathbf{p}_4 = \begin{bmatrix} 1 \\ 1 \\ 4 \end{bmatrix}$$

$$\mathbf{p}_5 = \begin{bmatrix} 1 \\ 0 \\ 0 \end{bmatrix} \quad \mathbf{p}_6 = \begin{bmatrix} 0 \\ 1 \\ 0 \end{bmatrix} \quad \mathbf{p}_7 = \begin{bmatrix} 0 \\ 0 \\ 1 \end{bmatrix}$$

The initial tableau is shown in Fig. 8.6 with $\mathbf{p}_5$, $\mathbf{p}_6$, and $\mathbf{p}_7$ as the initial feasible vectors. It can be seen that 5 is the largest of $p_q - z_q$; thus the vector $\mathbf{p}_4$, $q = 4$, should be inserted into the basis. Upon calculating the u_i/γ_{i4} (where the current u_i's are in the column under $\mathbf{p}_0$), there results

$$\frac{u_5}{\gamma_{54}} = \frac{5}{1} \qquad \frac{u_6}{\gamma_{64}} = \frac{2}{1} \qquad \frac{u_7}{\gamma_{74}} = \frac{4}{4}$$

The smallest is $u_7/\gamma_{74} = 1$, and thus the vector $\mathbf{p}_7$ is to be replaced with $\mathbf{p}_4$. To do this, divide the $\mathbf{p}_7$ row by $\gamma_{74} = 4$, multiply the $\mathbf{p}_7$ row by γ_{i4}/γ_{74}, $i = 5$ and 6, and subtract element by element from the $\mathbf{p}_5$ and $\mathbf{p}_6$ rows. This yields the results shown in the second tableau of Fig. 8.6. New values of z_q are then calculated by using $z_q = \sum_{i=1}^{3} \gamma_{iq} p_i$ followed by the corresponding $p_q - z_q$. The element under the $\mathbf{p}_1$ column is, as illustration,

$$z_1 = 4 \times 0 + 2 \times 0 + 0 \times 5 = 0$$

and the corresponding $p_q - z_q = p_1 - z_1 = 1 - 0 = 1$. This completes one step in the iteration. The profit has gone from $P = 0$ to $P = 5$ ($P = 5 \times 1$) in this transformation. The iteration could be continued, but this will not be done here.

	$\mathbf{P}_1$	$\mathbf{P}_2$	$\mathbf{P}_3$	$\mathbf{P}_4$	$\mathbf{P}_5$	$\mathbf{P}_6$	$\mathbf{P}_7$	$\mathbf{P}_0$	p_i
$\mathbf{P}_5$	4	3	0	1	1	0	0	5	0
$\mathbf{P}_6$	2	4	1	1	0	1	0	2	0
$\rightarrow \mathbf{P}_7$	0	1	3	4	0	0	1	4	0
p_q	1	2	3	5	0	0	0		
z_q	0	0	0	0	0	0	0		
$p_q - z_q$	1	2	3	5	0	0	0		
				$\uparrow$					

	$\mathbf{P}_1$	$\mathbf{P}_2$	$\mathbf{P}_3$	$\mathbf{P}_4$	$\mathbf{P}_5$	$\mathbf{P}_6$	$\mathbf{P}_7$	$\mathbf{P}_0$	p_i
$\mathbf{P}_5$	4	$\frac{11}{4}$	$-\frac{3}{4}$	0	1	0	$-\frac{1}{4}$	4	0
$\mathbf{P}_6$	2	$\frac{15}{4}$	$\frac{1}{4}$	0	0	1	$-\frac{1}{4}$	1	0
$\mathbf{P}_4$	0	$\frac{1}{4}$	$\frac{3}{4}$	1	0	0	$\frac{1}{4}$	1	5
p_q	1	2	3	5	0	0	0		
z_q	0	$\frac{5}{4}$	$-\frac{15}{4}$	0	5	0	$-\frac{5}{4}$		
$p_q - z_q$	1	$\frac{3}{4}$	$\frac{27}{4}$	5	-5	0	$\frac{5}{4}$		

FIG. 8.6. Initial and changed tableau for illustrative problem.

While this discussion has outlined the method of solving the linear-programming problem by the simplex method, a few further comments are in order. In addition to the method described, Dantzig and Orchard-Hays (14) have outlined a more efficient algorithm called the revised simplex method. This method will not be described here, but the paper of Wagner (38) is recommended to the interested reader. It has also been theoretically observed that in certain cases $\mathbf{p}_0$ can be expressed at some stage of the simplex algorithm by less than m linearly independent vectors. This means that one of the $u_1, u_2, \ldots, u_m$ is equal to zero. The system is now said to be degenerate, and the algorithm cycles, or returns again and again, to a previous nonoptimal solution. However, degeneracy occurs only when the f_i's bear a special relation to the coefficients of the u_i's and in practical and real systems may almost always be ignored.

From a digital-computer point of view the simplex method is relatively easy to use, but it does require a considerable amount of testing and bookkeeping. With the IBM 650 a linear-programming system of size $m \leq 97$, n unlimited, can be handled. For the IBM 704 or Remington Rand 1103A an $m \leq 255$ or $m \leq 242$, respectively, with n unlimited, can be handled. It is doubtful that physical systems will ever involve more variables than can be handled by these machines.

Now let us look at linear programming in a different light. The gradient of z (profit or cost) is a vector which expresses the local variation of z at some particular set of the independent variables. If the independent variables are denoted by $\mathbf{x}$, the gradient is $\nabla \mathbf{z}(\mathbf{x})$ or $\nabla \mathbf{z}$ and has elements $\partial z/\partial x_1, \partial z/\partial x_2, \ldots, \partial z/\partial x_n$, where $\mathbf{x} = [x_1x_2 \cdots x_n]^T$. This gradient vector determines the maximum rate of change of z and is perpendicular to one of the contour lines. In Example 7.4 $\nabla \mathbf{z}$ was called $\mathbf{G}(t_r)$ to fit that particular problem. In linear programming

$$z = z_1x_1 + z_2x_2 + \cdots + z_nx_n$$

where $z_1, z_2, \ldots, z_n$ are constants. Thus $\nabla \mathbf{z}$ in this case is a vector with constant elements $z_1, z_2, \ldots, z_n$. As the optimization proceeds, the gradient remains constant and never requires recalculation or estimation. This can be seen from Fig. 8.2, where the perpendicular to any of the contour lines P_1, P_2, or P_3 is always a constant. Based on this value of the gradient, linear programming then attempts to find a point on the constraint set which is as large as possible in the $\nabla \mathbf{z}$ direction. This is obviously the vertex at point B in Fig. 8.2. Thus the simplex method is an efficient computational device for finding this particular vertex along the constant direction of $\nabla \mathbf{z}$.

When the profit function is not linear, the gradient will be a varying quantity and another approach must be used. Example 7.4 illustrated one technique for handling this problem (7, 18, 31). An alternative procedure currently finding much favor is the projected-gradient method described by Rosen (34) and used by Singer (35) for optimizing a large oil refinery. In brief form, it starts with an initial feasible point and follows the gradient indicated until a constraint is reached. It then proceeds along this constraint, using gradient projections on the face of the constraint set (tangent hyperplanes), until a new constraint is met. This is continued until an optimum is reached or the gradient becomes zero. The final answer is then checked to make sure that it is a true solution.

While the methods detailed above will find the optimum operating conditions in, say, a single chemical reactor, the question soon arises with many systems as to how to optimize N interconnected reactors. Whereas each reactor requires the optimizing of M independent variables, the problem is now of magnitude MN. Fortunately, the technique of dynamic programming proposed by Bellman (Chap. 1, 4) as developed by Aris (4) proves ideal for handling this situation. The optimization is repeated N times, but at each stage in the optimization only M variables are involved.

8.6. System Dynamics

Once the static optimization has defined a more profitable operating condition, the following control problem can be discussed:

Given the state of the system at time t_0 (the values of concentrations and temperatures), how can the process be moved from its state at t_0 to the desired optimum state (or as close as possible) in the shortest time possible?

Control of this type is necessary only when the system dynamics are important. The initial state at time t_0 is indicated by the n-dimensional vector $\mathbf{y}(t_0)$ and the desired state by $\mathbf{y}^d$. The movement of the process from $\mathbf{y}(t_0)$ to $\mathbf{y}^d$ is to be accomplished by manipulating the control or forcing variables defined by the m-dimensional vector $\mathbf{x}$ in some optimum way.

In order to carry out this type of control, it is necessary to have some mathematical model of the process under consideration. This model could be one obtained from a purely theoretical analysis, one based only upon experimental data, or one formed from a combination of the two methods. In any event it will be assumed here that this model takes the form of the linear matrix differential equation

$$\frac{d\mathbf{y}}{dt} = \mathbf{A}\mathbf{y} + \mathbf{B}\mathbf{x} \tag{8.6.1}$$

with initial conditions

$$\mathbf{y} = \mathbf{y}(t_0) \qquad t = t_0 \tag{8.6.2}$$

The $\mathbf{A}$ matrix is $n \times n$, the $\mathbf{B}$ matrix $n \times m$, and the $\mathbf{x}$ and $\mathbf{y}$ vectors are $m \times 1$ and $n \times 1$, respectively. Of course, many models of interest to chemical engineers are not linear; some form of linearization must then be performed to yield an equation with the form (8.6.1). For the reader interested in this latter aspect, the papers of Kalman, Lapidus, and Shapiro (28, 29) and Amundson (2, 3) are recommended.

Since (8.6.1) involves time explicitly, the time-domain solution is important. First consider the system with the forcing term **x** equal to zero, i.e.,

$$\frac{d\mathbf{y}}{dt} = \mathbf{A}\mathbf{y} \tag{8.6.3}$$

If it is recalled that the solution to a scalar homogeneous equation of this form is given by an exponential function, the exponential matrix function

$$e^{\mathbf{A}t} = \sum_{i=0}^{\infty} \frac{(\mathbf{A}t)^i}{i!}$$

is probably, by analogy, a solution of (8.6.3). Because the exponential matrix function converges uniformly, it may be differentiated term by term to show that (see below)

$$\mathbf{y}(t) = e^{\mathbf{A}(t-t_0)}\mathbf{y}(t_0) \tag{8.6.4}$$

is a solution of (8.6.3). The symbolism

$$\mathbf{\Phi}(t;t_0) = e^{\mathbf{A}(t-t_0)} \tag{8.6.5}$$

will also be used for simplification in writing.

It is easy to show the following properties of the matrix $\mathbf{\Phi}(t;t_0)$ [or $\mathbf{\Phi}(t)$, with $t_0 = 0$]:

$$\mathbf{\Phi}^{-1}(t) = \mathbf{\Phi}(-t) \qquad \mathbf{\Phi}(0) = \mathbf{I} \qquad \mathbf{\Phi}(t_1)\mathbf{\Phi}(t_2) = \mathbf{\Phi}(t_1 + t_2) \tag{8.6.6}$$

Noting that

$$\frac{d}{dt}(e^{\mathbf{A}t}) = \lim_{h\to 0} \frac{1}{h}(e^{[\mathbf{A}(t+h)]} - e^{\mathbf{A}t})$$
$$= \lim_{h\to 0} \frac{1}{h} e^{\mathbf{A}t}(e^{\mathbf{A}h} - 1) = e^{\mathbf{A}t}\mathbf{A} = \mathbf{A}e^{\mathbf{A}t}$$

and substituting (8.6.4) into (8.6.3) with $t_0 = 0$ lead to

$$\frac{d\mathbf{y}}{dt} = \frac{d}{dt}[\mathbf{\Phi}(t)\mathbf{y}(0)] = \frac{d}{dt}[\mathbf{\Phi}(t)]y(0) = \mathbf{A}\mathbf{y}(t) = \mathbf{A}\mathbf{\Phi}(t)\mathbf{y}(0)$$

But since this holds for any $\mathbf{y}(0)$,

$$\frac{d}{dt}[\mathbf{\Phi}(t)] = \mathbf{A}\mathbf{\Phi}(t)$$

In other words $\mathbf{\Phi}(t)$ satisfies the homogeneous equation. Proceeding further,

$$\mathbf{A} = \frac{d}{dt}[\mathbf{\Phi}(t)]\mathbf{\Phi}^{-1}(t) = \frac{d}{dt}[\mathbf{\Phi}(t)]\mathbf{\Phi}(-t)$$

and differentiating $\mathbf{I} = \mathbf{\Phi}(t)\mathbf{\Phi}(-t)$ shows that, for any t,

$$\mathbf{A} = \frac{d}{dt}[\mathbf{\Phi}(t)]\mathbf{\Phi}(-t) = -\mathbf{\Phi}(t)\frac{d}{dt}[\mathbf{\Phi}(-t)] \tag{8.6.7}$$

The solution of the nonhomogeneous equation (8.6.1) can now be obtained directly. From (8.6.7)

$$\frac{d\mathbf{y}}{dt} = \mathbf{Ay} + \mathbf{Bx} = -\mathbf{\Phi}(t)\frac{d}{dt}[\mathbf{\Phi}(-t)]\mathbf{y} + \mathbf{Bx}$$

Multiplying by $\mathbf{\Phi}(-t)$ and transposing,

$$\mathbf{\Phi}(-t)\frac{d\mathbf{y}}{dt} + \frac{d}{dt}[\mathbf{\Phi}(-t)]\mathbf{y} = \frac{d}{dt}[\mathbf{\Phi}(-t)\mathbf{y}] = \mathbf{\Phi}(-t)\mathbf{Bx}$$

This can be integrated directly to yield

$$\mathbf{\Phi}(-t)\mathbf{y} = \int_{t_0}^{t} \mathbf{\Phi}(-\lambda)\mathbf{Bx}(\lambda)\,d\lambda + \mathbf{\Phi}(-t_0)\mathbf{y}(t_0)$$

or, with (8.6.6),

$$\mathbf{y}(t) = \mathbf{\Phi}(t;t_0)\mathbf{y}(t_0) + \int_{t_0}^{t} \mathbf{\Phi}(t-\lambda)\mathbf{Bx}(\lambda)\,d\lambda \tag{8.6.8}$$

This is the generalization of the well-known convolution integral formula. Equation (8.6.8) represents the complete solution, including initial conditions of the linear dynamic equations (8.6.1) and (8.6.2). In other words, (8.6.8) predicts the behavior of $\mathbf{y}(t)$ as a function of t and the other system parameters.

Now consider that the integration in (8.6.8) is to be performed only over a time interval τ and that over this interval the forcing function $\mathbf{x}(t)$ is to be held constant at its value at t_0. Thus $\mathbf{x}(t) = \mathbf{x}(t_0)$ for $t_0 \le t \le t_0 + \tau$. On this basis (8.6.8) can be written as

$$\mathbf{y}(t+\tau) = \mathbf{\Phi}(\tau)\mathbf{y}(t_0) + \mathbf{\Delta}(\tau)\mathbf{x}(t_0) \tag{8.6.9}$$

where

$$\mathbf{\Delta}(\tau) = \left[\int_0^{\tau} \mathbf{\Phi}(\tau-\lambda)\,d\lambda\right]\mathbf{B} \tag{8.6.10}$$

Equation (8.6.9) is a linear difference equation or recurrence formula which represents the dynamics of the process over a time interval of τ units. It is a specialized form of (8.6.8). If only the sequence of constant time periods τ, 2τ, 3τ, . . . is involved, (8.6.9) may also be written in the form

$$\mathbf{y}(k+1) = \mathbf{\Phi y}(k) + \mathbf{\Delta x}(k) \qquad k = 0, 1, 2, \ldots \tag{8.6.11}$$

since the matrices $\mathbf{\Phi}$ and $\mathbf{\Delta}$ are constant independent of k.

8.7. Dynamic Control

For dynamic control to have any quantitative meaning, it is necessary that some measure or criterion be available which can be used to specify how "good" the control is, i.e., how far away the process is from the desired condition. Consider the definition as presented by Kalman (27),

$$\beta^2 = [\mathbf{y}^d - \mathbf{y}(k)]^T\mathbf{Q}[\mathbf{y}^d - \mathbf{y}(k)] \tag{8.7.1}$$

where β^2 is defined by the right-hand side of the equation and $\mathbf{Q}$ is a positive semidefinite matrix. The expansion of (8.7.1) leads to a weighted sum of squares of the elements of $\mathbf{y}^d - \mathbf{y}$, with the weighting determined by the elements of $\mathbf{Q}$. If $\mathbf{Q}$ is the identity matrix $\mathbf{I}$, the weighting factors are unity. Thus this may be used to specify the deviation of the process from the desired condition at any time.

It is important to note the versatility of the use of this quadratic form. By suitably changing the elements in $\mathbf{Q}$ any one concentration or temperature can be made more important in specifying the control performance than any other item.

A performance index for the dynamic control may now be defined as

$$J = \sum_{k=1}^{N} [\mathbf{y}^d - \mathbf{y}(k)]^T\mathbf{Q}[\mathbf{y}^d - \mathbf{y}(k)] \tag{8.7.2}$$

and the control problem stated as follows:

Given a process governed by Eqs. (8.6.11), find that sequence of control vectors $\mathbf{x}(k)$, $k = 0, 1, 2, \ldots$, such that the index J of (8.7.2) is minimized as $N \to \infty$ as the process is moved from $\mathbf{y}(0)$ to $\mathbf{y}^d$.

Minimizing J tends to minimize the weighted sum of squares between $\mathbf{y}^d$ and $\mathbf{y}(k)$, that is, the desired optimum conditions and the actual conditions at the time $k\tau$. Further, the minimization involves the dynamics of the process, since $\mathbf{y}(k)$ occurs in J.

It is implicitly assumed here that the process is to be operated in a discrete fashion; changes in the control variables are needed only at multiples of τ, and not between. Such an arrangement would correspond to the use of a digital computer in the feedback loop of the process, since the computer can operate only in a discrete fashion.

The result of the minimization of (8.7.2) would be to yield a sequence of control vectors

$$\mathbf{x}(0),\ \mathbf{x}(1),\ \mathbf{x}(2),\ \ldots \tag{8.7.3}$$

which, when applied to the dynamic system, will move it from the initial $\mathbf{y}(0)$ to the closest possible state near $\mathbf{y}^d$. Unfortunately, there are many possible choices of the sequence (8.7.3) that will perform the desired linear transformation. Thus the object is to find that one sequence among the infinite set of possible sequences that will be optimal in the sense that (8.7.2) is minimized. This optimal sequence will be denoted as

$$\mathbf{x}^0(0),\ \mathbf{x}^0(1),\ \mathbf{x}^0(2),\ \ldots \tag{8.7.4}$$

and can be determined by a method outlined by Kalman (27) and Kalman, Lapidus, and Shapiro (28). To illustrate the mechanics of this process, however, it is easier to take J equal to

$$J = \sum_{k=1}^{N} \mathbf{y}^T\mathbf{Q}\mathbf{y} \tag{8.7.5}$$

as $N \to \infty$, rather than (8.7.2), because of mathematical manipulations.† In order to perform the minimization, N partial derivatives of J are taken with respect to $\mathbf{x}(k)$, $k = 0, 1, 2, \ldots, N-1$ and the results set equal to zero, starting with $k = N - 1$. This corresponds to starting at the final desired end condition and moving backward toward the initial starting condition. The reader may ask why the differentiation is started at seemingly the wrong end of the sequence. The idea here is much like that of dynamic programming (see Sec. 8.5), wherein the dimensionality of a particular minimization is brought down from MN to M repeated N times. In other words, if the differentiation is started at $\mathbf{x}(0)$, then it is impossible from a practical point of view to solve the large number of resulting equations. If, however, one starts at the other end, only a small set of equations must be solved at each step in the computation. First

$$\frac{\partial J}{\partial \mathbf{x}(N-1)} = 2\,\frac{\partial \mathbf{y}^T(N)}{\partial \mathbf{x}(N-1)}\,\mathbf{Q}\mathbf{y}(N) = 0 \tag{8.7.6}$$

In this expression

$$\frac{\partial \mathbf{y}^T(k)}{\partial \mathbf{x}(N-1)} = 0 \qquad k < N$$

† This new J could be obtained by merely changing variables such that

$$\mathbf{z}(k) = \mathbf{y}^d - \mathbf{y}(k)$$

since $\mathbf{y}(k)$ cannot be influenced by a control signal applied at a time greater than k, and

$$\frac{\partial \mathbf{y}^T(k)}{\partial \mathbf{x}(N-1)} = \mathbf{\Delta}^T \qquad k = N$$

Equation (8.7.6) thus becomes

$$\mathbf{\Delta}^T \mathbf{Q} \mathbf{y}(N) = 0$$

and by using (8.6.11)

$$\mathbf{\Delta}^T \mathbf{Q}[\mathbf{\Phi} \mathbf{y}(N-1) + \mathbf{\Delta} \mathbf{x}(N-1)] = 0$$

Solving for $\mathbf{x}(N-1)$,

$$\mathbf{x}(N-1) = -[(\mathbf{\Delta}^T \mathbf{Q} \mathbf{\Delta})^{-1} \mathbf{\Delta}^T \mathbf{Q} \mathbf{\Phi}] \mathbf{y}(N-1)$$

which may be written as

$$\mathbf{x}(N-1) = \mathbf{C}^{(N-1)} \mathbf{y}(N-1) \tag{8.7.7}$$

This may be substituted into (8.6.11) to yield

$$\mathbf{y}(N) = [\mathbf{\Phi} + \mathbf{\Delta} \mathbf{C}^{(N-1)}] \mathbf{y}(N-1)$$

or

$$\mathbf{y}(N) = \mathbf{\Psi}^{(N-1)} \mathbf{y}(N-1) \tag{8.7.8}$$

The entire process is now repeated with respect to $\mathbf{x}(N-2)$. Thus

$$\frac{\partial J}{\partial \mathbf{x}(N-2)} = 2 \frac{\partial \mathbf{y}^T(N)}{\partial \mathbf{x}(N-2)} \mathbf{Q} \mathbf{y}(N) + 2 \frac{\partial \mathbf{y}^T(N-1)}{\partial \mathbf{x}(N-2)} \mathbf{Q} \mathbf{y}(N-1) = 0$$

Substituting (8.7.8) and rearranging yields

$$\frac{\partial \mathbf{y}^T(N-1)}{\partial \mathbf{x}(N-2)} [\mathbf{\Psi}^{(N-1)T} \mathbf{Q} \mathbf{\Psi}^{(N-1)} + \mathbf{Q}] \mathbf{y}(N-1) = 0$$

and letting

$$\mathbf{P}^{(1)} = [\mathbf{\Psi}^{(N-1)T} \mathbf{Q} \mathbf{\Psi}^{(N-1)} + \mathbf{Q}]$$

results in

$$\frac{\partial \mathbf{y}^T(N-1)}{\partial \mathbf{x}(N-2)} \mathbf{P}^{(1)} \mathbf{y}(N-1) = 0 \tag{8.7.9}$$

But this equation is identical with (8.7.6) except that $\mathbf{P}^{(2)}$ replaces $\mathbf{Q}$ in (8.7.6) and the index on k has been dropped by 1. It immediately follows by analogy with (8.7.7) and (8.7.8) that

$$\mathbf{x}(N-2) = \mathbf{C}^{(N-2)} \mathbf{y}(N-2) \tag{8.7.10}$$

$$\mathbf{y}(N-1) = \mathbf{\Psi}^{(N-2)} \mathbf{y}(N-2) \tag{8.7.11}$$

This can be continued by differentiating J with respect to $\mathbf{x}(N-3)$, $\mathbf{x}(N-4)$, . . . , but it is already evident that a pattern has been set up in terms of

$$
\begin{aligned}
\mathbf{P}^{(i)} &= \mathbf{\Psi}^{(N-i)T}\mathbf{P}^{(i-1)}\mathbf{\Psi}^{(N-i)} + \mathbf{Q} \\
\mathbf{C}^{(N-i)} &= -(\mathbf{\Delta}^T\mathbf{P}^{(i)}\mathbf{\Delta})^{-1}\mathbf{\Delta}^T\mathbf{P}^{(i)}\mathbf{\Phi} \\
\mathbf{\Psi}^{(N-i)} &= \mathbf{\Phi} + \mathbf{\Delta}\mathbf{C}^{(N-i)}
\end{aligned}
\tag{8.7.12}
$$

with $\mathbf{P}^{(0)} = \mathbf{Q}$ and $\mathbf{\Psi}^{(N)} = \mathbf{0}$.

The iteration pattern of (8.7.12) will successively calculate the sequence of control vectors given by

$$\mathbf{x}(i) = \mathbf{C}^{(N-i)}\mathbf{y}(i)$$

but in a reverse manner to normal considerations. In other words, the last signal $\mathbf{x}(N-1)$ as applied to $\mathbf{y}(N-1)$ to yield $\mathbf{y}(N)$ is calculated first, followed by $\mathbf{x}(N-2)$, $\mathbf{x}(N-3)$, ... It can be shown that as long as $\mathbf{Q}$ is positive definite and $(\mathbf{\Delta}^T\mathbf{Q}\mathbf{\Delta})^{-1}$ exists, the matrices $\mathbf{C}^{(N-i)}$ always converge to a constant matrix as $N \to \infty$. Thus for N large enough (this would be determined by obtaining constant elements in $\mathbf{C}$) it is possible to write

$$\mathbf{x}(k) = \mathbf{C}\mathbf{y}(k)$$

or since these are the optimal values desired,

$$\mathbf{x}^0(k) = \mathbf{C}\mathbf{y}(k) \tag{8.7.13}$$

When (8.7.2) is used to define J, rather than (8.7.5), an analogous procedure to the above leads to

$$\mathbf{x}^0(k) = \mathbf{C}\mathbf{y}(k) + \mathbf{E}\mathbf{y}^d \tag{8.7.14}$$

where $\mathbf{C}$ is as before and

$$\mathbf{E} = (\boldsymbol{\varrho}^T\mathbf{Q}\boldsymbol{\varrho})^{-1}\boldsymbol{\varrho}\mathbf{Q} \qquad \boldsymbol{\varrho} = (\mathbf{I} - \mathbf{\Psi})^{-1}\mathbf{\Delta}$$

$\mathbf{\Psi}$ is obtained in the same iteration pattern as $\mathbf{C}$.

The final result of these manipulations is now available in the two equations (8.6.11) and (8.7.14),

$$
\left.
\begin{aligned}
\mathbf{y}(k+1) &= \mathbf{\Phi}\mathbf{y}(k) + \mathbf{\Delta}\mathbf{x}^0(k) \\
\mathbf{x}^0(k) &= \mathbf{C}\mathbf{y}(k) + \mathbf{E}\mathbf{y}^d
\end{aligned}
\right\} \qquad k = 0, 1, 2, \ldots
$$

The first equation represents the discrete system dynamics and the second equation is the discrete control equation. Starting with the known initial condition $\mathbf{y}(0)$, the second equation is used to calculate $\mathbf{x}^0(0)$, the control vector to be applied to the dynamic system at time $t_0 = 0$. When $\mathbf{x}^0(0)$ is known, the first equation is used to calculate $\mathbf{y}(1)$ by using $\mathbf{y}(0)$; in other words, when the initial condition $\mathbf{y}(0)$ and the forcing function $\mathbf{x}^0(0)$ at the time $t_0 = 0$ are known, the state of the process $\mathbf{y}(1)$ at the end of τ units of time can be calculated. This alternation is then continually repeated; knowing $\mathbf{y}^{(1)}$, calculate $\mathbf{x}^0(1)$ and in turn $\mathbf{y}(2)$, ...

In this way all the $\mathbf{x}^0(0)$, $\mathbf{x}^0(1)$, $\mathbf{x}^0(2)$, . . . and $\mathbf{y}(1)$, $\mathbf{y}(2)$, . . . are known for as far into the time domain as desired.

An important point resulting from this development is that the performance index [(8.7.2)] is minimized and the sequence of optimal control variables calculated by observing (or measuring) the system at the times

$$t_0,\ t_0 + \tau,\ t_0 + 2\tau,\ . . .$$

Actually it has been proposed above that the use of (8.6.11) and (8.7.14) is sufficient to predict the entire future evolution of the process. However, because of a possibly inaccurate knowledge of the matrix $\mathbf{\Phi}$, unknown disturbances acting on the process, and possible random effects of various kinds, the prediction based on (8.6.11) will become less and less correct as the prediction interval increases. By remeasuring the state of the system at the sampling instants, on the assumption that τ has been chosen small enough so that the one-step prediction is sufficiently accurate, the prediction errors are corrected and the control variables assume very nearly their optimal values at all times.

The procedure outlined is one which has considerable promise for application to the closed-loop computer control of dynamic chemical-engineering processes. The digital computer is a necessary adjunct, since it would be impossible to pass through the iteration cycle of (8.7.12) by using any other form of computation. This is especially true if the computation must be carried out quickly or if it must be repeated at periodic time intervals. If the process is sufficiently simple, however, only an off-line computation for the optimal control variable may be required. Other variations on this basic procedure are, of course, possible, but these will not be discussed here.

8.8. Numerical Examples

Example 8.1. Consider a train of six liquid-liquid countercurrent extraction units with a secondary feed to the third stage. A single solute in the main raffinate and the secondary feed streams is to be extracted by the extract phase. The solvents are assumed completely immiscible. The secondary feed is made up by suitable blending from two large storage reservoirs, each containing a constant (but different) composition of the solute. x and y are used to indicate raffinate and extract compositions; F and b are raffinate solvent-flow rates, and w is the extract solvent rate. If H and h are the holdups of the raffinate and extract phases (assumed constant for each stage), respectively, a material balance on any stage leads to the dynamic equations

$$\begin{aligned} h\frac{dy_n}{dt} + H\frac{dx_n}{dt} &= b(x_{n-1} - x_n) + w(y_{n+1} - y_n) && n = 1, 2 \\ h\frac{dy_n}{dt} + H\frac{dx_n}{dt} &= bx_{n-1} - b^*x_n + w(y_{n+1} - y_n) + Fx_F && n = 3 \qquad (8.8.1) \\ h\frac{dy_n}{dt} + H\frac{dx_n}{dt} &= b^*(x_{n-1} - x_n) + w(y_{n+1} - y_n) && n = 4, 5, 6 \end{aligned}$$

where $b^* = b + F$. F is the total feed rate of the secondary stream to the third stage, and x_F is the analogous solute composition. Upon assuming a linear-equilibrium relationship

$$y_n = \alpha x_n + \beta$$

and defining $d = \frac{b}{a} \qquad d^* = \frac{b^*}{a} \qquad p = \frac{w\alpha}{a} \qquad a = h\alpha + H$

(8.8.1) can be written in matrix form as

$$\frac{d\mathbf{x}}{dt} = \mathbf{A}\mathbf{x} + \mathbf{D}_1\mathbf{m}_1 + \mathbf{D}_2\mathbf{m}_2 \tag{8.8.2}$$

where

$$\mathbf{A} = \begin{bmatrix} -(d+p) & p & & & & \\ d & -(d+p) & p & & & \\ & d & -(d^*+p) & p & & \\ & & d^* & -(d^*+p) & p & \\ & & & d^* & -(d^*+p) & p \\ & & & & d^* & -(d^*+p) \end{bmatrix} = \text{tridiagonal matrix}$$

$$\mathbf{x} = \begin{bmatrix} x_1 \\ x_2 \\ \cdot \\ \cdot \\ \cdot \\ x_6 \end{bmatrix} \qquad \mathbf{D}_1 = \begin{bmatrix} d & 0 \\ 0 & \cdot \\ \cdot & \cdot \\ \cdot & \cdot \\ \cdot & 0 \\ 0 & p \end{bmatrix} \qquad \mathbf{D}_2 = \begin{bmatrix} 0 \\ 0 \\ \frac{F}{a} \\ 0 \\ \cdot \\ 0 \end{bmatrix} \qquad \mathbf{m}_1 = \begin{bmatrix} x_0 \\ \frac{y_7 - \beta}{\alpha} \end{bmatrix} \qquad \mathbf{m}_2 = [x_F]$$

Just as (8.6.8) was obtained, (8.8.2) can be integrated to yield

$$\mathbf{x}(t) = e^{\mathbf{A}t}\mathbf{x}(0) + \int_0^t e^{\mathbf{A}(t-\lambda)}\mathbf{D}_1 m_1\, d\lambda + \int_0^t e^{\mathbf{A}(t-\lambda)}\mathbf{D}_2 m_2\, d\lambda$$

where

$$e^{\mathbf{A}t} = \sum_{i=0}^{\infty} \frac{(\mathbf{A}t)^i}{i!}$$

$$\mathbf{x}(t) = \mathbf{x}(0) \qquad t = 0$$

Upon assuming that the inputs $\mathbf{m}_1$ and $\mathbf{m}_2$ are held constant over any sampling period τ, this integrated equation may be converted to

$$\mathbf{x}(k+1) = \mathbf{\Phi}\mathbf{x}(k) + \mathbf{\Delta}_1\mathbf{m}_1(k) + \mathbf{\Delta}_2\mathbf{m}_2(k) \qquad k = 0, 1, 2, \ldots \tag{8.8.3}$$

where

$$\mathbf{\Phi} = e^{\mathbf{A}\tau}$$

$$\mathbf{\Delta}_1 = \left(\int_0^\tau e^{\mathbf{A}\lambda}\, d\lambda\right)\mathbf{D}_1$$

$$\mathbf{\Delta}_2 = \left(\int_0^\tau e^{\mathbf{A}\lambda}\, d\lambda\right)\mathbf{D}_2$$

Note that (8.8.3) is a linear difference equation describing the dynamic behavior of the extraction train over any τ time units. It compares with (8.6.9) in the text but has an added term.

If it is further assumed (for convenience only) that x_0, the feed composition to stage 1, is held constant (this means that $\mathbf{\Delta}_1\mathbf{m}_1$ is also a constant) and that control of the extraction chain is to be achieved by blending the two flows from the external reservoirs, (8.8.3) can be put in a more familiar form. In effect, if x_{F1}, x_{F2} and F_1 and F_2 are the solute compositions and flow rates from the reservoirs 1 and 2, respectively, then for x_{F1} and x_{F2} held constant but F_1 and F_2 varying the input composition in the secondary stream can be manipulated as given by

$$x_{F1}F_1 + x_{F2}F_2 = x_F F$$

In so far as the extraction train is concerned, F is a constant and x_F is varied to achieve the desired control. In over-all terms, however, the variation in x_F is achieved by changes in the flow rates F_1 and F_2. Letting

$$\mathbf{x}^* = (\mathbf{I} - \mathbf{\Phi})^{-1}\mathbf{\Delta}_1\mathbf{m}_1 \qquad \text{and} \qquad \mathbf{z}(k) = \mathbf{x}(k) - \mathbf{x}^*$$

(8.8.3) becomes

$$\mathbf{z}(k+1) = \mathbf{\Phi}\mathbf{z}(k) + \mathbf{\Delta}_2\mathbf{m}_2 \qquad k = 0, 1, 2, \ldots \tag{8.8.4}$$

This equation now has the same form as (8.6.11) and the dynamic control calculation outlined in the text can be used directly.

It is necessary first to specify the problem itself in slightly more concrete terms. The following constant parameters are chosen (any convenient set of units applies):

$$\begin{aligned} w &= 60 & \alpha &= 2.20 \\ b &= 50 & \beta &= 0 \\ a &= 100 & y_7 &= 0 \text{ (pure solvent)} \\ F &= 50 \end{aligned}$$

These lead to

$$d = 0.50 \qquad d^* = 1.0 \qquad p = 1.32$$

and the control problem may now be specified in quantitative terms.

Given the extraction train at equilibrium, with inputs $x_0 = 0.0400$ and $x_F = 0.0300$, it is desired to move the process as quickly as possible to the equilibrium corresponding to $x_0 = 0.0200$ and $x_F = 0.0200$. In other words, the initial condition $\mathbf{x}(0)$ corresponds to using $x_0 = 0.0400$ and $x_F = 0.0300$ and the desired condition $\mathbf{x}^d$ to using $x_0 = 0.0200$ and $x_F = 0.0200$. Since both conditions are equilibrium points $[d\mathbf{x}/dt = 0$ in (8.8.2)], it is possible to calculate

$$\mathbf{x}(0) = \begin{bmatrix} 0.0245523 \\ 0.0187009 \\ 0.0164845 \\ 0.0105254 \\ 0.0060110 \\ 0.0025909 \end{bmatrix} \qquad \mathbf{x}^d = \begin{bmatrix} 0.0138795 \\ 0.0115611 \\ 0.0106829 \\ 0.0068211 \\ 0.0038955 \\ 0.0016791 \end{bmatrix}$$

These calculations involve solving a set of six linear algebraic simultaneous equations.

With this information in hand the details of Sec. 8.7 can be followed. This means using the dynamic difference equation (8.8.4),

$$\mathbf{z}(k+1) = \mathbf{\Phi}\mathbf{z}(k) + \mathbf{\Delta}_2\mathbf{m}_2$$

and the optimal control equation (8.7.14) in the form

$$\mathbf{m}_2{}^0(k) = \mathbf{C}\mathbf{z}(k) + \mathbf{E}\mathbf{z}^d \tag{8.8.5}$$

where $\mathbf{z}^d = \mathbf{x}^d - \mathbf{x}^*$ and $k = 0, 1, 2, \ldots$. The first step in the calculation is to evaluate the constant matrix $\mathbf{\Phi}$ and the constant vector $\mathbf{\Delta}_2$ by use of the definitions given in (8.8.3). In particular $\mathbf{\Phi}$ is obtained by the exponential expansion using up to 35 terms, and $\mathbf{\Delta}_2$ is obtained by performing the indicated integration on each term of the exponential and then postmultiplying the resulting sum by the constant vector $\mathbf{D}_2$. This leads (with $\tau = 0.20$) to

$$\mathbf{\Phi} = \begin{bmatrix} 0.2214669 & 0.2625844 & 0.1477837 & 0.0587518 & 0.0180606 & 0.0044012 \\ 0.0994657 & 0.2774455 & 0.2511197 & 0.1392115 & 0.0552448 & 0.0163935 \\ 0.0212040 & 0.0951211 & 0.2318090 & 0.2179857 & 0.1238636 & 0.0473681 \\ 0.0063861 & 0.0399482 & 0.1651407 & 0.2729136 & 0.2329446 & 0.1176540 \\ 0.0014872 & 0.0120099 & 0.0710879 & 0.1764731 & 0.2682093 & 0.1970596 \\ 0.0002746 & 0.0026999 & 0.0205951 & 0.0675241 & 0.1492876 & 0.1790774 \end{bmatrix}$$

$$\mathbf{\Delta}_2 = \begin{bmatrix} 0.0395470 \\ 0.1105056 \\ 0.2325049 \\ 0.0758054 \\ 0.0196469 \\ 0.0040299 \end{bmatrix}$$

Next the iteration cycle of (8.7.12) is used to determine the constant matrices **C** and **E** in (8.8.5). Note that, since $\mathbf{m}_2^0(k)$ is a 1×1 vector, **C** and **E** are now 1×6 vectors. The test on convergence of the iteration is taken as 1×10^{-7}. Table 8.1 shows the first element of each vector as the iteration proceeds; 10 iterations are required for convergence. At this point,

$$\mathbf{C} = \begin{bmatrix} 1.3582145 \\ 1.8726897 \\ 2.0675668 \\ 1.3201506 \\ 0.7539260 \\ 0.3249681 \end{bmatrix} \qquad \mathbf{E} = \begin{bmatrix} -0.3850683 \\ -0.9690016 \\ -1.4247159 \\ -1.3106808 \\ -0.8728042 \\ -0.4186988 \end{bmatrix}$$

and the control calculations can be completed by using (8.8.5) and (8.8.4) repeatedly.

TABLE 8.1. ITERATION VALUES FOR FIRST ELEMENTS OF **C** AND **E** VECTORS

C	**E**
1.3072585	−0.3405437
1.3541903	−0.3837107
1.3576975	−0.3853174
1.3581125	−0.3851569
1.3581914	−0.3850905
1.3582092	−0.3850736
1.3582133	−0.3850695
1.3582143	−0.3850686
1.3582145	−0.3850684
1.3582145	−0.3850683
1.3582145	−0.3850683

Table 8.2 shows the results of this calculation with x_6 (for illustration), F_1, and F_2 given at each sampling period; also shown is the normal transient response of the extraction train as obtained by evaluating (8.8.3). It can be seen that within 10 sampling periods the optimum control scheme has forced the process from the initial value $\mathbf{x}(0)$ to the final desired value $\mathbf{x}^d$. In contrast, the normal transient response requires about 90 sampling periods to reach the same point.

The reader will note that the use of the external reservoirs served the function of allowing flow rates to be controlled; however, in so far as the train of extraction units is concerned, the control is explicitly carried out by changing a composition x_F. In effect the reservoirs were used as a subterfuge to allow the more natural control variables of flow to be manipulated, rather than composition. To see why the flow rates F and b cannot serve as control variables, all that is necessary is to look at the **A** matrix in (8.8.2). If F or b is varied, **A** will no longer be a constant but will be time-varying. On this basis the technique for dynamic control discussed in this chapter can no longer be used without extensive modifications. The details of these modifications will not be presented here.

TABLE 8.2. FINAL CONTROL VALUES AND THE COMPOSITION OF STAGE 6 AS A FUNCTION OF TIME

Time	x_6	F_1	F_2	x_6 by solving (8.8.3)
0	0.0025909	0	50.0	0.0025909
0.2	0.0024437	6.145	43.855	
0.4	0.0020264	7.785	42.215	
0.6	0.0018078	8.142	41.858	
0.8	0.0017288	8.254	41.746	
1.0	0.0016999	8.298	41.702	0.0025875
1.2	0.0016884	8.317	41.683	
1.4	0.0016834	8.326	41.674	
1.6	0.0016811	8.329	41.670	
1.8	0.0016800	8.332	41.668	
2.0	0.0016795	8.332	41.667	0.0025654
.	.			
.	.			
.	.			
∞	0.0016791			

The calculations were performed on the IBM 704 in floating-point mode. Exclusive of output the machine time required was about 1 min.

BIBLIOGRAPHY

1. Acrivos, A.: *Chem. Eng.*, **63**: 215 (1956).
2. Amundson, N. R., and R. Aris: *Chem. Eng. Progr.*, **53**: 227 (1957).
3. Amundson, N. R., and R. Aris: *Chem. Eng. Sci.*, **7**: 121 (1958).
4. Aris, R.: "The Optimal Design of Chemical Reactors," Academic Press, Inc., New York, 1961.
5. Aris, R., R. Bellman, and R. Kalaba: Some Optimization Problems in Chemical Engineering, *Rand Corp. Rept.* P-1798, 1959.
6. Box, G. E. P., and G. D. Coutie: *Proc. Inst. Elec. Engrs. (London)*, **103**(B): 100 (1956).
7. Box, G. E. P., and K. B. Wilson: *J. Roy. Statistics*, **B13**: 1 (1951).
8. Charnes, A., and W. W. Cooper: *Management Sci.*, **1**: 49 (1954).

9. Charnes, A., C. E. Lemke, and O. C. Zienkiewick: *Proc. Roy. Soc.* (*London*), **251**(A): 110 (1959).
10. Chow, W. M.: *Communs. ACM,* **2**(7): 28 (1959).
11. Dantzig, G. B.: Computational Algorithm of the Simplex Method, *Rand Corp. Rept.* RM-1266, 1953.
12. Dantzig, G. B.: The Simplex Method, *Rand Corp. Rept.* P-891, 1956.
13. Dantzig, G. B., S. Johnson, and W. White: *Management Sci.,* **5**: 38 (1958).
14. Dantzig, G. B., and W. Orchard-Hays: Alternate Algorithm for the Revised Simplex Method, *Rand Corp. Rept.* RM-1268, 1953.
15. Dantzig, G. B., and W. Orchard-Hays: *Math. Tables Aids Comput.,* **8**: 46 (1954).
16. Debeau, D. E.: *Operations Research,* **5**: 429 (1957).
17. Dennis, J. B.: *J. Assoc. Comput. Mach.,* **5**: 132 (1958).
18. Dickinson, J. R.: A Computer Program for System Optimization, *Can. Gen. Elec. Co. Ltd. Rept.* 58, 1958.
19. Dreyfus, S. E.: A Comparison of Linear Programming and Dynamic Programming, *Rand Corp. Rept.* P-885, 1956.
20. Dwyer, P. S., and B. A. Galler: *J. Assoc. Comput. Mach.,* **4**: 308 (1957).
21. Eckman, D. P., and I. Lefkowitz: *Control Eng.,* **4**: 197 (September, 1957).
22. Fenech, E. J., and A. Acrivos: *Chem. Eng. Sci.,* **5**: 93 (1956).
23. Hall, C. R.: *Chem. Eng. Progr.,* **56**: 62 (February, 1960).
24. Kalman, R. E.: *Trans. ASME,* **80**: 468 (1958).
25. Kalman, R. E.: *J. Basic Eng.,* **1**: 35 (1960).
26. Kalman, R. E., and J. E. Bertram: *Trans. AIEE,* **77**(II): 602 (1958).
27. Kalman, R. E., and R. W. Koepcke: *Trans. ASME,* **80**: 1820 (1958).
28. Kalman, R. E., L. Lapidus, and E. Shapiro: *Proc. Joint Symposium on Instrumentation and Computation,* London, May, 1959.
29. Kalman, R. E., L. Lapidus, and E. Shapiro: *Chem. Eng. Progr.,* **56**: 55 (February, 1960).
30. Merriam, C. W.: *J. Franklin Inst.,* **267**: 267 (1959).
31. Neuwirth, S. I., and L. M. Naphtali: *Chem. Eng.,* **64**: 238 (1957).
32. Orchard-Hays, W.: Evolution of Computer Codes for Linear Programming, *Rand Corp. Rept.* P-810, 1956.
33. Orchard-Hays, W.: Evolution of Linear Programming Computing Techniques, *Rand Corp. Rept.* P-900, 1956.
34. Rosen, J. B.: *J. SIAM,* **8**: 181 (1960).
35. Singer, E.: Simulation and Optimization of Oil Refinery Design, presented at AIChE meeting, San Francisco, Cal., December, 1959.
36. Stout, T. M.: *ISA J.,* **6**: 98 (1959).
37. Symonds, G. H.: *Ind. Eng. Chem.,* **48**: 394 (1956).
38. Wagner, H. M.: *Operations Research,* **4**: 443 (1956).
39. Wagner, H. M.: *Operations Research,* **5**: 361 (1957).
40. Wagner, H. M.: *Operations Research,* **6**: 190 (1958).
41. Wagner, H. M.: *Operations Research,* **6**: 364 (1958).
42. Wersan, S. J.: *Communs. ACM,* **2**(9): 33 (1959).
43. Wolfe, P.: *Econometrica,* **27**: 382 (1959).

INDEX